D1616226

Industrial Wastewater Management Handbook

OTHER McGRAW-HILL HANDBOOKS OF INTEREST

American Institute of Physics · American Institute of Physics Handbook
American Society of Mechanical Engineers · ASME Handbooks
Engineering Tables | Metals Engineering—Processes
Metals Engineering—Design | Metals Properties
Baumeister and Marks · Standard Handbook for Mechanical Engineers
Brater and King · Handbook of Hydraulics
Burington · Handbook of Mathematical Tables and Formulas
Burington and May · Handbook of Probability and Statistics with Tables
Callender · Time-Saver Standards for Architectural Design Data
Chow · Handbook of Applied Hydrology
Condon and Odishaw · Handbook of Physics
Conover · Grounds Maintenance Handbook
Crocker and King · Piping Handbook
Croft, Carr, and Watt · American Electricians' Handbook
Davis and Sorensen · Handbook of Applied Hydraulics
DeChiara and Callender · Time-Saver Standards for Building Types
Fink and Carroll · Standard Handbook for Electrical Engineers
Flugge · Handbook of Engineering Mechanics
Hamsher · Communication System Engineering Handbook
Harris · Handbook of Noise Control
Harris and Crede · Shock and Vibration Handbook
Hicks · Standard Handbook of Engineering Calculations
Ireson · Reliability Handbook
Juran · Quality Control Handbook
Karassik, Krutzsch, Fraser, and Messina · Pump Handbook
Korn and Korn · Mathematical Handbook for Scientists and Engineers
LaLonde and Janes · Concrete Engineering Handbook
LeGrand · The New American Machinist's Handbook
Lewis · Management Handbook for Plant Engineers
Lewis and Marron · Facilities and Plant Engineering Handbook
Machol · System Engineering Handbook
Mantell · Engineering Materials Handbook
Maynard · Handbook of Business Administration
Maynard · Industrial Engineering Handbook
Merritt · Building Construction Handbook
Merritt · Standard Handbook for Civil Engineers
Morrow · Maintenance Engineering Handbook
O'Brien · Scheduling Handbook
Perry · Engineering Manual
Raznjevic · Handbook of Thermodynamic Tables and Charts
Rothbart · Mechanical Design and Systems Handbook
Smeaton · Switchgear and Control Handbook
Society of Manufacturing Engineers · Die Design Handbook
Society of Manufacturing Engineers · Tool and Manufacturing Engineers Handbook
Streeter · Handbook of Fluid Dynamics
Stubbs · Handbook of Heavy Construction
Truxal · Control Engineers' Handbook
Tuma · Engineering Mathematics Handbook
Tuma · Handbook of Physical Calculations
Tuma · Technology Mathematics Handbook
Urquhart · Civil Engineering Handbook
Watt and Summers · NFPA Handbook of the National Electrical Code
Woods · Highway Engineering Handbook

Industrial Wastewater Management Handbook

HARDAM SINGH AZAD *Editor-in-Chief*
Director, Environmental Projects
NUS Corporation, Rockville, Maryland

McGRAW-HILL BOOK COMPANY

New York St. Louis San Francisco Auckland Bogotá Düsseldorf
Johannesburg London Madrid Mexico Montreal
New Delhi Panama Paris São Paulo Singapore
Sydney Tokyo Toronto

Library of Congress Cataloging in Publication Data
Main entry under title:

Industrial wastewater management handbook.

Includes index.
1. Factory and trade waste—Handbooks, manuals, etc.
2. Water—Pollution—Handbooks, manuals, etc.
3. Sewage—Purification—Handbooks, manuals, etc.
I. Azad, Hardam Singh.
TD897.I44 628'.3 76-17884
ISBN 0-07-002661-0

TD
897
.I44

ENGINEERING
& PHYSICS
LIBRARY

Copyright © 1976 by McGraw-Hill, Inc. All rights reserved.
Printed in the United States of America. No part of this
publication may be reproduced, stored in a retrieval system,
or transmitted, in any form or by any means, electronic,
mechanical, photocopying, recording, or otherwise, without
the prior written permission of the publisher.

1234567890 KPKP 785432109876

*The editors for this book were Harold B. Crawford and Virginia Anne Fechtmann,
the designer was Naomi Auerbach, and the production supervisor
was George Oechsner. It was set in Caledonia
by Monotype Composition Company, Inc.*

Printed and bound by The Kingsport Press.

To my dear, understanding wife, Jagdesh;
daughter, Ishnella; and son, Jaspaul.

engineering
BNA
12-28-71

Contents

Index follows Chapter 11.

Contributors

OSMAN M. ALY *Manager, Environmental Quality, Campbell Soup Company, Camden, New Jersey (Chapter 5)*

HENRY C. BRAMER *President, Datagraphics, Inc., Carnegie, Pennsylvania (Chapter 9)*

STANLEY J. DEA *Manager, Environmental Process Engineering, NUS Corporation, Rockville, Maryland (Chapter 10)*

DAVIS L. FORD *Senior Vice President, Engineering-Science, Inc., Austin, Texas (Chapter 8)*

LOUIS C. GILDE, JR. *Director, Environmental Engineering, Campbell Soup Company, Camden, New Jersey (Chapter 5)*

MATTHEW GOULD *Corporate Director, Environmental Control, Georgia-Pacific Corporation, Portland, Oregon (Chapter 6)*

LEE HENRY *Director of Laboratories, The Mogul Corporation, Chagrin Falls, Ohio (Chapters 1 and 11)*

JERRY L. JONES *Manager, Environmental Control, Chemical Engineering Group, Stanford Research Institute, Menlo Park, California (Chapter 2)*

WILLIAM A. PARSONS *Director, Corporate Environmental Control, Arthur G. McKee & Company, Cleveland, Ohio (Chapter 7)*

GERRY L. SHELL *President, Gerry Shell Environmental Engineers, Brentwood, Tennessee (Chapter 3)*

J. DONALD WALKER *Chairman and Director of Research and Development, Peabody Welles, Inc., Roscoe, Illinois (Chapter 4)*

JAMES H. WRIGHT *Director, Environmental Systems Department, Westinghouse Electric Corporation, Pittsburgh, Pennsylvania (Chapter 10)*

Foreword

Industrial wastewater management has undergone vast changes since the enactment of PL 92-500 in 1972. Prior to that time, in many cases, industrial wastewater treatment requirements were drawn from domestic wastewater treatment criteria, usually resulting in 85 percent reduction of BOD and suspended solids. Little emphasis was placed on in-plant controls and optimization of end-of-pipe treatment. PL 92-500 has specified criteria of effluent quality for three levels, namely, BPTCA by July 1, 1977, BATEA by July 1, 1983 with a further zero discharge stipulation. BPTCA or Best Practical Technology Currently Available is generally defined as the equivalent of secondary treatment presently being practiced in the particular industrial subcategory. For example, this may be considered as the activated sludge process in the organic chemicals industry. BATEA or Best Available Technology Economically Achievable is generally defined as treatment technology that has been demonstrated on an advanced laboratory or pilot plant scale to be technically and economically feasible for a specific industrial category. Further, new industrial facilities are separately treated under a new source standards category.

Each of these criteria specify the allowable pollutant in pounds per unit production and include pollutants other than the conventional BOD and suspended solids. The permitting procedure specifies both an average effluent quality and a daily maximum.

From what the writer has seen to this point, meeting BPTCA requirements is generally being accomplished by end-of-pipe treatment. It should be recognized that within any industrial subcategory variations in raw waste load may result from differences in plant age and size, raw materials input, output product specifications, and variations in in-plant process operations. For example, in the pulp and paper industry raw waste load will be affected by the type of wood used, the quality and brightness of the bleached product and processing variants such as dry or wet debarking. These factors should be carefully considered in defining effluent limitations under BPTCA so that the treatment technology employed can, in fact, meet the requirements. There is some question at this time whether the BATEA effluent limitations presently being proposed will be changed prior to their implementation. In some cases the economics relative to the additional degree of treatment achieved are very poor. In any event, in most industrial categories attainment of BATEA effluent qualities will be achieved largely by in-plant controls, by-product recovery and recycle. In order to illustrate this point, a detailed study was made by Union Carbide for the Environmental Standards and Water Quality Information Advisory Committee on the economics of meeting BATEA levels. Considering secondary treatment in-place, the annual costs for in-plant waste reduction and effluent filtration was $1.3 million per year to achieve an effluent BOD of 28,000 lbs/day, a suspended solids of 13,800 lbs/day, and a COD of 22,500 lbs/day. If, as an alternative, advanced wastewater treatment employing filtration and activated carbon was added to the present secondary plant, the annual cost would be $4.1 million to achieve an effluent BOD of 25,700 lbs/day, a suspended solids of 9,200 lbs/day, and a COD of 17,850 lbs/day. It is apparent from these numbers that very little improvement in effluent quality is achieved by adding additional end-of-pipe treatment for a significant cost.

In the food processing industry it has been demonstrated that in-plant controls can generally meet BATEA levels at significant savings in cost over advanced end-of-pipe treatment. Consider a plant producing apple juice with a production capacity of 250 tons/day. Utilizing in-plant modifications and controls, the annual cost to meet present BATEA limitations would be $76,000 per year. Employing end-of-pipe treatment technology would result in an annual cost of $105,700. The favorable economics for in-plant controls are obvious. Considering the foregoing comments, the environmental engineer in industry today is faced with a complex problem of developing both a technical and economic solution to water pollution control. A well-defined sampling and monitoring program should be developed with all major sources of wastewater defined. Options for source control, recycle and recovery should be reviewed before consideration of end-of-pipe treatment. Treatment technology should be viewed in light of present and future effluent criteria.

This volume should be of great assistance to the environmental engineer seeking solutions to their problems. The fundamentals relative to establishing available technology and equipment are covered by well-qualified professionals. The experience in six major industrial categories should provide invaluable guidance as to the options available and the results obtainable.

W. WESLEY ECKENFELDER, JR.
Distinguished Professor
Environmental and Water Resources Engineering
Vanderbilt University
Nashville, Tennessee

Preface

Water may be the most reusable and recyclable commodity on earth. Since its supply is limited, we must learn to recycle and reuse it effectively. Different uses of water require different degrees and types of cleanliness. Industry needs water for drinking, steam making, manufacturing operations, cooling, plant and equipment cleaning, fire fighting, gardening, and many specialized purposes. The quality of water required for each of these duties is significantly different.

In today's world, water is not free. In fact, water conveyance and treatment systems cost great sums of money. Then, why turn water into wastewater after only one or two uses? Industrial management is recognizing the benefits of using water for several different duties in descending order of required cleanliness before calling it a waste. This multiple, cascade, or sequential reuse of water minimizes the need for new water supplies. Repeated use or recycle of water for the same duty such as cooling is practiced widely by industry now in reducing its net water consumption and use. In addition to saving water and associated costs, both of these techniques minimize the volume of wastewater that must be treated. A proper combination of these water recycle and reuse methods, coupled with the optimum conveyance and treatment facilities, *may* produce an economical closed-loop, zero discharge system that requires minimum make-up water to function.

"Industrial Wastewater Management Handbook" focuses on the practicality (and sometimes impracticality) of this philosophy. It deals in depth with the water pollution control problems of the six largest water polluting industries. Methods of pollution prevention and product recovery, relative pollution potential of competing manufacturing processes, quantification and characterization of wastewaters at significant sources, practicality and impracticality of zero discharge, and successful industrial wastewater treatment practices have received a major emphasis. Exclusion of other industries and related subjects such as air pollution control and solid wastes management have permitted its distinguished authors to cover the selected subjects in depth and disseminate significant practical data on successful industrial wastewater treatment engineering and management practices.

The chapters on Legislation and Standards, Effluent Discharge Guidelines, Wastewater Monitoring, Wastewater Treatment Technology, and Wastewater Treatment Equipment cover practical fundamentals that apply to all industries. Specific problems, solutions, and case histories of Food, Paper and Allied Products, Chemical, Petroleum, Metals, and Power Generation industries are discussed separately in the second half of the book for optimum industrial coverage. The industrial authors have tried to achieve a proper balance between the traditional manufacturing unit process and end-of-the-pipe wastewater treatment approaches in their problem solving task-force oriented presentations. They first point out how to minimize industrial wastewaters through manufacturing process change, product recovery, water reuse and recycle, stream segregation, and better housecleaning. Then, they show how to develop the most effective, fiexible, and economical wastewater treatment schemes for the wastewaters that must be treated prior to discharge or reuse.

This authoritative information is intended to orient the end-of-the-pipe treatment practitioners to wastewater prevention through product recovery and manufacturing process change for cost-effective water pollution control. Many successful industrial wastewater management case histories and other data presented in this book should provide practical guidance to its readers on determining the specific natures of the industrial wastewater problem and on selecting its optimum solution. Practicing engineers, related technical and middle management, students and teachers, regulatory agencies, libraries, and other concerned citizens should find this handbook valuable in achieving a proper understanding of the industrial wastewaters and their judicious management. We encourage and invite constructive comments from our readers so that the future revisions could be improved where possible.

Graham Garratt, book editor of another publishing concern, originally approached Monsanto Enviro-Chem Systems, Inc. in December 1971 to prepare a reference or handbook of this type. Dr. Clinton C. Kemp, then my superior at Monsanto, envisioned the need for such a book and assigned me to develop one. Monsanto Enviro-Chem also allowed Jerry Jones, then its employee, to contribute the chapter on Wastewater Monitoring. When the Editor-in-Chief joined Arthur G. McKee & Co. in mid-1972, William F. Richards and Robert L. Perry (McKee's management) kindly assumed this corporate committment. Bill Richards also encouraged Dr. William A. Parsons to contribute the chapter on Chemical Industry.

The management of Arthur G. McKee & Company permitted me to devote huge amount of time, paid for many long-distance telephone calls and out-of-town travel, and provided the much needed secretarial assistance for completing most of this handbook. It clearly shows that McKee has excellent professional outlook and very enlightened management. I am grateful to Bill Richards, Bob Perry, Bob Verner and other fine McKee managers for their unforgettable encouragement and material help.

Current affiliations of our contributors indicate major assitance from so many other businesses for this handbook. The McGraw-Hill Book Company, all authors, and I sincerely appreciate this generous industry support.

HARDAM SINGH AZAD, PH.D.

Industrial Wastewater Management Handbook

Section 1
Fundamentals

Chapter 1

Legislation and Standards: Status, Trends, and Significance

LEE HENRY

Director of Laboratories, The Mogul Corporation,
Chagrin Falls, Ohio

INTRODUCTION

Municipalities and industries account for the largest portion of waste discharges that occur in the United States. In the six New England states, New York, and Pennsylvania can be found 20 percent of the nation's pollution. In the same states 52 percent of the sewered population is not provided with waste handling facilities. It has been estimated that the municipal waste loads will increase nearly four times in the next 50 years.[1]

Industries discharge an enormous variety of materials which include the largest volume of waste and the most toxic of pollutants. It has been estimated that there are over 300,000 water-using factories in the United States. Industrial waste sources, like municipal wastes, are concentrated in specific areas of the country. As the population expands, so does the need for manufactured goods. Consequently, the volume of industrial wastes is growing several times as fast as that of sanitary sewage. Some of the industrial wastes can be treated in municipal sewage treatment plants, but others must be pretreated at the source.

Environmental control is a very complex science. The trend is to move in the direction of pollution avoidance rather than control. This will add a tremendous cost to industrial budgets as well as increase the taxes of every working American. The public has tolerated pollution until recently, but the condition has increased to the point that many may suffer or even die because of it.

In addition to standards, this book will describe monitoring of wastes, control equipment, and engineering techniques. It will also discuss specific problems in several typical industries. The industries will include food, paper and allied products, chemicals, petroleum, metals, and power generation.

This chapter will concentrate on the effluent and water quality standards and will attempt to describe their effects relative to industry in general.

The current regulations cannot be placed in the proper perspective unless the history of water quality legislation is understood. It is necessary then that we briefly review this subject.

WATER QUALITY LEGISLATION

The first attempt, in an indirect way, to control pollution began with the River and Harbor Act which was approved March 3, 1899. Next came the Federal Water Pollution Control Act in 1912 in which the U.S. Public Health Service was authorized to investigate pollution. Then in 1948, the U.S. Public Health Service was authorized to provide technical information to the states and a Water Pollution Control Division was established within the Public Health Service. The act of 1956 provided for studying pollution problems and for matching grants for local sewage disposal plants. 1965 marked the entry of the federal government into the pollution control field. At that time, the states were directed to prepare stream quality standards. By 1970, the federal government had a strong desire to enforce pollution control but did not have a law of recent vintage to use. Consequently, the River and Harbor Act of 1899 was used to require a permit for all who discharged wastes into navigable waterways. The federal government indicated that such a permit would be granted if the discharge did not violate the Federal Water Pollution Control Act; therefore, the 1899 act ("Refuse Act") became another amendment to the Federal Water Pollution Control Act.[2] The River and Harbor Act of 1899 had several limitations and subsequently fell into disuse because of several legal battles over the lack of definition of "navigable waterways," and the need to "establish environmental impact statements" at each outfall.

The current law, the Federal Water Pollution Control Act Amendments, was established on October 18, 1972. This law has been found to be free of most federal limitations.

FEDERAL WATER POLLUTION CONTROL ACT AMENDMENTS OF 1972

It is the objective of the current law to restore and maintain the chemical, physical, and biological integrity of the nation's waters. All discharge of pollutants is to be eliminated by 1985. Also, an "interim goal" is that water quality will be achieved "which provides for the protection and propagation of fish, shellfish, and wildlife and provides for recreation in and on the water" by July 1, 1983.[3] It is the national policy that discharge of toxic pollutants in toxic amounts be prohibited, federal financial assistance be provided to construct publicly owned treatment works, and areawide waste treatment management planning processes be developed and implemented to assure adequate control of sources of pollutants in each state.

The public is invited to participate in the development, revision, and enforcement, and is encouraged and assisted by the Administrator of the Federal Environmental Protection Agency. The Administrator, on the other hand, in cooperation with the states, must develop and publish regulations specifying the minimum guidelines and standards of performance and pretreatment.

A permit system has been initiated by the current law which is known as the *National Pollutant Discharge Elimination System* (NPDES). One of the peculiarities of this particular part of the law is that municipal as well as industrial plants are included in the permit program. At the time that the current law was initiated, the Refuse Act Permit Program, which had been controlled by the U.S. Corps of Engineers, was turned over to the Federal Environmental Protection Agency. Many industries had already applied for a Refuse Act permit. Some of the applicants had filled out their application forms completely and correctly, some had filled out the forms incompletely, or incorrectly, still others had not applied for a Refuse Act permit at all. The National Pollutant Discharge Elimination System takes these three situations into account. If an applicant had completely and correctly filled out the Refuse Act permit and it was accepted, then no further application was needed until January 1975. If the application was incorrectly or incompletely filled out or if no permit application had been made at all, then the applicant had to apply for the National Pollutant Discharge Elimination System permit under the current Federal Water Pollution Control Act Amendments of 1972.

FEDERAL GOVERNMENT AGENCIES RESPONSIBLE FOR THE ENVIRONMENT

The key federal group that is responsible for the protection of the environment is the Environmental Protection Agency (EPA). Another federal agency with important environmental protection activities is the Council on Environmental Quality. The key agency that has the responsibility for the protection of the oceans is known as the National Oceanic and Atmospheric Administration. The Department of Interior still carries on several important environmental functions, and at one time it was responsible for nearly all federal environmental protection operations as well as supervision of the use of public lands. The Army Corps of Engineers and the Department of Agriculture also are involved in environmental matters and should be considered with this group.

An understanding of the National Environmental Protection Act of 1969 and the Environmental Quality Act of 1970 is important when considering the basic federal government environmental agencies.

The passage of the National Environmental Policy Act of 1969 (NEPA) attempted to create a frame of reference within which the federal government's activities involving effects on the environment could operate. An attempt was made to internalize agency approaches concerning environmental impact.

The original 1969 bill was introduced as Senate Bill 1075 by Senator Henry Jackson of Washington. It had three purposes:

1. To establish a national environmental policy
2. To authorize research concerning natural resources
3. To establish a Council of Environmental Advisors.[2]

The bill that was introduced by Senator Jackson unfortunately did not contain any procedures that would assure implementation of the policy. After a brief hearing, Section No. 102(2)(C) was added to S. 1075 which provided for an "action-forcing" measure to supplement the bill. This new section requires federal agencies to prepare an environmental impact statement if any action proposed affects the environment.

The Environmental Quality Improvement Act of 1970 related to findings, declarations, and purposes. It first of all stated that Congress finds,

> that man has caused changes in the environment; that many of these changes may affect the relationship between man and his environment; and that population increases and urban concentration contribute directly to pollution and the degradation of our environment.[2]

It next declared

> that there is a National Policy for the environment which provides for the enhancement of environmental quality. This policy is evident by statutes here-to-fore enacted relating to the prevention, abatement, and control of environmental pollution, water and land resources, transportation and economic and regional development.[2]

It further stated that

> the primary responsibility for implementing this policy rests with State and local governments. The Federal Government encourages and supports implementation of this policy to appropriate regional organizations established under existing law.[2]

The purposes of this title are:

> To assure that each Federal Department and Agency conducting or supporting public works activities which affect the environment shall implement the policies established under existing law; and to authorize an Office of Environmental Quality, which, notwithstanding any other provision of law, shall provide the professional and Administrative staff for the Council on Environmental Quality established by Public Law 91–190.[2]

Environmental Protection Agency

The Environmental Quality Improvement Act of 1970 became Public Law 91–224 on April 3, 1970. Subsequently, on December 2, 1970, the United States Environmental Protection Agency was established. This created for the first time a single agency that has the major environmental control within the federal government. The EPA was given the responsibility to develop a force that was integrated and coordinated on environmental problems. This would involve air pollution, water pollution, solid waste management, pesticides, radiation, and noise. By putting all of these problems under one agency, the entire problem was attached at once to one integrated agency with one major purpose, and that is to once and for all end the nation's environmental problems that are bringing about destruction to the environment and death to individuals throughout the United States.

The EPA is a regulatory agency. It must establish and enforce environmental standards. Establishment of the standards is a central responsibility of EPA in the pollution control effort.

Research and monitoring are also principal areas of concern for EPA. It is the purpose of the EPA to research and suggest solutions. At the same time it has the obligation to monitor and analyze the environment. In doing so, it will conduct scientific studies in an effort to find causes and effects of pollution. Once the causes and effects are known, control techniques can be established.

Technical and financial assistance are also important aspects of the EPA activity. There are 10 regional offices in the United States. These offices are under federal control directly answerable to the Administrator but, at the same time, they are autonomous in that they have certain authority to deal with local matters. Funds are available through EPA to develop new technology. This assistance is provided to independent organizations and to state and local governments.

Finally, the EPA is responsible for personnel development. It is the responsibility of the agency to develop the highest skilled personnel possible to meet and subdue the environmental problems. Many educational programs are available at various EPA schools throughout the United States.

In Fig. 1 the reader can study the organization of the Environmental Protection Agency, and Table 1 lists current environmental personnel.

Council on Environmental Quality

The Council on Environmental Quality was established by the National Environmental Policy Act of 1969. Its duty is to formulate and recommend national policies that will promote the improvement of environmental quality. The Council consists of three members appointed by the President of the United States. The appointment is made by the President but by and with the consent of the U.S. Senate. Mr. Russell E. Train was originally the Chairman of the Council on Environmental Quality. At the time of this writing, Mr. Train is the Administrator of the U.S. Environmental Protection Agency.

The activities of the Council consist in developing and recommending to the President certain national policies that will promote environmental quality. Trends are to be studied in the preparation of an annual environmental quality report to the Congress.

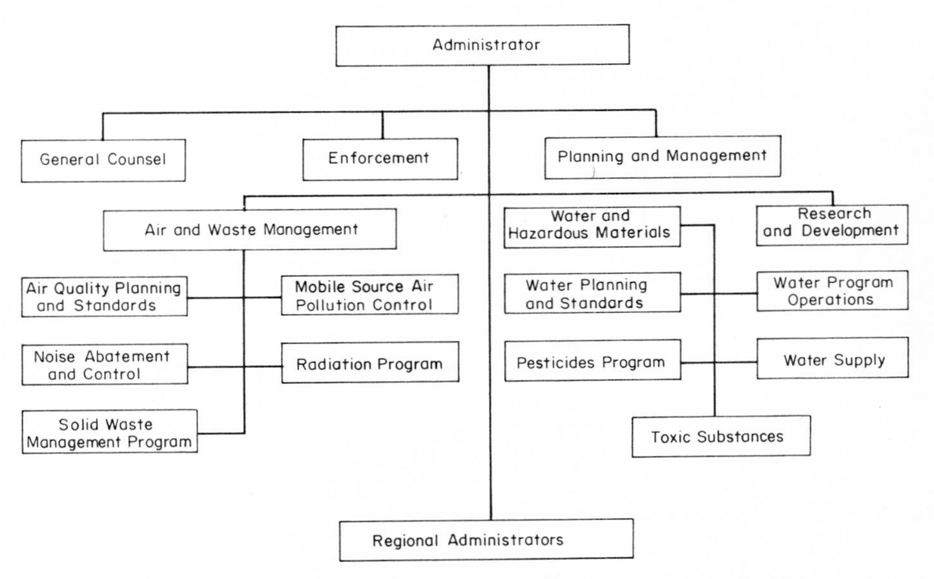

Fig. 1 United States Environmental Protection Agency, April 1975.

EPA Advisory Committee

Dr. Martha Sager is Chairman of the Effluent Standards and Water Quality Information Advisory Committee (ES&WQIAC). The nine-member committee was selected from the scientific community in an effort to advise the EPA Administrator on effluent limitations, water quality information, and toxic substances. The members of the committee operate on a workshop or seminar basis. It is the purpose of the committee to collect information from industries and to determine production variables. At first the efforts were somewhat fruitless because many industries had not collected sufficient data for decisions to be made.

Twenty-seven industries are involved in the study by the committee. These industries are specified in the Federal Water Pollution Control Act Amendments of 1972, Section 306(b)(1)(A). The committee first divided the 27 industries into groups of three. Dr. Sager has made individual committee members responsible for the

TABLE 1 Who's Who in the Environmental Administration—April 1975

U.S. ENVIRONMENTAL PROTECTION AGENCY (EPA)	
Telephone "locator" for Washington officials	202/755-2673
Russel E. Train	Administrator
John R. Quarles, Jr.	Deputy Administrator
Maurice Eastin	Industry Affairs Consultant to the Administrator
Alvin L. Alm	Assistant Administrator for Planning and Management
Alan G. Kirk II	Assistant Administrator for Enforcement and General Counsel
James L. Agee	Acting Assistant Administrator for Water and Hazardous Materials
Mrs. Lillian D. Regelson	Deputy Assistant Administrator for Water Planning and Standards
Roger Strelow	Assistant Administrator for Air and Materials Disposal
Bernard J. Steigerwald	Deputy Assistant Administrator for Air Quality Planning and Standards
Albert C. Trakowski, Jr.	Acting Assistant Administrator for Research and Development
Willis B. Foster	Deputy Assistant Administrator for Monitoring Systems
EPA REGIONAL ADMINISTRATORS	
Region I (Boston)	John A. McGlennon
Region II (New York)	Gerald M. Hensler
Region III (Philadelphia)	Daniel J. Snyder III
Region IV (Atlanta)	Jack E. Ravan
Region V (Chicago)	Francis T. Mayo
Region VI (Dallas)	Arthur W. Busch
Region VII (Kansas City)	Jerome H. Svore
Region VIII (Denver)	John A. Green
Region IX (San Francisco)	Paul DeFalco, Jr.
Region X (Seattle)	L. Edwin Coate (acting)
EPA EFFLUENT STANDARDS & WATER QUALITY INFORMATION ADVISORY COMMITTEE (ES & WQIAC)	
Dr. Martha Sager	Chairman
COUNCIL ON ENVIRONMENTAL QUALITY (CEQ)	
Russel W. Peterson	Chairman
John A. Busterud	Council Member
Dr. Beatrice Willard	Council Member
Steven Jellinek	Staff Director
Gary Widman	General Counsel
U.S. DEPARTMENT OF INTERIOR	
Rogers C. B. Morton	Secretary
Jack O. Horton	Assistant Secretary for Land and Water Resources
Lance Marston	Director, Office of Land Use and Water Planning
Curt Berklund	Director, Bureau of Land Management
(Vacant)	Assistant Secretary for Energy and Minerals
King Mallory	Deputy Assistant Secretary for Power Resources and Regulations
S. William Gouse, Jr.	Director, Office of Coal Resources
DEPARTMENT OF TRANSPORTATION	
Gen. Benjamin O. Davis, Jr.	Assistant Secretary for Environmental, safety, and consumer affairs
DEPARTMENT OF COMMERCE	
Dr. Sidney R. Galler	Deputy Assistant Secretary for Environmental Affairs

industries discussed and each will act as a Seminar Director. This would allow several workshops to proceed simultaneously on different industries.

It is important to note that the members of the committee are not federal employees. The members are selected from the scientific academic community. Dr. Sager stated in an interview,

> We have had an excellent response from industry in translating their day-to-day flowsheets into the kind of formula we requested. Their cooperation has been

magnificent. We feel that industry needs to have its input to the EPA through the committee because there is no one who is more expert for example, in the manufacture of steel than the steelmakers. Their inputs are more valuable than any other. We feel that it's the only place from which data can come. After the data have been reevaluated by the members in charge, comments are circulated to all members, suggestions are considered, editing is completed, and the final document is sent to EPA.[12]

It is also the responsibility of the ES&WQIAC to get advice on toxic substances. A number of recommendations have been sent to the EPA Administrator in the past several months.

The federal approach to environmental control has brought about a single-driver responsibility for a massive vehicle. Each part of that vehicle is unique with environmental problems that may be different from those of any other member. The EPA has attempted to allow the states to resolve their own individual problems if they desire. Before they can be given permission to resolve their own problems, however, they must show in a documented way that they are most desirous and capable of handling their own problems. Many of the states have been able to accept the responsibility, but many are still dependent upon the federal government. It is the opinion of the author that the vehicle would be pulling in 50 different directions if the federal system of control had not been adopted. Now that the direction has been established by the 1972 amendments, and the responsibility of enforcement has been accepted by the U.S. Environmental Protection Agency, the states can more easily direct their separate counties, which can effectively direct their separate towns, which can successfully direct local industries and other polluters in the cleanup and control of the nation's environment.

GENERAL EFFLUENT LIMITATIONS

The EPA Administrator has been given specific instructions to interpret and give meaning to the "best practicable technology currently available (BPTCA)." In doing so, he had to distinguish between the total cost of pollution control and balance it with the effluent reduction benefits. This activity might eliminate the application of technology which would be high in cost in comparison to the minimal reduction in pollution which might be achieved.

In addition to that responsibility, the "best available technology economically achievable (BATEA)" must be determined by the Administrator. This must involve the highest degree of technology that has been demonstrated as capable of being designed for plant-scale operation, so the cost for this treatment may be much higher than for treatment by best practicable technology. The economic feasibility will also be a factor in interpreting best available treatment. In addition to the best practicable control technology currently available, and best available technology economically achievable, the Administrator has been given the responsibility to promulgate guidelines which will be used to determine what "effluent limitations" will be imposed upon dischargers. In doing so, he must identify the degree of effluent reduction attainable through the application of the best practicable control and best available technology, which will be done in terms of amounts of constituents and chemical, physical, and biological characteristics of pollutants. Control measures must be identified. Regulations must identify control measures and practices to eliminate the discharge of pollutants.

SPECIFIC EFFLUENT LIMITATIONS

All publicly owned treatment works must meet effluent limitations by July 1, 1977. This will be based on the use of information supplied by the EPA Administrator regarding chemical, physical, and biological characteristics of pollutants. The effluent limitations must be met through the application of secondary treatment. Private point sources that are discharging into publicly owned treatment works must not be detrimental in any way to the fulfillment of the final discharge into navigable waters. If the waste from private point sources is detrimental, then the effluent must comply with pretreatment effluent standards. Effluent standards have been proposed for certain toxic pollutants. The pollutants that have been listed are:

1. *Aldrin* (1,2,3,4,10,10-hexachloro-1,4,4a,5,8,8a-hexahydro-1,4,-endo-exo-5,8-dimethanonaphthalene)
2. *Dieldrin* (1,2,3,4,10,10-hexachloro-6,7-epoxy-1,4,4a,5,6,7,8,8a-octahydro-1,4-endo-exo-5,8-dimethanonaphthalene)
3. *Benzidine* and its salts (4,4′-diaminobiphenyl)
4. *Cadmium* and all cadmium compounds
5. *Cyanide* and all cyanide compounds
6. *DDD* (TDE) [1,1-dichloro-2,2-bis(*p*-chlorophenyl) ethane and some o,p′-isomer]
7. *DDE* [1,1-dichloro-2,2-bis(*p*-chlorophenyl) ethylene]
8. *DDT* [1,1,1-trichloro-2,2-bis(*p*-chlorophenyl) ethane and some o,p′-isomer]
9. *Endrin* (1,2,3,4,10,10-hexachloro-6,7-epoxy-1,4,4a,5,6,7,8,8a-octahydro-1,4-endo-endo-5,8-dimethanonaphthalene)
10. *Mercury* and all mercury compounds
11. *Polychlorinated biphenyls* (PCB's) mixtures of chlorinated biphenyl compounds with various percentages of chlorination
12. *Toxaphene* (chlorinated camphene)

"Toxic pollutants," "toxic substances," and "toxic materials," are frequently noted in Water Quality Standards. The "substances" are usually not defined. Caswell[4] has described several factors that must be considered in the determination of "toxic substances" which have a controlling influence on the level of toxicity. They are:

1. Temperature
2. pH
3. Dissolved solids
4. Dissolved oxygen
5. Relative concentration of "toxic materials"
6. Species of organic life forms involved
7. Ages, and/or stage of development, of individual units within the species grouping
8. Synergistic effects that may occur when two toxic substances or a toxic and nontoxic substance are mixed in the same solution
9. Length of time of exposure, i.e., "immediate toxicity" versus "chronic toxicity"

In addition to the above list of toxic pollutants, the federal Environmental Protection Agency is examining a wide range of pollutants. Among those are:

1. Arsenic
2. Selenium
3. Chromium
4. Lead
5. Asbestos
6. Sevin
7. Zinc
8. Chlordane
9. Lindane
10. Acridine
11. Hydroquinone
12. Ortho-chlorophenol
13. Beta-naphthol
14. Alpha-naphthol
15. Beryllium
16. Nickel
17. Antimony
18. Heptachlor
19. Camphor
20. Methyl parathion
21. Parathion
22. Di-*n*-butyl phthalate

NEW SOURCE PERFORMANCE STANDARDS

New sources of pollution are especially considered by the EPA. Most new factories, and industries in general, are subject to national standards of performance. A list of New Source Performance Standards has been published by the EPA. This includes a list of categories of sources which must include 27 major types of industries. The 27 categories are:

1. Pulp and paper mills
2. Paper based, builder's paper and board mills
3. Meat product and rendering processing
4. Dairy product processing
5. Grain mills
6. Canned and preserved fruits and vegetables

7. Canned and preserved seafood processing
8. Sugar processing
9. Textile mills
10. Cement manufacturing
11. Feed lots
12. Electroplating
13. Organic chemicals manufacturing
14. Inorganic chemicals manufacturing
15. Plastic and synthetic materials manufacturing
16. Soap and detergent manufacturing
17. Fertilizer manufacturing
18. Petroleum refining
19. Iron and steel manufacturing
20. Nonferrous metals manufacturing
21. Phosphate manufacturing
22. Steam electric power plants
23. Ferro alloy manufacturing
24. Leather tanning and finishing
25. Glass and asbestos manufacturing
26. Rubber processing
27. Timber products processing

Best practicable control technology is not the only controlling factor. If water quality standards cannot be protected by this measure, or by secondary treatment for municipal wastes before 1977, then effluent limitations must be achieved which will protect water quality standards. Also, if the best available treatment and its equivalent for municipal facilities will not contribute to attainment of water quality by 1983 (which will protect public water supplies, agricultural, and industrial uses, protection of the population of fish and wildlife, and allow recreational activities) more stringent effluent limitations will be imposed.[5]

SECONDARY TREATMENT FOR MUNICIPAL WASTES

Minimum Levels

Minimum levels of effluent quality have been established for municipal wastes. These will be achieved by secondary treatment and will not exceed the concentration of the following parameters:

1. *Biochemical oxygen demand (BOD).* "The arithmetic mean of the values for effluent samples collected in a period of 30 consecutive days shall not exceed 30 milligrams per liter" and "shall not exceed 45 milligrams per liter" when collected in a period of 7 consecutive days.

2. *Suspended solids.* "The arithmetic mean of the values for effluent samples collected in a period of 30 consecutive days shall not exceed 30 milligrams per liter" and "shall not exceed 45 milligrams per liter" when collected in a period of 7 consecutive days.

3. *Fecal coliform bacteria.* "The geometric mean of the value for effluent samples collected in a period of 30 consecutive days shall not exceed 200 per 100 milliliters," and "shall not exceed 400 per 100 milliliters" when collected in a period of 7 consecutive days.

4. *pH.* "The effluent value for pH shall remain between 6.0 and 9.0."

Special considerations have been given for secondary treatment: "Secondary treatment may not be capable of meeting the percentage removal requirements during wet weather in treatment works which receive flows from combined sewers (sewers designed to transport both storm water and sanitary sewage)."[6] In that case, the decision must be made on a case-by-case basis. For some industrial categories the discharge to navigable waters of biochemical oxygen demand and suspended solids allowed may be less stringent than the values stated above. In those cases where waste is introduced from an industrial category into a publicly owned treatment system, "the values for biochemical oxygen demand and suspended solids may be adjusted upwards provided that the permitted discharge which is attributable to the industrial category would not be greater than that which would be detrimental to sewage treatment works in meeting the NPDES permit requirements."[6] This means that the same stringency is placed on industry as if it were to be discharging directly into navigable waters. "In those cases where the flow or loading of pollutants introduced by an industry exceeds 10 percent of the designed flow or loading of the publicly owned treatment works, values of biochemical oxygen demand and suspended solids may be adjusted upward from the limits."[6]

Sampling and Test Procedures

Sampling and test procedures have been developed for biochemical oxygen demand and for suspended solids. These must be done in accordance with guidelines promulgated by the Administrator of the Federal Environmental Protection Agency. "Chemical Oxygen Demand (COD) or Total Organic Carbon (TOC) may be substituted for Biochemical Oxygen Demand (BOD) when a long-term BOD:COD or BOD:TOC correlation has been demonstrated."[6]

POINT SOURCE CATEGORIES

Space will not allow thorough coverage of all 27 industries in this book. An extensive table has been developed covering the current effluent guidelines and standards of these industries and is included as Chap. 11. The table lists the various categories and subcategories of the 27 industries that were described in the Federal Water Pollution Control Act Amendments of 1972. The effluent characteristics have been included for each subcategory and subpart. Both the metric and English units have been given for the maximum for any one day, and the average of daily values for 30 consecutive days for the best practical control technology currently available, the best available technology economically achievable, and the new source standards of performance. The metric and English units have also been included in Chap. 11.

The information given in the table of the 27 categories will help the reader to understand the differences that the authorities expect of industry. By studying it and relating the information to that in the other nine chapters, the reader will (hopefully) be in a position to visualize the trends and significance of the requirements.

The EPA has considered the effluent limitations for existing sources as well as standards of performance and pretreatment standards for new sources. The Federal Water Pollution Control Act Amendments of 1972 require that the EPA Administrator must promulgate pretreatment standards at the same time the standards of performance for new sources are made.

Known Significant Pollutants

Effluent limitations guidelines and standards of performance were developed in the following manner: Each point source category was first studied to determine if separate limitations and standards were necessary for different subcategories. This then determined if differences in the raw materials, product, manufacturing process, age, size, wastewater characteristics, and other variables would require consideration of separate limitations and standards for each different segment of the point source category. Raw waste characteristics were then identified for each subcategory. This involved the measurement of source, flow, and volume of water used in process and each source of waste and wastewater in a plant. Also included were the constituents of all wastewater. Control and treatment technologies that exist within each of the subcategories were determined. Also included was the identification of chemical, physical, and biological characteristics of pollutants, and the effluent level expected for application of each of the technologies. Problems, limitations, and reliability of each control technology were described. Known "significant pollutants" were then assigned to each source category.

Table 2 describes some of the significant pollutants that will be present in the 27 point source categories. Discrete subcategories have been established that help to pinpoint both the problems and the solutions. If the subcategories are not included, unfair restrictions develop when attempting to assign known significant pollutants.[7]

An individual personally responsible for a company's water pollution control will want to become very familiar with Tables 2 and 3 and with Chap. 11.

Monitoring

The National Pollutant Discharge Elimination System requires self-monitoring. Analysis requirements can be daily, weekly, monthly, annually, or in any other consistent routine that the state and/or federal authorities feel is necessary.

If a commercial laboratory is chosen to assist with monitoring requirements, care must be taken to ascertain that the contracting laboratory is not "an analytical numbers factory." In other words, the contractor should be asked for assistance with the evaluation of the results relative to the permit limitations. There should be evidence of an on-going, extensive quality control program. If the contractor is going to do the sampling or is supplying containers, the proper size and type of containers as well as preservatives should be used according to federal and/or state specifications.

The laboratory should keep all data in a bound, numbered workbook that will readily be acceptable in a court of law.

Be skeptical of the contractor's expertise if he or she refuses to be available as an "expert witness" in court. On the other hand, be assured that the laboratory representative has had court experience and that all records to be considered are complete. If the representative becomes flustered or if the records are confusing, the witness will be of more harm than help.

Preparing for Court

The authorities are concerned with the attitude of the accused as well as with progress in the cessation of pollution. It is therefore very important to have an active file of an on-going monitoring program. This should include:

1. Pollution control program plan
2. Wastewater survey
3. Mass balance
4. Sewer map
5. Location of sampling stations
6. List of parameters and concentrations
7. Flow measurement data

All record books should be bound and numbered. No erasures should be allowed in records.

The plant environmental officer is responsible for the results submitted to the authorities. Blatant refusal to cooperate or inaccurate data can result in a financial loss or a jail sentence or both.

WATER QUALITY CRITERIA

The amendments of 1972 also required the Administrator of the Federal Environmental Protection Agency to publish criteria for water quality. He must also include information for restoring and maintaining aquatic integrity, as well as the measurement and classification of water. Volume I (released in October, 1973) of this two volume series[8,9] contains criteria for water quality for the "protection of human health and for the protection and propagation of desirable species of aquatic biota." Volume II of the series contains information on the "maintenance and restoration, measurement, and the classification of waters."

The National Water Quality Standards Program was initiated when the Federal Water Pollution Control Act of 1965 was passed as noted in Section 10(c) of the act. The water quality standards are comprised of:

1. Use designations for each water body or portion thereof.
2. Water quality criteria to support the use designations.
3. Implementation plans for scheduling the construction of the necessary treatment facilities.[8]

Prior to the act, the water quality standards applied only to interstate waters and their tributaries. An extension of the act now applies to intrastate streams. State standards will be or are already revised to cover this extension of the law.

In implementing the act, the EPA has established a "stream use classification policy" that provides for the "*protection of all waters* to sustain recreational uses in and on the water and for the preservation and propagation of desirable species of aquatic biota." These levels of protection will make all waters suitable for other uses such as "public water supply, agriculture and irrigation."[8]

TABLE 2 Known Significant Pollutants for the 27 Industries

Categories of sources	Known significant pollutants
1. Pulp and paper mills	BOD, COD, SS, bac, WSL, NH_3, DS, biocides
2. Paperbased, builder's paper and board mills	BOD, COD, SS
3. Meat product and rendering process	BOD, DS, SS, N, NO_3, NH_3, O&G, P, bac.
4. Dairy product processing	pH, BOD, COD, DS, SS, set. s.
5. Grain mills	BOD, SS, pH, DS, N, P, heat
6. Canned and preserved fruits and vegetables processing	BOD, SS, pH
7. Canned and preserved seafood processing	BOD, COD, SS, DS, O, fecal coliform, Cl
8. Sugar processing	BOD, COD, SS, DS, coli, NH_3, pH, heat
9. Textile mills	BOD, COD, DS, color, SS, O&G, heavy metals, (Cu, Cr, Zn)
10. Cement manufacturing	DS, SS, pH, heat
11. Feedlots	BOD, DS, SS, NO_3, P, coli
12. Electroplating	Heavy metals, (Cr, Zn, Ni, Cd, others) CN, acidity, pH, DS, SS
13. Organic chemicals manufacturing	O, Unreacted raw materials, BOD, COD, SS, acidity or alkalinity, heavy metals and heat
14. Inorganic chemicals manufacturing	Divided into 22 discrete subcategories* BOD, DS, COD, pH, heat
15. Plastic and synthetic materials manufacturing	BOD, COD, SS, heavy metals, pH, (subcategories vary extensively)
16. Soap and detergent manufacturing	BOD, COD, SS, O&G, surf, pH
17. Fertilizer manufacturing	
Subpart A—Phosphate type	pH, P, F, Cd, As, V, U.
Subpart B—Ammonia	pH, N, O
Subpart C—Urea	pH, N
Subpart D—Ammonium nitrate	pH, N, NO_3
Subpart D—Nitric acid	pH, N, NO_3
18. Petroleum refining	O, S, Phen, NH_3, BOD, COD, heavy metals, alkalinity
19. Iron and steel manufacturing	Phen, CN, NH_3, O, SS, heavy metals, (Cr, Ni, Zn, Sn) DS, acidity and heat
20. Nonferrous metals manufacturing	BOD, SS, DS, COD, CN, pH, color, turb, heavy metals, P, N, O&G, heat
21. Phosphate manufacturing	F, As, P, H_3PO_4, H_2SO_3, H_2SO_4, HCl, SS, Cr, DS, NH_3
22. Steam electric power plants	BOD, SS, DS, COD, CN, pH, surf, color, O&G, phen, turb, heavy metals, VS, P, N, heat
23. Ferroalloy manufacturing	
Subpart A—Open electric furnaces with wet air pollution control	SS, Cr, Cr^{6+}, Mn, O, phen, PO_4

The criteria in Volume II are arranged alphabetically by water use, with limits for each pollutant followed by the supporting scientific rational. The numerical criteria are included here as Table 3. Volume II, entitled "Water Quality Information," contains information on factors necessary for the "restoration and maintenance of the integrity of the Nation's waters; the protection of fish, wildlife and human health; the identification of pollutants; and the measurement and classification of water quality."[8] Volume II provides information on "sources of polluting constituents (manmade and natural), mean levels in major river basins, techniques for biological and physical measurements, methodology for bioassays, and overall classification of water quality and the types of pollutants suitable for maximum daily load measurements."[9]

Water quality criteria as compiled in Volume I are defined as the "acceptable limits of constituents in receiving waters based on the evaluation of the latest scien-

TABLE 2 Known Significant Pollutants for the 27 Industries (Continued)

Categories of sources	Known significant pollutants
23. Ferroalloy manufacturing (Continued)	
Subpart B—Covered electric furnaces with wet air pollution control	SS, Cr, Cr^{6+}, CN, Mn, O, phen, PO_4
Subpart C—Slag processing	SS, Cr, Mn, O
Subpart D—Noncontact cooling	Heat, SS, Cr, Cr^{6+}, O, PO_4
24. Leather tanning and finishing	BOD, COD, DS, alkalinity, hard, color, NaCl, SO_3, S, amines, Cr, Na_2CO_3, O&G
25. Glass and asbestos manufacturing	
Glass	NH_3, pH, color, turb, heat, phen, BOD, COD, DS, SS, O&G
Asbestos	SS, BOD, pH
26. Rubber processing	BOD, CID, N, surf, color, Cl, S, O&G, phen, Cr.
27. Timber products	BOD, COD, SS, DS, color, TOC

Definitions of Parameters

phen	Phenols	P	Phosphate
BOD	Biochemical oxygen demand	bac	Bacteria
COD	Chemical oxygen demand	coli	Total coliform
DS	Dissolved solids	F	Fluoride
SS	Suspended solids	As	Arsenic
O	Oil	H_3PO_4	Phosphoric acid
G	Grease	H_2SO_3	Sulfurous acid
set. s.	Settleable solids	H_2SO_4	Sulfuric acid
Cl	Chloride	HCl	Hydrochloric acid
Cu	Copper	Cr	Chromium (total)
Zn	Zinc	WSL	Waste sulfite liquor
Ni	Nickel	NaCl	Sodium chloride
Cd	Cadmium	hard	Hardness
CN	Cyanide	Mn	Manganese
alk	Alkalinity	V	Vanadium
surf	Surfactants	U	Uranium
NH_3	Ammonia	S	Sulfide
pH	pH	Sn	Tin
color	Color (APHA) and or dyes	VS	Volatile solids
turb	Turbidity	Cr^{6+}	Chromium hexavalent
heat	Thermal	SO_3	Sulfite
N	Nitrogen (organic or Kjeldahl)	Na_2CO_3	Sodium carbonate
NO_3	Nitrate	TOC	Total organic carbon

* Inorganic chemicals manufacturing sub + categories

1. Aluminum chloride
2. Aluminum sulfate
3. Calcium carbide
4. Calcium chloride
5. Calcium oxide
6. Chlorine, sodium hydroxide, potassium hydroxide
7. Hydrochloric acid
8. Hydrofluoric acid
9. Hydrogen peroxide
10. Nitric acid

tific information by the Environmental Protection Agency." They are to form the basis for the 1983 interim goal of "improving the Nation's waters to a quality that provides for the protection and propagation of fish and wildlife, and for the health of humans and their pursuit of recreation in and on these waters." (8)

The criteria proposed relate to toxicity studies and other field and laboratory tests that measure the effects of pollutants on agricultural crops, domestic livestock, aquatic life, wildlife, and people. Acceptable limits for pollutants which exhibit toxic effects were established by using lethal dose or lethal concentration data in a manner that provides a "margin of safety" to test organisms. Criteria for substances that impair aquatic habitats, cause taste and odor problems, or reduce aesthetic or recreational quality were established on the basis of field and laboratory investigations. Acceptable levels of toxic materials were determined by applying an application factor to locally derived LC_{50} data. (LC_{50} is defined as "the concentration of the

TABLE 3 Tabular Summary of Numerical Criteria[8]

Constituent	Agriculture		Freshwater			Marine water, aquatic life	Recreational waters
	Irrigation	Livestock	Aquatic life	Wildlife	Public supply		
pH	4.5–9.0		6.0–9.0	6.0–9.0	5.0–9.0	6.5–8.5	Acceptable = 6.5–8.3 Must be = 5.0–9.0
Alkalinity			75% natural level	30–130 mg/l	No limit*		
Acidity			Addition of acids unacceptable		No limit		
BOD	No limit						
Al	5.0 mg/l 20.0 mg/l (20 yr)	5.0 mg/l				1/100 (0.01) 96-hr LC_{50}¶ 1.5 mg/l 1/10 LD_{50}¶¶	
NH_3			1/20 (0.05) LC_{50} 0.02 mg/l		0.5 mg/l	0.4 mg/l	
Sb						1/50 (0.02) 96-hr LC_{50} 0.2 mg/l	
As	0.10 mg/l 2.0 mg/l (20 yr)	0.2 mg/l			0.1 mg/l	1/100 (0.01) 96-hr LC_{50} 0.05 mg/l	
Ba					1.0 mg/l	1/20 (0.05) LD_{50} 1.0 mg/l	
Be	0.1 mg/l 0.5 mg/l (20 yr)	No limit				1/100 (0.01) 96-hr LC_{50} 1.5 mg/l	
Bi						No limit	
B	0.75 mg/l sen. 1.0 mg/l semi-tol. 2.0 mg/l tol.	5.0 mg/l			1.0 mg/l	1/10 (0.1) 96-hr LC_{50}	

Br					0.1 mg/l (free) 100 mg/l (ionic)
HCO_3	No limit				
Cd	0.01 mg/l 0.05 mg/l (20 yr)	50 μg/l	0.03 mg/l hard H_2O 0.004 mg/l soft H_2O	0.01 mg/l	1/100 (0.01)† 96-hr LC_{50} 0.01 mg/l
Cl (free)	No limit		0.003 mg/l 0.05 mg/l (30 min)		1/10 (0.1) 96-hr LC_{50} 0.01 mg/l
Cl_2 (Chloride)	No limit			250 mg/l	
Cr	0.1 mg/l 1.0 mg/l (20 yr)	1.0 mg/l	0.03 mg/l	0.05 mg/l	1/100 (0.01) 96-hr LC_{50} 0.1 mg/l
Co	0.05 mg/l 5.0 mg/l (20 yr)	1.0 mg/l			
Cu	0.20 mg/l 5.0 mg/l	0.5 mg/l	1/10 (0.1) 96-hr LC_{50}	1 mg/l	1/100 (0.01) 96-hr LC_{50} 0.05 mg/l
(CN)			1/20 (0.05) 96-hr LC_{50}	0.2 mg/l	1/10 (0.1) 96-hr LC_{50} 0.01 mg/l
F	2.0 mg/l 1.0 mg/l (Sandy soil) 15.0 mg/l (20 yr)	2.0 mg/l			1/10 (0.1) 96-hr LC_{50} 1.5 mg/l
H_2S			See sulfides		1/10 (0.1) 96-hr LC_{50} 0.01 mg/l
Fe	5.0 mg/l 20.0 mg/l (20 yr)	No limit		0.3 mg/l	0.3 mg/l
Pb	5.0 mg/l 10.0 mg/l	0.1 mg/l	0.03 mg/l	0.05 mg/l	1/50 (0.02) 96-hr LC_{50} 0.01 LD_{50}

TABLE 3 Tabular Summary of Numerical Criteria[8] (Continued)

Constituent	Agriculture		Freshwater			Marine water, aquatic life	Recreational waters
	Irrigation	Livestock	Aquatic life	Wildlife	Public supply		
Li	2.5 mg/l 0.075 mg/l					0.01 LD_{50} 24-hr max. 0.05 mg/l	
Mn	0.20 mg/l 10.0 mg/l (20 yr)	No limit			0.05 mg/l	1/50 (0.02) 96-hr LC_{50} 0.01 mg/l	
Hg Inorganic		1.0 μg/l	0.2 μg/l tot. conc. 0.05 μg/l avg. conc. 0.5 μg/g Body burden Conc. tot. Hg	0.5 μg/g in fish	0.002 mg/l total	1/100 (0.01) 96-hr LC_{50} 0.1 mg/l	
Organic			0.2 μg/l tot. conc. 0.05 μg/l avg. conc. 0.5 μg/g Body burden Conc. tot. Hg				
Mo	0.01 mg/l 0.05 mg/l	No limit				1/20 (0.05) 96-hr LC_{50}	
Ni	0.2 mg/l 2.0 mg/l (20 yr)		1/50 (0.02) 96-hr LC_{50}			1/50 (0.02) 96-hr LC_{50} 0.1 mg/l	
(NO_3)	No limit	100 mg/l Combined NO_3 and NO_2			10 mg/l		
(NO_2)		10 mg/l			1 mg/l		

P					No limit	1/100 (0.01) 96-hr LC_{50} 0.1 μg/l	25 μg/l lakes and reservoirs 50 μg/l at confluence 100 μg/l streams
Se	0.02 mg/l	0.05 mg/l			0.01 mg/l	1/100 (0.01) 96-hr LC_{50} 0.01 mg/l	
Na	No limit				No limit		
Ag					0.05 mg/l	1/20 (0.05) 96-hr LC_{50} 5.0 μg/l	
Tl						1/20 (0.05) 96-hr LC_{50} 0.1 mg/l	
U						1/100 (0.01) 96-hr LC_{50} 0.5 mg/l	
V		0.1 mg/l				1/20 (0.05) 96-hr LC_{50}	
Zn		25 mg/l	3/1,000 (0.003) 96-hr LC_{50}		5 mg/l	1/100 (0.01) 96-hr LC_{50} 0.1 mg/l	
Viruses					No limit		
Microorganisms		5,000 coliforms/ 100 ml‡ 20,000/100 ml§		2,000/100 ml	10,000/100 ml		
Fecal coliforms	1,000/100 ml	1,000/100 ml‡ 4,000/100 ml§		2,000/100 ml	2,000/100 ml		2,000/100 ml avg. 4,000/100 ml max. log mean 2n 200/100 m <10% samples in 30 days to exceed 400/100 ml

TABLE 3 Tabular Summary of Numerical Criteria[8] (Continued)

Constituent	Agriculture		Freshwater			Marine water, aquatic life	Recreational waters
	Irrigation	Livestock	Aquatic life	Wildlife	Public supply		
Dissolved solids (tot) (total)	2,000–5,000 mg/l (tolerant) 500–1,000 mg/ (sensitive)		Bioassays		No limit		
Hardness			(See TDS)		No limit		
Suspended and settleable solids	No limit		80 mg/l				
Temperature	No limit		See text	(Minimized) maintain natural pattern	Not to detract from potability	2.0 (3.6° F)9–5 1.0 (1.8°F) 6–8	86°F
Toxic algae		Heavy growth of blue-green not acceptable		No limit			
Botulism				Minimizes factors which promote disease			
Pesticides		See public water standards	1/100 (0.01) 96-hr LC_{50} Those for which no toxicity data available. See also Tables 1 and 2			1/100 (0.01) 96-hr LC_{50}	
Dalapon	0.2 μg/l				Silvex 0.03		
TCA	0.2 μg/l				2,4,5-T 0.002		
2,4-D	0.1 μg/l				0.02 μg/l		
Insecticides	No limit			DDT 1 mg/kg wet weight	Organophosphates 0.1 mg/l		
Turbidity			<10% change in C.P.		No limit		Clarity—4 ft Secchi
Carbon adsorbable					0.3 mg/l CCE 1.5 CAE		
Foaming agents					0.5 mg/l (ABS)		

NTA					No limit	
Phenols					1 μg/l	
Color			Comp. pt. not changed by >10%		75 platinum-cobalt units	
Radioactivity	See federal drinking water standards	See federal drinking water standards	See federal drinking water standards		See federal drinking water standards	See federal drinking water standards
Salinity		3,000 mg soluble salts/liter		No rapid fluctuation		
D.O.					No limit saturation preferred	6.0 mg/l
Sulfate					250 mg/l	
Sulfides			0.002 mg/l			
Detergents			1/20 (0.05) (LAS) 96-hr LC_{50} 0.2 mg/l max.			
Oils			No visible oil 1/20 (0.05) 96-hr LD_{50} Hexane extractable sediments 1,000 mg/kg	No visible floating oils		No film or odor No tainting of fish No onshore oil deposit
Phthalate esters			0.3 μg/l		No limit	
PCB's			0.002 μg/l (in water) 0.5 μg/g (in tissue)	No increase	No limit	
Odor					Free	
Light				<10% change in C.P.		

¶ LC_{50}—Lethal concentration of 50 percent of the individuals.
¶¶ LD_{50}—Median lethal dose (refers to toxicant actually received inside of body).
* Where it appears in this table, "No limit" refers to constituents that were addressed but for which insufficient data existed for prescribing limits.
† If more than 1 mg/l of copper or zinc is present, then AF = 0.001 LC_{50}.
‡ Average of a minimum of two samples per month.
§ Individual sample.

constituents in the water in question which causes death within 96 hr to 50 percent of the test group of the most sensitive important species in the locality under consideration.")[8] Criteria based on pollutant effects on the most "sensitive and important species" introduce local variations which allow water quality standards to depend on local conditions.

An "important species" in the criteria is defined as an organism that:

A. Is commercially or recreationally valuable;

B. Is rare or endangered;

C. Affects the well-being of some species within *A* and *B;*

D. Is critical to the structure and function of the ecological system. A rare or endangered species is any species so officially designated by the U.S. Field and Wildlife Service.[8]

Several choices or levels of protections are provided for such parameters as pH, dissolved oxygen, settleable and suspended solids. The recommendations provide a level of protection as required by the 1972 act. Water quality standards based on these criteria are to be developed on a "local basis to minimize impairment."[8] Synergistic effects of certain combinations of pollutants cause greater detriment to the environment than the simple effect of each pollutant; however, most of the criteria are "not based upon synergistic studies."[8] Judgment should be used and additional safety factors should be applied in cases where there is a *known potential* for synergistic effects of specific pollutants in a water system.

Major Uses of the Criteria

Water Quality Standards, Toxic and Pretreatment Standards, Water Quality Inventory (monitoring), Toxic and Pretreatment Effluent Standards, National Pollutant Discharge Elimination System, and the Ocean Discharge Criteria are the key water pollution control programs designed to improve the quality of the nation's waters and will undoubtedly be the major users of the criteria. Water Quality Criteria and Effluent Limitations are the two scientific/technical supporting structures of the entire National Water Quality Improvement Program and thus provide the foundation for the 1983 interim goal and the 1985 goal of zero discharge.

Effluent limitations are based on control technology relative to variations in application costs due to "benefit, equipment age, engineering, and non-water quality environmental impact."[8] Federal EPA water quality criteria will be incorporated into state water quality standards by means of "policy guidelines" developed by the EPA Office of Water Planning and Standards. Provisions are made for waters to be exempted for scientific criteria on a case-by-case basis for certain periods when "naturally occurring conditions" exceed the limits of the criteria or other unavoidable conditions develop that result in a need for such an exemption.

The criteria are based on "current knowledge of the effects on health and welfare of the presence of various pollutants in receiving waters."[8] Certain considerations must be made when making decisions in establishing standards based on the criteria. Some of these are:

1. The environmental impact of the presence of pollutants in water (e.g., long or short term, temporary or permanent, localized or widespread, etc.).
2. The economic and social impact of standards and control measures, and the impact of the environmental damage to be alleviated.
3. The practicality and enforceability of the standards and control measures, including the availability of techniques and instrumentation for determining whether particular standards are being met.[9]

PRETREATMENT OF DISCHARGE TO PUBLICLY OWNED TREATMENT WORKS

Federal guidelines for the pretreatment of discharges to publicly owned treatment works give the following policies:

1. Joint treatment of domestic wastewaters and adequately pretreated industrial wastewaters is encouraged where it is the economical choice.
2. In-plant measures to reduce the quality of strength of industrial wastewater flows can be beneficial to joint treatment and should be encouraged.
3. Pretreatment for removal of compatible pollutants is not required by the Federal pretreatment standards.
4. In recognition of the broad spectrum of industries, waste constituents, and

treatment plants, state and municipal pretreatment requirements should be based on an individual analysis of the permitted effluent limitations placed on a publicly owned treatment works and on the potential for adverse effects on such works.[10]

Federal Pretreatment Standards

Standards have been issued for pretreatment of pollutants discharged into publicly owned treatment works. The standards were designed to protect the operation and prevent the introduction of pollutants which would pass through insufficiently treated.

Although national in scope (by intention), the pretreatment standards may have to be supplemented by state and municipal laws to cover local situations. The purpose of the guidelines is to furnish information to states and municipalities for assistance in the development of supplemental pretreatment requirements.

State and Local Pretreatment Requirements

It is the objective of the 1972 act that pretreatment standards be established by state or local law not in conflict with the federal standards. For this reason, the federal standards were developed on the basis that "each publicly owned treatment works may require pretreatment by users, consistent with applicable state or municipal law." State or local pretreatment requirements can consider other factors (i.e., treatment processes and plant capacities) which are not national in scope.

Materials which Inhibit Biological Treatment Processes

The EPA has considered various materials which can inhibit four types of biological treatment processes:

1. Activated sludge
2. Trickling filter
3. Anaerobic digestion
4. Nitrification

TABLE 4 Classification[10]

Waste constituents	Low	Average	High	Extremely high
BOD_5, mg/1	<200	200–300	300–1000	>1,000
COD, mg/1	<300	300–450	450–1500	>1,500
Suspended solids, mg/1	<300	200–300	300–1000	>1,000
Temperature, °C	<15	15–25	>25	
pH	<6 (acid)	6–9	>9 (alkaline)	

The information came primarily from data that have been reported in technical literature. Much of the data on the subject are limited. This is especially true of synergistic effects of many constituents in wastewater. For this reason, care in application of the guidelines must be exercised relative to specific situations. The guidelines instruct:

> The wastewaters must be analyzed to determine the presence of inhibitory materials and their potential impact upon treatment plant performance. This includes consideration of intermittent batch discharges, variations in concentration and background levels already present in the wastewater. When inhibitory materials are present, testing the public water supply will provide an indication of the domestic source of the inhibitory materials. However, it must be realized that materials of this type can be added during domestic water usage.[10]

Description of the characteristics of industrial wastewater in relation to sanitary sewage is provided by Table 4.

The guidelines state that wastewater characteristics information can be used to identify conditions which should be carefully evaluated when establishing pretreatment requirements for a specific industry and in the design of the joint treatment works. Specifically, they can be used as a guideline when establishing a wastewater testing program for an industry.

Three types of municipal secondary treatment processes are identified which are considered necessary for industrial wastewaters. These processes are:

1. Suspended Biological System (activated sludge process including modifications, aerated lagoon processes).
2. Fixed Biological Systems (Trickling Filter and modifications, rotary disc).
3. Independent Physical/Chemical Systems (Chemical addition, sedimentation, pH adjustment, filtration, carbon adsorption).[10]

Pretreatment Ordinances

It is important that no discharge to a publicly owned treatment system causes physical damage, interferes with the treatment process, or results in a violation of effluent limitations. All discharges therefore must be carefully controlled. It has been found to be necessary in many cases to establish a local system to allocate waste loads to industrial users to prevent inhibition of biological treatment processes and to ascertain that effluent limitations are not exceeded.

Many state and local authorities have published instructions to dischargers. These should be studied and adapted to specific problems in particular industries.

TRENDS

Stream standards, rather than effluent standards, are preferred by both municipalities and industries for legal purposes. The reason is that plants in the United States usually are located near large rivers and pollution discharges occur many times at wide intervals, allowing time for dilution. On the other hand, effluent standards are preferred by most authorities because they are easier to enforce. Effluent restrictions seek to prevent pollution rather than control it. The control of water pollution was assigned to the Public Health Authorities early in the century, to sanitary engineers in the mid-1960s, and now to attorneys. The trend has followed this same pattern in the establishment of standards.

Standards were at first only concerned with maintaining water sources that were potable. As the population grew, so did industrial complexes. This resulted in the need to develop standards that control water use for cooling purposes, process water, power, agriculture, and many other needs. As the population expanded, so did the need for recreation and transportation. Aesthetics and protection of nature became the vogue. As the control was passed from public health to sanitary engineering, the desire to do something about the total problem became a reality. At that point, degeneration of our environment had advanced far beyond easy control. Some of the nation's lakes and rivers were destroyed, almost to a point of no return. Many shorelines were fouled with dead and dying plants as well as with animals. Algae blooms have been prevalent at many outfalls from municipal treatment plants. In addition to this, oil and floating debris have been found where clean clear water once was. Sanitary engineers have had a desire to resolve the total problem but have had little power of control.

No federal control has existed, indeed little desire was noted even at the congressional level. Many of the states have had mixed emotions concerning water quality improvement, ranging from complex laws with little enforcement power to no law at all. The federal government was powerless unless the problem crossed state boundaries. Even then, little could be done because no federal law with sufficient "teeth" existed. The Federal Water Pollution Control Act has grown continuously stronger since 1965. The current amendments give significant power to the federal government, and the standards are under the jurisdiction of attorneys who prefer and are getting effluent standards. As stated before, effluent standards are easier to enforce than are stream standards. They also control the problem at the source, thus not allowing degeneration of the nation's water resources at all. From past experience, we can expect all discharges to navigable waters to eventually be controlled by effluent standards. At the present time, the states are required by the federal government to enforce pollution laws and at the same time are backed by the federal government with their enforcement needs. The enforcement is being assisted by the general attitude of the people, who are demanding a cleanup of the nation's waterways. Careless and avoidable pollution will no longer be tolerated by the authorities nor by the public in general.

The Cost of Control—Who Should Pay?

The cost of the elimination of water pollution will be staggering. By what formula should these costs be assessed? The federal government has not been too concerned with water problems that have affected citizens within a state until recently and, consequently, has played a relatively minor role in financing pollution control projects. The National Water Commission records indicate that, "of total capital expenditures for public waste treatment facilities and sewers from the time records began to be kept through June 30, 1971, only $4.9 billion out of a total of $84 billion (adjusted to 1972 price levels) were financed by Federal funds."[14] The federal government will assume a greater portion of the financing burden in the future.

The costs of waste treatment can be allocated by relying upon federal income taxes. This will result in a large amount of revenue quickly. On the other hand, federal allocation by income taxes will cause the local decision makers to lose sight of the "necessary" expenditures. When citizens are spending their own local money, "necessity" can take on a whole new meaning than when using donated money.

The federal government will finance most high costs of treatment plants for municipalities but will require that the money be paid back over a long-term contract. Who should pay this bill? The most equitable plan will be to tax the influent contributors according to their pollution load. Under this "polluter pay" requirement, the industries will be taxed highly in many cases. This cost can be expected to be passed on to consumers. The net result is still the same as income tax contributions but will retain local control of the "necessity" costs.

Regulation of Costs

Policy formulation, translation, and administration will be the responsibility of federal, state, and local governments.

Formulation will be the responsibility of the federal government. Although the design of the programs will be assumed by the federal government, implementation, planning, and administration will be assigned to the states. If the states do not perform as requested, then the federal government may assume all of the responsibilities.

Control will be a shared responsibility between federal and state authorities. This concept is basically sound. It will put the responsibility on the local plane as needed and prevent unilateral federal action that would destroy local initiative.

The entry of the federal government will improve the effectiveness of pollution abatement programs. This is especially true in research activities and with financial assistance. Many of the problems are similar, therefore one well-financed research effort will be of national significance. It will give equal assistance to poor and rich communities alike.

As stated earlier, the cost of water pollution control is tremendous. Financing by the federal government will make goals achievable that would otherwise be impossible.

Problems that Improved Regulations Do Not Solve

Pollution control, for the most part, removes pollutants from wastewater discharges. This presents another serious problem. What can be done with the solids accumulated?

We can incinerate the waste and pollute the air. We can dump it in the ocean and pollute it. Or, we can bury it in an already overburdened landfill which will add to the solid waste problem.

Chicago is, in one program, transporting its sludge (900 tons/day) to agricultural areas in central Illinois and applying it to crop lands. In another program, it is transporting it to an area near Peoria and spreading it on strip-mined land in an effort to "reclaim the land."[14]

The rapidly accelerating program will require many competent personnel who can plan, administer, and operate programs as well as facilities.

The EPA has estimated that "approximately 12,700 additional employees will be required to man wastewater treatment facilities proposed for construction during the 1972 to 1976 period. Of these, 16% are for professional positions, 65% for operators and maintenance workers, and the remaining 19% are for administrative support."[14]

Implementation of the Federal Water Pollution Control Act Amendments of 1972 will require a mutual effort of federal, state, and local authorities as well as the cooperation of all involved industries, municipalities, and citizens.

The trend is to clean up the nation's waters. This will be done by removal of pollutants or by the avoidance of pollution. Pounds of solids per period of time will be the unit of measurement and dilution will not be allowed. This approach will eventually result in the cleanup of our water resources and will give a healthy as well as an aesthetic environment to our heirs.

SIGNIFICANCE

The present amendments to the Federal Water Pollution Control Act are very complex and cover a broad area of control. Present regulations have had to be written in a short period of time. The standards now cover a wider spectrum by relating to general, rather than specific, sources. The problem is more complex than the current law implies.

The success or failure of the current law will depend heavily upon an informed public. The amendments of 1972 appear complete but are written more for legal enforcement than for easy understanding. This is exemplified by the technique of constantly referring to other sections, while attempting to relate to a requirement. The reader becomes rapidly confused if the significance of the other sections is not known. Professionals prefer to communicate with individuals trained in their own disciplines. Attorneys are no exception to this general rule. Unfortunately this puts the general public in a quandary when trying to understand a requirement that is so very important to them.

It is the opinion of the author that the public in general realizes the need for good water improvement and wants to cooperate. Some industries have done nothing in the past because of lack of proper guidance by knowledgeable authorities, whereas others have continued degradation of the nation's waterways because of the severe personal costs that control would bring. In either case, complete, scientifically based regulations are needed. The pollution problem has been used as a "grandstand" issue. It is for this reason that the public must be appraised of progress as well as alerted to the hazards of pollution.

The current laws require that standards be established to measure and control the "total problem." For this reason, industry can expect to have authorities looking at and measuring each problem based on the raw *waste load* and *flow per unit of production.*

This will mean the problem will be based on pounds of pollutants per unit of production (or its metric counterpart), which is an equitable way to measure the pollution impact at each source. It requires more expertise on the part of the individuals who are sampling proportionate to flow. Even though the monitoring will be costly and time-consuming, it will be economically better for dischargers in general.

The Federal Water Pollution Control Act Amendments of 1972 represent a giant step forward in a national commitment to solve the water pollution problems and will eventually result in clean water. It was the intent of Congress to strengthen the federal and state programs so that the commitment could be achieved. Standards have been made more stringent, available funds for research have increased, and enforcement has been "beefed up" in an effort to fulfill the commitment. This act is one of the greatest achievements relating to the cleanup of America's waters that the legislature has accomplished. The passage of this law represents the climax of many years of discussion, argument, and conclusions concerning water pollution control.

The act was not met with high acclaim at its inception. That is because it was written primarily for enforcement rather than for understanding. The deadlines were impossible to meet. At this point in time, more than two years after the enactment of the amendments of 1972, the Environmental Protection Agency readily admits that it has not met most of the deadlines and is approximately 6 months behind in issuing the National Pollutant Discharge Elimination System (NPDES) permits.

The important point to make here, which has great significance regarding the outcome, is the general attitude of the Environmental Protection Agency. Even though the Administrator was given a very complex law to enforce, with deadlines that were impossible to meet, he has made progress with a program that has accomplished much in the last two years. During this time, lawsuits have been filed against the EPA in an effort to obtain performance.

Specifics of the 1972 Law and EPA's Accomplishments

Looking briefly at the law, we can develop a better understanding of the requirements relative to accomplishments by EPA.

Approval of state permit program The law requires that EPA shall approve the state permit programs. The states must meet certain requirements as specified in the act. After they are approved, the states must assume the basic responsibility for issuing the NPDES permits. Interim state permit programs were approved initially, but expired 5 months after the enactment of the law. This was based upon the assumption that the state programs would be approved by the 5-month deadline. The multitude of changes in statutes and regulations, plus the changes in the 50 different states' programs, resulted in an overall inability to meet this deadline. In fact, not one state program had qualified for final approval by April 1973. Most of the states' programs have been reviewed and will eventually be approved by the federal government. Federal control of this program is necessary to kindle the water pollution control desires of the nation, but each state must do its part. Federal control of a local ordinance is not impossible, and is certainly legal under the Constitution, but it is virtually impossible when the complexity of the overall problem is considered.

Effluent guidelines The Effluent Guidelines were to be published within 1 year after the enactment of the amendments. As of January 1974, not one of the standards was promulgated. Proposed Effluent Guidelines and Standards were available by that time, and now, more than 2 years after the enactment, the rules are almost completely resolved. During this time the EPA continued to prepare industrial and municipal permits and did not wait for the Effluent Guidelines to be completed. In one respect, the EPA understood the complexity of forming a complete list of Effluent Guidelines and Standards (which Congress apparently did not) and, on the other hand, could readily see the 1977 compliance date approaching rapidly.

Toxic pollutants Great technical difficulty has been encountered by the EPA in the development of a "sound basis for regulating Toxic Pollutants." The toxicity of waste is one of the most critical problems of a water pollution control program. An initial list of toxic pollutants was proposed, which is by no means the entire list of hazardous substances. The statute specified that these "toxic pollutants" must have standards which will be met, "within one year after they are established." Congress apparently did not foresee the problems of implementing this part of the act. It has been nearly impossible to develop "intelligent standards" that will specify the desired degree of control over the toxic pollutants within the timing framework as specified in the statute.

Construction grants Due to pending regulations, the expectation and achievement of federal grants for municipal waste treatment facilities have not been realized. In January 1973, the approval of grant applications was delayed because the EPA had not yet issued the basic regulations under the new statute. After the regulations were issued, the program was slowed down over the statutory requirement that "no grants could be approved after March 1, 1973, unless they complied with cost recovery and user charge requirements," and the EPA has not yet issued those regulations. The states had to develop a new priority list for projects to be funded. The $5 billion that was available on January 1, 1973 was reduced to $2 billion. A great controversy developed which was centered on the President's budget that reduced funding for this need. Of the $18 billion authorized by the law, the President released only $9 billion. The need had grown from an estimated $18 billion to an apparent $60 billion. This is based on a survey made by the EPA. Further study might even increase this fantastically large number.

Throughout this series of blunders, the EPA has proven itself to be a dedicated part of the federal government. Individuals from that department have worked many nights and weekends in an effort to meet the deadlines. It is the author's opinion that the weakness does not lie in the administrative inabilities of EPA, nor does it reflect the incompetence or lack of dedication of the department in general, but instead relates to the lack of depth that Congress visualized when this statute was developed and promulgated.

The understanding of the solutions, of course, was not the responsibility of Congress. Very few of the members of Congress are technically qualified to describe the basic problems and certainly are not equipped to proclaim the solutions. Nevertheless, they are qualified to legislate and did create one of the best water pollution control acts that has been available in our history. We have a need now to focus on the practical and the realistic, and we must use common sense to obtain the goal of zero discharge of water pollutants. Even though industries are frustrated, they must not panic if they are to achieve this goal.

The situation was summarized by Mr. John R. Quarles, Jr., U.S. EPA Deputy Administrator, in a speech that he gave to the Midwest Research Institute's Conference on Industry and Clean Water, in Kansas City, Missouri, January 17, 1974. He stated:

> There is one final message which also becomes clear as we look ahead. It is that the war against water pollution is by no means won, yet. We continue to have a long road to travel, and progress down this road will continue to demand intensive public support. This is most clearly true with regard to the clean-up of municipal sewage. Until recently, we thought we were facing an $18 billion job that we could tackle in 3 bites of $6 billion a year. But now we see ourselves facing a $60 billion job which we are pecking away at [at] the rate of $3 or $4 billion a year. With regard to industrial pollution, the facts are not so dramatic. But there also, I am sure, we will need a continuous tightening of standards and increasing vigilance for many years into the future. In short, the battle against water pollution is neither virtually won nor about to be over. We are making progress, and that is heartening. In the next several years visible progress should become evident around the country. But a real solution to infinitely complex pollution problems can be achieved only through a sustained national effort over a long period of time. Those responsible for management of the pollution program in government must build it with an eye to continuing improvement in the years ahead.[11]

Mr. John B. Malloy, Director, Water Enforcement Division of the EPA, stated at a meeting in Alexandria, Virginia, on November 11, 1974, that "2900 major pollutor NPDES permits will be issued by December 31, 1974. The remainder of the permits will be issued by mid-1975."

Industrial Water Engineering magazine reported in its September/October, 1974 issue:

> EPA hopes to roughly double its current year's efforts to clean up the Nation's waters. Highest priorities are placed on the issuance of discharge permits for industries and municipalities (14,545 expected by the end of fiscal 1974 and 32,012 by the end of fiscal 1975), and a rise in the value of construction grants awarded (from $1.9 billion in fiscal year 1974 to $4.1 billion in fiscal year 1975).[13]

In the meantime, enforcement will increase to assure that the water pollution control desires of Congress and the nation will eventually be realized.

REFERENCES

1. U.S. Department of the Interior, Federal Water Quality Administrator: *Clean Water for the 1970's—A Status Report,* June, 1970.
2. Reitze, A. W., Jr.: "Environmental Law," North American International, Washington, D.C., 1972.
3. *Federal Water Pollution Control Act Amendments of 1972—Conf. Rept.*, 92d Cong., 2d Sess., House of Representatives, rept. no. 92–1456, ordered to be printed September 28, 1972.
4. Caswell, C. A.: Pandora's Box of Toxic Substances—A Commentary, *Industrial Water Engineering*, vol. XX, September/October 1973.
5. U.S. Environmental Protection Agency: "The National Water Permit Program," Office of Enforcement and General Counsel, June 1, 1973.
6. "Secondary Treatment Information," *Federal Register,* vol. 38, no. 159, pt. 133, August 17, 1973.
7. "Organic Chemicals Manufacturing," *Federal Register,* vol. 38, no. 241, pt. II, December 17, 1973.

8. U.S. Environmental Protection Agency: "Proposed Criteria for Water Quality," vol. I, October, 1973.
9. U.S. Environmental Protection Agency: "Proposed Criteria for Water Quality," vol. II, October, 1973.
10. U.S. Environmental Protection Agency, Water Program Operations: "Federal Guidelines—Pretreatment of Discharges to Publicly Owned Treatment Works," 1973.
11. Quarles, J. R., Jr.: Expectations vs. Achievements: Some Reflections on the Water Act, remarks to Midwest Research Institute's Conf. on Industry and Clean Water, Kansas City, Mo., January 17, 1974, reprinted in *Environmental News,* January 1974.
12. Interview—ES&WQIAC's Marth Sager, *Environmental Sci. and Tech.,* vol. 7, no. 13, December, 1973.
13. Perspective—Clean Water Efforts to Double in 1975, *Industrial Water Engineering,* vol. 11, no. 5, September/October 1974.
14. Luce, Charles F.: *Water Policies for the Future,* page 6 final report to the President and to the Congress of the United States by the National Water Commission, Water Information Center Publication, 1973.

Chapter 2

Monitoring: Requirements, Skills, Methods, and Instruments

JERRY L. JONES

Environmental Control, Chemical
Engineering Laboratory, Stanford Research Institute,
Menlo Park, California

INTRODUCTION

The purpose of this chapter is to describe the types of skills which are necessary for evaluating water pollution problems efficiently and to emphasize the importance of monitoring or data collection in problem definition. Acquiring people with adequate skills and experience and giving them reliable data on which to base their decisions are the two most important steps an organization can take to ensure finding the optimum problem solution.

In order to know what types of skills are necessary, a review of the tasks involved in studying water problems will be required. In order to be able to evaluate the validity of data, knowledge of what problems to expect in monitoring and an understanding of the limitations of equipment, techniques, and the individuals gathering the data will also be required. Because of space limitations and the fact that no rigid procedures can be written to include all water monitoring situations, references will be made to specific papers, publications, or vendors where detailed information may be obtained.

The mention or listing of trade names or commercial products in this chapter is for illustration and general information purposes only. An attempt is made to inform the reader of the many available suppliers of different types of equipment; however, such a listing does not constitute either endorsement or recommendation for use by the author.

SKILLS AND INPUTS REQUIRED

The individual in charge of water pollution control for a manufacturing facility must have many talents. Depending on the assignment of responsibility and the size of a facility's technical staff, the environmental control manager or engineer must be able to do some or all of the following:

1. Interpret ordinances and regulations
2. Establish monitoring programs for recording of water and waterborne emissions
3. Interpret data and report emission levels of specified pollutants to regulatory agencies
4. Direct in-plant pollution abatement programs and obtain necessary permits
5. Coordinate plant activities with consulting engineers or the company engineering department
6. Coordinate evaluations of plans for treatment systems, process changes, or product recovery systems
7. Gather data for design of water treatment or reuse systems
8. Keep operating departments and management informed of the possible or probable economic effect of new or proposed regulations for water discharges
9. Prepare statements for various government agencies on the environmental impact of present or proposed plant operations
10. Handle company public relations work on environmental issues

The fact that chemists, biologists, mechanical engineers, civil-sanitary engineers, and chemical engineers are now holding positions in major corporations where they have responsibility for water pollution control indicates that job requirements cut across conventional professional classifications. Depending on the type of operation and the specific problems, a biologist may be better qualified for the job requirements than an engineer, or vice versa. Because of the many specialized topics usually involved in studying water pollution problems, it is necessary for one to be familiar with many fields of science and engineering.

In general, the person working on the water problems of a given industry will need to have a thorough understanding of the technology of that particular industry as well as a basic working knowledge—or support from consultants—in the following subjects:

1. *Chemistry.*
   - Interaction of various waste constituents
   - Chemical equilibria and kinetics

- Qualitative and quantitative methods for inorganic and organic compounds in water
- Measurement of physical characteristics of water

2. *Environmental health.* Acute and chronic toxicity effects of elements and compounds on various forms of flora and fauna including man and a knowledge of which compounds may be classified as carcinogens, mutagens, or teratogens
3. *Aquatic biology.* Significance of various forms of aquatic life as characteristic of certain types of impurities in water
4. *Water quality requirements.* Water quality needs for various beneficial uses
5. *Hydrology and geology.* Surface and groundwater resources—use and contamination
6. *Monitoring techniques and technology*
   - Hydraulics—flow measurement
   - Sampling techniques
   - Sample preservation and handling
   - Automatic instrumental analysis
   - Data management
7. *Water and wastewater treatment technology and economics.* Conditioning or renovating water for specific process needs, reuse, or discharge
8. *Environmental laws.* Local, state, and federal
9. *Management skills.* Optimum utilization of company personnel, consultants, and government services

One could also add that the individual must have a crystal ball and be able to foresee changes in manufacturing processes and products as well as changes in regulations. It is now quite apparent that, as a rule, no one individual can successfully handle all aspects of a water pollution control job. Management skills were mentioned last in the list, but these skills are as crucial to the environmental engineer's success as is overall technical competence.

Solution of water problems requires a multidisciplinary team. Often, if a manager does not involve an adequate number of internal personnel and/or consultants at an early stage in water problem definition, a great deal of time and money is wasted.

In Table 1 the various types of activities which could be underway during the problem definition phase have been listed, and the groups or individuals making contributions indicated.

The importance of gathering information on all aspects of future plant operations including expected product changes, increasing or changing production levels, and changing process technology, cannot be overemphasized. It is impossible to accurately specify the seriousness of a current water problem for planning purposes if forecasts are not available for review. It would make little sense to pursue a course of action without consulting marketing research or process research and development teams, which might either complicate or completely eliminate certain pollution problems.

Assuming now that the environmental engineer or manager is given the personnel needed, the main problem is optimum utilization of these people. The environmental engineer's recommendations, as well as those of other specialists, can be no better than the technical data on which they are based. Water monitoring to gather data will be necessary; but will several grab samples be adequate, or will continuous sampling and on-stream instrumental analysis be required? How does one decide how much time and effort should be expended to obtain representative data for water characterization?

Monitoring of water volume and quality has been discussed in numerous texts and papers, but no one source to date has discussed all the topics which may be of concern to an engineer in industry. For certain manufacturing facilities it may be necessary only to monitor one sewer before discharge to a municipal or regional system. The operations may be such that effluent quality and quantity are consistent, and several grab samples will be adequate to determine the pollution load. At another site, an engineer may need data on water usage and water discharges for specific processes and the flow rate and waste quality in various sewers, as well as data on the quality of the body of water to which wastes are being discharged.

The remainder of this chapter will delve into the broad topic of water monitoring. It will include discussions of flow measurement, sampling, and automatic instrumental analysis techniques and equipment.

It is not the intent of the following discussion to provide design formulas for flow measurement devices nor to give detailed analytical procedures. It is rather to summarize the current state of the art and to compare alternate methods of obtaining data. The reader will be referred to other sources for specific detailed procedures or information. This approach will give the reader a broad overview of what techniques are available for monitoring water, and it will then be the reader's responsibility to assemble the components of a monitoring system to suit his budget and particular situation.

TABLE 1 Manpower Requirements for a Facility's Water Pollution Control Activities

Activity	Groups or individuals involved
Analyze situations and determine action to be taken:	
Interpretation of regulations, permit applications, discussion of present and proposed regulations	Environmental control group
	Legal group
	Public relations group
	Consultants
Define problem:	
Plant survey—monitoring program	
1. Make theoretical material balance around specific processes	Production engineers
	Utility engineers
2. Identification of probable major problem areas	Production engineers
	Utility engineers
	Environmental control group
3. Verify problem areas and set up monitoring program to determine what, where, when, why	Environmental control group
	Production engineers
	Technology group (R&D)
	Market forecasting group
	Plant laboratory
	Consultant's laboratory
a. Measure present conditions	
b. Measure conditions or sample so as to predict waste if certain plant changes are expected from product changes or production changes	
4. Analyze data and indicate problem areas and economic effect on various operations	Environmental control group
	Production engineers
	Engineering department
	Consultant

NEED FOR WATER MONITORING

Past and Present Needs for Wastewater Monitoring

At one time, the importance of knowing what was leaving a plant in the form of waterborne wastes was considered only from a product loss standpoint. In some cases, toxic or nuisance wastes did require special precautions, but in general, wastewater could be discharged to municipal sewers or surface waters with little if any treatment or monitoring required by law. Within the past decade more attention has been focused on industrial water discharges. It is now necessary to qualify and quantify, to varying degrees of accuracy, all plant water uses and discharges.

Monitoring may be necessary for a number of reasons, such as:

1. To define water problems (what, where, why, when)
2. To measure waste parameters for use in calculation of waste treatment charges for municipal or regional treatment systems
3. To measure waste parameters to allow detection and triggering of emergency actions in case of spills or process upsets
4. To measure the effect of a wastewater discharge on the quality of a receiving body of water

5. To measure the quantity and quality of all process wastes as well as influent liquid raw materials for material balance purposes

6. To gather enough information on water use and contamination to allow design of pretreatment and/or reclamation systems

Companies discharging to municipal or regional treatment systems are being ordered to monitor their wastewater discharges or allow monitoring by others. Unless industry is billed its "fair share" of treatment costs in the form of "user charges," no federal grant funds will be forthcoming. However, because of a lack of personnel at this time, many municipalities or regional treatment authorities may base treatment charge distributions on limited or inadequate sampling data. If there is doubt as to the validity of reported pollution levels, then it may behoove an industry to pay for its own monitoring program to be approved by the local regulatory body.

Upsets of municipal treatment plant aerobic or anaerobic biological systems are usually attributed, whether rightly or wrongly, to industrial dumps of "toxic compounds." Routine monitoring of the total plant effluent or of specific sewers where problem compounds could be accidentally discharged might prevent unfair accusations or allow early detection and sufficient time to prevent treatment plant upsets.

An example of a preventive monitoring system is one which will sound an alarm if the pH drops below a specified level or a certain compound is detected in the sewer. Emergency actions (such as pumping the waste to holding lagoons or dumping chemicals to bring the effluent back to acceptable quality) can be initiated by a signal from the monitoring equipment.

For facilities discharging directly into a body of water, monitoring within the plant or at the final point of discharge may not be adequate. To accurately assess the environmental effect of a discharge, samples of the receiving body of water must be analyzed, as well as the flora and fauna. For a new grassroots facility, the quality of the local aquatic environment before construction and operation is valuable information to use as a baseline for assessing the plant's actual impact on the local environment.

Future Role of Water Monitoring

If it is in fact possible that industry can even closely approach the "zero discharge" level by 1985, as specified by the Water Pollution Control Act Amendments of 1972, then one might think that everything will be bottled up and monitoring will be done on at most one effluent water stream from each plant. But on the contrary, the role of monitoring should become considerably more important, more sophisticated, and more expensive. Wastewater monitoring will be difficult to differentiate from water supply monitoring because of recycle and reuse.

With drastically increased reuse of water, many new water monitoring stations within plants will be required. Depending on specific processing needs, each manufacturing area within a plant may require a special water system because of certain contaminants which can or cannot be tolerated. In a case where many different quality requirements are necessary, it might be more economical to regenerate the water to varying degrees of purity for different uses rather than to regenerate all of the plant water to a single given quality. This is already being done, of course, in the cases of boiler feedwater, water for beverage manufacture, cooling water, and rinse waters. As the costs rise for water treatment and reclamation, each process or production area will have to be charged accurately for its appropriate share of the cost for water. Granted, some products will undoubtedly disappear from the market, and new processes eliminating water use will be developed; but wet processing is not going to disappear in the near future.

RESPONSIBILITY FOR MONITORING

The assignment of responsibility for plant water monitoring depends on

The size of the plant

The ultimate uses of the data

The complexity of the monitoring system stations and components

Smaller plants may not be able to afford a separate group to monitor water, so the task will be given to various production units. As monitoring systems become more complex with additional automatic analytical instrumentation, a person specially trained in routine maintenance of the equipment and instruments will probably be required. Despite claims of troublefree operation from many manufacturers of sampling equipment and instruments, this equipment usually requires maintenance on a very frequent and routine basis. As a rule, the more varied the waste stream as to solids, oils, salts, or gummy residues, the higher the frequency of the maintenance.

If the plant size and the complexity of the monitoring network are such to justify a central water pollution control group, then several advantages usually exist over having the work done by production personnel. The central group ensures

- More uniform procedures
- Efficient coordination of overall plant waste reduction programs
- Successful tracing of spills or process upsets

Tracing sources of wastes is a problem which has been observed at many large industrial complexes. A process upset may cause problems with a downstream treatment system's operation. The problem substance is not readily identifiable, and no one in the plant seems to know anything about a dump or spill. In some cases the actual problem substance may be a result of interactions of contaminants in the sewer system; but if the inventory system allows failure to report operation errors, such errors will in many cases be hidden.

In an attempt to reduce the frequency of process upsets, some plant managers have adopted the practice of fining production groups for upsets. This cost shows up on a department's monthly cost reports, and the fact that the boss has set this fine has quite an effect on production personnel. In order to trace spills, a detection system may consist of multiple monitoring points about the plant. Complex separation and identification techniques may also be required for specific chemicals in a chemical complex, or for identifying fermentable sugars, alcohol, or yeast in a brewery effluent.

Another approach taken by some plant managers involves essentially putting operating departments "in concrete bathtubs" to eliminate problems of operating personnel's dumping bad batches. All bad batches must be pumped to holding facilities.

One last point which should be mentioned about plant monitoring concerns credibility between industry and regulatory bodies on reporting the volume of wastewater and the level of the contaminants present. At certain times regulatory agencies are going to want samples taken and analyzed either by their own personnel or by a neutral third party such as a consultant or independent testing laboratory. In the latter case, it is important for plant personnel formally to explain previous monitoring problems to those responsible for monitoring in order to make sure that accurate, representative samples will be obtained.

COMPONENTS OF A WATER MONITORING SYSTEM

The water monitoring operation can be broken down into three basic categories:

1. Measurement of the water flow
2. Sampling and sample handling
3. Analysis for identification and quantification of specific constituents in the water

These three topics, of course, are not independent with regard to the design of a monitoring system, and a firm understanding of each topic is necessary in order to enable one to assemble components for optimally measuring water contamination.

The field of hydraulics provides adequate techniques to permit accurate measurement of flows in gravity-flow channels or pressure conduits. Sampling, however, is not nearly as developed a science as hydraulics. At present, sampling tends to be the weak point in designing and operating a monitoring system. This situation is unlikely to change soon because of the serious problems inherent in trying to take a small representative sample from a large volume of water. Further development of automatic analytical measurements which initiate sampling cycles based on contaminant concentration, as well as flow volume, should improve the accuracy of sampling immensely. These developments will be discussed in detail later.

In the area of analysis, a great deal of work is now being done to perfect various instrumental techniques leading toward complete automation of various methods. This automation will allow more rapid detection of problems in many situations where certain parameters or contaminants change rapidly with time. Continuous or semicontinuous measurement will allow better control of wastewater treatment or reclamation processes and, in many cases, result in considerable savings in system design because of its ability to allow rapid corrective action if the feed changes drastically in character.

DESIGN CONSIDERATIONS FOR A WATER MONITORING SYSTEM

One should answer the following four questions when preparing to establish a water monitoring program:

1. What must be or should be monitored?
2. When should specific parameters be monitored and for what duration?
3. Where should samples be collected and monitoring equipment located?
4. How should the monitoring be done? (Collection of samples, storage, analysis.)

These four questions cannot always be completely answered in the sequence shown; usually information is gathered and tabulated and several questions are answered simultaneously. Conflicts may arise with selection of a monitoring station at a hazardous location because the proper type of explosionproof equipment necessary for the area is not available or is prohibitively expensive. In this case the "where" and "how" are not compatible and a compromise must be made.

What

Regulations will usually indicate what must be monitored with regard to certain physical, chemical, or biological parameters. Regulations regarding discharges to bodies of water will, of course, vary somewhat from state to state as well as within various communities. To indicate what is expected of industry, the federal government is issuing pretreatment requirements and effluent guidelines for specific industries as discussed in Chapter 11.

In certain cases the parameters which must be monitored by law may not be adequate for the needs of a given manufacturing facility. Gross measuring parameters such as biochemical oxygen demand (BOD), chemical oxygen demand (COD), total organic carbon (TOC), or total oxygen demand (TOD) do not indicate precisely what substances are actually responsible for the pollution.

If the sources of certain contaminants are not known, it may be wise also to monitor influent raw materials and the water supply for contaminants. Often a plant has found that considerable contamination in effluent water results from raw material contamination, such as heavy metals present in acids from smelter off-gas acid plants or mercury-contaminated caustic.

As mentioned earlier, in some cases a routine determination should be made of the quality of the water into which wastewater is being discharged. For such studies, physical or chemical parameters may not be indicative of the actual effect of the discharge on the body of water. Certain chronic effects may be visible only as changes in flora and fauna of a stream or lake. Dumps of substances which may not coincide with a stream study may be evidenced by an ecological change in the stream. Two very good compilations of articles on such biological studies are "Biology of Water Pollution,"[1] and "Biological Problems in Water Pollution."[2] Several other publications which can provide useful, practical guidelines are by Velz,[3] Kittrell,[4] Jackson,[5] and Rainwater and Thatcher.[6]

In certain situations it may be advisable to conduct continuous biomonitoring of effluent streams to ascertain whether or not aquatic life is endangered. Fish movement patterns may be monitored in a unit shown in Fig. 1 or breathing rates may be determined from polygraph recordings of breathing signals.

When

The number of products manufactured and whether the processing is continuous or discontinuous can greatly affect the frequency of sampling and duration. If there are multiple products from batch operations, the effluent may be out of compliance with regulations for some contaminants for only several minutes a day or for 24 hr/day during several months when a specific product is being manufactured. In such cases, sampling periods must be staggered in order to sample the waste streams under different production conditions.

Some areas of the country also have regulations which make allowance for influent contamination; thus, knowledge of influent water contaminant concentration fluctuations may be the difference between compliance and noncompliance with certain regulations. Therefore, if a facility uses water from wells or streams, and the quality of such intake water varies significantly from season to season, more frequent sampling during certain seasons may be necessary.

Many regulatory agencies require 24-hr composite samples, intermittent grab samples and, in some instances, recording of the maximum concentration for some parameter during a 24-hr period. For some purposes, however, such required information may not be adequate. If data are being collected for design of a wastewater treatment system, it may be necessary to define fluctuations in waste characteristics more accurately than would be required by law. Frequent analysis of discrete samples is necessary for exact determination of chemical feed rate requirements and design parameters necessary for good process control. For design of a neutralization system, grab samples should be taken at frequent intervals (approximate frequency

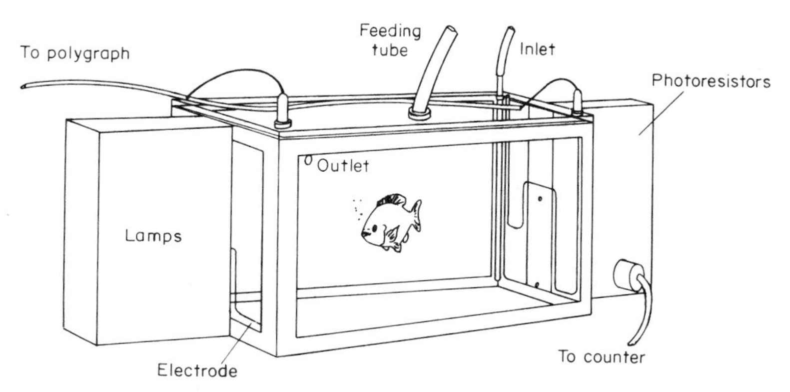

Fig. 1 Biomonitoring test unit. Test chamber for monitoring system, showing the electrodes for recording fish breathing and the light-beam system for recording fish movement. For details on monitoring fish movement patterns using the light-beam interruption technique, see Cairns et al., *J. Water Pollution Control Federation,* vol. 42, no. 5, pp. 685–703, 1970.

equal to one-half the predicted retention time), and the acidity measured to determine buffering and reaction time with different neutralizing agents. For a waste with very great fluctuations in acidity, a 24-hr composite sample can indicate the effect equalization would have on system size and cost.

Where

In evaluating alternative sampling positions in a wastewater stream, the first consideration should be to decide at what points problems may exist and where mixing will be adequate to allow taking a representative sample. In some cases it may be necessary to conduct experiments involving the sampling of various cross sections of a stream and to inspect for bottom deposits or floating scum in sewers.

The frequency of monitoring and the type of monitoring will also significantly affect the choice of the monitoring site. If composite samples are to be taken and certain parameters measured and recorded continuously, then the monitoring station should be at a point easily accessible and in an environment suitable for operation of the required instruments. Because no sampling and monitoring equipment is maintenance free, it should be as close as possible to areas where plant personnel can frequently check on the operation. Hazardous locations which would require installation of special explosionproof instruments might be rejected in favor of areas where such special precautions would be unnecessary.

Sampling of aboveground pressure or gravity flow lines should be attempted wherever possible, instead of below-ground sewer lines. Maintenance of flow-measuring devices in buried lines and unclogging sampling equipment in manholes can be extremely hazardous because of sewer fumes and the possibility of falls when an employee is entering or working in a manhole. Some plants have removed all rungs from manholes to prevent plant personnel from entering. They have also instituted very rigid safety procedures, including use of fresh air blowers, independent oxygen supply, safety lines, and protective clothing; they also require a minimum of two people aboveground when one person enters a sewer manhole. Such procedures are quite costly, and if monitoring must be done at a manhole, every effort should be taken to keep maintenance of equipment in the manhole to an absolute minimum. Reference 7 describes safety measures for municipal sewer work. For many industrial plants these procedures may not be adequate; however they will provide general guidance.

As regards monitoring a stream, the location may vary from a specified distance from the outfall to perhaps many miles downstream. Samples from various depths, from the surface to the bottom sediments, may be necessary. Estuary sampling may present many problems not encountered in lake or stream sampling. Gunnerson[8] has discussed estuary sampling and indicated how the ebb and flow of tides provides dilution as well as causing particular water masses (including pollution slugs) to pass a particular point several times. Jenkens[9] has indicated how analytical methods may have to be modified for such locations because of salinity variations. Another point that cannot be overemphasized is that stream, estuary, and lake sampling can be dangerous. [This was tragically demonstrated in 1971 when a federal Environmental Protection Agency (EPA) biologist drowned while sampling Mississippi River sediment directly across from downtown St. Louis.] Such work, in most instances, should be left to professional water quality sampling teams. In addition to the need for precautionary measures in such work, special techniques and equipment are required which are not likely to be available to plant personnel.

How

After deciding which streams or areas are to be monitored, the frequency and duration of such monitoring, and the possible physical locations for monitoring equipment, one must then decide how to take the samples and measure the contaminant levels. Depending on the location of the monitoring station and the nature of the waste, various types of monitoring systems might be possible. There are no off-the-shelf items or set procedures that will fit all circumstances. Where questions of plant wastewater toxicity to aquatic organisms are of particular concern, it may be advisable to set up test chambers with fish exposed to a continuous flow of the plant wastewater diluted with stream water. Physical-chemical measurements alone may not indicate a problem resulting from synergistic effects of various contaminants.

To date, the federal EPA has not specified rigid methods for monitoring because of the impossibility of considering all potential problems. The EPA, however, has released a "Handbook for Monitoring Industrial Wastewater"[10] which should provide guidance to industrial personnel responsible for monitoring. Therefore, in order to determine *how* to do the monitoring, it is necessary to be aware of what equipment and instruments are available and the advantages and limitations of each.

SELECTION OF MONITORING SYSTEM COMPONENTS

Flow Measurement*

To understand the principles of flow metering, a basic understanding of fluid mechanics is vital (including the concepts of the equation of continuity, conservation of energy, and the Bernoulli equation). The basic flow measurement techniques can be divided into two classifications:

Flow in conduits under pressure

Nonpressure conduit and open-channel flow

For either pressure flow or open-channel flow, the device that actually measures the flow of water is referred to as a *primary device*. In Tables 2 and 3, numerous

* The reader's attention is particularly directed to Reference 129, an extremely useful publication for those responsible for industrial wastewater management.

TABLE 2 Flow Measurement Devices and Techniques for Pressure Flow in Conduit

Technique or primary device	References	Vendors
Differential pressure—fixed flow-area devices:		
Venturi-type tubes (Herschel type, Dall tube, Gentile flow tube, universal venturi, twin throat venturi)	10, 12, 13–21	V-12, V-47, V-51, V-60, V-65, V-90
Flow nozzles	10, 14, 15, 17–19	V-9, V-12, V-47, V-60, V-90
Orifices (segmental, eccentric, concentric)	10, 14, 15, 19–21	V-51, V-78, V-90
Elbow meters	19, 22, 23	
Variable flow area—fixed differential pressure devices (rotameters)	10, 19, 20, 24	V-47, V-127
Point velocity techniques:		
Pilot tube	10, 17, 19	
Annubar	19	V-41
Current or velocity meters:		
Propeller meter		V-111, V-114
Turbine meter	19, 25	V-2, V-20, V-48, V-56 to V-58, V-64, V-68, V-74, V-83
Positive displacement meters:	18	V-104
Rotary piston		V-2, V-74
Nutating disk	19	V-83, V-124
Dynamic force measurement	18	V-51, V-98
Thermal techniques:	26	V-24, V-34, V-122
Probe type		V-48, V-121
Perimeter of conduit		V-121
Electromagnetic devices:		
Pipeline meter	10, 13, 19	V-12, V-19, V-47, V-51, V-60, V-117
Probe-type meter		V-47
Sonic techniques:		
Wetted transducer	19, 27	V-85, V-132
Clamp-on		V-31, V-108
Vortex shedding	19	V-38, V-130
Fluidic oscillation	28	V-80
Catch and weigh or measure volume per unit time (bucket and stop watch, sump)	17	
Tracer and dilution techniques:		
Salt dilution (lithium chloride)	13, 29–31	V-49
Fluorescent dyes	13, 32, 34	V-50
Radioactive tracers	13, 17, 33	
Computation techniques:		
Open pipe discharging to atmosphere	17, 10	
On-off time on pumps	10	

TABLE 3 Flow Measurement Devices and Techniques for Open-channel Flow

Technique or primary device	References	Vendors: Primary device	Vendors: Secondary device
Differential head devices:			
Weirs (V-Notch, rectangular, Cippoletti)	10, 13, 17, 32, 35, 39	V-81, V-112	V-9, V-43, V-47, V-51, V-98, V-103, V-112, V-115, V-128
Flumes (Parschall, Palmer Bowlus, Leopold Lagco)	10, 13, 17, 32, 35, 39, 37	V-12, V-46, V-47, V-49, V-52, V-59, V-60, V-93, V-106, V-128	V-9, V-43, V-46, V-47, V-51, V-60, V-98, V-103, V-115
Orifice (sluice gate, miner's weir)	21, 36, 38		
Nozzles (Kennison)	10, 13, 17	V-9, V-12, V-46, V-90	V-9, V-12, V-46, V-90
Velocity measurement techniques:			
Pilot Tube (very limited use)	10, 17		
Current meters	10, 13, 17, 35, 39	V-45, V-54, V-67, V-107	
Thermal techniques		V-121	V-24, V-34, V-121, V-122
Sonic techniques		V-132	V-132
Catch and weigh or measure volume per unit time (sump, bucket, and stop watch)	17		
Tracer techniques:			
Salt dilution	13, 19, 31, 39	V-49	
Fluorescent dyes	13, 35, 39–41, 43, 44	V-50	
Radioactive tracers	13, 17, 33, 45, 46		
Computation techniques:	17		
Chezy and Darcy Weisbach equations	13		
Kutter formula	13		
Manning formula	13		
Hazen-Williams formula	13		
California pipe method	10, 13, 17		

primary devices have been listed for pressure flow and open-channel flow. Figures 2 and 3 show some of the more commonly used devices. The primary device produces a signal which must be transmitted and converted into an indication of flow rate. The *secondary device* performs this function. Secondary devices are differentiated according to the types of information supplied and the method of transmission of information from the primary device.

The information supplied by a secondary device may be instantaneous flow rate, total volume over a certain period of time, continuous recording of the flow rate, or a combination of these.

The signal from the primary device may be sensed and transmitted mechanically, electrically, pneumatically, or by a combination of these methods. For open-channel measurements, the level fluctuations behind a weir or flume may be sensed by float gages in a float well or in the flow channel, by a bubbler tube, or by a capacitance probe. A pneumatic or mechanical signal from the primary device is often converted to an electrical signal for further transmission.

In designing a flow-metering installation, one must consider both the primary and secondary metering devices and their compatibility with possible samplers and on-line analyzers. A list of points to consider in meter selection is shown below:

1. *Physical location*

   DANGEROUS PRODUCTION AREAS. Are special requirements necessary for electrical equipment because of explosive environment? Are explosive sewer gases present?

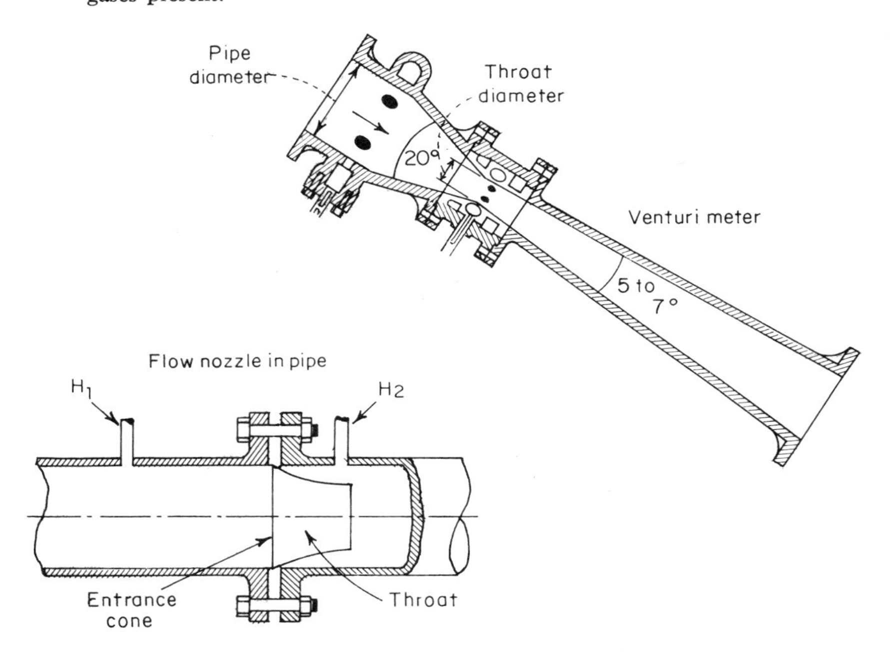

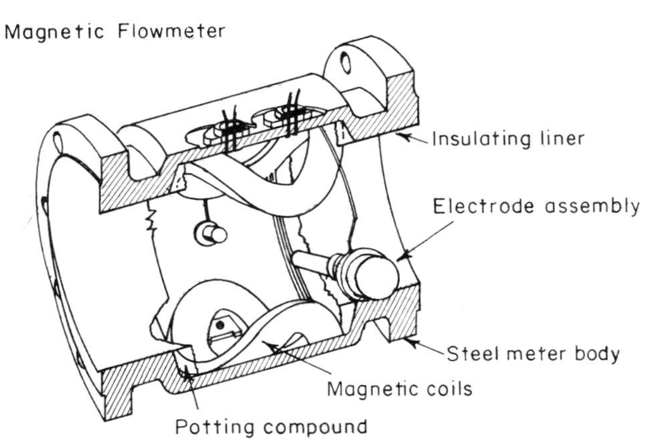

Fig. 2 Three commonly used primary flow-measurement devices for pressure flow in pipes.

Corrosive Conditions. Is either the atmosphere or wastewater corrosive?

Operator Convenience. Does the location provide easy access for reading of charts and sample pickup?

Safety for Maintenance. Would the additional costs for implementing rigid safety procedures at a chosen site offset the additional costs for installation at another point in the plant? Overhead pipe racks and deep sewers are not the ideal locations for meters.

Laying Length of Primary Device. The actual length of pipeline, sewer, or channel required for meter installation varies considerably for different primary devices.

Installation Position. Devices such as rotometers must be installed in a vertical position. A thermal or magnetic meter may be installed in a vertical or a horizontal position. Vertical installation for streams with high suspended solids concentrations will usually yield a more uniform solids distribution than a horizontal pipe. However, the solids concentration may not be representative. This is an important consideration for sampling purposes.

With upflow, there is slippage between the continuous and discontinuous phases, which causes some holdup of the discontinuous phase. Therefore, the concentration of heavier particles will exceed the system average. Downflow will produce the opposite effect.[11]

Upstream and Downstream Piping or Flow Conditions. Ells or valves in upstream piping, drops in sewers, or excessive turbulence may strongly affect the accuracy of certain primary devices.

Availability of Power. If the location is not served by plant instrument air or electricity, it may be cheaper to buy and operate a self-contained unit than to supply power from an external source. Sampler and analytical instrument power requirements must also be considered.

Distance between Primary and Secondary Devices. Mechanical transmission is limited to very short distances. Pneumatic transmission is usually not used for distances over 1,500 ft. Electrical transmission can be used for any length of transmission with telemetering installations transmitting signals many miles.

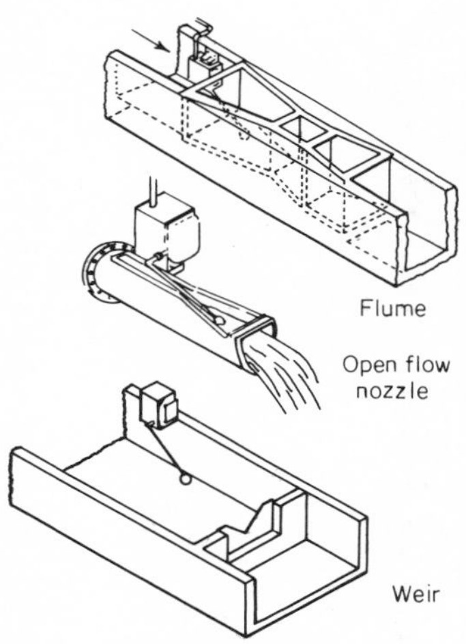

Flume

Open flow nozzle

Weir

Fig. 3 Three commonly used primary flow-measurement devices for open-channel flow.

2. *Size of primary device and flow rangeability*. Many primary devices are commonly manufactured in only certain pipe sizes or, for open-channel flumes, certain throat widths. Special fabrication is usually quite expensive. The range of flow over which a specific device can measure varies, depending on the type of primary device. For flow in pipes, differential pressure devices have a range of approximately 4:1.

Thermal, sonic, and electromagnetic devices have ranges of 10:1, 20:1, and 30:1, respectively. Open-channel metering devices such as V-notch weirs have a flow range of 30:1.

3. *Pressure drop*. The head loss through primary devices used for pressure-flow measurement ranges from essentially the equivalent length of pipe for electromagnetic and sonic techniques to as high as 15 psi for some water meters. Orifices generally have a much greater head loss than do venturis or flow tubes. If water is being pumped, the pressure drop may increase pumping costs, and should be included in the initial cost estimates when comparing different primary devices.

For open-channel flow the Palmer-Bowlus (V-59) or Leopold-Lagco (V-46) flumes offer the lowest head loss and have the added advantage over a Parshall flume (see Fig. 3) in that they may be placed on a level section of floor in a sewer manhole. The head loss for a Palmer-Bowlus flume is about half that of a Parshall flume and one-fifth to one-tenth that for various types of weirs.[10] Figure 4 shows the various shapes of Palmer-Bowlus flumes available.

4. *Accuracy.* For differential head-flow meters, the measurement of differential pressure becomes decreasingly sensitive as the flow rate drops. The transmitter errors related to the differential pressure thus increase relative to the flow rate as the flow drops. Because of this problem, differential pressure devices have a flow range of about 4:1. Vendors' quoted accuracy for differential pressure meters varies from

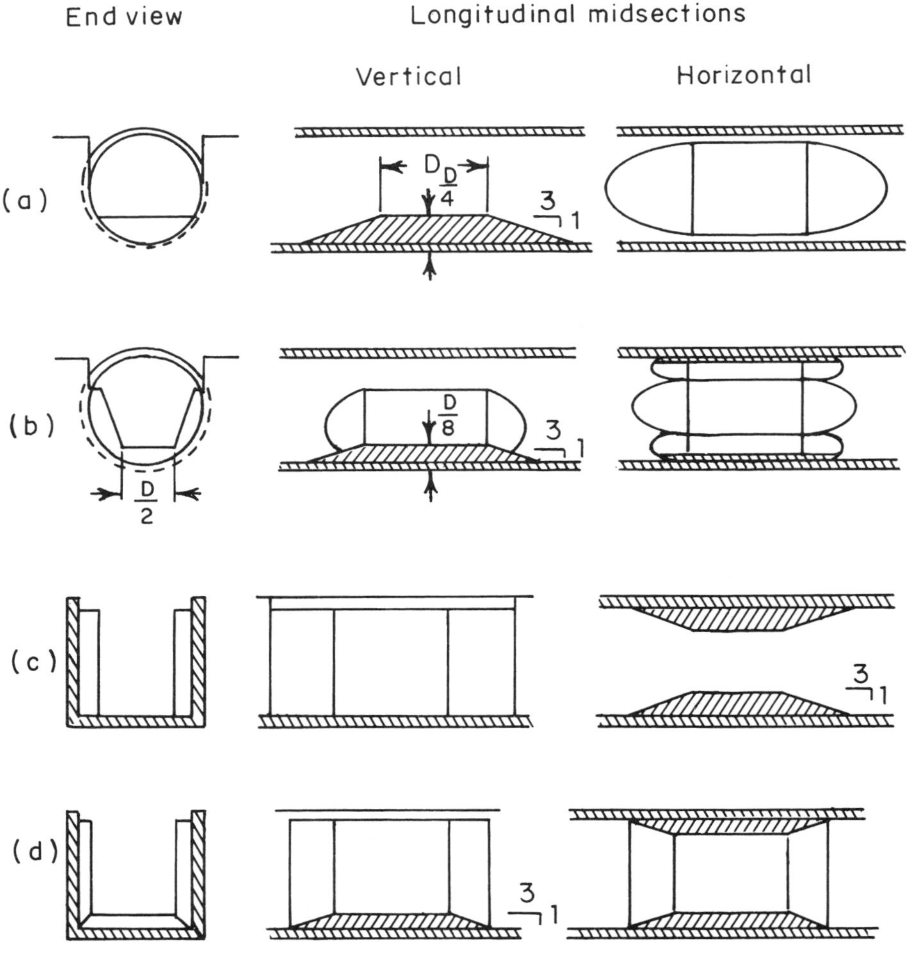

Fig. 4 Various shapes of Palmer-Bowlus flumes.

± 1 to 3 percent. The accuracy of flume and weirs depending on the secondary device should never be considered to be better than ± 3 to 5 percent. Computational techniques using friction factors or Manning factors may be in error by 25 percent or more.

The best way to ensure that an instrument will provide accurate readings is to establish a routine maintenance and calibration schedule. Also, some additional capital investment for continuous flushing of float wells for flumes or for water purging of pressure-sensing lines on orifice installations will reduce maintenance costs and improve accuracy. Installation of new pressure sensors operating on the null-balance principle may significantly reduce fouling problems for differential pressure devices measuring streams with high concentrations of scum and solids.

5. *Wastewater characteristics.* The various primary devices are affected differently by scum, oil, or suspended solids. In some applications where grease and solids are present, magnetic flowmeters may require liner heaters and ultrasonic electrode cleaning devices. As was mentioned previously, safeguards can be taken to reduce problems arising from grease and solids for differential pressure devices or flumes. In open-channel flow situations, a flume may be chosen instead of a cheaper weir because of an expected solids buildup problem behind the weir.

In selecting the materials of construction, one should consider not only erosion and corrosion, but changes in system properties with widely fluctuating temperature. For instance, some liner materials for magnetic flowmeters must not be exposed to temperatures exceeding 150°F.

6. *Primary device read-out.* In pressure pipe flow, the flow rate through a differential pressure device is directly proportional to the square root of the pressure drop across the device. For open-channel flow, the flow rate is directly proportional to the head above the primary raised to a power. To linearize these measurements requires expensive instrumentation, thus both the cost of the primary device and the secondary instrumentation must be considered in calculating installed cost. As indicated in Table 4, thermal, sonic, and electromagnetic techniques produce a direct linear signal.

7. *Cost.* Equipment purchase price and installation costs may be roughly estimated from published instrument cost tables such as those by Lipták.[47] In estimating installation cost, it may be wise to consult vendors concerning the effort required for initial calibration. This cost may be very large for some instruments. Operating costs were mentioned previously with relation to pressure drop. In choosing an instrument, the purchaser should try to find as simple a device as will suit his accuracy and flow rangeability needs. Instrument maintenance is expensive.

Sampling

After it is known how often sampling must be done, approximately where the sampling will be done, and which parameters are to be measured, numerous other factors must then be considered. One must decide how to actually obtain the sample, estimate the approximate volume needed, select the type of container, and determine whether special handling or preservation will be necessary. The method of sampling may vary, depending on whether physical, chemical, or biological parameters are to be measured. If the sample is not to be analyzed immediately, certain parameters may change with time and in contact with air. Numerous publications are available which give information on sample preservation, and volume requirements on specific parameter determinations (see Refs. 10 and 48 to 52). Because of current wide use of refrigeration and freezing to preserve samples,[52] special mention will be made of Agardy's and Kiado's experiments in preservation techniques. In this study they investigated the effect of "refrigerated storage" and "frozen storage" on analytical results for measurement of wastewater suspended solids, volatile suspended solids, total solids, COD, and 5-day BOD. They also determined the effect of length of storage on analytical results. Their recommendations may be summarized as shown in Table 5.

These findings may not be valid for every waste stream, but the points they have mentioned should be considered before selecting a preservation technique.

In some cases a preservation technique for a given contaminant may alter the concentration of other contaminants in the sample. In such a case, the sample will have to be divided and various aliquots preserved according to the analysis to be performed. An example of a preservation technique's interfering with other analyses is Schaumburg's method of mercury poisoning.[53] Before a BOD analysis begins, a chelating agent is added to tie up the mercury which was added. This agent would also complex with other heavy metals and invalidate subsequent metals analyses.

The sample container and sampler lines also must be chosen carefully. Coyne and Collins,[54] for example, have reported notable losses of mercury (>50 percent) from

TABLE 4 Comparison of Flow Measurement Devices for Pressure Flow in Conduit

Metering device	Size range or capacity	Flow range ability	Pressure drop	Accuracy, %	Requirements for Up-stream piping	Requirements for Down-stream piping	Effect of oils, grease	Effect of suspended solids	Type of readout	Installed cost
Differential pressure—fixed flow area devices	<1–48 in.	3:1–4:1	5–100% of differential	1–3	5-50D	None	Minor to severe	Minor to severe	Square root	Low to high
Variable area—fixed differential pressure devices	<1–400 gpm	10:1	0–12 psia	1–5	None	None	Minor to severe	Minor to severe	Linear	Moderate
Point velocity techniques	No limit	3:1	Negligible	1–3+	None	None	Severe	Severe	Square root	Low
Current or velocity meters	½–24 in.	10:1–15:1	0–7 psia	0.15–2	D-10D	None	Severe	Minor to severe	Linear	Moderate to high
Positive displacement meters	½–16 in.	10:1–20:1	0–15 psia	0.1–2	None	None	Severe	Severe	Linear	Moderate to high
Dynamic force measurement devices	½–60 in.	10:1	0–5 psia	0.5–2	. . .	. . .	None	None	Linear	High
Thermal techniques	No limit	10:1	Negligible	5	. . .	. . .	Minor to severe	Minor to severe	Linear	High
Magnetic meters	½–78 in.	30:1	Negligible	0.5–2	Minor to none	None	Minor	None	Linear	High
Sonic techniques	No limit	. . .	Negligible	0.5–1	25-40D	5D	Minor	None	Linear	High
Vortex shedding	1–42 in.	30:1	0–6 psia	0.5–1	10-30D	. . .	Severe	Severe	Linear	High

water samples resulting from adsorption of mercury by the sample container. Both glass and polyethylene sample bottles exhibit this phenomenon. Rubber stoppers in contact with acidic wastewater samples may contaminate the sample with the zinc which is used in the rubber vulcanization process.[55] Other metals such as cadmium have reportedly been leached or extracted from sample containers.[56]

Sample volume requirements may vary significantly depending on the type and particular method of analysis as well as the contaminant concentration. Volume requirements are listed in standard references such as 10 and 48 to 51. For contaminants present in very low concentrations (such as chlorinated hydrocarbon pesticides in surface water), extraction and further concentration techniques may be necessary before an analysis can be performed. Such contaminants may be present in such low concentration that many thousands of gallons may be passed through activated carbon beds for concentration of the trace contaminants on the bed.[57–59] The contaminants on the carbon bed may then be removed by some type of extraction technique. In other cases, several gallons of water may be contacted directly with a solvent for concentration of the trace contaminants in the solvent.[60]

Aeration during sampling or storage is another point to consider with regard to parameters to be measured. References 48 to 51 and 61 give detailed listings of the constituents which will or will not be altered by contact with air. Some parameters which may be affected by sample aeration include dissolved oxygen, acidity or alkalinity, ammonia, carbon dioxide, chlorine, hardness, iron, nitrites, pH, sulfides, and sulfites.

TABLE 5 Sample Storage

Analysis	4°C	Frozen
Total solids	Acceptable	Acceptable
Suspended solids	Up to several days	No
Volatile suspended solids	Up to several days	No
COD	Up to several days	Acceptable
BOD	Up to one day in composite sampling systems	Use fresh sewage seed

After all of the above-mentioned points have been considered, one should look at the available sampling techniques and equipment. There are essentially three techniques for water sampling:

- Grab sampling (manual or automatic)
- Composite sampling (manual or automatic)
- Continuous sampling (automatic)

A grab sample is simply an aliquot removed in such a way as to be representative, it is hoped, of the contaminants present in a stream or body of water at the instant of sampling. Such a sample may be taken from a pump discharge, dipped from a tank or stream, or automatically collected through use of a solenoid valve or a scoop mechanism.

A composite sample is a mixture of incremental grab samples over a specified period of time. The composite sample may be prepared manually or automatically. The sample frequency can be controlled by a timer, or by a flow totalizer which generates a signal to energize the sampler after a certain volume of water has been recorded. The incremental grab samples which comprise the composite sample may be of constant volume—as, for instance, a bucket on a chain—or of variable volume, such as a contoured scoop for dipping a flow proportioned sample behind a flume. If the frequency is controlled by a timer, the accuracy of the composite sample will usually be enhanced if taken in proportion to the flow at the instant of sampling.

A continuous sample involves an indefinite number of grab samples or continuous flow. It is possible to maintain a constant ratio of sample flow according to wastewater stream flow, but normally this is not done because of complexity of proportional controls. Note Table 6 for instances where the various sampling techniques may be used.

Number of phases present If a stream or body of water consists of essentially one homogeneous phase or if only the continuous phase is of interest, then sampling accuracy is mainly a function of

1. Finding a point where the continuous water phase is completely mixed
2. Discovering the flow and soluble contaminant variations in the water phase to establish the sample frequency for adequate quantification of soluble contaminant loads
3. Knowing how the sample must be taken and handled to avoid changes in physical or chemical parameters being monitored

To improve mixing in pipes, turbulent conditions may be established by reducing the cross-sectional area of flow, installing disk and donut baffles, or using an in-line

TABLE 6 The Three Basic Sampling Techniques and Typical Applications

Method	Applications
Grab sampling	Stream or lake studies with multiple monitoring stations, bottom deposit sampling, samples of flora or fauna Preliminary design of a manufacturing facility's monitoring system Determination of specific parameter fluctuations—many discrete samples are required Sampling of a stream for immediate laboratory analysis of a given parameter Characterization of a stream with relatively constant composition Sampling for scum or oil Sampling of a stream with a high concentration of suspended solids with a nonuniform distribution Sampling of streams with semicontinuous discharges
Composite sampling (semicontinuous)	Sampling for waste parameters which are stable with time or can be stabilized Quantify waste loads with incremental samples taken proportional to flow Situation where continuous-flow sampling is impossible because large incremental samples are necessary to assure a representative measurement with multiple phases present Feed to an instrument which requires a sample at specified time intervals
Continuous sampling	Feed to instruments which can continuously measure and record parameters such as temperature, color, turbidity, pH, or dissolved oxygen Sampling of a homogeneous waste stream or for parameters of the continuous phase in a multiple-phase system

static mixer. If mixing is not possible, as for instance in large open channels, then cross-sectional sampling is an alternative. This technique involves establishing concentration and/or flow profiles and then sampling at specific depths or locations in cross-sectional segments of a pipe or channel.[4, 39, 61, 62] Flow profiles may be determined using previously listed flow measurement techniques such as a pitot tube, current meters, and dye or salt dilution techniques.

When there are multiple phases present (such as suspended solids or organic liquids of densities greater or less than that of water), sampling is extremely difficult. In general, any multiple-phase system will have a nonuniform or nonrepresentative distribution. For such a system, the greater the density difference between the phases, the greater the chance that a nonuniform distribution exists.

In some cases it is impossible to get one sample which is representative of the average concentration of all the contaminants in the wastewater stream. The word "representative," as used above, is important. A sample should be representative of the specific parameters being measured and not necessarily of all the physical, chemical, and biological parameters of the waste stream. A sample which is representative of dissolved materials in the continuous water phase may be quite different from a sample which is representative of suspended solids or floating material.

As an example of a difficult sampling problem for a material less dense than water, we will briefly consider sampling for oily material which is insoluble. Kawahara[63] has described methods for grab sampling of oily materials that involve equipment such as a wide-mouthed glass filtering funnel, a paint-free dustpan with stopcock attached to handle, or a large household sponge mop with a wringer attachment. To use the methods he describes, it may be necessary to allow the oily material to accumulate behind a skimming bar at a pond or sump pit discharge, or to actually remove a 55-gal drum sample and allow the oil to separate. Therefore, several procedures or steps may be necessary to obtain a large enough representative sample of the oily material in the water. (For further information on an oil-sampling device see Ref. 64.)

If a representative sample of several phases is desired, isokinetic sampling should be considered. *Isokinetic sampling* means withdrawing the sample at the same velocity into the probe as the velocity upstream of the probe. Houser[65] has indicated that, in general, if the sample velocity is higher than the water stream, the heavier phase will be lower in concentration in the sample than it is in the water stream and the converse applies. Rushton[66] has studied the continuous removal of mixed phases from a mixing tank and concluded that anisokinetic withdrawal conditions are least serious when the particle size, as well as the density, is small. Deviations from isokinetic conditions have large and serious effects when particle size and density are large.

Problems with nonuniform distributions and sampling have been discussed in detail by Shelley and Kirkpatrick[67] with relation to design of storm- and combined-sewer samplers. They state that one of the greatest problems in the design of a wastewater sampler is concerned with the sampler intake. It must be designed and positioned so as to obtain a representative sample, even in a stratified flow condition. It should also be relatively invulnerable to clogging. As Houser also mentioned, for a nozzle pointing directly into the flow, the most representative sample of a fluid-suspended solids mixture will be obtained when the sampling velocity is equal to the flow velocity. Shelley and Kirkpatrick[67] expanded on this point by considering the relative effects on sampling accuracy from

1. Deviation from normal sampling rate or inlet velocity
2. Deviation from straight-into-flow position of the sample probe
3. Deviations in size and shape of the probe
4. Disturbance of the sample by nozzle appurtenances

For the particular conditions of the experiments discussed, the sample inlet velocity was the most crucial parameter. For a probe velocity range of from 0.4 to 4 times the stream velocity, the error was ±4 percent for 0.06-mm-diameter sand particles, compared with +45 to −25 percent error over the same range for 0.45-mm-diameter sand particles. Note that the 0.06-mm-diameter particles are within the Stokes' law range, and the 0.4-mm particles are not. Shelley and Kirkpatrick also discussed experiments involving probes located at an angle of 90° to the direction of flow, and reached much the same conclusion concerning probe inlet velocity. Particles in the Stokes' law range are much easier to sample in a representative manner than are larger, more dense particles, which is in agreement with Rushton's[66] conclusions.

From a practical standpoint, it is seldom possible to maintain isokinetic sampling conditions at all times. The anisokinetic conditions must be tolerated, and the resulting effect on accuracy of the sampling method recognized.

Continuous-flow sampling deserves some special mention with regard to isokinetic sampling considerations. All continuous sampling systems necessarily require a probe in the stream to be sampled. If the sample stream is flowing to a sample container, total sample-size limitations usually necessitate a rather small flow. Isokinetic conditions then, in many cases, dictate a probe tube of small diameter, which would easily clog. Using a probe that would not clog with the same sample flow would mean a very low velocity in the sample tube. This could lead to an unrepresentative sample with respect to suspended matter.

There are two alternatives to the above-mentioned continuous sampling problem. First, a larger total sample volume can be accommodated, or second, a high-frequency composite (semicontinuous) sampler may be used. In many cases of multiple-phase systems, a *composite scoop sampler* which takes relatively large incremental grab samples by cutting across the waste stream, or a waste side stream, may be far more accurate than a continuous sampler. It should be borne in mind that the continuous sampler probe is usually located at one point in the stream, will not cut across the stream, and surely will not sample materials at or near the surface.

For the composite sampler which takes large incremental grab samples, the problem of composite sample volume may also exist. Holding the sampling frequency constant, we note that the larger the size of the incremental grab sample, the larger is the volume of the composite sample.

One very common mistake is to settle for a small incremental sample or low sampling frequency, rather than to deal with a very large composite sample. In a situation with rapid, unpredictable, and severe contaminant concentration fluctuations, the sampling frequency should be high. Large samples may be handled by storage in drums or small tanks; they should then be agitated before aliquots are taken from the tanks. After removal of an aliquot, the contents of the tank can be redischarged into the sewer. If sample preservation by refrigeration is a problem, perhaps collection on a shift basis instead of daily basis would alleviate the problem. Figure 5 shows a portable flow-proportioned composite sampling device which was used successfully at a large brewery.[75] (Note the refrigeration technique utilized.)

Evaluation of alternative techniques To illustrate the difference in results obtained by various sampling techniques, one may refer to a study done by Tarazi, Hiser, Childers, and Boldt[68] for the Texas Water Quality Board. In the project they compared two sampling techniques. The first consisted of automatically sampling a wastewater stream proportional to flow and obtaining a composite sample. A dip-wheel sampler dipping into a side stream revolved at a speed proportional to the wastewater flow. The second technique consisted of automatically taking three grab samples per day and recording the waste stream flow at the time of sampling.

They summarize their results as follows:

> A definite difference in results existed between the two techniques, with the degree of the differences dependent on the overall time period for the wastewater characterization, the confidence levels desired, the variability of the wastewater stream as to quality and quantity, and whether concentration levels or material transport rates were desired. *The flow weighted composite sampler provides the sampling technique most suitable for universally obtaining representative samples of wastewater effluents.*

The major problem with many composite sampling techniques, however, is that samples are taken every time 100 or 1,000 gal are recorded, and critical component concentrations may vary in a manner unrelated to flow. Considerable amounts of certain contaminants could be dumped during low-flow periods and not be present in representative amounts in the composite sample because of lower sampling frequency during low-flow periods.

A relatively expensive sampling system designed to remedy the problem of mass rate fluctuations not directly correlated with flow was devised by Nedved, Fochtman, Langdon, and Sullivan.[62] The project was sponsored by the Army Corps of Engineers. In this study they desired to obtain a representative sample with respect to the suspended solids concentration. The instrument was to operate automatically, be self-contained and portable, have its own power source, and be suitable for installation and operation under conditions ranging from open-channel flow to full-pressure flow in conduits ranging from 1 to 6 ft in diameter.

The instrument they designed performed essentially two tasks:

1. Flow rate was measured and integrated by means of five pitot tubes and a level indicator.

2. A representative sample with respect to suspended solids was withdrawn from the outfall (10 different sampling probes were positioned across the flow path).

In order to determine the weight of suspended solids passed per unit time, a relationship between turbidity and suspended solids was assumed. After an average

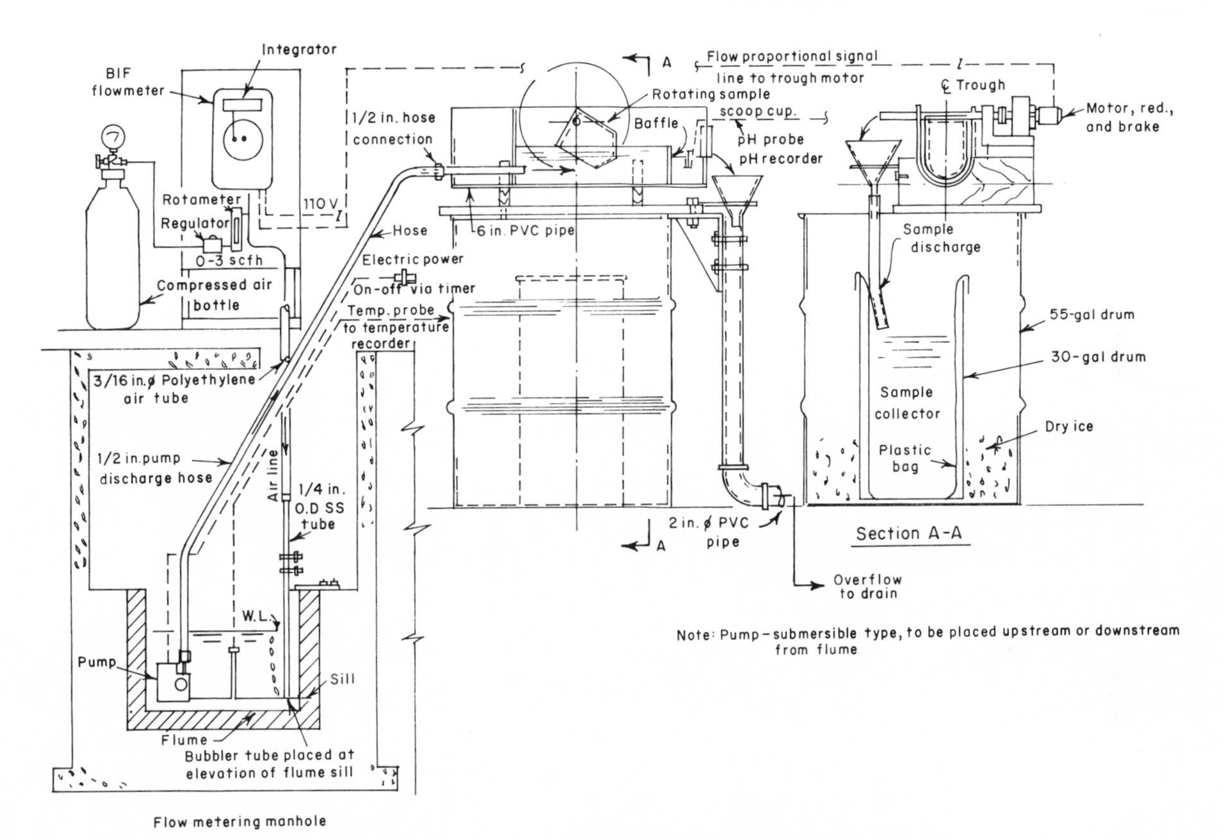

Fig. 5 Portable flow-proportioned composite sampling device.

turbidity reading for all of the sample probes was established, the reading was multiplied by the flow signal and a signal was produced proportional to the weight of suspended solids. An analog computer was used for calculation. This calculated weight was recorded and compared with a preset weight, and when the value equaled or exceeded the set value, a sample was taken.

The researchers claim that such a sampling instrument is extremely flexible and

TABLE 7 Grab-Sampling Equipment and Techniques

Application	Sampler description	Reference	Vendors
Pressure flow in conduit or tanks (for mixing tanks see Ref. 59)	Ram-type hand-operated valve	. . .	V-116
	Pinch valve	. . .	V-100, V-102
	Probe type—samples from different points in cross section	61	
	OPEN CHANNELS AND LARGE BODIES OF WATER		
Shallow stream or near surface sampling	Buckets, bottles	10, 9, 6, 50	
	Wide-mouth filtering funnel, dustpan, household sponge mop (for floating oily material)	63	
Sample taken at specific depth	Uniscoop (nonvolatile sample, not susceptible to aeration)	10	V-109
	Ohio type (will not aerate sample)	4, 49, 50	
	Juday bottle, Kemmerer, Van Dorn (will not aerate sample)	4, 49	
	Bellows-type bag sampler (sterile sampling)	. . .	V-54
	Nisken bottle	. . .	V-67
	Bottom sampler (only water sample at bottom)	6	
	Ball valve sampler	6	
	Foerst	6	
	Colorado River	6	
	Hand pump	. . .	V-28, V-61
Depth integrating samplers	Bottle and weighted frame support	6, 49, 50	
Bottom deposit samplers (macroinvertebrates)	Sand corers, dredges	49	V-67
	Surber square foot sampler	4, 49	
	Petersen dredge	4, 59	
	Eckmann dredge	4, 49	
	Shipek sediment sampler	49	V-63
	Ponar dredge	49	
	Orange peel dredge	49	
General biological sampling	Fungi	69, 70	
	Bottom deposits and organisms	4, 49, 8, 70	
	Plankton and periphyton	49, 70–72	
	Fish	70	
	Insects	49, 70	
	Algae	49, 70	
	Bacteria	49	

can be used for measurement of any variable which can be monitored continuously, such as pH, dissolved oxygen, specific conductance, or chlorides.

Another alternative to the sophisticated and expensive system described by Nedved et al. might be to go directly to the source of discharge for monitoring the problem contaminant. The cost of the additional installation might be far cheaper and more accurate than a monitoring station at a point further downstream.

Sampling equipment available Tables 7 to 9 list references and vendors for information on samplers. The grab-sampling information is self-explanatory. The

TABLE 8 Composite Sampling Equipment and Techniques

Application and principle of operation	Sampler	Price*	References	Vendors
Pressure flow in conduit	Tru Cut sampler (liquid and slurry)	B	. . .	V-27
	Isolok (liquid and slurry)	B	73	V-18
	Quality liquid sampler (liquids)		. . .	V-97
	Automatic liquid extractor (liquid sampling from slurry tanks)		. . .	V-109
	Solenoid valves (may become fouled or plugged)		10, 50	
	Pinch valves (high solids content)		. . .	V-100
	Hydragard pipeline sampler		. . .	V-8
	OPEN CHANNELS AND BODIES OF WATER			
Scoop or bucket:				
Scoop sampling directly from channel proportional to depth	Trebler sampler (installation behind weirs and flumes)	B	73, 67	V-123
	Wheel with buckets spaced at various distances from center of wheel		10	
Bucket elevator cup—sampling directly from channel	BIF Sanitrol (installation in manholes)	B	10, 67, 73	V-13
	QCEC Model E	B	67, 73	V-97
	Phipps and Bird dipper sampler	B	67, 73	V-92
Dip tube sampling directly from channel	HG4 Sonford sampler (installation in manholes)	A	67	V-113
	Can sampler		74	
Pump side stream from channel:				
Scoop or dip cup sampling flowing side stream which is pumped from channel	Chicago Tru Test (scoop type)	D	10, 67, 73	V-26
	Sentinel sampler (scoop type)	D	10, 67, 73	V-82
	Sirco cup sampler	C	10, 67	V-109
	Serco TC-2 cup sampler	D	67	V-113
	Infilco automatic	D	67	V-131
Sample cutter passing through free-falling pumped side stream	Denver wet sample cutters (pump sidestream from well-mixed channel)		. . .	V-33
Full side stream periodically diverted to sample container	Sirco diverter-type sampler	C	67	V-109
	Protech Model CEL-300	C	67	V-96
	BVS proportional composite samplers	D	67	V-17
	Collins composite sampler (portion of side stream diverted)	C	67	V-29
	N-Con Surveyor (portion of side stream diverted)	A	67	V-82
	Hydra-Numatic sampler	C	67	V-62
Vacuum-type samplers:				
Elevated chamber evacuated and sample drawn up through tubing	Sirco vacuum/compressor-type sampler (automatic purge or blowout of lines)	C	67	V-109
	"QCEC" effluent sampler "CVE"	B	10, 67	V-97
	Brailsford effluent sampler EV	B	67, 73	V-16
	Accura-flo samplers		. . .	V-59
Large sample tube in stream evacuated and sample collected	Rice Barton effluent sampler	D	. . .	V-101
Evacuated bottles opened by timer mechanism and sample drawn up through tubes	Serco automatic sampler	B	67	V-113

TABLE 8 Composite Sampling Equipment and Techniques (Continued)

Application and principle of operation	Sampler	Price*	References	Vendors
Pressure-type samplers:				
Flow proportional sample chamber in channel for use behind weir or flume	Hydragard automatic liquid sampler	A	. . .	V-8
	Alar Compositor 100	B	. . .	V-1
	Black Clawson-Krofta effluent samplers	B	. . .	V-15
Fixed-volume sample chamber in channel	Protech liquid sampling equipment	B	67, 73	V-96
	Markland automatic sampler	B	10, 67	V-77
	BVS composite sampler	B	67	V-17
	TMI fluid stream sampler	B	67	V-120
On-off peristaltic pump systems:				
	Isco sampler	B	67	V-66
	Sigmamotor samplers	B, C	. . .	V-110
	Milton Roy		. . .	V-79
	N-Con Scout, Sentry	A, B	67	V-82
	Brailsford DC-F	A	67, 73	V-20

* Base price: A < $500; B $500–$1,000; C $1,000–$2,000; D $2,000. (1973 Dollars)

composite or semicontinuous samplers listed in Table 8 are the most commonly used devices for routine monitoring in industry and will be discussed in detail. Table 9 shows that continuous-sampling devices mainly consist of centrifugal or peristaltic pumping systems. Some vacuum bottles or siphon-type devices are also commonly used.

Composite samplers are divided into two classifications: *pressure-pipe flow samplers* and *open-channel flow samplers.* Pressure-pipe flow samplers may also be used for sampling from tanks or at a point below the water surface in a gravity-flow pipe. The pressure-flow devices are usually either some type of valve or a positive displacement plunger. The open-channel devices are of five main types:

1. Scoop and buckets
   - Scoop dipped directly into channel-incremental sample proportional to flow (see Figs. 6 and 7)
   - Cup or chain dipped directly into channel-constant volume incremental samples
2. Side stream pumped from main channel
   - Sample scooped from a sidestream flow trough (see Fig. 5)
   - Sample caught by scoop passing through vertically falling side stream
   - Bucket dipped into side stream for sample
   - Side stream diverted by solenoid into sampler container
3. Sample forced up sample line by atmospheric pressure and waterhead when sample chamber is evacuated

TABLE 9 Continuous-flow Sampling Equipment and Techniques

Application and principle of operation	Sampler	Reference	Vendors
Continuous pumping from stream to sample and analysis train	Peristaltic pumps	10, 30	V-89, V-110
	Centrifugal pump, centripetal pumps	. . .	Many
Vacuum cannister	Evacuated cylinder	30	
Vacuum	Siphon sampler	10, 13, 61	

4. Sample forced up sample line by high-pressure air or other gas above liquid in the sample chamber (see Fig. 8)

5. Peristaltic or centrifugal pump actuated by timer or flow totalizer signal

When comparing these five types of automatic composite sampling devices, it is important to consider some or all of the following points, depending on the specific application:

LIFT OF SAMPLE. How high must sample be lifted and transported?

SAMPLER INTAKE. What is the size of opening and what is the sample inlet velocity?

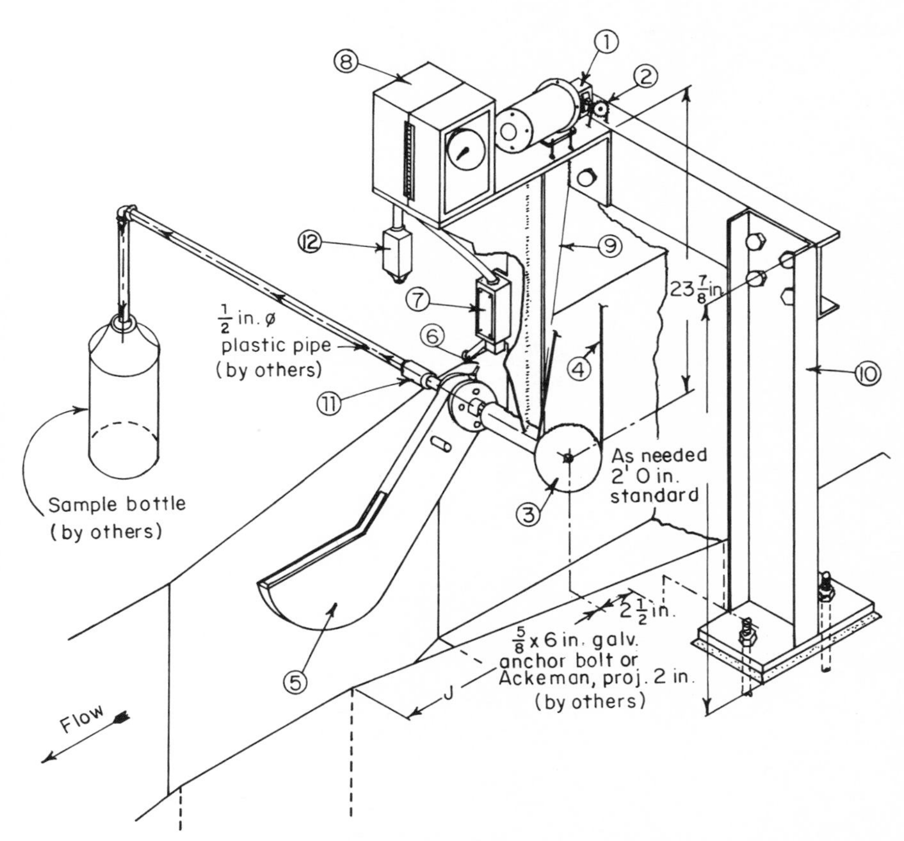

Fig. 6 Trebler sampler shown in Parshall flume. (1) motor reducer, (2) drive sprocket, (3) driven sprocket, (4) roller chain, (5) scoop, (6) scoop counterweight, (7) limit switch, (8) time clock, (9) aluminum sampler frame casting, (10) aluminum sampler support, (11) outlet coupling, (12) ½-in. Unilet body and cover.

INCREMENTAL SAMPLE SIZE AND SAMPLE REMOVAL METHOD. Can the incremental sample be varied? Will stream composition vary from top to bottom or side to side? If so, is the sample taken from one point in stream or from a cut or scoop cut across entire stream? Is incremental sample volume constant or proportional to flow rate at the instant of sampling?

FREQUENCY OF SAMPLING. Is the sampling cycle initiated by a flow recording device or a timer? Can sampling frequency be varied? Can frequency and incremental sample size be varied so as to obtain desired composite sample volume?

Method of Flow Proportioning Sample. Is scoop or sample chamber designed to take a sample volume proportional to the depth behind a weir or flume? Is sampler compatible with the intended flow-metering systems?

Environmental Requirements. Can sampler be installed in manhole? Can a heated shelter be provided as well as refrigeration? Will immersion damage or prevent operation of the sampler?

Sampler Storage. What composite sample volume can be stored in containers? Can multiple discrete samples be stored?

Maintenance Requirements. Are there automatic line purges to prevent pluggage? Are there valves, chambers, or lines which can easily be plugged or fouled?

Power or Energy Source for Sample Lift. Is necessary power source available for sampling site? Is it possible to find a self-contained unit?

Sampler Portability. If not a permanent installation, how easily can the equipment be moved? How versatile is the sampler for varying conditions such as lift, power source, sample frequency, sample volume, flow-measuring device?

Special Sample Consideration. What effect will sampling technique have on readily oxidizable materials? What is the bubble point of the sample?

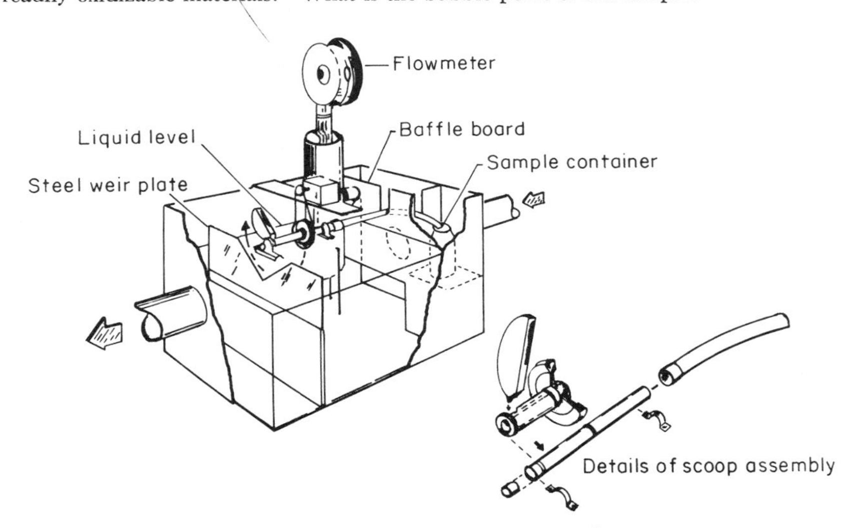

Fig. 7 Scoop-type composite sampler.

Materials of Construction—Corrosion and Erosion Considerations. Will the sampler lines or containers contaminate the sample?

Experience with sampling equipment Craft and Ingols[73] surveyed the market for automatic sampling equipment, as did Shelley and Kirkpatrick.[67] Table 8 indicates which samplers they evaluated or gathered user information for. Shelley and Kirkpatrick's[67] descriptions and evaluation of commercially-designed, as well as custom-designed, sampling equipment are one of the most thorough studies ever done.

In early 1975, the U.S. Army released the results of a sampler evaluation they conducted with 16 commercially available samplers.[180] The study included consideration of the devices' efficiency in sampling water for biological organisms, biodegradable substances, suspended solids, colloidal solids, dissolved gases, and volatile organics. This study should be very helpful in selecting a sampling device. Many shortcomings listed for individual devices may have been corrected since the evaluation was completed.

Craft and Ingols[73] indicated satisfaction by users of the Isolok sampler (V-18) for pressure flow in pipes, including some sewage treatment plant applications. A sampler operating on the principle of a continuous-flow side stream pumped from a sewer to a chamber where a scoop periodically dips out a sample (V-26, V-82) also received favorable reports from users, as did a scoop dipping directly from behind a flume or weir (V-123). Samplers of the conveyor chain type with attached scooper bucket (V-13, V-92, V-97) were generally satisfactory, but comments were made concerning jamming of the chain mechanism by rags or debris. Pressure-type samplers (V-96) were reported as satisfactory, but a number of users reported frequent clogging of liquid lines. Users of vacuum-type samplers (V-16) generally reported satisfaction, but it was noted that the flow-proportioning device operates on water level changes of 1-in. increments rather than continuously. Samplers utilizing peristaltic pumps (V-110) were generally considered satisfactory by users, but stoppage of the sample line by paper and other solids was reported.

One should realize that most of the comments made by users were concerned with mechanical problems and failure of the equipment to provide a sample. The representativeness of the sample does not seem to have been considered in detail.

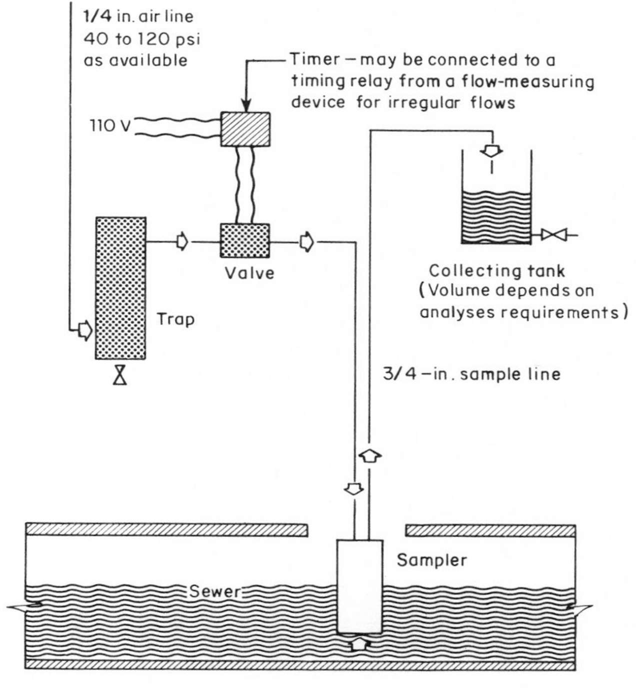

Fig. 8 Air-lift automatic sampler system.

Shelley and Kirkpatrick[67] indicate one possible problem with vacuum- or pressure-type samplers which have chambers submerged in a wastewater stream.

> Sampling chamber will fill immediately following discharge of the previous aliquot, resulting in a sample not necessarily representative of conditions in the sewer at the time of the next triggering signal. Representativeness is also questionable at high flow rates.

In some situations, this phenomenon may not produce significant errors when sampling frequency is high relative to waste variability. Some vacuum- or pressure-type samplers avoid this problem by not reopening the sample-collection chamber until another sample is to be taken (V-1).

A sampling system with a submersible pump continuously pumping a side stream to a chamber where a dip or scoop mechanism periodically removes a sample is one of the best operating systems available.[75] Several modifications, however, of commercially available systems may be necessary to provide troublefree operation. Screens on pump intakes should be backwashed periodically by stopping the pump and allowing the aboveground sampling trough and line to drain back through the screen to the sewer. In some cases it may be necessary to backwash with a separate pump and water storage system.

Shelley and Kirkpatrick[67] also mention that in instances where a sampler body or other appurtenances exist in a wastewater stream (i.e., submersible sampling pump), the probe should be extended a short distance upstream to allow collection of a representative sample. This procedure should prevent errors resulting from flow disturbances around the large obstruction.

On-Stream Analysis

The number of analytical instruments and suppliers of such instruments is increasing at a rate bewildering to those who are not full-time analytical chemists. In reviewing manufacturers' literature, one will find systems which automatically perform wet chemical analysis. Other systems involve specific ion electrodes, various opacity or light-scattering techniques, ultraviolet or infrared spectrophotometry, conductivity

TABLE 10 Some Basic Analytical Techniques Utilized for On-Stream Monitoring

Method	Measurement of	Parameters
Electrolytes or electrochemical sensors:[77]		
Potentiometric	Potential at zero faradic current	pH, Cl^-, ORP, specific ion electrodes (many ions)
Polarographic	Current at controlled potential or controlled potential variation	Dissolved oxygen
Coulometric Titration	Current passed through solution during reaction of substance with titrant generated in solution	Arsenic (not yet developed)
Charge transport	Conductivity	(Estimate dissolved salt concentration)
Spectrophotometer:		
Visual spectra Ultraviolet spectra Infrared spectra	Measures amount of light or radiant energy transmitted through a solution as a function of wavelength	
Light transmission or reflectance—turbidity		

measurements, or combustion of samplers followed by measurement of off-gas concentrations. Reading about the specific methods for measurement leaves most of us in a state of total confusion.

Craft and Ingols[73] have surveyed the field of on-stream analytical instrumentation, using a simple classification descriptive of function rather than the specific analytical method.

TYPE I instruments are continuously recording devices which yield a direct and almost instantaneous response to variations in a given parameter.

TYPE II instruments are devices which produce continuous readings by automatically adding reagents to a continuously flowing sample stream, followed by detection with a sensor of the Type I variety.

TYPE III instruments produce readings on a discontinuous basis. These devices take a sample and subject it to chemical and/or physical treatment. *Type I* devices may then be used on a discontinuous basis for detection.

Some of the analytical methods which one will read about in surveying the literature are summarized in Table 10. Under potentiometric electrochemical sensors, specific ion electrodes deserve some special mention as an example of developing technology. The electrodes measure the concentration of ionized material.

Riseman[76] has stated that about 20 specific ion electrodes are commercially available, 9 being of interest for wastewater monitoring. Electrodes for calcium, chloride, fluoride, sodium, and sulfide may be used in both fresh- and saltwater, while electrodes for determination of fluoroborate, cyanide, nitrate, and total water hardness are limited to freshwater use. Indirect electrode-based methods have also been developed for determination of aluminum by reaction with fluoride, chlorine by reaction with iodide, and sulfate by reaction with lead.

Suffet and Radziul[77] have discussed in some detail the problems associated with using specific ion electrodes for continuous on-stream monitoring. Analytical problems discussed include electrode response to interferences, ion complexing agents, and waste variability. Also mentioned are problems with the electrodes themselves, including leakage, adsorption or physical entrainment of ions at electrode surface, length of electrode response time, and drift.

In reviewing literature on previous on-stream applications, one should determine whether the installation was for municipal or industrial water supply, lake, stream, or estuary situation, or for wastewater or reclaimed wastewater quality monitoring. Problems associated with these three applications of on-stream instrumentation may be quite different. For municipal and/or industrial water supply, on-stream instrumental techniques for monitoring chlorides, chlorine, color, conductivity, fluoride, hardness, pH, turbidity, and temperature are quite well-developed. For stream or lake monitoring of water quality, pH, specific conductance, chlorides, dissolved oxygen, temperature, and turbidity have been monitored continuously in numerous applications. Wastewater and water recycle streams have been monitored by on-stream instrumental techniques for numerous parameters. Possible interferences and problems with limited rangeability of certain instruments do mean, however, that each situation must be carefully studied before an instrument is purchased.

To date only certain instrumental techniques are approved by the United States Environmental Protection Agency. In the *Federal Register* of October 16, 1973,[78] the EPA issued Guidelines Establishing Test Procedures for Analysis of Pollutants. Here reference is made to "Standard Methods,"[49] "ASTM Standards,"[51] and "EPA Methods"[48] in these guidelines for description of acceptable methods. If one wishes to utilize an on-stream instrumental technique or different lab technique for certain parameters, the guidelines provide procedures for obtaining approval. In many cases, continuous monitoring may not be required by law, but may be desirable for other reasons. In such cases, composite samples may be taken for laboratory analysis and reporting to a regulatory body and continuous monitoring utilized for spill control, wastewater treatment process control, or as a process safeguard where recycled water is being utilized.

In order to keep abreast of this rapidly changing field, the EPA financed a study entitled *Operation of the Analytical Methodology Information Center (AMIC)* conducted by Darby and Little.[79] The AMIC was established to assist government and private laboratories in searching the literature and identifying, procuring, evaluating, and computerizing relevant information on methods for determining the identity, concentration, and ecological effects of pollutants and measuring water quality. Information is distributed to the public through publication by the National Technical Information Service.[80]

The National Science Foundation has also been active in the area of environmental monitoring. The Lawrence Berkeley Laboratory is conducting a comprehensive survey titled *Instrumentation for Environmental Monitoring*[115] under an NSF grant. Volume II of this survey should provide the most up-to-date information on analytical instrumentation for both laboratory and field analysis of water quality. This is a necessary reference for anyone involved in water monitoring. The first release of information in looseleaf binder form was in February 1973, and the survey was completed in 1974. The topics to be covered are listed in the first release as follows:

- Metals
- Halides and cyanide
- Nitrogen, phosphorus, sulfur
- Biological parameters
- Dissolved gases

- Pesticides
- Phenolics
- Petrochemicals
- Oil and grease
- Physical parameters

Three other sources of information on advances in analytical techniques are the Annual Literature Review of the *Journal of the Water Pollution Control Federation,*[81] the Annual Reviews in *Analytical Chemistry,*[82] and the Research Briefs in *Environmental Science and Technology.*[83]

For a basic review of water chemistry, laboratory quality control, and instrumental analysis, reference works or texts by Sawyer and McCarty,[84] the EPA,[85] and Mancy[86] are helpful.

The text edited by Mancy[86] is particularly useful for background information on the following topics:

- Concentration and separation techniques
- Instrumental analysis techniques
- Continuous monitoring systems
- Automated chemical analysis
- Remote optical sensing techniques
- Analysis for organics, metals, inorganic anions and dissolved gases

Evaluation of instruments In evaluating many on-stream instruments, it may be necessary to review laboratory experience because of limited field data. Elving[87] has suggested criteria for use as a basis for selection of instruments. These include:

ACCURACY. Degree of difference between observed and known values

PRECISION. Reproducibility of results

SELECTIVITY. Lack of interference from other compounds, ions

SENSITIVITY. Lowest concentration or amount detectable

SPEED. Lag time between sample injection and information output

TYPE OF DATA PRESENTATION. Form of output data

In addition to these, one should also consider the following points very carefully:

INSTRUMENT RANGE. Concentration range over which instrument can produce a reading—variation in instrument accuracy and precision over the entire range

STABILITY. Frequency of recalibration required

MAINTENANCE. Amount of instrument cleaning and adjustment, need for ultrasonic cleaning devices to lower routine maintenance

PERSONNEL REQUIREMENTS. Laboratory technician, chemist, instrument engineer

TEMPERATURE COMPENSATION. Automatic compensation may be required

TYPE OF SAMPLING DEVICE. Sample transportation, conditioning and injection

This last item, concerning sampling, is one of the biggest problems encountered in moving an instrument from a laboratory to field location for on-stream monitoring. Problems encountered with obtaining representative samples were discussed in detail earlier. Sensors located at a representative point in a given stream may, of course, eliminate the need for a sampling train. A sample must usually be removed from the stream, sewer line, or sump, however, and transported to the monitoring equipment.

Houser[65] has prepared a very comprehensive publication for the Instrument Society of America on the design of process analysis systems, in which he discusses:

1. Sample transportation—sizing sample lines, phase preservation, adsorption, diffusion
2. Sample conditioning—cleaning, cooling, pressure reduction, pumping
3. Sample switching for stream sequencing
4. Sample disposal or venting
5. Corrosion considerations

Although water analysis systems are not specifically covered, Houser does discuss the actual design, installation and start-up of process analysis systems. This reference should be of great help to anyone desiring to design an on-stream analytical instrumentation system.

Summary of on-stream instrumental methods As an aid to individuals interested in analysis for specific parameters, a number of those which may be monitored by on-stream instrumental methods have been listed in Table 11. Note that an X

TABLE 11 On-Stream Instrumental Analysis Summary

Parameter	Continuous		Semi-continuous,	Method	Labora-tory use reported	Successful field use reported	References	Vendors
	Type 1	Type 2	Type 3					
Alkalinity			X	Automatic analyzer	X		48, 93	V-99, V-118
Ammonia	X			Specific ion electrode	X	X	73, 85, 115	V-88, V-137
			X	Automatic analyzer	X	X	48, 73, 93, 88, 90, 115	V-118
		X		Continuous spectrophotometer			73	V-32
Bromide	X			Specific ion electrode	X			V-88
Cadmium	X			Specific ion electrode	X		73, 115	V-88, V-134
Calcium	X			Specific ion electrode	X		94	V-42, V-88, V-134
Chloride	X			Specific ion electrode	X	X	85, 115	V-4, V-42, V-51, V-88, V-103, V-134
			X	Automatic analyzer	X	X	93, 115	V-118
Chlorine	X			Polarographic devices		X	73	V-23, V-47, V-51, V-60, V-127
		X		Colorimetric analyzer		X	73	V-32, V-55
Chrome (total and hexavalent)			X	Automatic analyzer		X	73, 115	V-32, V-55, V-99, V-118
Color	X			Spectrophotometric analyzer		X	73, 115	V-32, V-55
Copper	X			Polarographic device		X	73	V-47
	X			Specific ion electrode	X	X	73, 115	V-51, V-88, V-134
			X	Automatic analyzer and colorimetric		X	73, 115	V-32, V-55, V-99
Cyanide	X			Specific ion electrode			73, 85, 115	V-51, V-88, V-134
			X	Automatic analyzer				V-118
Dissolved solids (electrolyte detected)	X			Specific conductance	X	X	10, 73, 115	V-4, V-11, V-32, V-44, V-51, V-55, V-73, V-75, V-79, V-99, V-103, V-126, V-134
Filtrable solids	X			Inductance or capacitance	X	X		

TABLE 11 On-Stream Instrumental Analysis Summary (Continued)

Parameter	Continuous		Semi-continuous,	Method	Laboratory use reported	Successful field use reported	References	Vendors
	Type 1	Type 2	Type 3					
Fluoride	X			Specific ion electrode	X	X	48, 85, 90, 94, 95	V-42, V-51, V-88, V-134
		X		Colorimetric analyzer	X	X		
Hardness		X	X	Automatic analyzer		X	73, 96	V-55, V-99
	X			Polyvalent ion electrode	X	X	73, 96	V-51, V-88
Iron			X	Automatic analyzer		X	115	V-99
		X		Colorimetric, spectrophotometer		X	115	V-32, V-55
Mercury			X	Flameless ultraviolet absorption		X	73, 93, 115	V-87
Nitrate; nitrite	X			Specific ion electrode	X		48, 73, 90, 93, 115	V-42, V-88, V-134
		X		Spectrophotometer	X		48, 73, 90, 93, 115	V-32
			X	Automatic analyzer	X		48, 73, 90, 93, 115	V-118
Nitrogen (Kjeldahl)			X	Automatic analyzer	X		73, 88	V-118
Oil	X			Ultraviolet light transmittance		X	73, 97	V-21, V-119
	X			Light reflectance		X	98	V-37
Oxidation reduction potential	X			Use of pH equipment with substitution of platinum electrode for glass membrane electrode	X	X	73, 115	Contact manufacturers of pH control equipment
Oxygen demand								
Chemical oxygen demand (COD)			X	Wet oxidation; CO formation ($CO_2 + C \rightarrow CO$)	X		56, 88, 99–101, 115	V-22, V-91, V-95, V-118
Total organic carbon (TOC) or Total carbon (TC)			X	Combustion; wet oxidation with persulfate	X	X	49, 77, 84, 88, 101, 103, 115	V-6, V-7, V-11, V-22, V-35, V-86, V-91, V-99, V-125
Total oxygen demand (TOD)			X	Combustion	X	X	73, 84, 93, 101, 115	V-6, V-44, V-69
Biochemical oxygen demand (BOD)			X	Respirometer	X	X		V-5, V-10

Oxygen (dissolved)	X			Thallium and reference electrode, polarographic systems	X	X	73, 94, 104–106, 113, 115	V-4, V-11, V-25, V-32, V-39, V-40, V-42, V-44, V-60, V-67, V-69, V-75 V-95, V-99, V-103, V-105, V-126, V-130, V-134, V-135
Phenols and other dissolved organics	X			Ultraviolet spectrophotometry			73, 107–109, 115	V-119
			X	Automatic analyzer	X		56, 115	V-118
							93	V-36
Phosphorus			X	Flame emission photometry	X		110	
			X	Automatic analyzer		X	73, 88, 93, 115	V-55, V-69, V-99
		X		Colorimetric			73, 93, 115	V-32
pH	X			Potentiometric (electrode device)	X	X	73, 115	V-11, V-30, V-32, V-44, V-55, V-72, V-73, V-79, V-99, V-103, V-126, V-134
Silver	X			Spectrophotometric			73, 115	V-32
Sulfide	X			Specific ion	X	X	115	V-51, V-88, V-134
Suspended solids	X			Light scattering or opacity		X	62, 73, 111, 115	V-14, V-71
Temperature	X			Thermistor, thermocouple	X	X	21, 73, 115	V-4, V-32, V-40, V-42, V-44, V-54, V-60, V-67, V-99, V-103, V-134
Turbidity	X			Light scattering or opacity, reflectance		X	73, 115	V-4, V-32, V-42, V-51, V-53, V-55, V-60, V-67, V-70, V-84, V-99, V-103, V-134

mark in the column labeled "Successful field use reported" should not be considered an endorsement nor should a lack of reports be considered a rejection of the method. Successful applications may have occurred in situations completely different from one which the reader is considering. Also, because instruments are constantly being modified to eliminate problems encountered by customers, it would be unfair and unwise to eliminate any instrument or manufacturer from consideration. It is also quite probable that many users of such equipment never report either successes or problems in the literature.

As a general guide to determining the amount of time and care one should invest in evaluating instruments for specific parameters, Craft and Ingols'[73] recommendations to the Air Force should prove to be helpful. They are listed in Table 12.

Instrument costs and operating expenses Craft and Ingols[73] and Ballinger[93] have published information on the purchase prices for on-stream instruments for measuring some specific parameters. Their cost figures as well as some information from other sources have been summarized in Table 13.

TABLE 12 Recommendations for On-Stream Instrumental Analysis for the Air Force by Craft and Ingols[73]

Equipment available "off the shelf" with sufficient information to recommend use		
Chlorine residual	Oxidation-reduction potential	
Conductivity	pH	
Dissolved oxygen	Temperature	
Hydraulic loading	Turbidity	
Equipment available "off the shelf" but not recommended at this time (1973)		
Ammonia	Cyanide	Organic loading
Cadmium	Iron	Phenols
Chromium	Lead	Phosphate
Color	Nitrate	Silver
Copper	Nitrite	Suspended solids
Research and development required for continuous monitoring		
Color	Nickel	
Cyanide	Nitrogen	
Mercury	Organic loading	
Manual laboratory procedures with automatic sampling recommended		
Cadmium	Oil and grease	
Filtrable solids	Phenols	
Lead	Surfactants	
Nickel	Suspended solids	
Nitrogen, Kjeldahl	Zinc	

Data Management

By this time you may be wondering how all of the information that will be generated from a monitoring program will be logged, stored, and utilized. Even if composite samples are gathered and analyzed in a laboratory, the data generated can become cumbersome. On-stream analyzers for numerous parameters can generate overwhelming amounts of data.

Recently released EPA Effluent Guidelines are based on the mass of specific pollutants discharged per unit of production or unit of raw material processed. This means that not only monitoring data must be readily accessible but also plant production information. One advantage to such a data system is that tracking down problem areas in a plant may be several orders of magnitude simpler if observed pollution loads can be correlated rapidly with production data.

It should be apparent that optimum use of monitoring information will not be possible without a rapid and efficient data reduction, storage and retrieval system. The read-out from a strip-chart recorder is obviously not a very convenient data form for the person in a plant or at corporate headquarters who must evaluate a plant's environmental performance. Also, it should be remembered that water, air, and solid waste discharges are probably all going to be monitored, and this may compound the problems already mentioned.

Many companies are now using off-line computers for storage of data and calculation of pollution discharges over various time periods. These systems, however, involve data reduction and logging by laboratory and plant engineering personnel before the data are converted to an intermediate storage form, as on punched cards. Barrett[117] has discussed a planned multiple-brewery surveillance system for the Joseph Schlitz Brewing Company. An off-line computer would have access to production data and raw material usage as well as pollution monitoring information. With this data system, Barrett hopes to reduce the time and effort required by corporate management to assess the environmental performance of the various breweries and to detect problem areas rapidly. Schlitz, as well as other companies, realizes though that in order to obtain maximum control over pollutant discharges, on-stream analyzers will be necessary. As the number of parameters being monitored increases, the lag time between data acquisition and retrieval usually increases. Manual data handling becomes almost impossible.

The ultimate answer to this information problem seems to be the on-line digital computer. During the last 5 to 10 years there has been a tremendous increase in the use of on-line or sensor-based computers. These digital systems are being used for

TABLE 13 Purchase Prices for Miscellaneous On-Stream Instruments

Parameter	Range of purchase prices for on-stream device*
Chlorine residual	$1,700–$3,700
Chrome (hexavalent)	~$3,000
Color	$2,500–$3,000
Copper	$2,000–$4,000
Iron	$3,000–$3,400
Mercury	~$20,000
Nitrates	~$3,000
Oil	~$10,000
Organics—oxygen demand:	
TOC	~$10,000
COD	~$6,000
TOD	~$9,000
Phenols	$4,000–$10,000
Phosphate	$1,600–$5,000

* 1973 dollars.

process control in refineries, automobile exhaust emission testing control, and laboratory data processing as well as for automatic data logging and processing for air and water quality field-monitoring stations.

Eggleston[118] has discussed the rapid turnaround time possible between data acquisition and use of such information for decision making from use of sensor-based systems. He indicates that one of the major challenges for a company using sensor-based systems will be integration of the entire data acquisition capability with the total information system. Balancing of input and output from sensor-based computers to the data base/data communications facility must be achieved to allow optimum usage of information.

Depending on the type and amount of data to be handled, there are numerous types of equipment available. One may purchase systems to scan analog outputs from various sensors automatically, convert such signals to digital output, and store the information on tape. The information may also be telemetered and printed out at a central location or stored in a central data bank. In certain applications, data reduction may be needed and a real-time minicomputer can control the data acquisition as well as perform calculations. Outputs from this type of system may be used for process control or for feeding preprocessed information into a central computer system.

For general information on the type of computers available, the reader should refer to Noonan.[119] Ewy[120] has presented more detailed information including network diagrams for automated measurement systems. Schagrin[121] has presented cost information for minicomputers, and Stout[122] has utilized some of Schagrin's information to indicate how to justify the use of minicomputers. For up-to-date information the reader should contact vendors. A listing of vendors has been provided by *Chemical Engineering*.[123]

REMOTE MONITORING

It was mentioned during the preliminary discussion of monitoring that sampling is usually the weak point in a monitoring program. This is particularly true when one considers the many miles of streams and shorelines from which pollutants are discharged, as well as discharges from ships or platforms. In the future, remote monitoring techniques may be developed to a point where floating materials, suspended matter, and dissolved matter can be identified and quantified from aerial observation. If this comes about, the monitoring techniques used now will not be replaced, but instead will be utilized more efficiently. Problem areas can be spotted from airplanes and even by satellite camera along large river systems, in lakes, or along the coastline. After spotting such problems, routine sampling and analysis programs can be initiated by field-monitoring teams in well-defined areas.

At this time, the field of remote monitoring of water quality is very much in the developmental stages. Temperature is really the only parameter which can be quantitatively measured. Sensing may be accomplished by electromagnetic methods, or by other means such as sonic techniques. Hom[124] states that the amount of information potentially obtainable by remote sensing of electromagnetic energy is so great, however, that methods other than electromagnetic energy techniques are relatively unimportant.

The EPA's National Field Investigation Center at Denver, through an agreement with the U.S. Air Force, has been using jet aircraft to carry water pollution monitoring equipment. By remote sensing methods, the EPA has detected and attempted to assess the extent and physical effects of oil spills, heat discharges, untreated waste discharges, and algal growths. In one study, aerial photographic techniques were used for detection and recording of over 200 wastewater discharges to San Francisco Bay.[125]

Mills[126] has described an Airborne Remote Sensing System for coastal zone pollution monitoring established by the Coast Guard. Under this program, six EU-16-E aircraft have been outfitted with sensors capable of real-time detection of petroleum pollutants and a recording system furnishing a permanent record of any pollutants detected. The equipment may be operated during daylight and nighttime periods. The six aircraft are assigned computer-generated search plans based on an analysis of coastal traffic patterns.

For further information on remote monitoring, the reader should review Refs. 86, 127, and 128.

REFERENCES

1. Keup, L. E., W. M. Ingram, and K. M. Mackenthun: "Biology of Water Pollution—A Collection of Selected Papers on Stream Pollution, Waste Water, and Water Treatment," U.S. Dept. of the Interior, 1967.
2. Tarzwell, C. M.: "Biological Problems in Water Pollution—1962," Public Health Service Publication No. 999-WP-25.
3. Velz, C. J.: "Applied Stream Sanitation," Wiley Interscience, New York, N.Y., 1970.
4. Kittrell, F. W.: "A Practical Guide to Water Quality Studies of Streams," U.S. Dept. of the Interior, CWR-5, 1969.
5. Jackson, H. W.: Biomonitoring of Industrial Waste Effluents, *Proc. Purdue University Industrial Waste Conf., 1966*, Purdue University, West Lafayette, Ind.
6. Rainwater, F. H., and L. L. Thatcher: "Methods for Collection and Analysis of Water Samples," Geological Survey Water Supply Paper 1454, 1960.
7. WPCF Safe Work Procedure No. 1—Preparations for Manhole Work, *J. Water Pollution Control Federation,* vol. 42, no. 2, part 1, pp. 333–339, February 1970.

8. Gunnerson, C. G.: Optimizing Sampling Intervals in Tidal Estuaries, *J. Sanitary Engrg. Div., Proc. Am. Soc. of Civil Engineers,* vol. XX, pp. 103–125, April 1966.
9. Jenkins, D.: Analysis of Estuarine Waters, *J. Water Pollution Control Federation,* vol. 39, no. 2, pp. 159–180, February 1967.
10. Associated Water and Air Resources Engineers, U.S. Environmental Protection Agency: "Handbook for Monitoring Industrial Wastewater," Technology Transfer Section, Washington, D.C., August 1973.
11. Fair, J. R., B. B. Crocker, and H. R. Null: Trace Quantity Engineering, *Chem. Engrg.,* vol. 79, p. 60, August 7, 1972.
12. Davis, C. V., and K. S. Sorenson: "Handbook of Applied Hydraulics," 3rd ed., McGraw-Hill, New York, N.Y., 1969.
13. Metcalf & Eddy, Inc.: "Wastewater Engineering," McGraw-Hill, New York, N.Y., 1972.
14. Halmi, D.: Practical Guide to the Evaluation of the Metering Performance of Differential Procedures, *Am. Soc. Mech. Engrs. paper No. 72-WA/Fluid Meters No. 2.*
15. "Fluid Meters," 6th ed., Am. Soc. Mechanical Engineers.
16. Daneker, J. R.: Reproduction of Pressure Differentials at Sensed Piezometer Openings, paper presented at Conf. Water and Wastewater Equipment Manufacturers Assoc., March 1973.
17. "Manual on Disposal of Refinery Wastes—Flow Measurement," American Petroleum Institute, New York, N.Y., 1969.
18. Byrne, E. J.: Measuring and Controlling, *Chem. Engrg.,* vol. XX, pp. 189–193, April 14, 1969.
19. Zientara, D. E.: Measuring Process Variables, *Chem. Engrg.,* vol. X, pp. 23–25, September 11, 1972.
20. Perry, R. H., C. H. Chilton, and S. D. Kirkpatrick: "Chemical Engineers' Handbook," 4th ed., McGraw-Hill, New York, N.Y., 1963.
21. Benedict, R. P.: "Fundamentals of Temperature, Pressure and Flow Measurements," pp. 267–344, Wiley, New York, N.Y., 1967.
22. Moore, D. C.: Easy Way to Measure Slurry Flow Rates, *Chem. Engrg.,* vol. X, p. 96, October 2, 1972.
23. Pierce, J. W.: Mass Flow Measurements of Mining Slurries, *Trans. AIME,* vol. 223, pp. 34–37, 1962.
24. McCabe, W. L., and J. C. Smith: "Unit Operations of Chemical Engineering," pp. 117–123, McGraw-Hill, New York, N.Y., 1956.
25. May, D. L.: Accurate Flow Measurements with Turbine Meters, *Chem. Engrg.,* vol. X, pp. 105–108, March 8, 1971.
26. Eshleman, P. W., and R. A. Blase: *A Thermal Wave Flowmeter for Measuring Combined Sewer Flows,* U.S. Environmental Protection Agency, EPA-R2-73-145, Washington, D.C., March 1973.
27. Zacharigs, E. M., Jr., and D. W. Fran: Sound Velocities Monitor Process Streams, *Chem. Engrg.,* vol. X, pp. 101–108, January 22, 1973.
28. Liquid Flowmeter is Based on Fluidic Oscillations, *Chem. Engrg.,* vol. X, p. 66, September 3, 1973.
29. *Planning and Making Industrial Waste Surveys,* prepared by the Metal Finishing Industry Action Committee of the Ohio River Valley Sanitation Commission, Cincinnati, Ohio, April 1952.
30. Hodges, P. B.: Unique Sampling and Flow Measurement Devices for In-Plant Waste Control, *Proc. Purdue University Industrial Wastewater Conf., 1959,* Purdue University, West Lafayette, Ind.
31. Jones, J. L., and W. F. Suchanek: *Procedure for Flow Measurement Using Lithium Chloride Dilution Method,* Monsanto Enviro-Chem Systems, Inc., Chicago, Ill., 1970. Unpublished data.
32. Kilpatrick, F. A.: Flow Calibration by Dye-Dilution Method, *Civil Engrg.,* vol. XX, pp. 74–76, February 1968.
33. Hull, D. E., M. Macomber, and J. H. Easthagen: Flow Measurement by Radiotracer, *Sewage and Industrial Wastes,* vol. XX, pp. 45–52, January 1959.
34. Wilson, J. F.: *Fluorometric Procedures for Dye-Tracing—Techniques of Water Resources Investigation of the U.S. Geological Survey,* book 3, chap. A-12, U.S. Dept. of Interior, Geological Survey, 1968.
35. U.S. Bureau of Reclamation, Department of the Interior: "Water Measurement Manual," 1967.
36. Stevens, J. C.: "Hydrographic Data Book," 8th ed., Leopold & Stevens, Inc., Portland, Ore.

37. Walker, W. R., G. V. Skogerboe, and R. S. Bennett: Flow Measuring Flume for Wastewater Treatment Plants, *J. Water Pollution Control Federation,* vol. 45, no. 3, pp. 542–551, March 1973.
38. Crocker, S.: Irrigation Piping, in Reno C. King (ed.), "Piping Handbook," 5th ed., pp. 21–41, McGraw-Hill, New York, N.Y., 1967.
39. Rabosky, J. G., and D. L. Koraido: Gaging and Sampling Industrial Wastewaters, *Chem. Engrg.*, vol. XX, pp. 111–120, January 8, 1973.
40. Wright, R. R., and M. R. Collings: Application of Fluorescent Tracing Techniques to Hydrologic Studies, *J. Am. Water Works Assoc.*, vol. XX, pp. 748–754, July 1964.
41. Smith, A. S., and L. G. Kipple: Infiltration Measure in Sanitary Sewers by Dye Dilution Method, *Water & Sewage Works,* vol. XX, pp. 58–61, January 1972.
42. Feuerstein, D. L., and R. E. Selleck: Fluorescent Tracers for Dispersion Measurement, *J. Sanit. Engrg. Div., Am. Soc. Civil Engrs,* vol. 89, pp. 1–21, 1963.
43. Cobb, E. D., J. F. Baily, and F. A. Kilpatrick: *Surface Water Techniques—Measure of Discharge by Dye Dilution Methods,* book 1, chap. 14, U.S. Department of Interior, Geological Survey, 1965.
44. Deaner, G. S., Effect of Chlorine on Fluorescent Dyes, *J. Water Pollution Control Federation,* vol. 45, no. 3, pp. 507–514, March 1973.
45. Timblin, L. O., and A. J. Peterka: *Use of Radioisotopes for Open Channel Flow Measurements,* report from Office of Chief Engineer, Bureau of Reclamation, Denver, Colo.
46. Siegel, H., A. Telfer, and E. L. Bastin: Radioisotope Tracing of Oil Refinery Wastewater Dilution, *J. Water Pollution Control Federation,* vol. 44, no. 8, pp. 1637–1642, August 1972.
47. Lipták, B. G.: Costs of Process Instruments, *Chem. Engrg.*, vol. XX, pp. 60–76, September 7, 1970.
48. U.S. Environmental Protection Agency: *Methods for Chemical Analysis of Water and Wastes,* Water Quality Office, Cincinnati, Ohio, 1971.
49. "Standard Methods for the Examination of Water and Waste Water," 13th ed., American Public Health Association, 1971.
50. "Manual on Disposal of Refinery Wastes, Volume IV—Sampling and Analysis of Wastewater," American Petroleum Institute, New York, N.Y., 1957.
51. "ASTM Annual Book of Standards, Part 23, Atmospheric Analysis," Am. Soc. for Testing and Materials, Philadelphia, Pa.
52. Agardy, F. J., and M. L. Kiado: Effects of Refrigerated Storage on the Characteristics of Waste, *Proc. Purdue University Industrial Waste Conf., 1966,* Purdue University, West Lafayette, Ind., 1966.
53. Schaumburg, F. D.: A New Concept in Sample Preservation—Poisoning and Depoisoning, *J. Water Pollution Control Federation,* vol. 43, no. 8, pp. 1671–1680, August 1971.
54. Coyne, R. V., and J. A. Collins: Loss of Mercury from Water During Storage, *Analytical Chem.*, vol. 44, no. 6, pp. 1093–1095, May 1972.
55. Davis, B. C.: *Contamination of Water Samples from Sample Containers,* Monsanto Enviro-Chem. Systems, Inc., Chicago, Ill., 1971. Unpublished data.
56. Foresman, M. R.: Private communication, Monsanto Industrial Chemicals Co., Sauget, Ill., 1972.
57. Braus, H., F. M. Middleton, and G. Waltor: Organic Chemical Compounds in Raw and Filtered Surface Waters, *Analytical Chem.*, vol. 23, no. 1160, 1951.
58. Middleton, F. M., A. A. Rosen, and R. H. Burttschell: Taste and Odor Research Tools for Water Utilities, *J. Am. Water Works Assoc.*, vol. 50, no. 21, 1958.
59. Breidenbach, A. W., et al.: "The Identification and Measurement of Chlorinated Hydrocarbon Pesticides in Surface Waters," U.S. Department of the Interior, Federal Water Pollution Control Administration, 1968.
60. Kawahara, F. K., et al.: Semiautomatic Extraction of Organic Materials from Water, *J. Water Pollution Control Federation,* vol. 39, no. 4, pp. 572–578, April 1967.
61. "Manual on Water," 3rd ed., Am. Soc. for Testing and Materials, Philadelphia, Pa. 1969.
62. Nedved, T. K., et al.: Instrumentation for Measurement of Wastewater Flow, *J. Water Pollution Control Federation,* vol. 44, no. 5, pp. 820–828, May 1972.
63. Kawahara, F. K.: "Laboratory Guide for the Identification of Petroleum Products," U.S. Department of the Interior, Div. of Water Quality Research, Cincinnati, Ohio, 1969.
64. Schatzberg, P., and D. F. Jackson: "Remote Sampler for Determining Residual Oil Contents of Surface Water," U.S. Coast Guard, Washington, D.C., November 1972. (Available through NTIS, No. AD-760217; see Ref. 80.)

65. Houser, E. A.: *Principles of Sample Handling and Sampling System Design for Process Analysis,* Instrument Society of America, Pittsburgh, Pa., 1972.
66. Rushton, J. H.: "The Continuous Removal of Mixed Phases from a Mixing Tank," Am. Inst. of Chem. Engrs., *I Ch.E Symp. Ser.,* no. 10, 1965.
67. Shelley, P. E., and G. A. Kirkpatrick: *An Assessment of Automatic Sewer Flow Samplers,* U.S. Environmental Protection Agency, EPA-R2-73-261, Washington, D.C., June 1973.
68. Tarazi, D. S., et al.: Comparison of Wastewater Sampling Techniques, *J. Water Pollution Control Federation,* vol. 42, no. 5, part 1, pp. 708–731, May 1970.
69. Cooke, W. B.: "A Laboratory Guide to Fungi in Polluted Waters, Sewage, and Sewage Treatment Plants," Public Health Service Publication No. 999-WP-1, 1963.
70. Stewart, K. R., W. M. Ingram, and K. M. Mackenthun: "Selected Biological References on Fresh and Marine Waters," U.S. Department of the Interior, Federal Water Pollution Control Administration, 1966.
71. Weber, C. I., and R. L. Raschke: "Use of a Floating Periphyton Sampler for Water Pollution Surveillance," U.S. Department of the Interior, Federal Water Pollution Control Administration, September 1966.
72. Weber, C. I.: "Methods of Collection and Analyses of Plankton and Periphyton Samples in the Water Pollution Surveillance System," U.S. Department of the Interior, Federal Water Pollution Control Administration, July 1966.
73. Craft, T. F., and R. S. Ingols: *Wastewater Sampling and Testing Instrumentation,* U.S. Air Force System Command, Kirtland Air Force Base, N. Mex., tech. rept. no. AFWL-TR-73-69, July 1973. (Available through NTIS No. AD-76489; see Ref. 80.)
74. Meritt, A. D., and J. T. Golden: Low Cost Continuous Sampler for Plant Effluents, *Chem. Engrg.,* vol. XX, p. 124, January 24, 1972.
75. Davis, B. C., J. L. Jones, and B. Sparks: Unpublished data, Monsanto Enviro-Chem Systems, Inc., Chicago, Ill., 1972, 1973.
76. Riseman, J. M.: Specific Ion Electrodes as Transducers in Continuous Monitoring Applications, in J. W. Scales (ed.), "Water Quality Instrumentation," vol. 1, Instrument Society of America, Pittsburgh, Pa., 1972.
77. Suffet, I. H., and J. V. Radziul: Continuous Quality Measurement Present Status and Future Trends, in J. W. Seales (ed.), "Water Quality Instrumentation," vol. 1, Instrument Society of America, Pittsburgh, Pa., 1972.
78. Guidelines Establishing Test Procedures for Analysis of Pollutants, *Federal Register,* vol. 38, no. 199, part II, October 16, 1973.
79. Darby, R. L., and R. L. Little: *Operation of the Analytical Methodology Information Center,* U.S. Environmental Protection Agency, EPA-R4-73-011, Washington, D. C., April 1973.
80. "Environmental Pollution and Control," National Technical Information Service, U.S. Department of Commerce, Springfield, Va. 22161
81. Annual literature reviews in *J. Water Pollution Control Federation,* 3900 Wisconsin Ave., Washington, D.C.
82. Annual reviews in *Analytical Chem.,* American Chemical Society, 1155 16th St., N.W., Washington, D.C.
83. Research briefs in *Environmental Sci. and Tech.,* American Chemical Society, 1155 16th St., N.W., Washington, D.C.
84. Sawyer, C. N., and P. L. McCarty: "Chemistry for Sanitary Engineers," McGraw-Hill, New York, N.Y., 1971.
85. "Handbook for Analytical Quality Control in Water and Wastewater Laboratories," Analytical Quality Control Lab., U.S. Environmental Protection Agency, Cincinnati, Ohio, June 1972.
86. Mancy, K. H.: "Instrumental Analysis for Water Pollution Control," Ann Arbor Science Publishers, Inc., Ann Arbor, Mich., 1973.
87. Elving, P. J.: The Need for Instrumental and Automated Analytical Techniques, *J. Water Pollution Control Federation,* vol. 39, no. 12, pp. 2055–2062, December 1967.
88. Stack, V. T., Jr., and N. S. Zaleiko: A Comprehensive Instrumentation System for Simultaneous Monitoring for Multiple Chemical Parameters in a Municipal Activated Sludge Plant, in J. W. Scales (ed.), "Water Quality Instrumentation," vol. 1, Instrument Society of America, Pittsburgh, Pa., 1972.
89. McFarren, E. F., and R. J. Lishka: The Use of Collaborative Studies to Evaluate Water Analysis Instruments, *J. Water Pollution Control Federation,* vol. 43, no. 1, pp. 67–72, January 1971.
90. Ostendorf, R. G., and J. F. Byrd: Modern Monitoring of a Treated Industrial

Effluent, *J. Water Pollution Control Federation,* vol. 41, no. 1, pp. 89–91, January 1969.
91. Cochran, L. G., et al.: Pollution Instrumentation Techniques, *Chem. Engrg. Progress,* vol. 68, no. 8, pp. 76–79, August 1972.
92. Neal, R. C.: Unpublished data, Monsanto Enviro-Chem. Systems, Inc., Dayton, Ohio, 1970.
93. Ballinger, D. G.: Instruments for Water Quality Monitoring, *Environmental Sci. and Tech.,* vol. 6, no. 2, pp. 130--133, February 1972.
94. Andleman, J. B.: Ion Selective Electrodes—Theory and Application in Water Analysis, *J. Water Pollution Control Federation,* vol. 40, no. 11, part 1, pp. 1844–1860, November 1968.
95. Bellack, E.: "Fluoridation Engineering Manual," U.S. Environmental Protection Agency, Washington, D.C., 1972.
96. Oliver, R. T., and R. F. Marion: Ion Selective Electrodes in Process Control: Water Hardness Measurement of Ion-Exchange Treated Water, in J. W. Scales (ed.), "Water Quality Instrumentation," vol. 1, Instrument Society of America, Pittsburgh, Pa., 1972.
97. Keyes, A. C., and J. M. Walsh: Oil in Water Pollution Monitors, paper presented at the 13th Ann. Marine Chemists' Assoc. Seminar, Minneapolis, Minn., July 1971.
98. Witmer, F. E., and A. Gollan: Determination of Oil Concentration and Size Distribution in Ship Ballast Waters, *Environmental Sci. and Tech.,* vol. 7, no. 10, October 1973.
99. Stenger, V. A., and C. E. Van Hall: Analyses of Municipal and Chemical Wastewaters by an Instrumental Method of COD Determination, *J. Water Pollution Control Federation,* vol. 40, no. 10, pp. 1755–1763, October 1968.
100. Fahrner, W. J.: Joseph Schlitz Brewing Company, Milwaukee, Wis., 1973.
101. "Notes on Water Pollution," Water Pollution Res. Library, Elder Way, Stevanage, Hertfordshire, U.K., December 1972.
102. Oliver, R. T., and R. F. Marion: Ion-Selective Electrodes in Process Control—Water Hardness Measurement of Ion-Exchange Treated Water, in J. W. Scales (ed.), "Water Quality Instrumentation," vol. 1, Instrument Society of America, Pittsburgh, Pa., 1972.
103. Boucher, F. R., and R. Ricci: Continuous Monitoring for Total Organic Carbon in Water and Wastewater, in J. W. Scales (ed.), "Water Quality Instrumentation," vol. 1, pp. 114–125, Instrument Society of America, Pittsburgh, Pa., 1972.
104. Mancy, K. H., and T. Jaffe: "Analysis of Dissolved Oxygen in Natural and Waste Waters," Public Health Service Publication No. 999-WP-37, April 1966.
105. Reynolds, J. F.: Comparison Studies of Winkler vs. Oxygen Sensor, *J. Water Pollution Control Federation,* vol. 41, no. 12, pp. 2002–2009, December 1969.
106. Pijanowski, B. S.: Salinity Corrections for Dissolved Oxygen Measurements, *Environmental Sci. and Tech.,* vol. 7, no. 10, October 1973.
107. Martin, J. M., Jr., et al.: Ultraviolet Determination of Total Phenols, *J. Water Pollution Control Federation,* vol. 39, no. 1, pp. 21–32, January 1967.
108. Mrkva, M.: Investigation of Organic Pollution of Surface Waters by Ultraviolet Spectrophotometry, *J. Water Pollution Control Federation,* vol. 41, no. 11, part 1, pp. 1923–1931, March 1968.
109. Ogura, N., and T. Hanya: Ultraviolet Absorbance as an Index of the Pollution of Seawater, *J. Water Pollution Control Federation,* vol. 40, no. 3, part 1, pp. 464–467, March 1968.
110. Prager, J. M.: *Automated Water Monitoring Instrument for Phosphorous Contents,* U.S. Environmental Protection Agency, EPA R4-73-026, Washington, D.C., 1973.
111. Fleming, G.: Suspended Solids Monitoring: A Comparison between Three Instruments, *Water & Water Engrg. (G.B.),* vol. 73, no. 377, 1969.
112. Talley, D. G., J. A. Johnson, and J. E. Pilzer: Continuous Turbidity Monitoring, *J. American Water Works Association,* March 1972.
113. McKeown, J. J., L. C. Brown, and G. W. Gove: Comparative Studies of Dissolved Oxygen Analysis Methods, *J. Water Pollution Control Federation,* vol. 39, no. 8, pp. 1323–1336, August 1967.
114. Munoz, J. A.: Unpublished data, Monsanto Industrial Chemicals Co., Sauget, Ill., 1972.
115. *Instrumentation for Environmental Monitoring—Vol. 2—Water,* Lawrence-Berkeley Lab., University of California, Berkeley, Calif., 1973.
116. Bromberg; A. W., and M. Caramers: Experience with Operating an Automatic Water Quality System in an Estuarine Environment, *Proc. Natl. Symp. on Data and Instrumentation for Water Quality Management,* University of Wisconsin, Madison, Wis., July 1970.

117. Barrett, P.: Private communication, Joseph Schlitz Brewing Company, Milwaukee, Wis., 1973.
118. Eggleston, W. W.: Perspectives in Sensor-Based Computing, in *Data Processor,* vol. 15, International Business Machines Corp., White Plains, N.Y., November 3, August 1972.
119. Noonan, R. P.: What Kind of Computer for Your Plant? *Chem. Engrg.*, vol. XX, pp. 112–116, June 2, 1969.
120. Ewy, M. D.: Automated Measurement Systems, in B. M. Oliver and J. M. Cage (eds.), "Electronic Measurements and Instrumentation," chap. 18, pp. 704–720, McGraw-Hill, 1971.
121. Schagrin, E. F.: How Much Do Mini Computer Systems Cost? *Chem. Engrg.*, vol. XX, pp. 103–109, March 22, 1971.
122. Stout, T. M.: Justifying Process Control Computers: Selection and Costs, *Chem. Engrg.*, Deskbook Issue, vol. XX, pp. 89–93, September 11, 1972.
123. Instrumentation and Process Control Directory, *Chem. Engrg.*, Deskbook Issue, vol. XX, pp. 95–125, September 11, 1972.
124. Hom, L. W.: Remote Sensing of Water Pollution, *J. Water Pollution Control Federation,* vol. 40, no. 10, pp. 1728–1738, October 1968.
125. *Remote Sensing Report—San Francisco Bay Area,* U.S. Environmental Protection Agency, San Francisco, Calif., April 1972.
126. Mills, B. C.: Coast Guard Airborne Remote Sensing System, abstract of paper presented at the 2nd Joint Conf. on Sensing of Environmental Pollutants, Instrument Society of America, Washington, D.C., December 10–12, 1973.
127. Van Lopek, J. R., G. S. Rambie, and A. E. Pressman: Pollution Surveillance by Noncontract Infrared Techniques, *J. Water Pollution Control Federation,* vol. 40, no. 3, part 1, pp. 425–438, March 1968.
128. Duntley, S. Q.: Optical Methods for Detection of Water Pollution, *Proc. Environmental Sensor Workshop in Las Vegas, Nev.*, U.S. Environmental Protection Agency, Washington, D.C., December 1971.
129. Kulin, G., and P. R. Compton, *A Guide to Methods & Measurement of Water Flow,* National Bureau of Standards, Washington, D.C., (May 1971) NBS-SP-421 Available through NTIS, Report COM-75-10683/1WP.
130. Barkley, J. J., et al, *Water Pollution Sampler Evaluation,* Army Medical Bioengineering Research and Development Laboratory, Fort Detrick, Maryland (January 1975) (Available through NTIS, Report AD-A009-079.)

LIST OF VENDORS

(V-1)
Alar Engineering Corp.
Burbank, Ill. 60459

(V-2)
A. O. Smith Meter Systems
Erie, Pa. 16512

(V-3)
Aqua Test Corporation
Arlington, Mass. 02174

(V-4)
Aquatronics
Philadelphia, Pa. 19133

(V-5)
Arthur Bros. Co.
P. O. Box 1222
Fond du Lac., Wis. 54935

(V-6)
Astro Ecology Corporation
P. O. Box 58159
Houston, Tex. 77058

(V-7)
Automated Environmental Systems, Inc.
Woodbury, L.I., N.Y. 11797

(V-8)
Automatic Samplers
Lebanon, Ore. 97355

(V-9)
Badger Meter, Incorporated
Instruments Division
Milwaukee, Wis. 53223

(V-10)
Badger Meter, Incorporated
Precision Products Division
Tulsa, Okla. 74101

(V-11)
Beckman Instruments
Fullerton, Calif. 92634

(V-12)
BIF
A Unit of General Signal Corp.
Providence, R.I. 02901

(V-13)
BIF Sanitrol
P. O. Box 41
Largo, Fla. 33540

(V-14)
Biospherics Incorporated
Rockville, Md. 20852

(V-15)
Black Clawson Co.
Middleton, Ohio 45042

(V-16)
Brailsford & Company
Rye, N.Y. 10580

(V-17)
Brandywine Valley Sales Co.
P. O. Box 243
Honey Brook, Pa. 19344

(V-18)
Bristol Engineering Co.
Box 568
Yorkville, Ill. 60560

(V-19)
Brooks Instrument Division
Emerson Electric Company
Hatfield, Pa. 19440

(V-20)
Brooks Instrument Division
Emerson Electric Co.
Statesboro, Ga. 30458

(V-21)
Bull & Roberts, Incorporated
Murray Hill, N.J. 07974

(V-22)
Calibrated Instruments, Inc.
Ardsley, N.Y. 10502

(V-23)
Capital Controls Company
Advance Lane
Colmar, Pa. 18915

(V-24)
CGS/Datametrics
Watertown, Mass. 02172

(V-25)
Cherne Scientific, Inc.
Edina, Minn. 55436

(V-26)
Chicago Tru Test
Chicago Pump
Chicago, Ill. 60614

(V-27)
Cliff Mock Co.
Houston, Tex. 77021

(V-28)
Cole-Parmer Instrument Co.
Chicago, Ill. 60648

(V-29)
Collins Products Company
P. O. Box 382
Livingston, Tex. 77351

(V-30)
Condra-Tech Inc.
Concord, Calif. 94518

(V-31)
Controlotron Corporation
Farmingdale, N.Y. 87401

(V-32)
Delta Scientific Corporation
Lindenhurst, N.J. 11757

(V-33)
Denver Equipment Division
Joy Manufacturing Co.
P. O. Box 5268
Denver, Colo. 80217

(V-34)
DISA Electronics
Franklin Lakes, N.J. 07417

(V-35)
Dohrmann-Envirotech
Mountain View, Calif. 94040

(V-36)
Du Pont Instrument & Equipment Division
Wilmington, Del. 19898

(V-37)
Durham Associates, Incorporated
Milford, N.H. 03055

(V-38)
Eastech, Incorporated
South Plainfield, N.J. 07080

(V-39)
Edmont-Wilson
Coshocton, Ohio 43812

(V-40)
Electronic Communications, Inc.
P. O. Box 12248
St. Petersburg, Fla. 33733

(V-41)
Ellison Instrument Division
Dieterich Standard Corporation
Boulder, Colo. 80302

(V-42)
FMR-Instruments
Weston Instruments Inc.
Box 3041
Sarasota, Fla. 33578

(V-43)
Endress & Hauser, Incorporated
Beverly, Mass. 01915

(V-44)
Enviro Control, Incorporated
Rockville, Md. 20852

(V-45)
Epic, Incorporated
New York, N.Y. 10038

(V-46)
F. B. Leopold Co., Inc.
Zelienople, Pa. 16063

(V-47)
Fischer & Porter Company
Warminster, Pa. 18974

(V-48)
Flow Technology, Incorporated
Tempe, Ariz. 85281

(V-49)
Foote Mineral Company
Exton, Pa. 19341

(V-50)
Formulabs
Escondido, Calif. 92025

(V-51)
Foxboro Company
Foxboro, Mass. 02035

(V-52)
Free Flow, Incorporated
P. O. Box 4067
Benson Station
Omaha, Neb. 68104

(V-53)
Gam Rad Inc.
Detroit, Mich. 48221

(V-54)
General Oceanics, Inc.
Miami, Fla. 33127

(V-55)
Hach Chemical Company
P. O. Box 907
Ames, Iowa 50010

(V-56)
Halliburton Services
Duncan, Okla. 73533

(V-57)
Hays Manufacturing Division
Erie, Pa. 16512

(V-58)
Hersey Products Inc.
Dedham, Mass. 02026

(V-59)
Hinde Engineering Co.
P. O. Box 56
Saratoga, Calif. 95070

(V-60)
Honeywell
Industrial Division
Fort Washington, Pa. 19034

(V-61)
Horizon Ecology Company
Chicago, Ill. 60648

(V-62)
Hydra-Numatic Sales Company
Hackensack, N.J. 07602

(V-63)
Hydro Products
P. O. Box 2528
San Diego, Calif. 92101

(V-64)
HydroVane Meter Company
P. O. Box 351
Brea, Calif. 92621

(V-65)
Infilco
Tucson, Ariz. 85702

(V-66)
Instrumentation Specialties Co.
P. O. Box 5347
Lincoln, Neb. 68505

(V-67)
Inter Ocean Systems, Incorporated
San Diego, Calif. 92110

(V-68)
In-Val-Co
Division of Combustion Engineering, Inc.
P. O. Box 556
Tulsa, Okla. 74101

(V-69)
Ionics, Incorporated
Watertown, Mass. 02172

(V-70)
Jacoby-Tarbox
Yonkers, N.Y. 10703

(V-71)
Keene Corp.
Aurora, Ill. 60507

(V-72)
Kernco Instruments Co., Inc.
Huntington Station, N.Y. 11746

(V-73)
Kerotest Manufacturing Corp.
Pittsburgh, Pa. 15222

(V-74)
Kimmon Marsano Corporation
P. O. Box 1082
Berkley, Mich. 48072

(V-75)
Leeds & Northrup
North Wales, Pa. 19454

(V-76)
Manning Environmental Corporation
Santa Cruz, Calif. 95060

(V-77)
Markland Specialty Engrg. Ltd.
Box 145
Etobieski, Ontario, Canada

(V-78)
Meriam Instrument
Cleveland, Ohio 44102

(V-79)
Milton Roy Company
Michigan City, Ind. 46360

(V-80)
Moore Products Company
Spring House, Pa. 19477

(V-81)
N B Products
New Britain, Pa. 18901

(V-82)
N-Con System Company
Larchmont, N.Y. 10538

(V-83)
Neptune Meter Company
Long Island City, N.Y. 11101

(V-84)
Nuclarus Limited
Toronto 18, Ontario, Canada

(V-85)
Nusonics, Incorporated
P. O. Box 248
Paramus, N.J. 07652

(V-86)
Oceanography International Corp.
P. O. Box DB
College Station, Tex. 77840

(V-87)
Olin Custom Analytical Instruments
Stamford, Conn. 06904

(V-88)
Orion Research Incorporated
Cambridge, Mass. 02139

(V-89)
Paul Noascono Company
Collinsville, Ill. 62234

(V-90)
Permutit
Paramus, N.J. 07652

(V-91)
Phase Separations Limited
Queensferry, Flintshire, England, U.K.

(V-92)
Phipps & Bird, Inc.
Richmond, Va. 23205

(V-93)
Plastic Fab
P. O. Box 644
Beaverton, Ore. 97005

(V-94)
Polcon, Incorporated
St. Louis, Mo. 63109

(V-95)
Precision Scientific
Chicago, Ill. 60647

(V-96)
Pro-Tech, Incorporated
Malvern, Pa. 19355

(V-97)
Quality Control Equipment Co.
P. O. Box 2706
Des Moines, Iowa 50315

(V-98)
Ramapo Instrument Co.
Bloomingdale, N.J. 07403

(V-99)
Raytheon Company
P. O. Box 360
Portsmouth, R.I. 02871

(V-100)
Red Valve Company
Carnegie, Pa. 15106

(V-101)
Rice Barton Corporation
P. O. Box 1086
Worcester, Mass. 01601

(V-102)
RKL Controls, Incorporated
Hainesport Industrial Park
Hainesport, N.J. 08036

(V-103)
Robertshaw Controls Company
Richmond, Va. 23226

(V-104)
Rockwell International
Pittsburgh, Pa. 15208

(V-105)
Rustrak Instruments
Gulton Industries
Manchester, N.H. 03103

(V-106)
R. W. Fowler and Assoc. Inc.
Atlantic Beach, Fla. 32233

(V-107)
Scientific Instruments of
Wisconsin, Incorporated
Milwaukee, Wis. 53212

(V-108)
Scorpa Laboratories, Inc.
Metuchen, N.J. 08840

(V-109)
Sirco Controls Limited
Seattle, Wash. 98119

(V-110)
Sigma Motor, Inc.
Middleport, N.Y. 14105

(V-111)
Simmonds Precision
Bellows Falls, Vt. 05101

(V-112)
Singer-American Meter Division
Philadelphia, Pa. 19116

(V-113)
Sonford Products Corp.
Minneapolis, Minn. 55402

(V-114)
Sparling Meter
Division of Envirotech
El Monte, Calif. 91731

(V-115)
Stevens Hydrographic Instruments
Leopold & Stevens, Inc.
P. O. Box 688
Beaverton, Ore. 97005

(V-116)
Strahman Valves, Inc.
Florham Park, N.J. 07932

(V-117)
Taylor Instrument
Rochester, N.Y. 14601

(V-118)
Technicon Industrial Systems
Tarrytown, N.Y. 10591

(V-119)
Teledyne Analytical Instruments
San Gabriel, Calif. 91776

(V-120)
Testing Machines, Inc.
Amityville, N.Y. 11701

(V-121)
Thermal Instrument Company
Trevase, Pa. 19047

(V-122)
Thermo-Systems, Inc.
St. Paul, Minn. 55113

(V-123)
Trebler Sampler
Lakeside Engineering Corp.
Chicago, Ill. 60606

(V-124)
Tuthill Pump Company
Chicago, Ill. 60658

(V-125)
Union Carbide Corporation
Instrument Department
White Plains, N.Y. 10601

(V-126)
Universal Interloc, Inc.
Santa Ana, Calif. 92705

(V-127)
Wallace & Tiernan
Belleville, N.J. 07109

(V-128)
Warminster Fiberglass Company
Southampton, Pa. 18966

(V-129)
Western Marine Electronics
Seattle, Wash. 98109

(V-130)
Westinghouse Electric Corporation
Computer & Instrument Division
P. O. Box 402
Orville, Ohio 44667

(V-131)
Westinghouse Electric Corporation
Infilio Division
Box 2118
Richmond, Va. 23216

(V-132)
Westinghouse Electric Corporation
Ocean Research & Engineering Center
P. O. Box 1488
Annapolis, Md. 21401

(V-133)
Weston & Stack, Inc.
Malvern, Pa. 19355

(V-134)
Whitney Underwater Instruments
Montedoro Corporation
P. O. Box 1401
San Luis Obispo, Calif. 93401

(V-135)
Yellow Springs Instrument Co.
Yellow Springs, Ohio 45387

Chapter 3

Industrial Wastewater Treatment Technology

GERRY L. SHELL

President
Gerry Shell Environmental Engineers
Brentwood, Tennessee

CLASSIFICATION OF WASTEWATER POLLUTANTS

Before embarking on a description and explanation of the available industrial water pollution treatment processes, it is pertinent to define the various types of pollutants that occur in industrial wastewaters. Generally, pollutants can be classified into three basic categories: floating, suspended, and dissolved.

Floating pollutants These consist of oil, grease, and other materials lighter than water. The presence of floating pollutants in a receiving water causes an unsightly appearance, retards plant growth, and is a general nuisance. Oils in particular interfere with natural reaeration, thus endangering aquatic life. Flammables can be a fire hazard when excessive amounts accumulate.

Suspended pollutants This type of pollutant can be either organic or inorganic. The presence of suspended solids can make receiving waters unsightly and can retard aquatic life because when they settle to the bottom, these solids tend to smother plant life. If the suspended pollutants are organic they could decompose, utilizing the available dissolved oxygen.

Dissolved pollutants Pollutants such as acids, alkalis, heavy metals, insecticides, and various types of organics can make receiving waters unusable and may possibly destroy aquatic life. Very small concentrations of certain dissolved pollutants, such as phenols, can cause objectional tastes and odors. Again, organic decomposition could occur, possibly depleting the receiving water of oxygen and causing noxious gases and odors.

Other Pollutants

Other forms of pollutants include heat, color, taste, odor, and radioactivity. Changing the temperature of the receiving water can result in an imbalance of the natural biota system. Such an imbalance can result in a pollution problem.

Color Color is a pollutant that is objectionable mainly from an aesthetic standpoint. It does not necessarily cause harm but may interfere with normal aquatic life.

Taste and odor Alteration in taste and the introduction of unpleasant odors can render a relatively clean water unsuitable for use. Materials such as phenols and hydrogen sulfides in small concentrations can be very objectionable.

Radioactivity Water containing radioactive pollutants even in very small amounts may be harmful to the environment and should never be used for drinking.

Chemical and biological pollutants Pollutants can be categorized further as chemical and biological. Chemical pollutants include an extremely wide variety of impurities which may occur naturally. Acids, alkalis, arsenic, cyanides, fluorides, iron, manganese, and other chemical compounds at specific concentrations can be considered pollutants. Biologically degradable materials are considered pollutants since nature tends to decompose them and if the demand for oxygen were in excess of the available oxygen resources, a polluted condition would exist.

WASTEWATER TREATMENT PROCESSES

The unit processes used in the treatment of industrial wastewaters are numerous. In most industrial wastewater treatment problems the final approach used is somewhat unique. Fig. 1 shows a typical approach to the treatment and reuse of wastewaters from a processing plant. Note that the weak wastewaters are kept separate from strong wastewaters to facilitate reuse at the least treatment cost. The sequence of treatment is not important as it will depend on the treatment objectives.

Fig. 2 shows the sources and possible treatment of the sludges produced during wastewater treatment. Some of these processes (oil recovery by dissolved air flotation) may be used to recover raw materials. Again, the processes used will be somewhat unique for each wastewater in order to achieve specific treatment objectives.

Treatment cost for each unit process is difficult to define due to changing conditions. An attempt to quantify total unit operation costs is made in Fig. 3. The total accumulated cost of treatment for the removal of organics is shown. Note that simple gravity sedimentation of a wastewater can have a gross effect on organics removal at a very low relative cost, whereas carbon adsorption may achieve only a small organic removal at a relative high cost. The costs shown are based on a

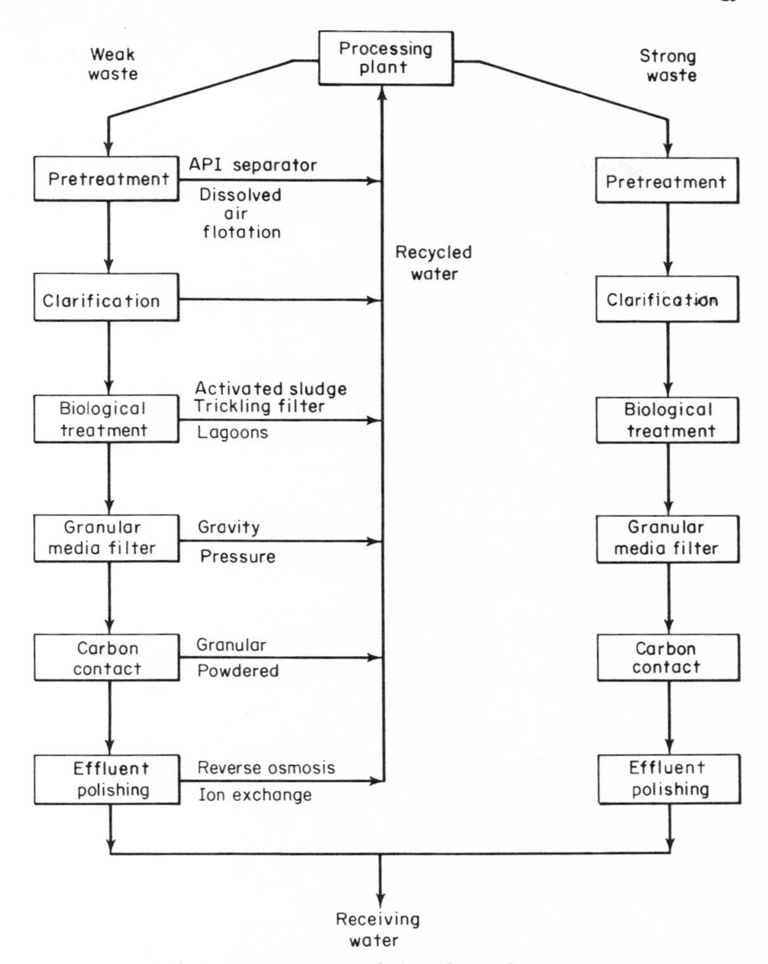

Fig. 1 Typical unit processes used in industrial wastewater treatment.

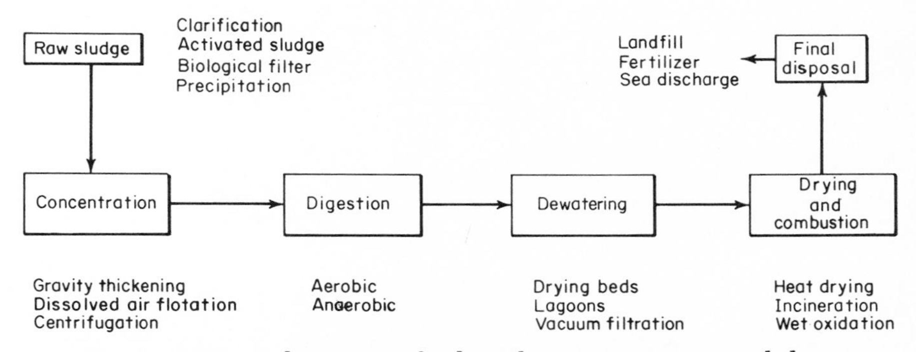

Fig. 2 Sources and treatment of industrial wastewater treatment sludges.

10-mgd plant and include operation, maintenance, and replacement. Inflation has had a gross effect on all costs and therefore the data in Fig. 3 should be used only for relative comparisons.

Dissolved Air Flotation

Dissolved air flotation is a useful tool for solving difficult wastewater treatment problems such as those resulting from wastewaters containing fats, grease, or oily material, which float naturally and present a difficult removal problem to conventional clarifying equipment. Dissolved air flotation has also been used for the thickening of hydroxides and biological flocculant sludges.

Flotation consists of attaching fine gas bubbles to suspended or oily material, causing a net reduction of specific gravity. The micron-size bubbles are produced by dissolving gas into the wastewater at elevated pressures followed by subsequent release to atmospheric pressure. When the pressure is reduced to atmospheric conditions, the dissolved gas (in excess of saturation) is released as extremely fine gas bubbles.

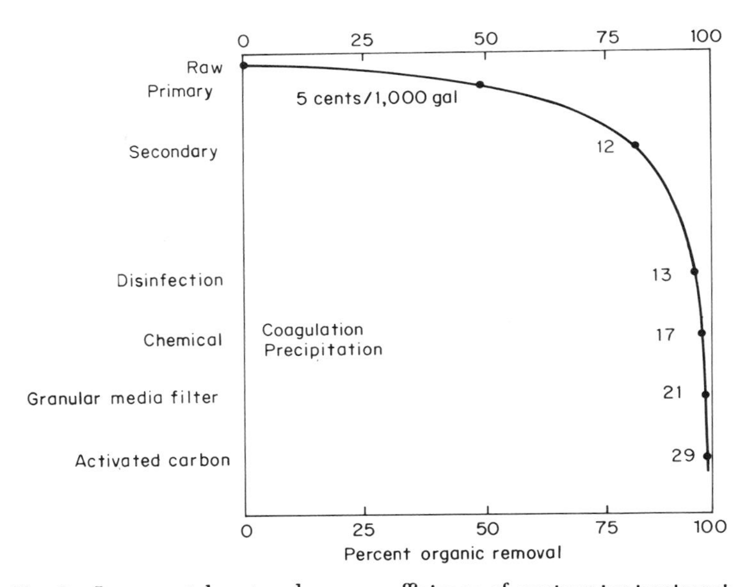

Fig. 3 Incremental cost and process efficiency of wastewater treatment.

Figure 4 shows a simplified flowsheet of a dissolved air flotation system. When the wastewater enters the flotation vessel, the oil or solid with air bubbles attached rises to the liquid surface since the specific gravity of the combination is less than the specific gravity of the liquid.

The amount of gas that can be dissolved in water follows Henry's law ($C = KP$). This law states that for gases of low solubility, the mass dissolved varies with its partial pressure. The quantity of gas theoretically released from solution when the pressure is reduced to atmospheric conditions is calculated from the following equation:

$$S = Sg\left(\frac{P}{14.7} - 1\right) \qquad (1)$$

where S = gas released at atmospheric pressure, mg/l
Sg = gas saturation at atmospheric conditions, mg/l
P = absolute pressure, psia

Equation (1) may be modified to Eq. (2) by taking into consideration the dissolving efficiency of the physical system used:

$$S = Sg\left(\frac{fP}{14.7} - 1\right) \tag{2}$$

where f = system dissolving efficiency, fraction.

Attachment of micron-size gas bubbles to suspended solids or oily material occurs by several mechanisms illustrated in Fig. 5. Some or all of these mechanisms may occur during the flotation process. The suspended solids/gas combination is carried to the surface of the flotation vessel after

1. Adhesion of a gas bubble to the suspended solids by precipitation of the gas on the particle or collision of the rising gas bubble with a particle
2. Trapping of rising gas bubbles by the floc
3. Adsorption for gas bubbles by floc formed or precipitated around the gas bubble

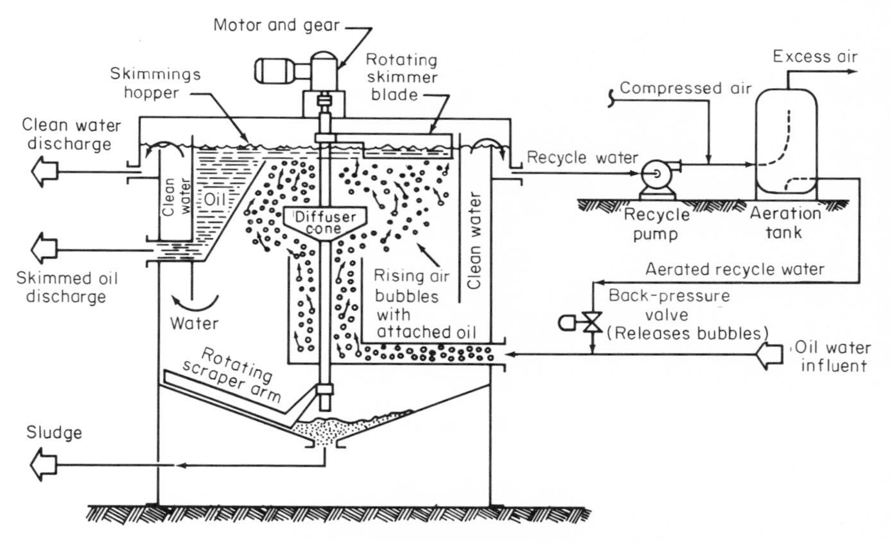

Fig. 4 Dissolved air flotation unit with recycle flow pressurization.

Pressurization systems Three types of pressurization systems, illustrated in Fig. 6, are used to effect flotation.

Full-flow Pressurization. This system is used for wastewaters containing large amounts of oily material that may pass through the intense mixing zone which occurs in the pressurization system without affecting the treatment results.

Partial-flow Pressurization. This system is used for moderate to low concentrations of oily material, where again intense mixing of the wastewater does not affect treatment results. The amount of pressurization flow is usually based on the air/solids weight ratio (A/S) required for treatment. Air/solids weight ratios ranging from 0.01 to 0.06 have been demonstrated to be effective. A design A/S ratio of 0.02 is appropriate for most applications. In many cases where total- or partial-flow pressurization is employed, an arbitrary air volume of 3 percent of the pressurized flow has been used successfully.

Recycle Pressurization. The recycle pressurization system is used for flotation of solids or oily material which would degrade or be destroyed by the intense mixing occurring in the pressurization system. Recycle pressurization is used with chemical treatment of oil emulsions or for clarification and thickening of flocculant suspensions. The recycled pressurized stream is the clarified or treated effluent. Gas is dissolved in this stream at an elevated pressure and mixed with the wastewater just downstream of the pressure release valve. Mixing of these streams prior to entering the flotation zone results in intimate contact of the precipitated gas and suspended solids to effect efficient flotation. The recycle pressurization mode is required for most wastewaters containing light flocculant solids, such as waste biological or hydroxide sludges. The major drawback of recycle pressurization is that the flotation area must be larger since the required clarification area is based on both feed and recycle flows.

Table 1 shows typical design parameters and performance results of dissolved air flotation on various industrial wastewaters.

Sedimentation

Clarification of wastewater involves the removal of settleable solids. Suspended solids are usually defined as the particles retained on a glass filter mat or a 0.45-

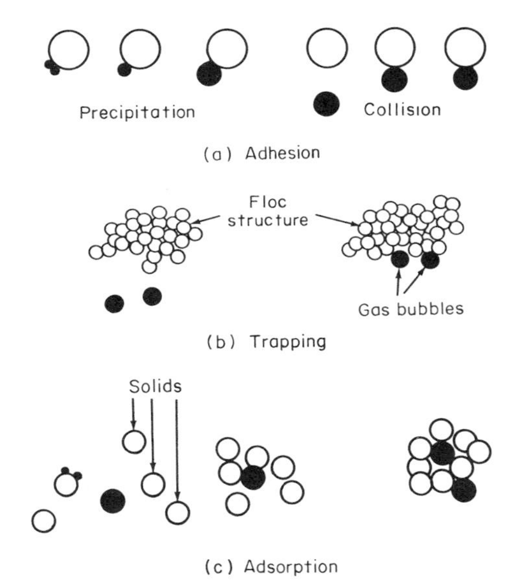

Fig. 5 Methods of gas-bubble attachment for dissolved air flotation.

micron filter. Any material passing these filters is defined as soluble. Settleable solids can be defined as those solids removed during a 2-hr quiescent settling.

The oldest method of clarification is retention in a basin for a period of time to allow settleable suspended solids to separate by gravity. Any suspended solids remaining will require additional treatment to achieve removal.

There are several properties of the liquid and the suspended solids that influence gravity sedimentation. These properties are liquid temperature, specific gravity, size, and shape of the suspended solids.

Temperature The settling velocity of a particle varies inversely with the kinematic viscosity of the liquid, which is related to liquid temperature. The ratio of kinematic viscosity at 50°F to that at any other temperature will indicate the effect of liquid temperature change on the settling velocity of a particle. For example, changing the liquid temperature from 50 to 86°F would increase the settling velocity of a particle by 1.63. Similarly, reducing the temperature from 50 to 32°F would reduce the settling velocity by 0.73. Thus, liquid temperature has an important effect on the design of gravity sedimentation basins.

Specific gravity The higher the specific gravity of the suspended particle, the higher will be its settling velocity. A turbid water may contain suspended matter whose specific gravities range from 2.65 for sand to 1.03 for flocculated particles of organic matter and mud containing 95 percent water. Floc particles resulting from chemical coagulation with alum or iron oxides may have a specific gravity as low as 1.02 to 1.10. The specific gravity may be increased by the presence of clay or silt, or it may be drastically reduced by the presence of organic matter, entrained or adsorbed water. The specific gravity of particles resulting from precipitation of calcium may be as high as 1.2.

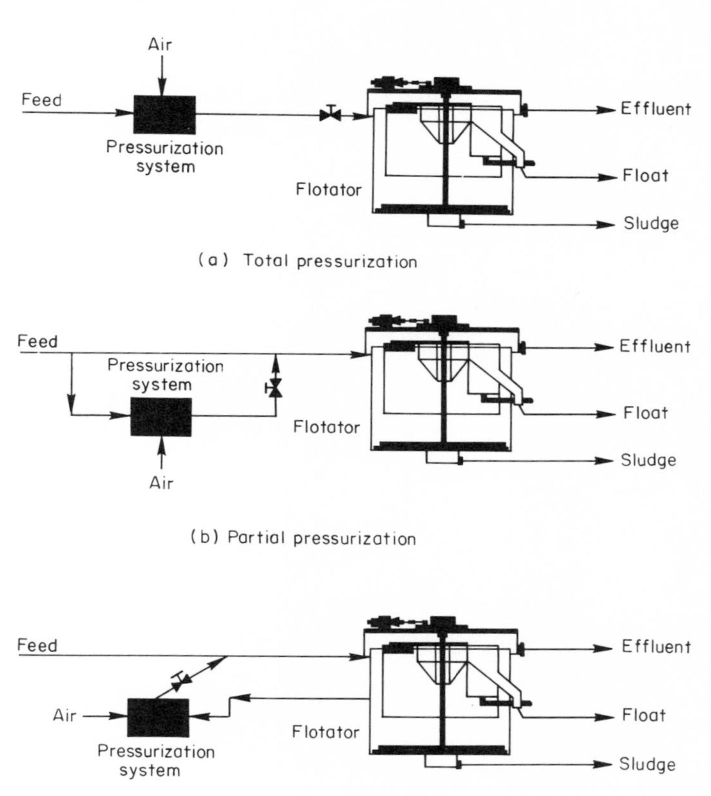

Fig. 6 Three dissolved air flotation systems.

Size and shape The size and shape of the suspended particle also affect gravity sedimentation. As shown in Table 2, a silt particle of 0.004-mm diameter settles at a rate of only 0.0247 mm/sec compared to fine sand at 0.04-mm diameter which settles at 2.0 mm/sec. Both have the same specific gravity (2.65).

A spherical suspended particle will settle much faster than a flat particle. The settling rate can, therefore, be increased if a large dense floc is formed. Bulky biological and hydroxide floc contains a great deal of entrained water which reduces the specific gravity even though the size is increased. All of the above-mentioned liquid and solids properties should be considered to achieve proper design and application of gravity sedimentation.

Efficiency The treatment efficiency of a sedimentation basin depends on both the settling properties of the suspended solids and the basin hydraulic properties. The

TABLE 1 Typical Design Parameters and Performance of Flotation Units

Type of wastewater	Overflow rate, gpm/ft²	Characteristics (typical) of wastewater	Amount of air required	Removals or performance	Coagulation or flotation aids
Oil processing	2.0–2.5	200–1,000 mg/l oil	3 vol %, P or T	Nearly all of free-floating oils; 70–80% SS removal. No soluble or emulsified oils removed.	None
	1.3–1.8	200–1,000 mg/l oil	3 vol % or 0.02 A/S ratio, R	Removals of up to 90% free-floating and emulsified oils. No soluble oil removed.	Alum, lime, polyelectrolyte
Meat packing	2.5	500–5,000 mg/l SS 1,000–2,000 mg/l grease	3 vol %, P or T	Removal of all free-floating grease; 40–60% SS removal.	None
	1.5 or 2.0 lb SS/(sq ft)(hr)	500–5,000 mg/l SS 1,000–2,000 mg/l grease	0.02 A/S ratio, R	Up to 90% removal of emulsified grease and SS.	Alum, lime, polyelectrolyte
Tannery	1.5 or 2.0 lb SS/(sq ft)(hr)	3,000–8,000 mg/l SS	3 vol %, P or T	Removal of 80% fat; 60% SS removal.	None
Soluble or cutting tool oil	1.5	3,000–8,000 mg/l SS	0.02 A/S ratio, R	Removal of 95% fat; 95% SS removal. No solubles removed.	Alum, lime, polyelectrolyte

Paper	1.5	200–3,000 mg/l SS	0.02 A/S ratio, R	Removes 90% of fiber.	Alum, polyelectrolyte
Laundry	1.5 or 2.0 lb SS/(sq ft)(hr)	2,000–5,000 mg/l SS 500–1,500 mg/l grease	0.02–0.04 A/S ratio, R	Up to 90% removal of SS and grease.	Alum, ferric polyelectrolyte
Poultry	1.5–2.0	200–2,500 mg/l SS, 30–1,000 mg/l grease	0.02–0.04 A/S ratio or 3 vol %, R, P, or T	40–60% SS removal and up to 90% removal of grease.	None
	1.25–1.75	200–2,500 mg/l SS, 30–1,000 mg/l grease	0.02–0.04 A/S ratio or 3 vol %, R	Up to 90% removal of emulsified grease and SS.	Alum, lime, polyelectrolyte
Cannery	0.5–1.5	200–2,500 mg/l SS	0.02 A/S ratio, R	80–90% removal SS.	Polymer
Metal finishing and plating waste	1.5–2.5	200–1,000 mg/l SS	3 vol %		
Municipal waste activated sludge thickening	1.25–1.5 or 2.0 lb SS/(sq ft)(hr)	5,000–10,000 mg/l SS	0.02 A/S ratio, R	80–90% SS removal, 3–4% solids float.	None
				90–95% SS removal, 3–4% solids float.	Polyelectrolyte
Cannery waste activated sludge thickening	0.5–1.5	5,000–10,000 mg/l SS	0.02 A/S ratio, R	80–90% SS removal, 2.5–3.5% solids float.	None
				80–95% SS removal, 2.5–3.5% solids float.	Polyelectrolyte

P = Partial pressurization, R = Recycle pressurization, T = Total pressurization.

TABLE 2 Velocities at which Particles of Sand and Silt Subside in Still Water

Diameter of particle, mm	Classification	Hydraulic subsiding rate, mm/sec	Comparable overflow rate, gpm/sq ft
10.0	Gravel	1,000.0	1,475.0
1.0		100.0	148.2
0.6		63.0	93.0
0.4	Coarse sand	42.0	62.0
0.2		21.0	31.0
0.1		8.0	11.8
0.06		3.8	5.6
0.04	Fine sand	2.1	3.1
0.02		0.62	0.91
0.01		0.154	0.227
0.004	Silt	0.0247	0.036

Note: Temperature, 10°C (50°F); specific gravity of sand and silt particles, 2.65; values for 10-mm particles from Hazen's experiments; values for 0.02- to 0.004-mm particles from Wiley's formula; intermediate values interpolated from connecting curve.

basin hydraulic properties depend on both geometry and flow. Sedimentation basins may be rectangular, square, or circular. Circular basins may be either center feed with radial flow, peripheral feed with radial flow, or peripheral feed with spiral flow. In a rectangular basin, the flow is essentially rectilinear with flow lines parallel and in one direction. Sedimentation basin design strives to achieve the ideal condition of equal flow velocity at all points on each vertical line in the settling zone. Flow enters the basin through some type of inlet device, travels through the basin, and exits over some type of outlet device.

Practically all sedimentation basins are operated on the continuous-flow principle and are provided with equipment for sludge removal. The primary purpose of a settling basin is to retain wastewater, thus reducing flow velocity to allow for gravity sedimentation. To minimize flow disturbances that would interfere with the settling process, four major zones in a sedimentation basin must be considered.

1. *Inlet zone.* The inlet design must provide energy dissipation and a smooth flow transition from the influent pipe into the basin.
2. *Settling zone.* Design of the settling zone must provide the liquid sufficient time for gravity sedimentation.
3. *Outlet zone.* The outlet device must provide uniform removal of clarified wastewater from the basin.
4. *Sludge zone.* The design of the sludge zone must provide quiescent storage and achieve some thickening.

The typical gravity sedimentation unit shown in Fig. 7 is commonly used for industrial wastewater treatment.

The design overflow rates for clarifiers can vary widely. The overflow rate employed in design will depend on the characteristics of the solids to be removed and the desired percentage of removal. Table 3 shows clarifier design data for several industrial wastewaters.

Gravity sedimentation units are utilized in biological treatment to clarify the effluent from biological treatment processes. Clarifier design overflow rates for secondary biological plants can range from 750 to 1,500 gpd/sq ft. Retention times for most clarifiers range from 1.5 to 3.0 hr.

Chemical Treatment

Removal of very small particles by gravity sedimentation requires excessively long retention periods. Typically, these solids are bacteria, viruses, colloidal organics, and fine minerals. Chemical treatment of wastewater containing these solids results in the precipitation of chemical agents which causes flocculation (particle growth) and rapid settling. Solids requiring chemical treatment for removal are generally classified as colloids and lie within the size range of 0.001 and 0.5 micron. Particles from 0.5 to about 15 microns in diameter exhibit properties of colloids and usually require chemical treatment for removal.

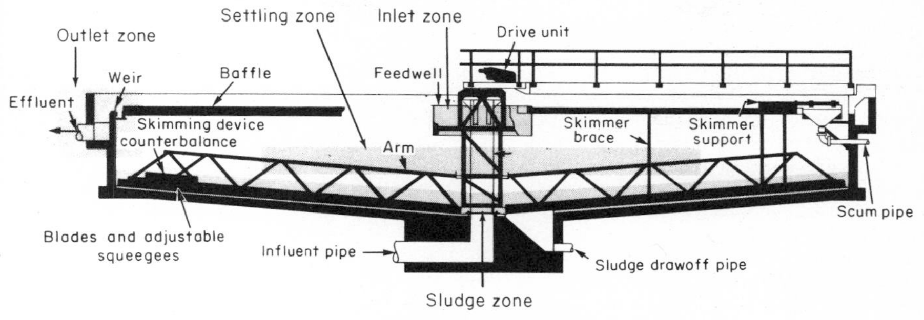

Fig. 7 Typical gravity sedimentation unit.

Hydrolyzable trivalent metallic ions of aluminum (Al^{3+}) and iron (Fe^{3+}) salts are established coagulation chemicals. The hydrolysis species of Al^{3+} or Fe^{3+} destabilize colloidal pollutants and render them amenable to flocculation (particle growth) which enhances settleability. The gelatinous floc precipitated from these metallic ions enmeshes finely divided pollutants, removing them by sedimentation.

Adding lime to wastewater results in the elevation of pH and precipitation of calcium phosphate, calcium carbonate, and magnesium hydroxide. Magnesium hydroxide, precipitated at elevated pH (pH = 10.0), acts as a coagulant, destabilizing and enmeshing colloidal pollutants. The chemistry of lime treatment is generally

TABLE 3 Clarifier Design Data

Application	Percent solids		Unit area, sq ft/(ton)(day)	Overflow rate, gpm/sq ft
	Feed	Underflow		
Bicarb distiller waste	2–4	10–14	20–30	
Brine purification	0.1–2	8–15	...	0.2–0.5
Coal refuse	0.5–6	20–40	...	0.3–0.7
Coking water	1–3	50	...	0.6
Flue dust:				
Blast furnace	0.2–2	40–60	...	0.6–1.5
BOF	0.2–2	30–70	...	0.4–0.7
Foundry wastewater	1.0	...	...	0.3–0.4
Pulp and paper waste treatment:				
Kraft waste	0.01–0.05	2–5	...	0.35–0.5
Deink waste	0.01–0.05	4–7	...	0.4–0.5
Paper mill waste	0.01–0.05	4–10	...	0.5–0.9
Pickle liquor and rinse water	1–8	9–18	35–50	
Plating waste	2–5	5–30	...	0.5
Sewage:				
Primary	2 hr detention		...	0.4
Secondary	1.5–2.0 hour detention		...	0.55–0.7
Water treatment:				
Clarification	3 hr detention		...	0.4–0.55
Softening-lime soda	2 hr detention		...	1.5

described by water-softening reactions. However, the presence of dissolved organics and condensed phosphates in wastewaters results in some interference with water-softening reactions, such as the precipitation of calcium carbonate ($CaCO_3$).

Organic polyelectrolyte flocculation aids have proved effective in promoting suspended solids removal. The addition of polyelectrolytes does not cause chemical precipitation, but promotes particle growth. Polyelectrolytes are effective for both wastewater suspended solids and precipitates formed by chemical treatment. The generally accepted action of polyelectrolytes on suspensions is the bridging between particles resulting in floc growth.

Sludge production An inherent burden of improved suspended solids removal by chemical treatment is the production of significant quantities of chemical sludge. The thickening and dewatering properties of chemical wastewater sludge are often deteriorated from those for the wastewater sludge alone because of the presence of hydroxide sludges and increased amounts of colloidal pollutants.

The addition of alum to a wastewater containing a suitable quantity of alkalinity produces a chemical floc. As a general rule approximately 1 lb of suspended solids (chemical floc) is produced for each 0.25 to 0.40 lb of *aluminum* added or 0.3 lb of chemical sludge is produced per pound of *alum* added.

The chemical sludge produced by lime addition to wastewater depends on the chemical characteristics of the water, the treatment pH, and the method of operation. The net chemical sludge production is a result of an interaction of these three parameters. Current knowledge indicates that lime treatment of low hardness ($\leq$ 200 mg/l as $CaCO_3$) and low alkalinity ($\leq$ 150 mg/l as $CaCO_3$) wastewaters should be accomplished in two stages, at treatment pH's of 11.0 to 11.5 and 9.5 to 10.0, respectively, in each stage. Chemical sludge production under such conditions will be about 4,000 to 5,500 lb/million gal. For high hardness ($\geq$ 350 mg/l as $CaCO_3$) and high alkalinity ($\geq$ 250 mg/l as $CaCO_3$) wastewaters, single-stage treatment at a pH of 10.5 to 11.0 is recommended. Chemical sludge production under such conditions will be about 5,500 to 6,500 lb/million gal. The addition of organic polyelectrolytes to aid in settling at a dosage of less than 1 mg/l does not result in a significant increase in chemical sludge production.

Chemical sludge produced by pH adjustment of industrial wastes will depend on a variety of factors. The initial concentration of chemical pollutants to be precipitated and the efficiency of the liquid-solids separation step are the major factors.

Suspended solids removal Suspended solids removal by chemical treatment is accomplished by a series of three unit operations: rapid-mixing, flocculation, and sedimentation. First, the chemical reagent must be completely dispersed into wastewater. This is especially important when using an inorganic coagulant such as alum, where precipitation reactions occur immediately. For lime treatment, the lime slurry should be dispersed throughout the wastewater in the presence of previously formed precipitate (recycled sludge). The purpose of recycled sludge is to provide an abundance of surface area on which the chemical precipitates can form. Failure to provide sludge recycle results in gross deposition (scaling) of $CaCO_3$ on tank walls and other available surfaces.

Rapid mixing is accomplished in 10 to 30 sec in a basin with a turbine mixer. About ¼ to 1 hp/mgd is used for rapid mixing. A mean temporal velocity gradient in excess of 300 ft/(sec)(ft) is recommended.

After achieving effective coagulation-precipitation reactions (rapid mix), promotion of particle growth by flocculation is the next step. The purpose of flocculation is to bring coagulated (destabilized) particles together by mechanically inducing velocity gradients within the liquid. Flocculation is accomplished in 15 to 30 min in a basin containing a turbine or paddle-type mixer. Mean temporal velocity gradients of 40 to 80 ft/(sec)(ft) are recommended. The lower value is for fragile floc (aluminum or iron) and the higher value is for lime treatment.

Following flocculation, clarification is achieved by gravity sedimentation. Conventional clarifier design is suitable. Sludge withdrawal facilities should be incorporated to waste the accumulated sludge and prevent septic conditions.

Solids-contact treatment unit A more recent development in chemical treatment of wastewater is the use of solids-contact treatment units. Solids contacting is beneficial for lime treatment because of reduced deposition problems which are inherent in once-through rapid-mix flocculation systems. Solids contacting is achieved by recycling previously formed precipitates for contacting with the incoming wastewater and added lime. The solids-contact treatment approach was originally developed for lime-softening water treatment, but it has recently proven effective for chemical treatment of wastewaters.

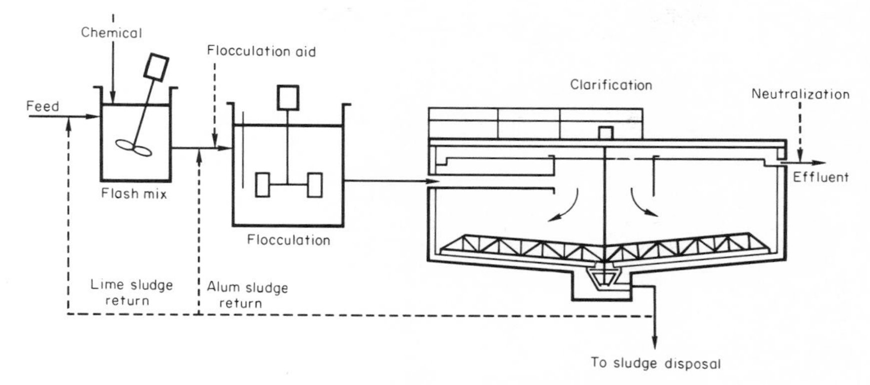

Fig. 8 Three-stage chemical treatment system.

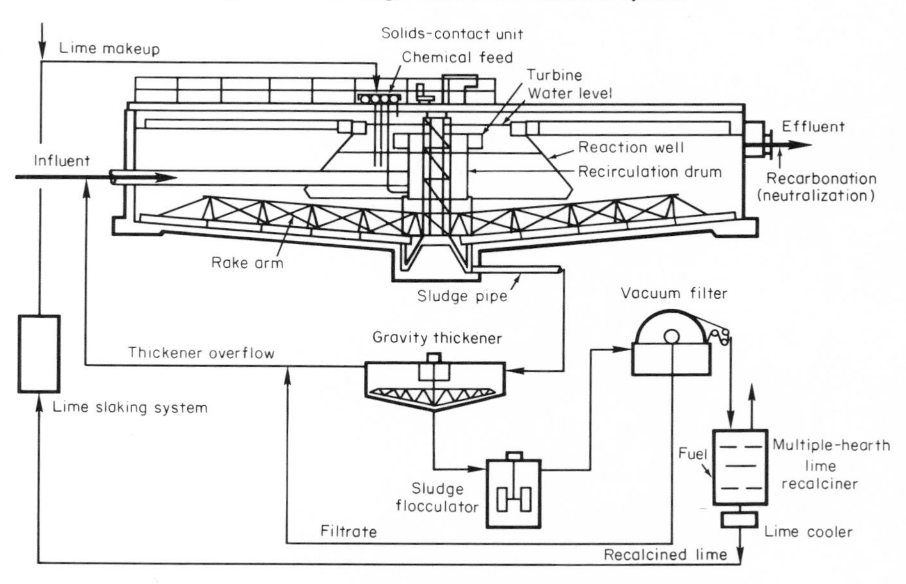

Fig. 9 A typical solids-contact chemical treatment system.

Figure 8 shows a typical three-stage chemical treatment system and Fig. 9 shows a typical solids-contacting chemical treatment system.

Costs The principal cost of chemical treatment is the cost of the added chemicals. An estimate of chemical dosage required can be obtained from laboratory jar tests and/or pilot-plant studies. Daily, weekly, and seasonal variations in wastewater characteristics will necessitate adjustment of chemical dosage during plant operation to minimize dosage consistent with providing the desired solids removal. Typical chemical dosages required for industrial wastewater are presented in Table 4.

TABLE 4 Chemical Treatment of Wastewater

Criteria	$FeCl_3$	Alum	$Ca(OH)_2$
Dose, mg/l	80–120	100–150	350–500
Hydraulic loading, gpm/sq ft*	0.3–0.4	0.2–0.4	0.5–0.8
Chemical sludge production, lb/million gal	350–700	250–500	4,000–7,000
Chemical cost, cents/lb	4–5	3–4	1
Treatment chemical cost, cents/1,000 gal	2.5–5	2.5–5	3–4

* Without use of polyelectrolyte.

Figures 10, 11, and 12 show typical flowsheets for chemical treatment of industrial wastewaters.

Hydraulic loading is used as the basis of determining suspended solids removal efficiency. Normally, high removal efficiencies are sought and, therefore, low hydraulic loadings are employed. Table 4 presents recommended average hydraulic loading design to achieve 80 to 90 percent suspended solids removal.

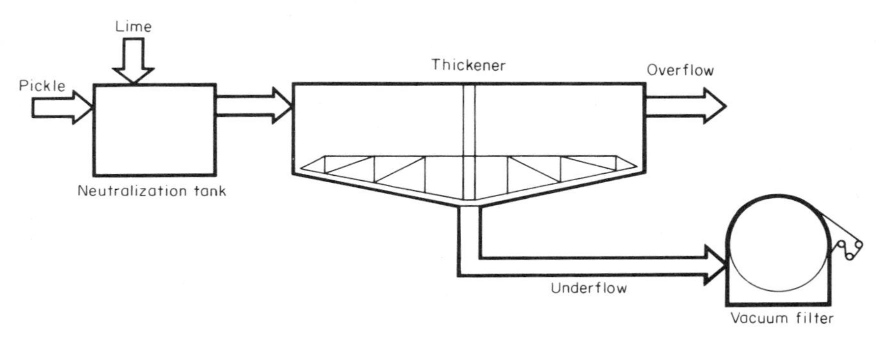

Fig. 10 Neutralization of waste pickle liquor.

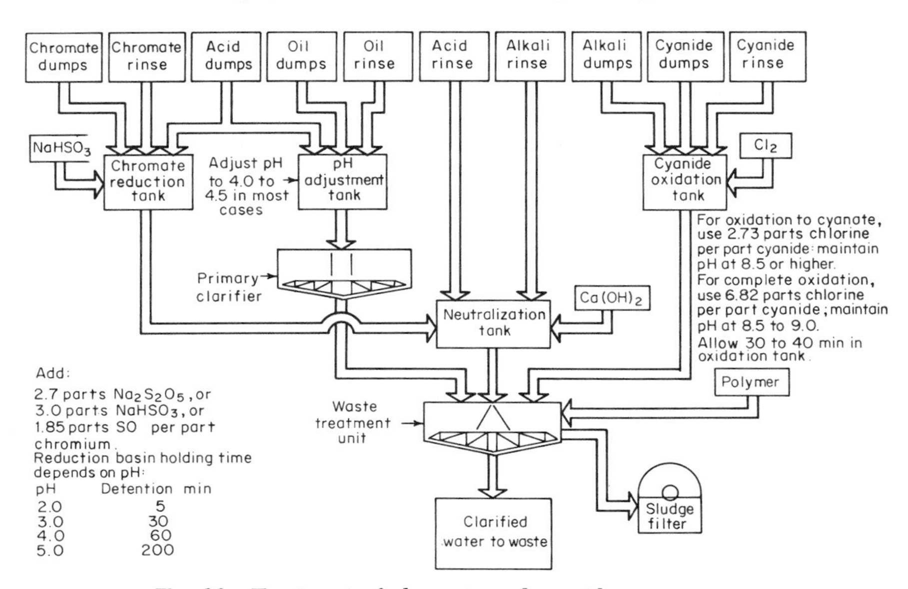

Fig. 11 Treatment of chromate and cyanide wastewaters.

The addition of polyelectrolyte at a dosage of 0.25 mg/l or less will at least double the chemical-sewage floc-settling rates. Normally it is less expensive to provide twice the clarifier area than to add polyelectrolyte. For new plant construction, a thorough analysis of polyelectrolyte addition versus reduced clarifier area should be made. For upgrading existing facilities, use of polyelectrolytes may be justified to meet effluent requirements.

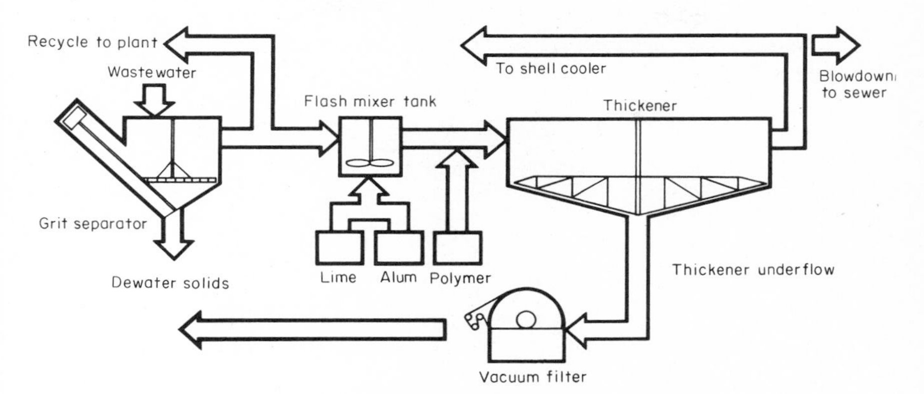

Fig. 12 Chemical clarification of cooler water.

Biological Treatment

Organic wastewaters can be stabilized by biological treatment processes through the metabolic activities of heterotrophic microorganisms. These microorganisms convert organics to end products such as carbon dioxide, water, and methane gas. A general description of a biological process is shown in Fig. 13. When available organics are used or when only a limited amount remains, the microorganisms are sustained by consuming their own protoplasm. This process is termed *endogenous respiration.* If starvation or limited organics were continued, the organisms would consume protoplasm until all that remained was a relatively stable humuslike organic residue that resists further degradation. The "inert" organic residue represents about 20 to 25 percent of the initial biological cell mass, both for aerobic and anaerobic microorganisms.

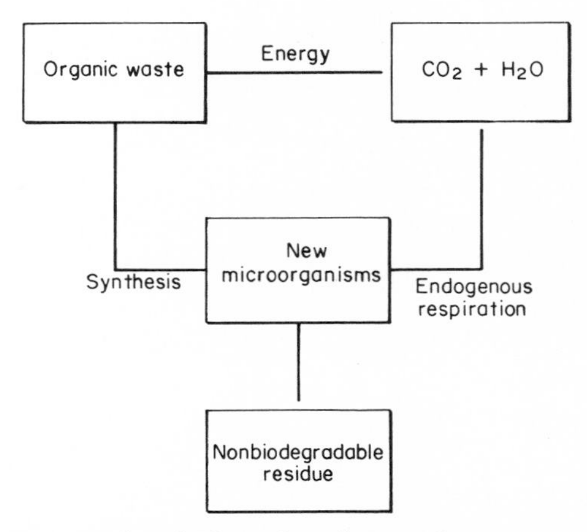

Fig. 13 Complete biological oxidation of organic wastes.

Microorganism growth has three major phases. A typical growth curve is shown in Fig. 14. The log growth phase occurs when organics are not limiting and the microorganisms are at the maximum growth rate. Under these conditions the microbial mass increases logarithmically. Organics will be consumed until the concentration is sufficiently low to limit the rate of microbial growth; then the declining growth phase occurs. As the organic concentration is reduced to a minimum, the endogenous respiration phase occurs. During this phase the only organic source available for energy is their own protoplasm, and the microbial mass decreases with time. Endogenous respiration occurs during all of the above phases, but is predominant in the food-limiting phase.

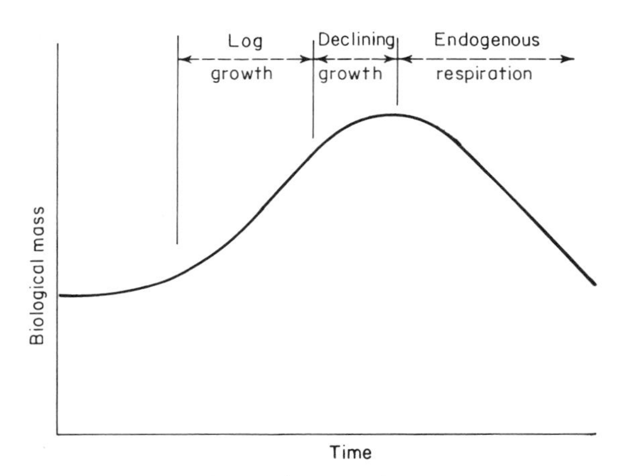

Fig. 14 Typical growth curve for microorganisms.

Microbial growth as a function of time has been approximated by equations similar to

$$\frac{dM}{dt} = a\frac{dF}{dt} - bM \tag{3}$$

where dM/dt = growth rate of microorganisms, mass per unit time
dF/dt = rate of waste utilization, mass per unit time
M = mass of microorganisms present
a = growth yield constant, lb cells per lb organics removed
b = endogenous respiration rate constant, per day

The rate of microbial growth is proportional to the rate of organics utilization (dF/dt) minus the loss of microbial mass due to endogenous respiration (bM). The decrease in microbial mass is proportional to the active mass present and not to the total mass which includes humus residue of dead microorganisms. A measurement of the active mass is frequently assumed to be equal to the mixed liquor volatile suspended solids (MLVSS). Active mass may represent only a fraction of the organic suspended solids present.

The rate at which microbial organics are utilized has been shown to be a function of the limiting nutrient concentration. Organics normally represent the limiting nutrient required for cell growth, and inorganic nutrients (such as nitrogen and phosphorus) are usually in excess. However, some industrial wastes are limited by inorganic nutrients which must be added to achieve good treatment efficiency.

A basic relationship between microbial growth and essential nutrient concentration was noted by Monod as a function similar to the Michaelis-Menton equation. This relationship has been used for describing enzyme-catalyzed reactions. Microbial growth rate and organic utilization are related and can be described by

$$\frac{dF}{dt} = \frac{ksM}{K_s + s} \tag{4}$$

where k = maximum rate of organics utilization
K_s = organic concentration at which organic utilization is half the maximum rate
s = concentration of organics

Equation (4) is useful in describing microbial growth in general terms; however, biological systems are more complex, having many types of microorganisms. Direct use of this equation is sufficiently basic to indicate the parameters of importance in biological systems.

A typical activated sludge biological process flowsheet is illustrated in Fig. 15. The wastewater flow Q and organic concentration S_o are being treated in a reactor volume V. The microbial mass M metabolizes the organics and reduces the organic concentration to s. The microorganisms and wastewater continue to a settling basin where the microorganisms are separated from the treated wastewater. The settled microorganisms are recycled back to the reactor and mixed with the incoming wastewater for treatment. If wastewater is continuously added, the microorganisms concentration will increase until the system can no longer maintain them. At this point, excess microorganisms produced must be removed.

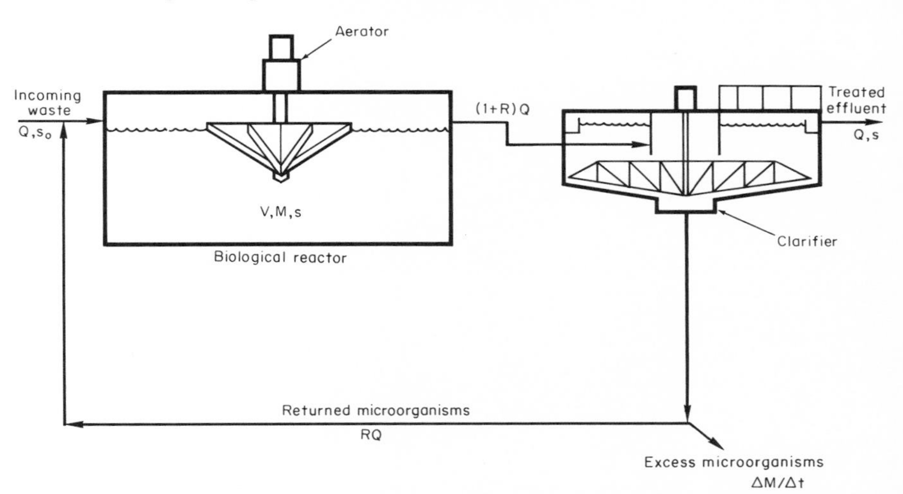

Fig. 15 Typical biological unit process. Q = wastewater flow; R = return sludge ratio; RQ = return sludge flow; $\Delta M/\Delta t$ = excess sludge produced/day; S_o = influent organic concentration; s = effluent organic concentration; V = reactor volume; and M = mass of microorganisms.

For steady-state conditions, the wastewater treatment efficiency is $(S_o - s)100/S_o$. High treatment efficiencies require that the organic concentration in the effluent s be small.

The reciprocal of growth rate is the solids retention time SRT. SRT is the average retention time of the microorganisms in the system:

$$\text{SRT} = \frac{M}{\Delta M/\Delta t} \tag{5}$$

or

$$\text{SRT} = \frac{\text{suspended solids in system}}{\text{suspended solids removed per day}}$$

where M = total suspended solids in system
t = time in days

$\Delta M/\Delta t$ is used since the average growth rate over a long period (day) is more important than the instantaneous growth rate. The suspended solids removed per day includes both the solids wasted deliberately and those lost in the effluent. If the microorganisms are lost faster than they are produced, then "washout" results.

Another design approach for biological waste treatment systems is the loading velocity or food/microorganisms ratio (F/M). The F/M ratio is equal to the organic material [5-day BOD, COD, or TOC total organic carbon] fed to the system divided by the total mixed liquor suspended solids (MLSS). The lower the food/microorganism ratio maintained, the lower will be the soluble effluent waste concentration. At very low F/M ratios (<0.1) (such as those used in extended aeration), the effluent quality sometimes deteriorates due to the dispersed floc produced which leaves with the effluent.

Either F/M or SRT may be used as the basis for biological system design and operation. However, the use of SRT has certain advantages. The quantity of active microorganisms has to be known in order to properly apply the F/M ratio. This is difficult to determine especially in anaerobic systems because of the presence of large quantities of other organic suspended solids. However, when applying SRT, such a differentiation is not required since for a given fraction of solids wasted, the same fraction of active microorganisms is wasted. For example, if it were desired to maintain the SRT at 5 days, this could be done by wasting 20 percent of the solids from the system every day. In this approach, 20 percent of the active microorganisms are also wasted. Application of the SRT design and operation approach to any biological system is similar to that just stated, that is, a percentage of the total mass in the system is wasted to maintain the required process results.

A by-product of all biological systems is excess sludge which must be removed periodically. The disposal of excess sludge is one of the most difficult and expensive operations associated with biological systems and should receive careful consideration in the overall design. One portion of this consideration is the estimation of the quantities of excess solids. The quantity of excess sludge produced will vary with the type of process, aerobic or anaerobic, and with the method of operation, long or short SRTs. Excess solids are composed of two major fractions:

The excess microorganisms produced

The solids in the raw waste not removed by previous treatment processes

Proper operation of biological systems depends on the presence of sufficient inorganic nutrients for growth. The major nutrients required are nitrogen and phosphorus, which serve as basic elements in the formation of cell proteins, enzymes, and nucleic acids. In general, the nitrogen and phosphorus requirements for biological treatment are as follows:

$$N = 5\ \text{lb}/100\ \text{lb BOD}_5\ \text{removed}$$
$$P = 1\ \text{lb}/100\ \text{lb BOD}_5\ \text{removed}$$

Nitrogen may be in the form of ammonia, nitrates, or nitrites for aerobic systems, but it should be in the form of ammonia for anaerobic systems since nitrites and nitrates can be lost by denitrification. Nearly any form of soluble phosphorus can be used.

Stabilization ponds Stabilization ponds are one of the major biological wastewater treatment systems. Success of stabilization ponds depends on good design, maintenance, and operational supervision.

Stabilization ponds are low-cost biological wastewater treatment systems which depend on natural processes and may be assisted by mechanical or diffused aerators. Stabilization ponds have been referred to as sewage lagoons, oxidation ponds, plain aeration, maturation ponds, facultative lagoons, anaerobic lagoons, and aerobic stabilization ponds.

Any biological wastewater system which has been designed to fulfill a biological waste treatment requirement (utilizing bacteria and/or algae) can be classified as a stabilization pond. Aerated ponds are those in which all or much of the oxygen requirement is supplied by mechanical or diffused aeration.

The design of stabilization ponds is based on mode of operation (aerobic, facultative, or anaerobic). Once the mode of operation is chosen, the organic loading and retention time are chosen to achieve the desired effluent quality. Other design factors such as temperature, light, operating conditions, and wastewater characteristics must be considered to assure a successful operation.

Costs. The capital and operational costs of stabilization ponds can be significantly less than other treatment methods. Aerated stabilization ponds have been shown to cost from 25 to 50 percent less than activated sludge treatment where land is readily available and inexpensive.

Efficiency. Treatment efficiency ranges from 50 to 95 percent BOD_5 removal depending on the wastewater and type of pond. Since liquid-solids separation is not normally included in this treatment approach, a highly polished effluent low in suspended solids is not achieved.

Design. Stabilization pond design is usually based on liquid retention time. Depending on design conditions, retention times of from 1 to over 100 days have been

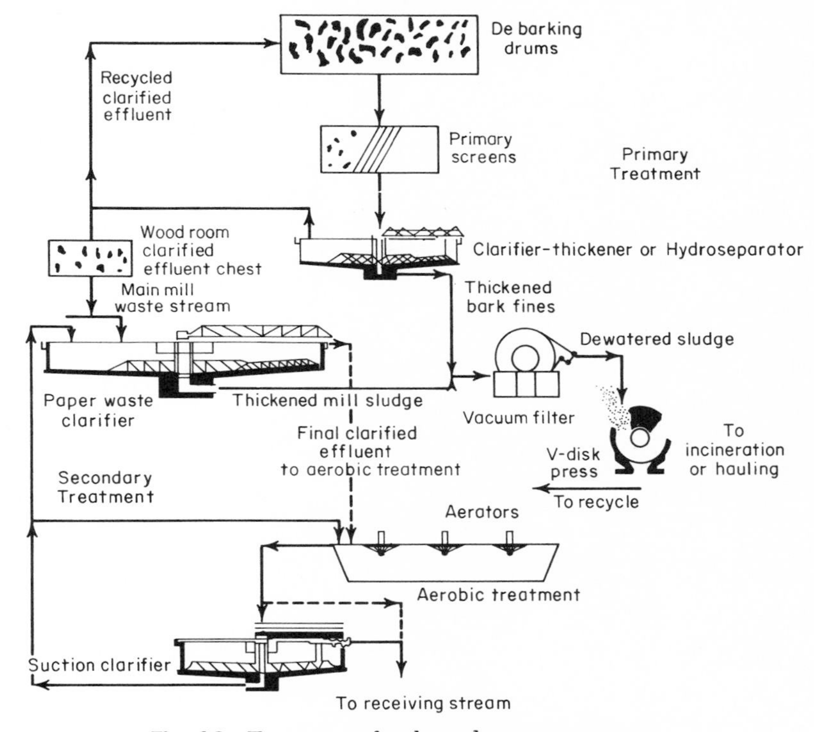

Fig. 16 Treatment of pulp and paper wastewater.

used. Laboratory tests can be used to determine the retention time required to achieve a given effluent quality.

Activated sludge treatment process The conventional activated sludge treatment process is designed for an F/M ratio varying from 0.2 to 0.5 lb BOD_5/(lb MLSS) (day). Industrial wastewater containing from 100 to in excess of 10,000 mg/l BOD_5 can be treated by proper design. The MLSS concentration will vary from 1,000 to 7,500 mg/l, depending on the design operation and MLSS settling characteristics. The degree of treatment achieved ranges from 75 to 95 percent BOD_5 and suspended solids removal. A typical wastewater treatment flowsheet for a pulp and paper mill is shown in Fig. 16.

Extended Aeration. The extended aeration activated sludge process has been equated to a 24-hr contactor retention time. For industrial wastewaters, 24-hr contact retention time may not be sufficient. Extended aeration activated sludge should be based on an F/M ratio of 0.1 or less. Design of the activated sludge process at this low F/M ratio results in a high degree of organics oxidation and a minimum of excess solids production. The low production of solids is the major advantage, since there is less sludge disposal problem. The extended aeration activated sludge process is normally used for small wastewater flows of 2 mgd or less. In small plant applications, the cost of sludge disposal equipment would be prohibitive. It is, therefore, more economical to design the contactor with a low F/M ratio to achieve maximum oxidation of organic material and minimum solids production.

Ammonia nitrogen is present in many wastewaters. If nitrifying bacteria are present in sufficient quantity in the activated sludge and if the liquid temperature is correct, then nitrification will occur. For conventional or high-rate activated sludge systems, little nitrification occurs due to the short solids retention time. As solids retention time increases, nitrification occurs. Nitrification involves the oxidation of ammonia nitrogen (NH_3) to nitrate nitrogen (NO_3) by specific nitrifying bacteria. A typical two-stage nitrification activated sludge system is shown in Fig. 17.

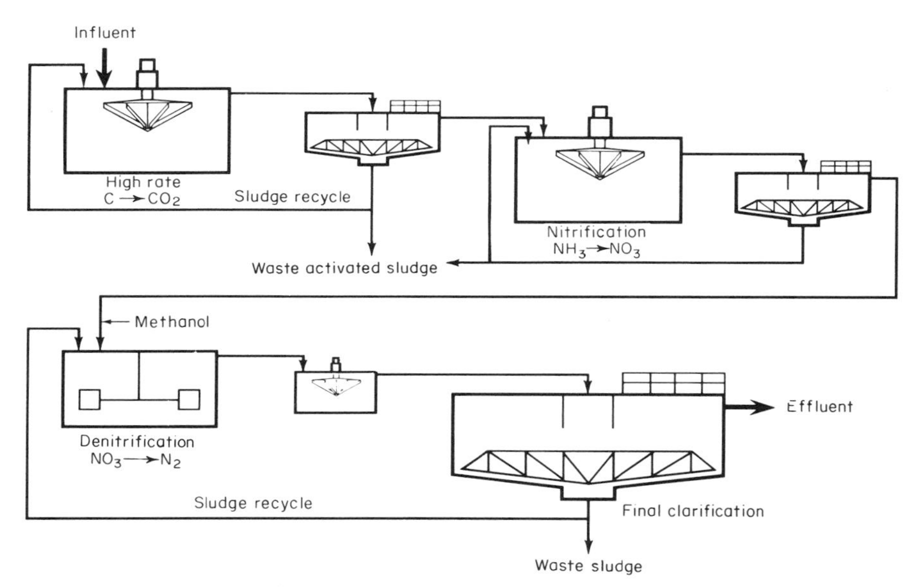

Fig. 17 A typical biological nitrification-denitrification treatment system.

Completely Mixed. Development of the completely mixed activated sludge system resulted from an understanding of both microbiology and basic unit operations. The completely mixed system involves contacting the wastewater with the contents of the contactor as rapidly as possible. The advantages of the completely mixed system are:

1. Less variation in organic loading in the contactor results in a more uniform effluent quality and a more uniform oxygen demand.
2. Dilution of the incoming wastewater into the entire basin volume results in reduced shock-loading effect either organic or toxic in nature.
3. The entire contactor contents is used at maximum efficiency at all times due to complete mixing.
4. Leveling out of organic loadings occurs, thus stabilizing operation.

The completely mixed system is the best approach that the design engineer has for overcoming many of the operational problems presently experienced by the activated sludge process. Figure 18 illustrates the simplicity of design of the completely mixed activated sludge system.

Pure Oxygen. The use of pure oxygen in the activated sludge process has gained attention. Although evaluated many years ago, an economical method of producing relatively pure oxygen was not available. With advances in oxygen-producing technology, the potential of pure oxygen usage in the activated sludge process appears to be feasible.

The saturation of oxygen in water is relatively low (9 mg/l at 20°C) for equilibrium conditions with atmospheric oxygen (21 vol % oxygen). Since the solubility of gases in water follows Henry's law of partial pressure, enrichment of oxygen in air up to 100 percent oxygen increases the saturation from 9 to about 45 mg/l. This increase in saturation of oxygen by the use of relatively pure oxygen gas (90 percent oxygen or more) results in an increase of about five times in the oxygen transfer capability of mechanical aeration equipment. As mentioned earlier, one process limitation to the activated sludge process is the capability of the aeration equipment to meet the oxygen demand of the system. With the use of a relatively pure oxygen gas, oxygen uptake rates of up to five times greater than presently designed can be achieved.

Figure 19 shows one approach to the pure oxygen system. Depending on the application and economics, single or multiple staging is used alone with covered or uncovered basins. Maximum use of oxygen is achieved with staging and covered basins.

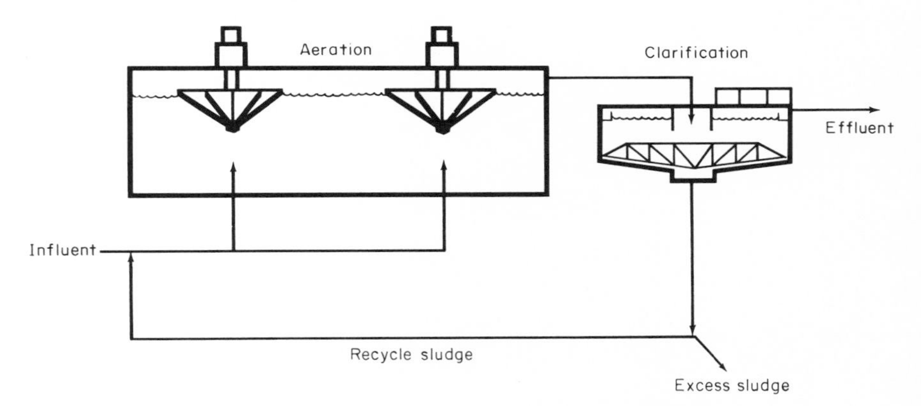

Fig. 18 Completely mixed activated sludge system.

The advantages claimed for the pure oxygen gas approach are:

1. Capability to meet high oxygen uptake rates
2. Ability to carry a reserve of oxygen in solution to meet variations in demand
3. Apparent superior settling characteristics of MLSS allowing a high concentration of solids to be maintained in the contactor

Aeration

Oxygenation and mixing must be provided to achieve good treatment results in aerobic biological processes. An efficient mechanical device to achieve both is desirable. Several methods are presently used to accomplish both oxygenation and mixing. Four methods are shown in Fig. 20.

Aeration devices Air diffusers are the earliest forms of aeration devices used. Compressed air (3 to 10 psig) is released from the diffuser as air bubbles. The larger the number and the smaller the size of the air bubbles produced, the more efficient will be the oxygen transfer achieved. Pumping caused by the release of air bubbles beneath the liquid surface results in the mixing of the contactor contents. Combination of compressed air and turbine mixing eliminates the troublesome clogging problems experienced with diffusers and adds versatility to mixing and oxygen transfer. With the submerged turbine aerator, mixing and oxygenation may be varied independently within a given operating range.

Low-speed Surface Aerator. A further development of aeration equipment resulted in the elimination of air compressors or blowers. The low-speed surface aerator utilizes atmospheric oxygen by causing extreme liquid turbulence at the liquid surface. This device has proven to be nearly twice as efficient in oxygen transfer as air diffusers.

Motor-speed Surface Aerator. The latest addition to the aeration field is the motor-speed surface aerator. This device operates at the liquid surface but does not have a gear reducer between the motor and impeller. Because there is no gear reducer,

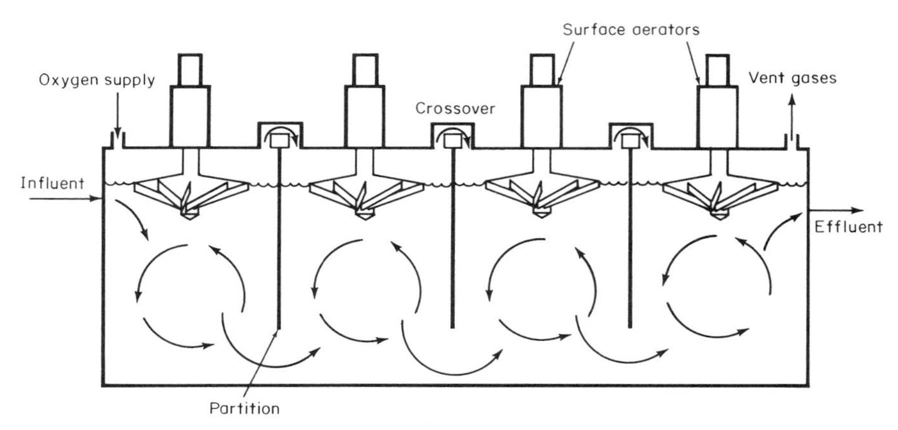

Fig. 19 Pure oxygen activated sludge contactor.

the cost is significantly reduced. This device has been used extensively to supplement oxygen requirements for oxidation ponds.

Selection The advantage of each aerator will vary with the physical conditions at which the units operate. The data listed in Table 5 are offered as a guide to selecting the various aeration systems that are available.

The sizing and selection of aerators are important to the successful operation of a treatment plant using aeration for biological or chemical oxidation. Accuracy of process data and the selection of factors determine the accuracy of the calculation.

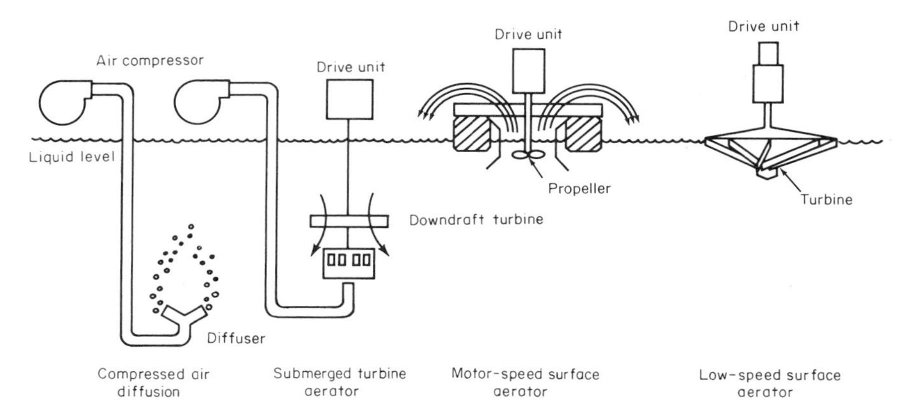

Fig. 20 Artificial oxygenation and mixing devices.

TABLE 5 Comparison of Mechanical Aerators

	Low speed					
	Standard	With lower turbine	With draft tube	Direct-drive propellor	Diffused	Submerged
Efficiency*	3.5 lb O_2/hp-hr	3.5 lb O_2/hp-hr	3.5 lb O_2/hp-hr	2.75 lb O_2/hp-hr	2.0 lb O_2/hp-hr	3.0 lb O_2/hp-hr
Pumpage	2–3 cfs/hp	2–3 cfs/hp	2–3 cfs/hp	1.75 cfs/hp	3–5 cfs/hp	2–3 cfs/hp
Tip speed	15–25 ft/sec	15–25 ft/sec	15–25 ft/sec	75–100 ft/sec	. . .	15–25 ft/sec
Fixed supports	Yes	Yes	Yes	Yes	Yes	Yes
Float supports	Yes	Yes	No	Yes	No	No
Application	†, ‡, §, ¶	†, ‡	†	‡, §, ¶	†, ‡, ¶	†

* Based on water tests conducted using 2.0 mg/l cobalt catalyst.
† Activated sludge.
‡ Aerated lagoon.
§ Facultative lagoon.
¶ Stream aeration.

The following example shows design calculations necessary to arrive at horsepower and sizing of aerators in a typical application:

Plant design flow, mgd	3.0, average, 4.5, peak
Influent BOD_5, mg/l	200
Desired BOD_5 removal, percent	93
Process	Completely mixed activated sludge
Loading, lb BOD_5/(lb MLSS)(day)	0.4
MLSS in aeration basin, mg/l	3,000
Influent temperature, °C	15
Barometric pressure P, in. Hg	29.92
Relative oxygen solubility β	0.9
C_L, dissolved oxygen to be maintained during treatment, mg/l	2.0
Relative oxygen transfer α	0.9

Because of the important effect of the variables listed above, accurate data and judgment regarding the selection of factors are important for the proper design and operation of a waste treatment plant using either mechanical or diffused aeration. Relative oxygen solubility and relative oxygen transfer coefficients vary for different wastes. They are best determined by tests on a representative waste sample, if available, using standard laboratory tests. There will usually be several possibilities for each aerator application. The selection should be based on aerator costs, desired basin configuration, and standby capacity. However, anticipated performance should be evaluated on the basis of the reliability of the data and the conservatism of the factors used in the calculations.

PRIMARY TREATMENT:

BOD_5 in raw waste: 3.0 mgd × 8.34 lb/gal × 200 mg/l = 5,000 lb/day
Assume primary removal of 35 percent BOD_5.
BOD_5 removed in primary: 5,000 × 0.35 = 1,750 lb/day

SECONDARY TREATMENT:

Total BOD_5 in raw waste	5,000 lb/day
BOD_5 removed in primary	1,750
BOD_5 to aeration	3,250 lb/day
Allowable BOD_5 in effluent (based on 93 percent overall removal)	350
BOD_5 to be removed by aeration	2,900 lb/day

Oxygen requirements For completely mixed activated sludge, use 0.8 lb O_2/lb BOD_5 removed.

$$\frac{2{,}900 \text{ lb BOD}_5\text{/day}}{24} \times 0.8 \text{ lb O}_2\text{/lb BOD}_5 = 96.7 \text{ lb O}_2\text{/hr}$$

Where peak flow may be 150 percent of average flow, it can reasonably be assumed that the oxygen demand will not increase in proportion to flow and the use of a 125 percent factor is suggested to supply the maximum oxygen requirement. For this example, adjustment for peak oxygen demand, assuming 125 percent of 24-hr average oxygen demand.

$$N_\alpha = 96.7 \times 1.25 = 121 \text{ lb } O_2\text{/hr transferred to waste}$$

Aerator sizing After N_α has been determined, the equivalent oxygen transferred to tap water N at standard conditions in pounds per hour is computed using Eq. (6).

$$N = \frac{N_\alpha}{\alpha\left(\frac{C_{sw} - C_L}{C_s}\right)(1.025)^{T-20}} \quad (6)$$

where $\alpha = \dfrac{\text{oxygen transfer rate to waste}}{\text{oxygen transfer rate to tap water}}$

C_{sw} = oxygen saturation value of the waste, mg/l, calculated from the expression:

$$C_{sw} = \beta C_{ss} P$$

where $\beta = \dfrac{\text{oxygen saturation of the waste}}{\text{oxygen saturation of tap water}}$

C_{ss} = oxygen saturation value of tap water at the specified waste temperature

$P = \dfrac{\text{barometric pressure at the plant site}}{\text{barometric pressure at sea level}}$

C_L = dissolved oxygen concentration to be maintained in the waste, mg/l

C_s = oxygen saturation value of tap water at 20°C and 1 atm pressure; use value of C_s = 9.17 mg/l

T = waste temperature, °C

From the design conditions, we have these values:

N_α = 121 lb O_2/hr
α = 0.9
β = 0.9
P = 1.0 atm
C_L = 2.0 mg/l
T = 15°C

$$C_{sw} = 0.9(10.15)1.0 = 9.14 \text{ mg/l}$$

$$N = \frac{121}{0.9\left(\frac{9.14 - 2.0}{9.17}\right)0.884} = \frac{121}{0.9 \times 0.78 \times 0.884} = 195 \text{ lb/hr}$$

Assume 3.5 lb O_2/hp-hr for surface aerators for estimating purposes. Therefore, the total horsepower required is

$$\frac{195}{3.5} = 55.8 \text{ bhp}$$

Activated Carbon Adsorption

Removal of soluble organics from wastewater can be achieved by adsorption on activated carbon. The outstanding feature of this treatment approach compared to biological treatment is that activated carbon is effective in removing most forms of organics. Furthermore, efficiency is not lost during conditions which would be toxic or inhibitory to biological treatment.

The critical design criteria are contact time and organic loading. Contact time determines adsorber size and carbon inventory. The amount of organic material removed per unit weight of carbon while maintaining the desired effluent quality determines the carbon usage rate. Carbon usage rate determines the regeneration furnace size and costs. Contact times of 20 to 60 min and organic loadings of 0.2 to 0.5 lb COD per lb carbon have been experienced. These values will depend on the effluent requirements and raw wastewater characteristics. Pilot-plant testing is usually required to established these design criteria.

Another important design criterion is the quantity of activated carbon required to remove a desired amount of soluble organics. The *maximum* carbon usage can be *estimated* based on equilibrium adsorption isotherm test results. Since regeneration equipment sizing depends on the amount of organics adsorbed per unit weight of activated carbon, reliable design data are very important.

In addition to the removal of soluble organics by physical adsorption, biological removal has been observed, thus complicating the estimation of carbon usage. It has been observed that anaerobic biological activity within the carbon contactors increases the adsorption capacity. This anaerobic biological activity is both good and bad. It is good because the overall organic removal capacity of an adsorption system may be more than doubled. This improvement is probably the result of both biological oxidation and in situ regeneration of activated carbon. The negative aspects of anaerobic biological treatment within the carbon contactor include the production of odors and the creation of corrosive conditions. Both of these negative aspects can be eliminated by the addition of oxygen or air to the contactor to maintain aerobic conditions. Air or oxygen addition is not recommended since aerobically produced solids (many times greater in quantity than those produced under anaerobic conditions) will cause clogging and require frequent and possibly special backwashing procedures.

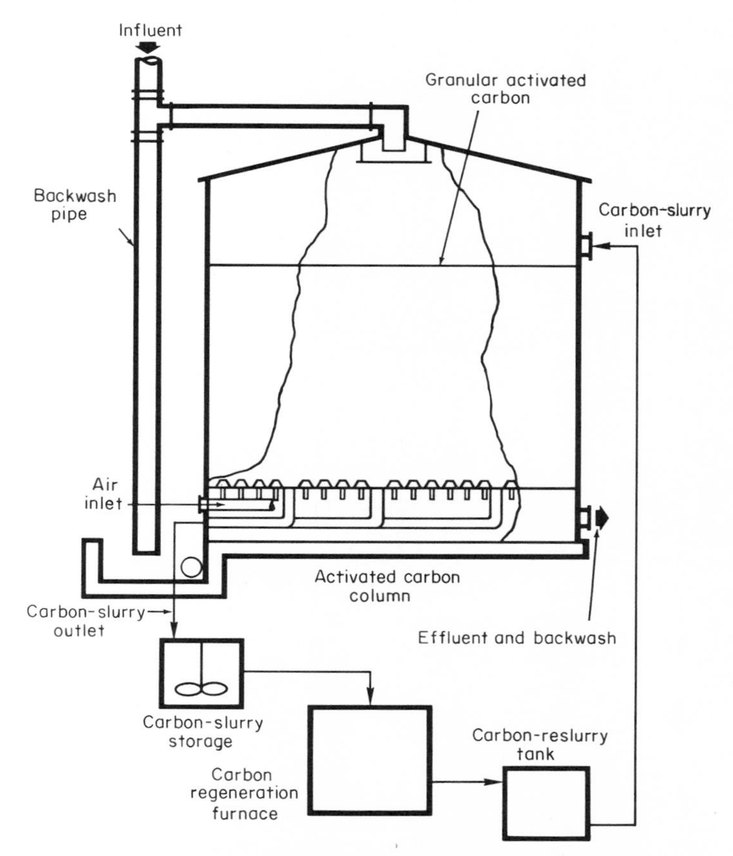

Fig. 21 A typical granular activated carbon adsorption system.

It is difficult, if not impossible, to determine the soluble organic removing capacity of an adsorption system because of the anaerobic biological oxidation effect. Laboratory equilibrium adsorption isotherm results indicate physical adsorption removal capacity of carbon, but the influence of biological activity can only be estimated. Carbon column studies operated to exhaustion will provide the desired design information. Figure 21 shows a typical granular activated carbon adsorption system for the treatment of wastewaters.

Figure 22 is a cross-sectional view of a multiple-hearth furnace used to regenerate granular activated carbon. The furnace consists of a steel shell lined with refractory material. The interior spaces are divided by horizontal brick arches into separate compartments called *hearths*. Alternate hearths have holes at the periphery or at the center for the carbon to drop through. A variable-speed drive located at the bottom of the furnace rotates the center shaft. It is sealed at the top and bottom to prevent air or gas leakage. The center shaft is hollow to allow for cooling air and has sockets where rabble arms are connected. The arms are fitted with rabble teeth placed at an angle so that as the shaft rotates, carbon is moved in or out on the hearths. Dewatered spent carbon enters the top of the furnace on hearth 1 and is rabbled in a spiral pattern through the furnace. Hot steam and flue gases travel upward through the hearths countercurrent to the movement of carbon.

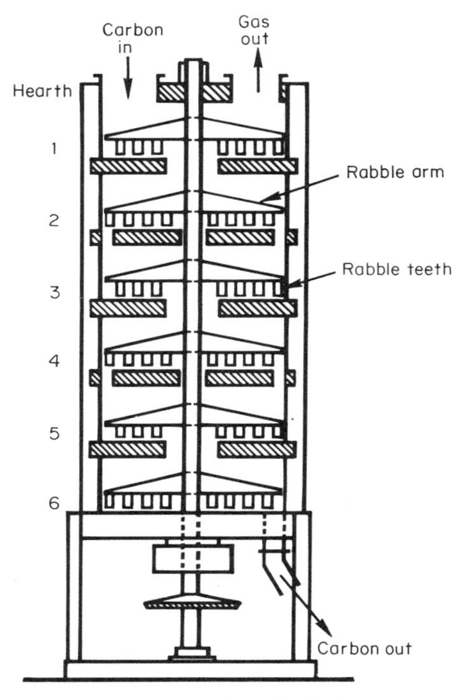

Fig. 22 Cross section of multiple-hearth furnace.

Burners are located at several hearths in the furnace to maintain the desired temperature. These burners can be of the nozzle-mixing or premixed type and are normally positioned on hearths 4, 5, and 6. Steam inlet tubes are also provided at these hearths. The temperature on these hearths is independently controlled by an automatic controller which is capable of maintaining the temperature within 10°F of the desired temperature. A proportional flowmeter is used to supply the desired mixture of air and gas to the burners. About 1 lb steam/lb carbon regenerated is recommended. Normal gas flow rates including steam are about 50 cu ft/lb carbon.

Drying occurs on the first three hearths for a period of about 15 min. Baking occurs on the fourth hearth for about 4 min, and activation occurs on the fifth and sixth hearths for about 11 min.

A number of safety devices are included in the furnace design. An ultraviolet scanner is used on each burner to detect a flameout in which case the furnace automatically shuts down. The furnace also automatically shuts down in the event of high or low gas pressures, high-combustion air pressures, low scrubber water pressure, high stack gas temperature, and inoperation of the shaft-cooling air fan. An air fan supplies cooling air through the hollow shaft to the rabble arms to prevent overheating.

Carbon regeneration off-gases exit at the top of the furnace and go to an afterburner where volatiles and noxious components are burned. A wet scrubber is provided to remove dust and odorous substances. It also cools the gases so that the induced-draft fan can handle them. The induced-draft fan is necessary to draw the gases through the system. The wet scrubber is fabricated of stainless steel because of the corrosive and abrasive properties of the wet carbon dust.

Carbon lost during the thermal regeneration cycle can be attributed to attrition in transporting, gasification and burning in the regeneration furnace, and thermal shock in the quench tank. Regeneration may also result in a decrease in the iodine number, and carbon adsorption capacity (X/M). Carbon losses in the range of 5 to 10 percent can be expected.

Figure 23 shows a carbon regeneration system for granular activated carbon. Granular carbon in a slurry form can be handled by eductors, centrifugal pumps, diaphragm pumps, and torque flow pumps. An eductor pumps the carbon/water slurry by the use of an auxiliary source of 60- to 80-psig water. Centrifugal pumps should be rubber-lined to protect the pump and minimize attrition of the carbon particles. A torque flow pump is a special type of centrifugal pump with a recessed impeller that effectively minimizes carbon particle attrition. A diaphragm pump uses an air- or water-pressure source to actuate the diaphragm. A 3-ft suction head is required for diaphragm pumps presenting a possible installation problem.

Carbon-slurry velocities should not be less than 3 ft/sec to prevent settling and not more than 6 ft/sec to minimize pipe abrasion and mechanical attrition of carbon particles. About 0.5 gal water per pound of carbon is recommended for transport design. Piping used for carbon transport should include a bend radius equal to twice the pipe diameter. Carbon regeneration equipment should be placed as close as possible to the carbon adsorption reactors to minimize pipe lengths.

Since spent carbon is transported in slurry form, a dewatering screw is used to dewater it to about 50 percent moisture prior to being fed to the regeneration furnace. For small installations the spent carbon storage tank may be located directly above the dewatering screw. The dewatering screw seals with the furnace by using a covered trough and flanged connection to the feed tank. The carbon serves as the sealing medium. Therefore, a rotary air-lock feeder is not necessary. The dewatering screw can be used as either a carbon feed device or a dewatering-feeding device.

Carbon discharge from the regeneration furnace drops into a quench tank. This tank is filled with water to a level set by a level controller or float valve. Carbon-slurry conveying equipment is used to transport the regenerated carbon from the quench tank back to contactors.

Powdered activated carbon Application of powdered activated carbon (PAC) normally involves three steps: rapid mix, contact mixing, and liquid-solids separation. Rapid mixing is required to disperse the carbon. Contact mixing provides time for adsorption. Clarification or liquid-solids separation is required to maintain the relatively expensive carbon in the system. Use of upflow solids-contact contactors combines the three in one unit operation. Solids-contact contactors require no chemical additives to achieve gravity clarification at overflow rates up to 0.8 gpm/sq ft. This clarification characteristic results from the natural flocculation characteristics of powdered carbon slurries.

Granular media filtration can be used as the final liquid-carbon separation step. A high degree of powdered carbon removal is required since as little as 10 to 15 mg/l results in a black, hazy effluent. Also, loss of powdered carbon may be undesirable since regeneration and reuse are possible at reasonable costs. Effective removal of powdered carbon can be achieved at filtration rates of 1 to 3 gpm/sq ft.

A typical granular media filter bed would consist of 1.5 ft of 1.0-mm anthracite coal and 1 ft of 0.5-mm sand. The removed carbon is typically a "weak floc" and a polyelectrolyte dosage of ⅛ to ½ mg/l may be required to produce a "tough floc" which will remain in the filter bed. A powdered carbon contacting system is shown in Fig. 24.

Due to its small particle size, powdered activated carbon can be dryed, baked, and activated very rapidly. Several approaches of thermal regeneration are possible. These include: wet air oxidation, transport reactor, and fluidized-bed furnace.

Fluidized-Bed Furnace. The fluidized-bed furnace approach has been extensively evaluated on a pilot-plant scale. The fluidized bed of sand serves as a controlled constant-temperature zone for regeneration. Fluidization occurs by the action of hot combustion gases passing upward through a distribution plate. The operating temperature of the bed is from 1300 to 1600°F. Dewatered carbon is pumped directly into the fluidized bed.

To prevent structural failure, the temperature in the firebox must be maintained at less than 2100°F. The firebox temperature is controlled by recycling inert stack off-gas. The regenerated carbon and gases are cooled to about 200°F by spraying

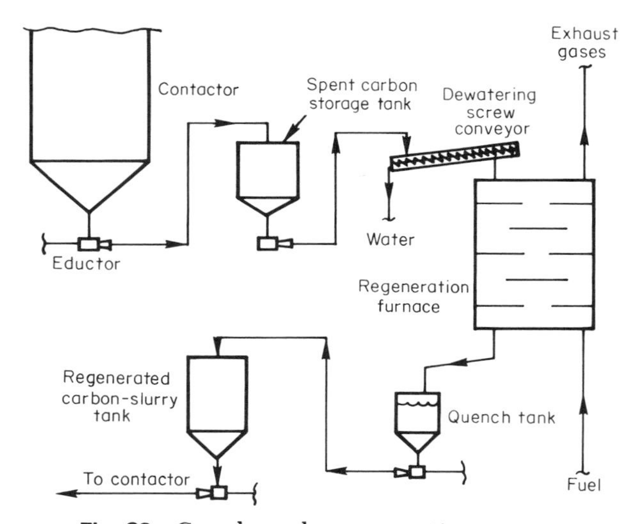

Fig. 23 Granular carbon regeneration system.

water directly into the regeneration furnace exit gas duct. After cooling, the gases and regenerated carbon are passed through wet venturi scrubbers. The scrubber water is collected in a carbon recovery and scrubber water recycle tank.

The fluidized-bed-furnace operation can be automated. Off-gas and burner air and gas flows are manually set to provide the desired fluidization velocity and exit oxygen concentration. Carbon is automatically fed to the furnace at a rate necessary to maintain a preset bed temperature. Regeneration losses of less than 10 percent fixed carbon appear to be possible with this system.

Wet Air Oxidation Systems. These systems involve subjecting a thickened powdered carbon slurry (about 6 to 8 percent solids) to detention in a pressurized, steam-heated reactor. The reactor product is passed through a decant tank prior to reuse.

Transport Reactor Systems. The transport reactor systems involve direct injection of thickened spent powdered carbon (about 10 percent solids) into a direct flame reactor at a temperature of 1400 to 1600°F. The carbon detention time in the reactor is approximately 1 sec. The powdered carbon is captured in water- and air-cooled jet condensers. Carbon losses of 10 percent and near complete recovery of adsorption characteristics are possible.

Granular Media Filtration

Granular media filters can be designed for low suspended solids removal efficiency (coarse roughing filters) at high filtration rates (15 gpm/sq ft or more) and/or with coarse media. Conversely, they can be designed for high suspended solids removal efficiency (polishing filters) at lower filtration rates (2 to 6 gpm/sq ft) and/or with fine media. Combined with chemical treatment, these filters can also affect polishing and phosphorus removal.

Efficient filtration results when suspended solids are removed over a large portion of the filter-bed depth. In-depth filtration is not screening of particles, but involves more complex processes occurring within the filter-bed voids (such as particle interaction, flocculation, sedimentation, etc.). Data concerning filterability of suspended solids to be removed is required for proper filter design. These data can be established by operating pilot-plant filters on the wastewater.

An example of filter application is the polishing of secondary biological effluents. Effluent standards requiring 5-day BOD and suspended solids concentrations of less than 5 mg/l indicate a need for excellent liquid-solids separation. Nearly all 5-day BOD present in a good quality secondary biological effluent is in suspended solids

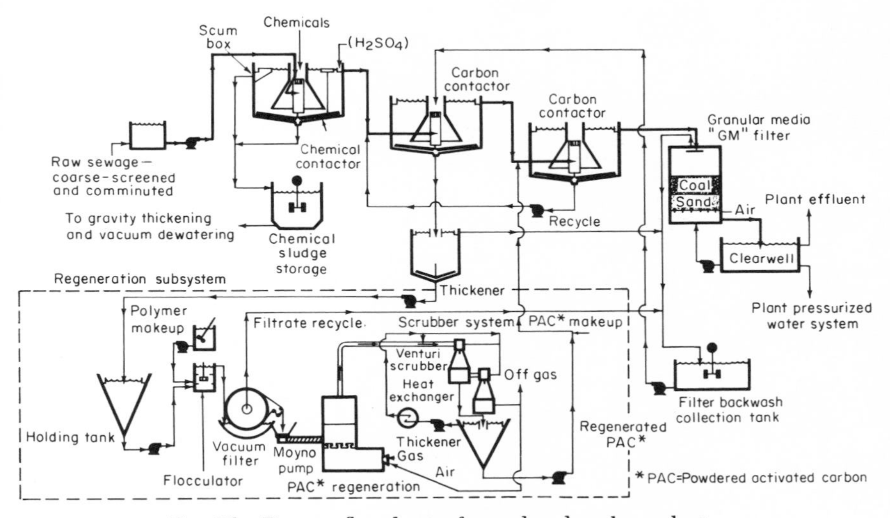

Fig. 24 Process flowsheet of powdered carbon plant.

form. Unfortunately, some of the suspended solids in biological effluents are colloidal and only about 50 to 70 percent removal can be achieved by filtration without chemical coagulation. In order to remove more than 50 to 70 percent of the suspended solids, some chemical coagulant (such as alum) and a floc toughener (polymer) are required. Figure 25 shows a typical filter flowsheet for polishing secondary biological effluent.

Another example of granular media filtration for polishing secondary biological effluents is the combination of suspended solids and phosphorus removal. Secondary biological effluents can be dosed with alum and polymer prior to entering the filter to effect nearly complete removal of both suspended solids and phosphorus. For suspended solids removal a minimum of alum is required since a settleable floc (requiring 25 to 50 percent additional alum) is not necessary or desired prior to filtration. The minimum alum dosage required will be that necessary to achieve coagulation (not settleability) of suspended solids *or* for precipitating phosphorus to a desired residual level. Careful consideration of filter-bed design and filtration rates can assure filter runs of from 10 to 20 hr for gravity filters having 6 to 10 ft of available waterhead.

An important design consideration for granular media filtration is the periodic cleaning or backwashing procedure. Cleaning of the filter media ranges from difficult to nearly impossible with methods commonly applied for backwashing potable water filters. The basic problem lies in the desire to achieve in-depth filtration along with biological slimes forming on the media. In-depth filtration is very desirable since more efficient use of the filter media is achieved resulting in greater water production and longer filter runs. The media acts as a flooded biological filter causing slimes to build up throughout the bed depth. Application of disinfectants (such as chlorine) may be effective in controlling such slime growths. Both of these conditions require that effective backwashing methods be used.

A combination of air scour and hydraulic backwash can be used to effectively clean filter beds treating biodegradable organic-containing wastewaters. Air is first applied at a rate sufficient to completely upset and scour the media (3 to 5 cfm/sq ft), then the hydraulic wash (15 to 25 gpm/sq ft) is used to flush away loosened suspended matter and restratify the media.

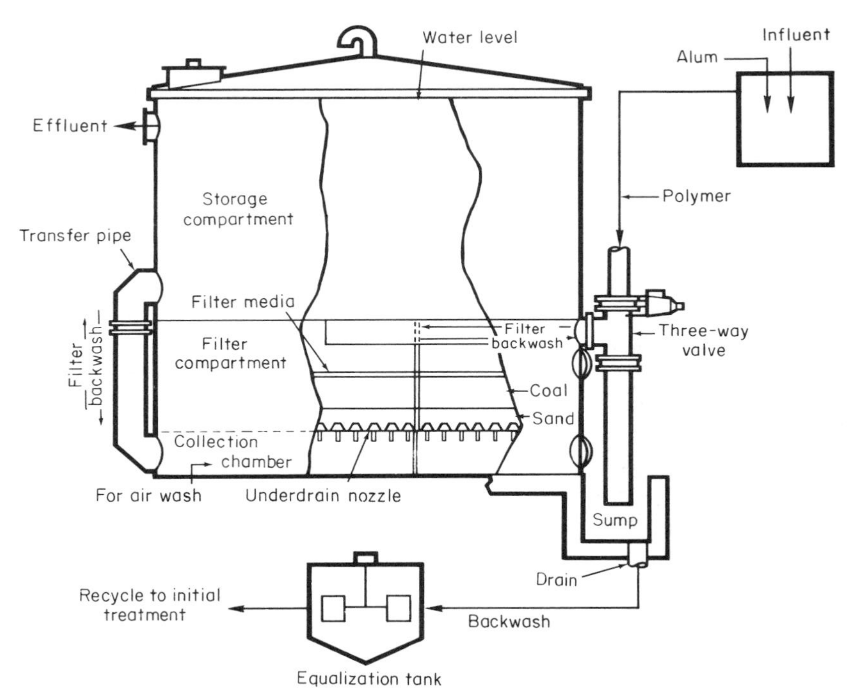

Fig. 25 Typical automatic granular media filter system.

SLUDGE HANDLING

In nearly all forms of wastewater treatment a residue of solids is produced. The treatment of these solids can result in a significant part of the total treatment cost. Sludge handling is normally discussed in three steps: thickening, dewatering, and disposal. Digestion and combustion are methods to reduce both volume and weight of the sludge to be disposed.

Thickening

Thickening is a process by which suspensions of solids are increased in concentration. The resulting thickened sludge can still be pumped. Sludge thickening can be differentiated from clarification by the primary objective of each. Clarification has the

TABLE 6 Effect of Sludge Thickening on Volume

Solids concentration, wt %	Water, wt %	Total liquid volume, gal	Volume remaining, %
1	99	100	
2	98	50	50
4	96	25	25
8	92	12.5	12.5
16	84	6.25	6.25

primary objective of effluent clarity while thickening has the primary objective of underflow solids concentration. The effect of sludge thickening on volume is illustrated by the information in Table 6.

Table 6 shows that if 100 gal of 1 percent sludge is thickened to 2 percent, 50 percent of the liquid is removed or 50 gal. If the 2 percent sludge were further concentrated to 4 percent sludge, again 50 percent of the liquid is removed but this time only 25 gal. This illustrates the value of thickening in reducing the hydraulic load to more expensive dewatering steps.

Gravity thickening is the most common method in use today. It is a sedimentation process which is simple and relatively inexpensive. Four basic zones occur in gravity thickening: clarification, settling, compression, and compacting.

The process parameters which affect the results achieved are: type of solids, temperature, feed concentration, sludge depth, detention time, agitation, and chemical addition. The effects of some of these parameters should be studied to determine design criteria. Standard laboratory thickening tests can be used to set design solids loading for nearly any type of sludge. Listed in Table 7 are the design solids loading used for several sludges.

Gravity thickeners are rarely designed on a hydraulic loading basis, but the liquid retention time without dilution should be in excess of 24 hr and the overflow rate less than 100 gpd/sq ft. If dilution were practiced to increase the thickening rate, retention time would decrease.

Operation of a gravity thickener is relatively simple if sludge wasting is continuous. For intermittent sludge wasting, upset conditions can occur. Care must be taken to avoid long solids retention time due to the production of odor and floating sludge. Normally, the gentle agitation of the picket arms releases accumulated gas to prevent both odor and floating sludge. Picket arms also assist in the thickening process by providing channels for the release water. A typical gravity thickener is shown in Fig. 26.

Dissolved air flotation can be applied to the thickening of wastewater sludge. This process was discussed earlier. Design factors for flotation thickening are: operating

TABLE 7

Sludge	Solids loading, lb/(sq ft)(day)	Percent solids
Primary		
60% volatile	20–30	8–15
40% volatile	30–40	10–20
Primary + trickling filter	10–15	6–10
Primary + WAS*	8–15	4–8
WAS	5–8	2–3
WAS + polymer	10–12	3–4
Primary + lime	20–30	10–20
Primary + alum + polymer	3–5	4–6

* WAS = waste activated sludge.

pressure, feed solids concentration, type and quality, solids and hydraulic loading, recycle ratio, retention time, air/solids ratio, and use of chemicals. Below are listed the range of these factors used for flotation sludge thickening:

Operating pressure, psig	40–70
Feed solids concentration, wt %	0.5–1
Solids loading, lb/(sq ft)(hr)	0.5–2.0
Hydraulic loading, gpm/sq ft	0.5–2.0
Recycle ratio	0.5–3.0
Retention time, min	15–60

Digestion

Anaerobic digestion is defined as the decomposition of organic matter in the absence of free molecular dissolved oxygen. Decomposition is not complete since by-products such as organic acids, ammonia, methane, and hydrogen sulfide are produced. A 60 to 75 percent reduction in volatile solids is normally achieved resulting in sludge stabilization. Digestion achieves stabilization, volume and weight reduction, a useful methane by-product, reduction of pathogenic organisms, and an easier sludge to dispose.

Fig. 26 Typical sludge gravity thickener.

The sludge fed to a digester should be as concentrated as possible to achieve maximum treatment, conserve heat, and minimize supernatant recycle. For standard and high-rate digesters, an organic loading of 0.04 to 0.1 and 0.15 to 0.40 lb MLVSS[1]/(cu ft)(day), respectively, are recommended. Digestion retention time averages about 40 and 15 days for standard and high-rate digestion, respectively. It is very important to keep a digester well mixed and in the temperature range of 90 to 120°F.

Operation of an anaerobic digester is tedious. Foaming, accumulation of grit, loss of gas production, scum blanket formation, clogged mixers, odors, and nonthickening sludge are a few key problems. Since many toxic materials tend to accumulate in the digesters due to the long retention time, these operational problems do not go away easily. Careful attention to operating conditions is required for successful treatment. Measurements such as pH, volatile acids, alkalinity, and gas production are used to indicate the conditions occurring within the digester.

Aerobic digestion is an extension of the activated sludge process whereby organic solids are stabilized. The organic solids are concentrated to 2 to 5 percent solids

[1] Mixed liquor volatile suspended solids.

by weight and aerated for an extended period of time. Design factors affecting aerobic digestion are organic loading, sludge age, sludge concentration, temperature, and oxygen uptake rate. Volatile solids reduction of 40 to 60 percent are normally achieved in a properly designed and operated system.

Although volatile solids loading has been used, the most common design parameter is detention time. Table 8 lists the recommended design detention times in days. The recommended aerobic digester mixing horsepower for mechanical low-speed aerators (surface or submerged) is listed in Table 9. For diffused-type aeration, air rates of 15 to 25 scfm/1,000 cu ft are adequate for mixing. With the proper mixing horsepower or air volume, more than sufficient oxygen will be supplied.

Operation of aerobic digesters is relatively easy compared to anaerobic digestion. The shorter retention time and aerobic condition reduces operation problems. The treated sludge is still difficult to dewater but is reasonably stable. The major disadvantage of aerobic digestion is the high power cost to achieve mixing and aeration.

TABLE 8 Detention Times

	Detention time, days	
	Sludge temperature	
Type of sludge	>60°F	>40°F
Biological sludge only	10	15
Biological + primary	15	20

TABLE 9

Solids, wt %	hp/1,000 cu ft
1	1.25
2	1.40
3	1.60
4	1.85
5	2.00

Dewatering

Vacuum filtration Vacuum filtration of wastewater sludge has been used for many years. The process consists of producing a vacuum on a drum which is covered with media. The media retains solids while moisture is drawn from the solids cake produced into a drainage compartment and receiver. A typical vacuum filter system is shown in Fig. 27.

The characteristics of the sludge that affect vacuum filtration are concentration, compressibility, chemical composition, and temperature.

The operating parameters are vacuum, drum submergence, drum speed, agitation, type of filter media, and sludge condition. The performance of the vacuum filter is based on cake moisture (weight percent), yield (pounds per hour per square foot), cake dischargeability, and filtrate solids concentration. Table 10 indicates the vacuum filter rates that have been observed on various types of sludges.

Use of polyelectrolyte for conditioning sludges has been successful. Polymer dosages of 0.2 to 2.0 lb/100 lb sludge have been used on primary and digested sludges to result in a filter yield of 4 to 20 lb/(hr)(sq ft).

Elutriation has been used on digested sludges to reduce chemical requirement. Elutriation is a method of sludge conditioning whereby dilution water is used to reduce alkalinity. By reducing the alkalinity, the chemical dosage for conditioning is reduced. Elutriation also removes fine solids.

TABLE 10 Typical Vacuum Filtration Results

Type of sludge	Thickened solids, wt %	Chemical requirements, wt %		Filter yield, lb/(hr)(sq ft)	Cake moisture, wt %
		$FeCl_3$	CaO		
Raw	6–10	1–2	5–7	5–7	65–70
Digested	6–10	1–4	6–10	6–8	70–75
Raw + trickling filter	5–7	2–4	8–12	6–8	75–80
Raw + activated sludge	4–6	2–4	8–12	3–5	75–80
Activated sludge	2–4	8–10	. . .	0.5–2	80–85

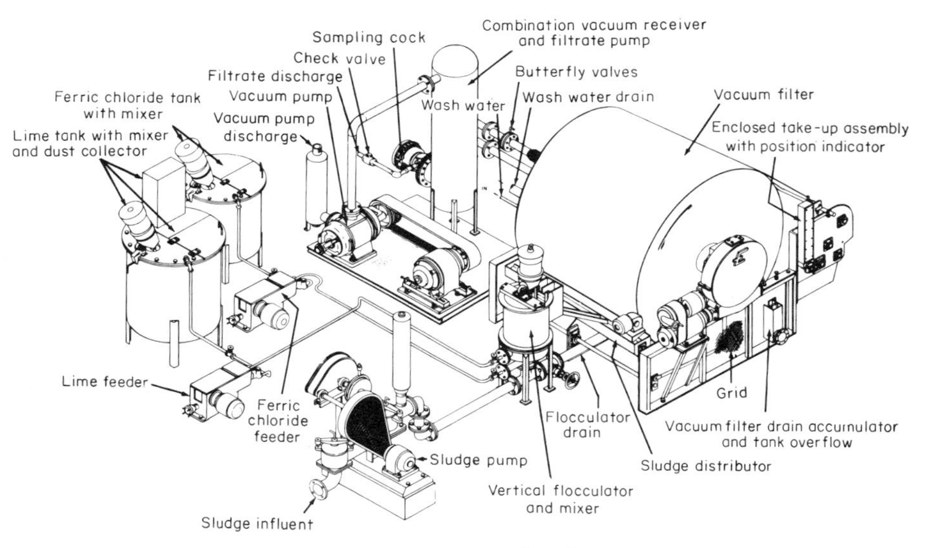

Fig. 27 Typical vacuum-filter sludge dewatering system.

Evaluation and performance of vacuum filters can be determined in the laboratory by leaf tests. A sample of sludge is tested first to determine the proper conditioning chemical(s) dosage. When the conditioning chemical dosage is established, the sample is then tested on an 0.1-sq-ft leaf using various types of media to determine the optimum filter yield, cake moisture, filtrate solids, and cake dischargeability. Then, by applying the proper scale-up factor, a full-scale unit can be sized.

Vacuum Filtration Sizing Calculations

Type of Sludge—Primary and Waste Activated

Anticipated thickener underflow concentration = 5 wt %
Total pounds dry solids (DS) per day = 5,100 lb DS/day
Operation = 8 hr/day, 5 days/week
20% lime slurry makeup
20% ferric chloride slurry makeup

I. Size of Vacuum Filter

$$\text{lb DS filtered/hr} = \frac{5{,}100 \text{ lb DS/day (7 days/week)}}{40 \text{ hr operation/week}}$$

$$= 893 \text{ lb DS/hr}$$

5% primary—waste activated
Filtration rate = 4.5 lb DS/(hr)(sq ft)

Filtration area required $= \dfrac{893 \text{ lb DS/hr}}{4.5 \text{ lb DS/(hr)(sq ft)}}$
$= 198$ sq ft

Use one 8-ft diameter by 8-ft face vacuum filter (see Table 11).

II. Sludge Pump Size

Sludge feed to filters $= \dfrac{893 \text{ lb DS/hr}}{(0.05)(8.34 \text{ lb/gal})(60 \text{ min/hr})}$
$= 36$ gpm

Use a 20- to 50-gpm sludge pump.

III. Ferric Chloride System

Required $FeCl_3$ dose = 4 wt %
20% $FeCl_3$ solution = 1.9 lb dry $FeCl_3$/gal

A. Feed Pump Size

gph 20% $FeCl_3$ solution required $= \dfrac{(0.04)(893 \text{ lb DS/hr})}{1.9 \text{ lb dry } FeCl_3\text{/gal}}$
$= 19$ gph

Use a 0- to 38-gph $FeCl_3$ pump

B. $FeCl_3$ Makeup Day Tank

Tank size (gal) = (38 gph)(8 hr)
= 304 gal

IV. Lime Feed Systems

Required lime dose = 10 wt %
20% lime solution = 1.95 lb dry CaO/gal
Assume 90% available CaO

A. Feed Pump Size

gph 20% lime solution required $= \dfrac{(0.10)(893 \text{ lb DS/hr})}{(0.9)(1.9 \text{ lb CaO/gal})}$
$= 50$ gph

Use a 0- to 120-gph lime pump

B. Lime Makeup Day Tank

Tank size (gal) = 100 gph (8 hr)
= 800 gal

From Table 5, use one 820-gal tank.

Centrifugation Centrifugation involves liquid-solids separation by means of sedimentation and centrifugal force. There are several types of centrifuge available for sludge dewatering: solids bowl, basket, nozzle, and disk. A typical unit is shown on Fig. 28. The most used wastewater sludge centrifuge is the horizontal, cylindrical-conical, solid bowl type.

Centrifugation has the following advantages in sludge dewatering:

Simple to operate and compact
Totally enclosed to minimize odor problem
Flexible operation
Can be used without chemicals
Low supervision required

The disadvantages of centrifugation are:

Low solids capture without chemical addition
Higher maintenance requirements

Design parameters are sludge feed rate, characteristics and concentration, temperature, conveyor and bowl speed, pool level, and chemical additions. Performance

TABLE 11 Standard Vacuum Filter Sizes, sq ft

	Face length									
Diameter	3	4	6	8	10	12	14	16	18	20
6 ft 0 in.	57	75	113	150	189					
8 ft 0 in.			150	200	250	300	350			
10 ft 0 in.				250	314	377	440	503	565	
12 ft 0 in.					377	452	528	603	679	754

TABLE 12

	Cake moisture, %
Primary	65–75
Trickling filter	75–80
Activated sludge	75–85

of centrifugation is based on solids recovery (centrate solids concentration), cake moisture, and cake production. Results of centrifugation of wastewater sludges are given by Table 12.

The centrate contains the fine, difficult-to-remove solids. These solids are usually recycled to the treatment system, resulting in fine solids buildup. Operation of a centrifuge with chemical addition is required to alleviate this problem.

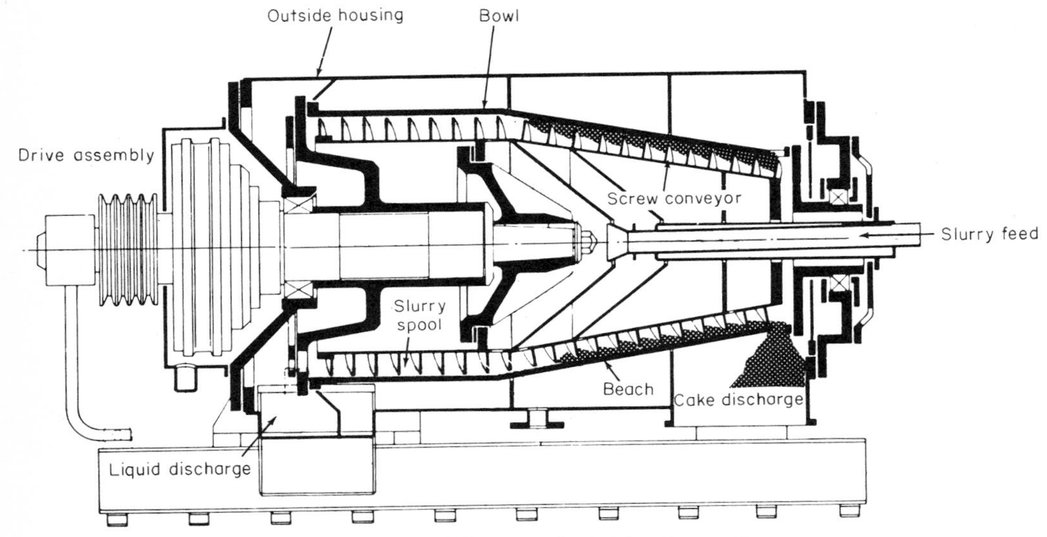

Fig. 28 Typical horizontal solid bowl centrifuge.

Disposal

Drying beds One of the most common ways of disposing of wastewater sludges is on drying beds. This approach is used for small plants since costs are low. Large land area may be required. Design factors such as sludge volume, characteristics and concentration, land value, weather and soil conditions are required for proper application. Drying beds can be open or covered, on natural soil or artificial media.

Table 13 shows the basic design loadings used for drying beds.

TABLE 13 Sludge Drying Bed Design Data

Sludge	Sludge loading, lb dry solids/(sq ft)(year)
Primary	20–30
Primary + trickling filter	20–30
Primary + activated sludge	10–15

Heat Treatment

Sludge conditioning Heating of wastewater sludge under pressure results in a breakdown of gel structure, coagulation, and, in general, an improvement in thickening and dewatering characteristics. The process involves heating the sludge to a temperature of 290 to 370°F for ½ to 1 hr at about 150 psig. To conserve heat, the treated sludge is passed through a dual-channel heat exchanger countercurrent to the incoming sludge.

Performance of the process has indicated that a treated primary plus trickling filter sludge will thicken to 8 to 10 wt % and dewater on a vacuum filter at rates up to 10 lb/(hr)(sq ft). One major disadvantage of this approach to sludge conditioning is that up to 25 percent of the organics present may be solubilized and recycled to the treatment system. A typical heat-treatment flowsheet for sludge conditioning is shown in Fig. 29.

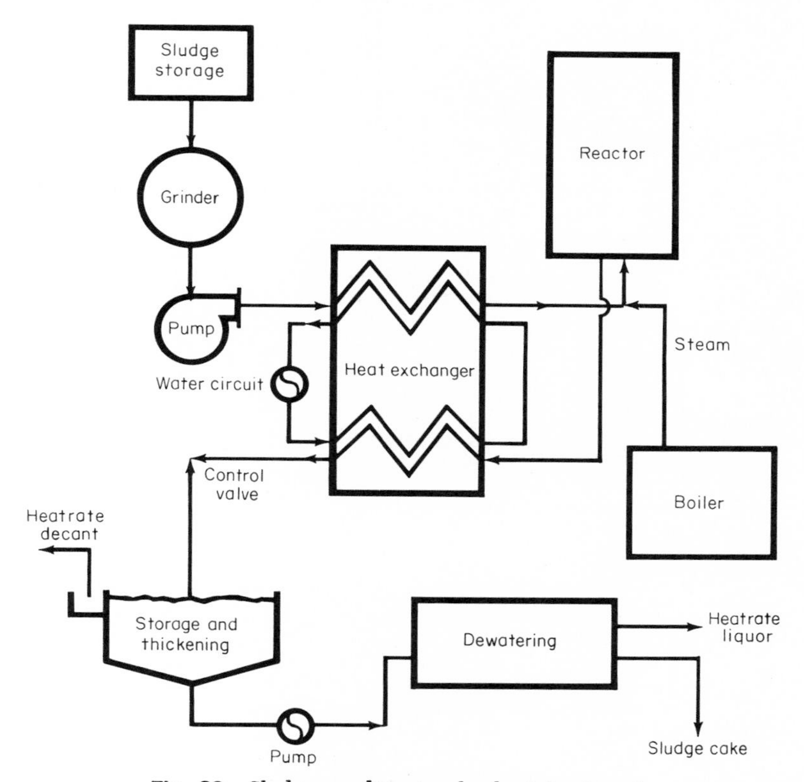

Fig. 29 Sludge conditioning by heat treatment.

Wet oxidation Wet oxidation differs from heat treatment in that destruction of organics is achieved. Up to 90 percent or more of the organics present may be oxidized by this treatment approach. Basically the organics in the sludge are oxidized by dissolved oxygen present in the reactor at elevated temperatures and pressure. The design parameters are operating temperature and pressure, sludge solids concentration, and oxygen supplied.

Incineration

Incineration processes involve the steps of drying and combustion. Combustion by definition is a rapid chemical reaction between fuel and oxygen. Time, temperature, and turbulence are necessary for complete reaction. The drying step should not be confused with the fact that preliminary dewatering, usually by mechanical means, precedes the incineration process. Wastewater sludges having a moisture content of about 75 percent are generally delivered to incineration furnaces. Typical sludges may contain about 3 lb of water for each pound of dry solids, so the heat required for evaporation of the water nearly balances the heat available from combustion of the dry solids. A slightly lower moisture content could allow autogenous burning of the sludge. This would depend, however, on the volatility of the sludge components.

Operation of an incinerator requires that air in excess of theoretical be supplied in order to ensure complete combustion of the fuel (sludge). Introduction of excess air has the effect of reducing burning temperature and increasing heat losses from the furnace. For this reason, close control over excess airflow is desirable for maximum thermal economy. The amount of excess air required varies with the type of burning equipment, the nature of the sludge to be burned, and the disposition of the stack gases.

Fuel and sludge burned in the furnace provide heat. Heat is lost by radiation, through stack gases, and with the ash. The remaining available heat is used to dry incoming sludge and warm incoming air. Self-sustained combustion is possible with dewatered sludge once the burning of auxiliary fuel raises incinerator temperatures to the volatile solids ignition point.

The primary end products of combustion are water, sulfur dioxide, carbon dioxide, and inert ash. The combustible elements of sludge and other fuels are carbon, hydrogen, and sulfur, which, when completely burned with oxygen, form compounds called *products of combustion.*

The products of complete combustion of substances like coal and sludge are carbon dioxide and water. Since oxygen required for combustion is supplied by air, the combustion products also contain a large amount of nitrogen. Sludge, like coal, contains small quantities of sulfur which burn mainly to sulfur dioxide. These products are also known as *stack gas, flue gas,* and *waste gas.* In addition to the combustible elements, sludge contains inert substances like oxygen, nitrogen, ash, and moisture that do not react with the oxygen. These elements only contribute to the weight and volume of flue gas.

Combustion occurs in accordance with the following reactions and the number to the far right is the amount of heat release.

$$\begin{array}{ccccc} \text{Carbon} & + & \text{oxygen} & \rightarrow & \text{carbon dioxide} \\ C & + & O_2 & \rightarrow & CO_2 \\ (1\ \text{lb}) & & (2.67\ \text{lb}) & & (3.67\ \text{lb}) \end{array} \qquad 14{,}600\ \text{Btu/lb dry solids} \tag{7}$$

$$\begin{array}{ccccc} \text{Hydrogen} & + & \text{oxygen} & \rightarrow & \text{water} \\ 2H_2 & + & O_2 & \rightarrow & 2H_2O \\ (1\ \text{lb}) & & (8\ \text{lb}) & & (9\ \text{lb}) \end{array} \qquad 62{,}000\ \text{Btu/lb dry solids} \tag{8}$$

$$\begin{array}{ccccc} \text{Sulfur} & + & \text{oxygen} & \rightarrow & \text{sulfur dioxide} \\ S & + & O_2 & \rightarrow & SO_2 \\ (1\ \text{lb}) & & (1\ \text{lb}) & & (2\ \text{lb}) \end{array} \qquad 4{,}500\ \text{Btu/lb dry solids} \tag{9}$$

In Eq. (7), the weight ratio of oxygen to carbon is $32 \div 12 = 2.667$; in Eq. (8), the weight ratio of oxygen to hydrogen is $32 \div 4 = 8$. Therefore, 1 lb of carbon will burn completely with 2.667 lb of oxygen to form 3.667 lb of carbon dioxide; and, 1 lb of hydrogen requires 8 lb of oxygen to burn completely, forming 9 lb of water.

Multiple-hearth furnace The multiple-hearth furnace is a combustion device. Unlike furnaces designed for the combustion of waste material (such as refuse), commonly referred to as incinerators, the multiple-hearth furnace employs no open burning grates and is, therefore, subject to different fundamentals of combustion than those developed for fuel on open grates.

The multiple-hearth furnace is a cylindrical, refractory-lined, steel shell containing a series of horizontal refractory hearths located one above the other. A typical furnace is depicted in Fig. 30. The hearths have alternate peripheral and central discharge locations. Sludge is moved across each hearth by rabble arms as it drops

TABLE 14 Sludge Heat Values

Description	Combustibles, percent	Ash, percent	Sludge heat value, Btu/lb
Grease and scum	88.5	11.5	16,750
Raw sewage solids	74.0	26.0	10,285
Fine screenings	86.4	13.6	7,820
Primary sewage sludge	. . .	. . .	8,990
Activated sewage sludge	. . .	. . .	6,540
Digested primary sludge	59.6	40.4	5,290
Grit	33.2	69.8	4,000

from one level to the next. These hearths create a multichamber effect and induce a countercurrent flow of wet sludge cake and hot combustion gas. Mechanical stoking is provided by a motor-driven, revolving, insulated central shaft to which are attached rabble teeth, similar to the ploughs of a circular clarifier, which move the material across the hearth to either the peripheral or the central openings. The central shaft and arms are cooled by air supplied from a blower which discharges into a housing at the bottom of the central shaft.

Return of hot air from the cooling air system to the combustion zone of the furnace obviates the necessity of expensive and troublesome preheating of combustion air. Combustion air is returned to the lowest hearth in the combustion zone after it has been raised from ambient temperature to approximately 400°F.

Combustion in the multiple-hearth furnace occurs in three distinct operating zones. The first zone, the drying zone, consists of the upper hearths, where a major portion

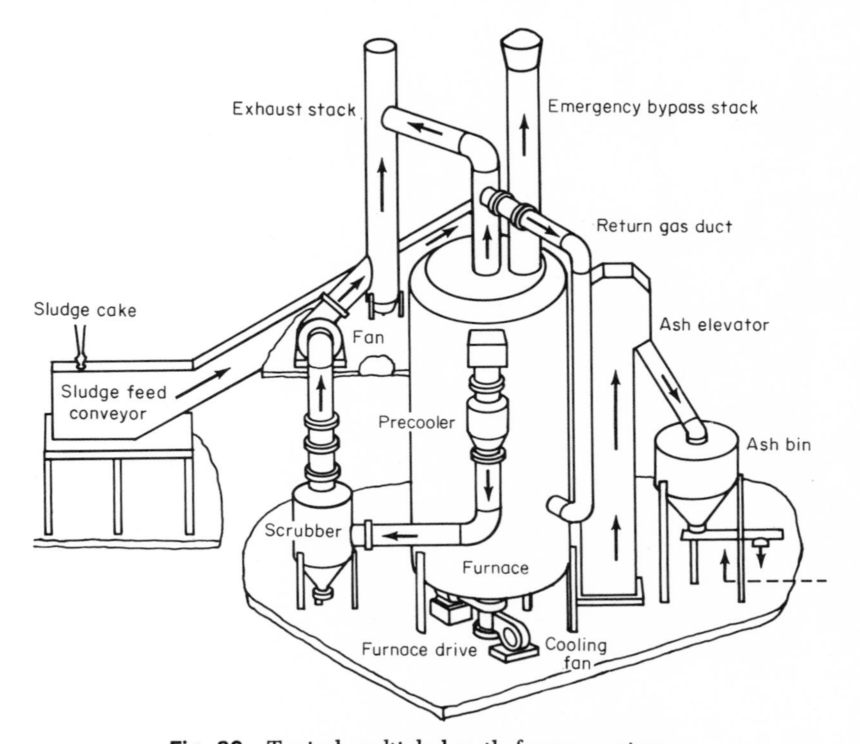

Fig. 30 Typical multiple-hearth furnace system.

of the free moisture in the sludge is evaporated. The second zone, the burning zone, is where the material to be destroyed is burned at temperatures generally in the range between 1400 and 1700°F. The third zone, the cooling zone, serves to cool the ash prior to discharge into the ash-quenching facilities. The sequence of these zones always remains the same; the instantaneous position varies as the characteristics of the sludge feed changes. If the sludge is sufficiently high in volatile content, auxiliary fuel will not be required. If fuel were required, any liquid type available can be used, for instance, natural gas, fuel oil, or even digester gas. Pilot lights can be automatically ignited, electrically or manually.

The hot gases from the combustion zone of the furnace give up heat to the incoming sludge, evaporating sludge moisture.

As the sludge is rabbled across the hearths, it is constantly agitated by the rabble teeth and reduced in particle size. This rabbling assures maximum surface exposure to the passing hot furnace gases, thus inducing rapid drying and burning. Off-gases leaving the furnace range in temperatures from 500 to 1200°F. Exit-gas temperature is dependent on the moisture and organic content of the incoming sludge. In general, the wetter the feed, the lower the gas outlet temperature and the cleaner the exhaust gas.

Generally, off-gas temperatures of 700 to 800°F indicate a wet sludge feed, low in volatile or calorific value requiring auxiliary fuel. Gas outlet temperatures of 800 to 1200°F indicate a sludge with high calorific values and low moisture content. In this case, additional air is brought into the furnace to stabilize the burning operation. Inasmuch as these operations are very efficient, particularly for wet sludges, the need for expensive external air preheaters is eliminated.

REFERENCES

1. Boyd, J. L., and G. L. Shell: Dissolved Air Flotation Application to Industrial Wastewater Treatment, Purdue Industrial Waste Conference, May, 1972.
2. O'Melia, C. R.: A Review of the Coagulation Process, *Public Works,* vol. 100, no. 87, 1969.
3. McCarty, P. L.: Thermodynamics of Biological Syenthesis and Growth, 2nd Int. Conf. on Water Pollution Research, Tokyo, Japan, August, 1964.
4. Eckenfelder, W. W., and D. J. O'Conner: "Biological Waste Treatment," Pergamon Press, New York, 1961.
5. Logan, R. P., and W. E. Budd: "Biological Treatment of Sewage and Industrial Wastes," Vol. I, Reinhold, New York, 1956.
6. Cassady, T., and G. L. Shell: "Selecting Mechanical Aerators," *Industrial Water Engineering,* July/August, 1973.
7. Culp, G. L.: Chemical Treatment of Raw Sewage, Part 1 and 2, *Water and Waste Engineering,* p. 61, July, 1967 and p. 55 October, 1967.
8. Bishop, D. F., T. P. O'Farrell, and J. B. Stamberg: Physical-Chemical Treatment of Municipal Wastewater, *Journal WPCF,* vol. 44, no. 3, p. 361, March, 1972.
9. Weber, W. J., Jr., C. B. Hopkins, and R. Bloom Jr.: Physico-chemical Treatment of Wastewater, *J. Water Pollution Control Federation,* vol. 42, no. 1, p. 83, January, 1970.
10. Davies, D. S., and R. A. Kaplan: Removal of Refractory Organics from Wastewater with Powdered Activated Carbon, *J. Water Pollution Control Federation,* vol. 35, no. 3, p. 442, 1966.
11. Ockershausen, R. W.: Phosphorus Removal-Chemical Requirements and Sludge Production, *Wastewater News,* Industrial Chemicals Division, Allied Chemical, Morristown, New Jersey.
12. Burns, D. E., and G. L. Shell: "Physical-Chemical Treatment of A Municipal Wastewater Using Powdered Activated Carbon," WPCF Conference, San Francisco, October, 1971.
13. Burd, R. S.: *A Study of Sludge Handling and Disposal,* Federal Water Pollution Control Administration, pub. no. WP-20-4, May, 1968.
14. McCarty, P. L.: "Anaerobic Waste Treatment Fundamentals," in four parts, *Public Works,* p. 107, September, 1964; p. 123, October, 1964; p. 91, November, 1964; p. 95, December, 1964.

Chapter 4

Industrial Wastewater Treatment Equipment

J. D. WALKER
Chairman and Director of Research and Development,
Peabody Welles, Inc., Roscoe, Illinois

INTRODUCTION

The purpose of this chapter is to review major wastewater equipment design and operation and suggest features and parameters for major equipment selection. Some operation experience is given along with a limited discussion of ancillary equipment. Wastewater plant operation tending toward zero discharge is rapidly becoming more involved and expensive so that much that is included here has to do with simplifying the manpower cost and problems of operation.

The major equipment discussed herein is used, with minor variations, for treating wastewater by most industries and municipalities. Mechanically desludged circular sedimentation equipment, for example, has long been used in the waste treatment works of the petroleum, metals, pulp and paper, and food processing industries and others, although there are some distinctive operating problems and solutions for each separate industry.

This chapter does not discuss process systems as such, although equipment application may involve process reasons.

Sludge treatment equipment is discussed only in some modes here. Sludge as a formidable by-product of wastewater treatment has to be disposed of eventually. Fortunate is the industrial operation which can thicken this sludge and haul or pump it to unending lagoons, wasteland, or even sanitary landfill. For them, waste sludge is no real problem because, importantly, there generally is no pathogenic or public health problem as there is with sanitary waste. For those who cannot dispose by land or by lagoon, the sludge problem can be as complicated as the liquid waste treatment was in the first place.

Some types of sludge can be conditioned with chemicals to assist in breaking the bound water bonds so they can be dewatered to an autogenous cake that is burnable or more easily hauled to landfill.

Sludges of high organic content, without accumulations of biopoisons, can be either digested anaerobically in closed, heated, and gas-mixed reactors (or, being already warm, in slowly stirred anaerobic ponds) or digested aerobically in mixed open aeration reactors. Both modes reduce the volatile organic content and render the sludges more dewaterable, with a relatively nonbiodegradable end product. Of course, this end product requires dewatering and disposal on the land.

Incineration, either multiple hearth or fluid bed, is employed to burn all types of heat destructible sludges that will not destroy the firebrick in the incinerators. As a prelude to incineration, the sludges are thickened and prepared as autogenous as practicable by vacuum filtration, centrifugation, or filter pressing.

PRETREATMENT

Pretreatment of wastewaters is often as important as subsequent wastewater and sludge treatment. The mill waste discharges, types, and concentrations are often so varied that meaningful blending is an absolute necessity as a prelude to design and operation of any waste treatment system. Constant rate of waste flow to the treatment works is also important for some types of systems. Little details like degritting and coarse screening or scalping also determine whether or not the treatment and sludge disposal systems can keep operating without trouble or even at all.

Pretreatment also involves a critical in-house survey to eliminate or abate some "clean" flow contributions and to abate some organic spills or even to alter the manufacturing process to partially eliminate wastewater pollution and/or easily disposable dilution water. In-house abatement problems will not be dealt with here even though they are frequently the most important.

Trash Screening (Scalping)

Often screening of the raw waste is omitted, more as an oversight than as a calculated risk. Without screens, both large and small pieces of trash, if present, can enter the treatment works and cause operating headaches. A good example of the need for adequate screening is in the treatment of wastes from pulp mills.

This discussion deals only with removing large particles or objects that cause mechanical troubles with scrapers, valves, transfer pumps, etc., and does not deal with microslot or micromesh screening. Those types of screening, in unusual cases, may be able to serve the suspended solids removal function of sedimentation tanks. There are a great many types of self-cleaning commercial trash screens; however, for most applications, selection can be narrowed to mechanically raked, coarse, vertical bar screens having about ¾-in. clear openings and traveling screens with continuous backwash means and mesh openings of about ⅜ to ½ in. Longitudinal vibrating screens and rotary medium-mesh screens may be applied to some specific problems.

In many heavy industries and in those using long, open channels to conduct flow to the wastewater works, the occurrence of suspended or bed-rolled debris may not warrant a mechanically cleaned screen station. In such cases, it may be sufficient to protect the influent with a series of heavy-mesh screen units disposed in vertical slides on the screen chamber wall.

Grits Separation

Grits included in an industrial waste stream can cause considerable trouble in plant operation, especially in clarifiers, mixing and flocculation basins, and aeration reactors. The removal of these grits is relatively easy and not costly, and more designers and operators should take advantage of a grit separation device. Borne or bed-rolled by streaming waste flow through influent conduits or channels, grits can shoal or classify into unbelievably hard masses capable of stopping the most rugged collector mechanism or hard-packing sludge blowdown lines and valves. Many a new primary clarification plant, without degritting, has been caught completely by surprise at start-up and has been forced to resort to "digging parties" to get into operation again, and then eventually resorting to degritting.

If in doubt, grit separation basins are relatively inexpensive and should at least be designed into the system so that the tank and hardware can be added later if required.

Fine or scalping screens are not, in general, a substitute for a gravity-type grit separator.

One effective way to separate grits from the influent stream is with a grit hydroseparator. This is a short-detention, relatively high-surface-rate (about 8 to 12 gpm/sq ft at maximum flow), selective sedimentation vessel using a shallow (about 4 ft) water depth. The flow is introduced across the square basin using adjustable flow straightening vanes on the input side and an overflow weir on the opposite side. The shallow, roiled cross flow within the hydroseparator effects a separation of fines down to about 0.2 mm (sand equivalent). A bridge-supported, rotating scraper mechanism plows the settled grits toward the outside of the circular scraper area, and thence down a peripheral side opening into an inclined side ramp. An endless-chain scraper-agitator, or hardened screw conveyor, drags the grit up the inclined drainage ramp and into a receiver.

Aerated grit separation vessels are sometimes used in a bioplant where 7-psig air is available, and the degritter protects the aeration tanks from acting as degritters. These units are designed with a short detention period (5 to 8 min at maximum flow) and are 10 to 15 ft liquid depth. An air diffusion means sets up an overall toroidal stirring effect which detrains grit and bed-rolls it to a hopper. From here, it is pumped (often by a simple air-lift pump) to an inclined dewatering ramp similar to that described for the grit hydroseparator. The free-surface design parameter for aerated separation units is about the same as for hydroseparators.

A common "package" variation of the grit hydroseparator is a shallow, rectangular, steel vessel, designed with a 3- to 8-min (at maximum flow) detention period. The settled grit is conveyed by chain-propelled steel flights spaced on 5-ft centers, and dragged along the length of the flat bottom and up the ramp. In this case, all underwater shaft bearings need to be very specially labyrinth grease-sealed against grit wear (mechanical seals cut out too rapidly). Malleable drag chains will require easy, occasional replacement (see Fig. 1).

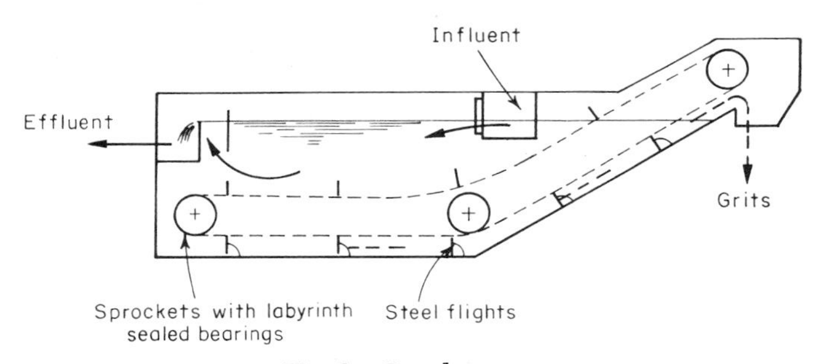

Fig. 1 Grit drag out.

A recent case history of the successful application of such equipment has to do with a large foundry dust waste treatment operation. Originally, the wastewater plant was equipped with a two-tray inclined vibrating screen which was expected to scalp out grits. The vibrating screen did not work and the grits classified on the floor of the flocculator-clarifier and stopped the scraper. The waste treatment plant could not be used until a "package" grit separator was installed, a delay of nearly 4 months—the "want of a nail" had stopped the entire sophisticated treatment works!

Equalization and Blending Basins

Most industrial wastes are variable in nature both from the characteristics of the originating streams and from process effect, perhaps resulting in hourly or diurnal variations. Variations in content, pH, strength and biopoisons of necessity should be at least blended on a long period basis, and preferably both blended and equalized to a nearly constant flow to the treatment works.

Large storage ponds cannot be blended well either by use of flow-through hydraulic kinetic energy or by multiple-feed discharge points and should be blended by surface aerator mixing. Mixing can be accomplished by use of floating surface aerators, either medium-speed direct drive or slow speed; or if aeration is of no value, by floating slow-speed plate turbine mixing devices.

Direct-drive, floating mechanical aerators are a good selection where both stirring and oxygenation are required. For example, one 75-bhp direct-drive surface aerator unit can serve a pond region about 100 ft square by 12 ft water depth (WD), adequately mixing the entire region and imparting about 250 lb of dissolved oxygen per hour into the liquid (assuming $\alpha = 1.0$) (see Fig. 2). The direct-drive, low-trajectory (minimum of ambient aerosol) surface mechanical aerator has been developed by old-line companies to the point where its dependability, even in large horsepower sizes, is excellent.

Where ice cap on the pond is a serious problem, the stirring can be effected, at a sacrifice of power, by closely spaced parallel strings of small subsurface air-lift eductor tubes.

Influent flow rate equalizing is accomplished by pumping from an equalizing pond to the waste treatment works at a constant rate, allowing the water level in the equalizing pond to rise and fall. Hence, the necessity in this case for mechanical mixing devices that function under substantial changes in water level in the blending and equalizing pond. In order to reduce the deposits that eventually will fill a pond, any grits and screening should be removed from the waste flow before discharge to the pond.

Fig. 2 Floating direct-drive aerators. (*Peabody Welles.*)

WASTEWATER SEDIMENTATION

The clarification basin is still the most reliable and cheapest way to separate settleable solids from the flow that bears them—be they plain solids, chemically coagulated or activated sludge solids. The clarifier basin proper may range from a sophisticated concrete basin as in municipal design, or a steel-walled basin or even a hole fashioned in the ground as is sometimes seen in industrial work. A modern clarifier always has several essential mechanical parts. These parts are an influent diffusing feed well and an effluent peripheral weir system along with a mechanical, collector-desludging device and controlled sludge pumping means.

There are three general types of mechanically cleaned sedimentation basins:

1. The plain sedimentation basin, which practices plain gravimetric sedimentation without chemical precipitation technique
2. The chemical sedimentation basin which does employ chemicals to coagulate and remove as much of the suspended matter and colloids as possible
3. The activated sludge (secondary) sedimentation basin which acts not only to produce a clarified effluent but also as phase separation for the process

All of this discussion pertains to circular clarification basins since they are the types most commonly used by industry.

Plain Primary Sedimentation

Simply stated, plain sedimentation (clarification) as applied to waste treatment involves a protracted period of quiescence in a basin where most of the settleable solids fall out of suspension by gravity; there being no chemical coagulant added. The solids fallout is mechanically collected on the bottom and pumped from the bottom as a sludge (or "mud") underflow, and the throughput overflows as a clarified effluent.

The relatively flat, conical bottom is equipped with a rotating mechanical scraper system, plowing sludge to a center hopper. Suction collector types, with rare exceptions, are never used to remove primary-type sludges. An influent feed well located in the center *tends* to distribute the influent radially, and a simple peripheral weir overflow system carries the effluent. Floating scum is trapped inside a peripheral scum baffle and squeegeed into a scum discharge box.

This workhorse for plain sedimentation is often referred to as a *thickener* because of the propensity of industrial operators to store industrial waste primary sludge in a deep blanket and to blowdown the thickest sludge possible as underflow. As

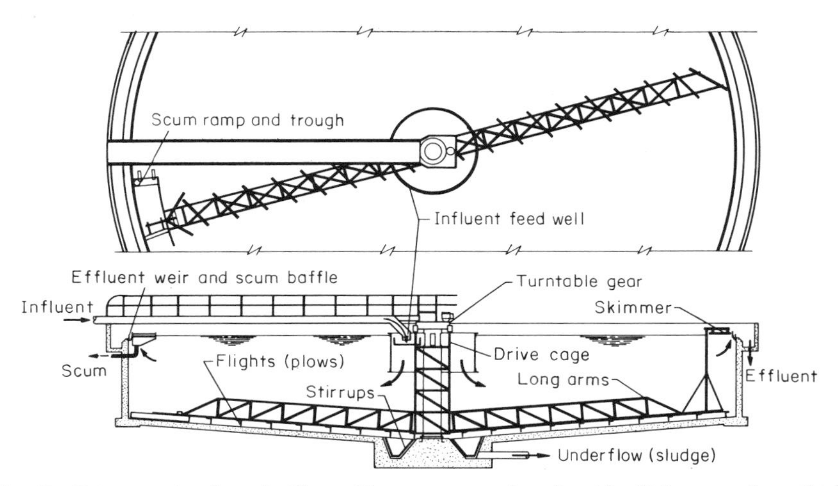

Fig. 3 Primary circular clarifier. Two arms equipped with flights to plow thick sludge to the center hopper, a peripheral effluent weir and scum baffle, and a mechanical skimmer. Influent feed is generally overhead along the bridge but may, with flocculant sludge, be underneath through the center pier.

regards thickening, the underflow sludges from clarifiers frequently are pumped into a *rethickener,* a mechanical gravity thickener where the partially thickened sludges from clarifiers undergo additional compaction.

Equipment

Mechanical Collector Unit. The unit consists of a center motor-driven turntable drive either bridge supported, i.e., supported by a bridge spanning the top of the tank, or pier supported by a vertical steel center pier. The turntable gear rotates a vertical cage or torque tube, which in turn rotates the truss arms (preferably two long and two short). The truss arms carry multiple flights (plows) on the bottom chord which are set at a 30° angle of attack, and literally "plow" heavy fractions of sludge and grits along the bottom slope toward the center blowdown hopper (Fig. 3).

Turntable Gear Housing. The turntable gear housing, rigidly fastened to the vertical steel center pier, rotates the drive cage, and receives the end reaction of the access bridge. All of the hanging influent structures, such as the feed well, etc., are suspended from this gear housing (Fig. 4). The center pier transmits the design maximum operating torque (Table 1) to the concrete foundation through rugged, hooked anchor bolts. The foundation under the center pier has to be strong enough to transmit the turntable gear torque and very stable so that the center of rotation of the collector will remain truly vertical.

The ring gear part of the turntable drive should always be furnished split. The split construction allows the maintenance crew to pull the gear apart without removing the bridge, etc., affording good access to the replaceable raceways and balls.

Overload warning devices. These commonly are used to warn the operator of collector overload from excessive buildup in thick sludge blanket. Electrical contacts cut off the drive (and sound an alarm) in the case of an overload. Extra contacts are sometimes used to start (and stop) underflow sludge pumps when collector load builds up.

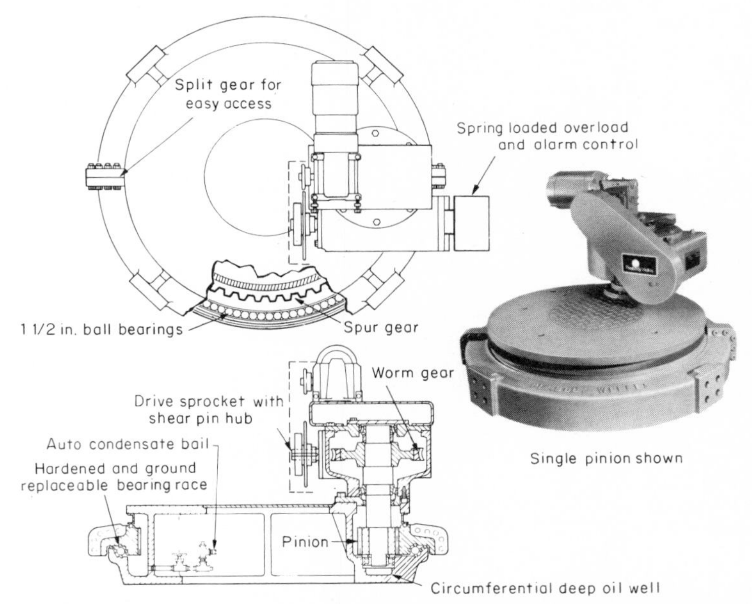

Fig. 4 Spur gear turntable drive. The large-diameter ballrace turntable supports and turns the collector arm system. The split gear enables replacement without dismantling the steelwork. A spring-loaded alarm and cutout control indexes off the thrust on the primary worm shaft.

Overload devices which are ampere-rated are not satisfactory because of the low percentage of operating load current to full load current of the drive motor. Accurate spring-type early warning and overload cutout devices, taking a signal from the operating thrust of the intermediate gear worm shaft, are quite reliable and are typically used.

Truss Arms. The best collector design for plowing heavy sludges, especially in large diameters, is to use two full-length arms, each extending radially from opposite sides of the drive cage, and also an auxiliary pair of short arms extending 90° to the long arms. These short arms extend to about one-third to one-half of the radius and are additionally used where plowed sludges are prone to be quite viscous or carry grits or large particles that will detrain or classify as they are slowly plowed into the center region (see Fig. 5).

The collector moves at a *very slow* rotational speed, especially near the center. With a tip speed of around 10 to 15 ft/min, medium to large-diameter collectors are afflicted with minuscule flight speeds around the center hopper region. The additional short arms make practicable the use of *deep spiral flights* which are required

TABLE 1 Clarifier Drive-Torque Calculation

Type of sludge settled	Load factor, lb/ft arm	Tangential tip speed, ft/min	Floor slope, in./ft radius
Hydroseparators:			
Foundry class grit	50	15–20	
Rolling mill scale	70	10–15	
Plain sedimentation	13	12–12	1–1¼
Lime coagulation:			
Primary solids sedimentation	30	10–15	1–1½
Tertiary sedimentation	15	10–12	1½–2
Secondary biodegradable sludge (suction)	8	12–18	Flat
Alum/iron coagulation:			
Low turbidity sedimentation	6	10–12	¾
Tertiary	7	6–8	1
Lime softening (cold)	15	10–12	1½
Flue dust "thickeners"	80	8–10	2½–3
BOF dust "thickeners"	70	8–10	2½–3
Rolling mill wastes	70	7–8	3
Rolling mill degritted + coagulants	35	7–8	2–2½
Pulp mill "thickeners"	40	10–12	2½
Paper mill white water	25	10–12	2
Rethickening:			
Lime sludge	40	10	2½–3
Primary sedimentation sludge	60	10–12	2½–3
BF flue or BOF	100	7–8	3–3½

The design continuous operating torque T required by the turntable drive, see load factor LF for:

$$T\text{, ft-lb} = 0.25(\text{diameter})^2 LF$$

When calculating the continuous operating torque requirements for clarifiers with more than two scraper arms, treat as two systems.

Example: 100-ft-diameter clarifier with two full-length arms with nonstaggered blades and two short arms extending for one-third of the radius.

$$T\text{, ft-lb} = 0.25(100)^2 LF + 0.25\left(\frac{100}{3}\right)^2 LF$$

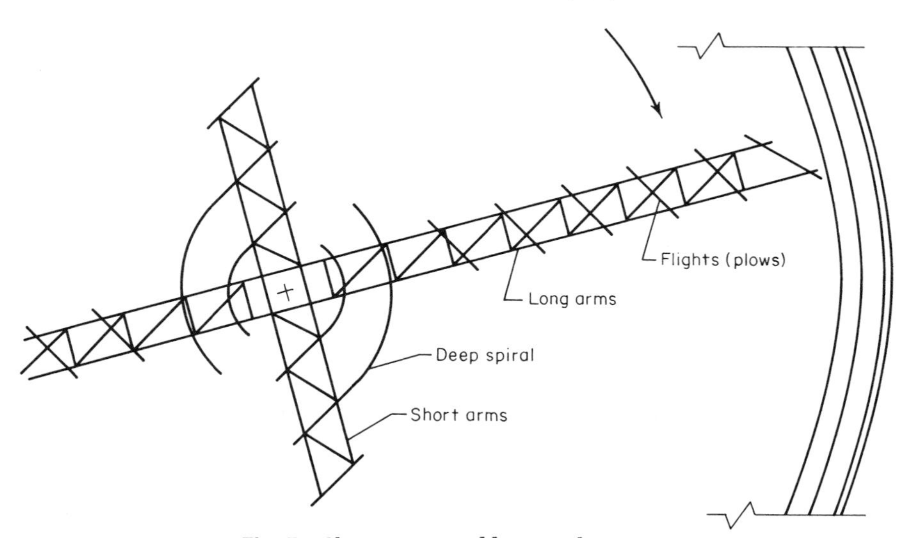

Fig. 5 Short arms in addition to long arms.

to aid in center-region plowing action to progressively move the converging, dense sludge into the underflow hopper (see Fig. 6). Ordinary shallow, straight plows are nearly useless in the center region, especially on large-diameter units.

If a two-arm collector (only) is employed, and if the density of sludge being pumped from an offset center hopper is observed, it will often be seen that each time an arm passes over the hopper, the sludge, as pumped, becomes remarkably thicker. As the arm passes away, the sludge will thin. Continued pumping during this thin phase of the cycle can result in *postholing*—breaking through the blanket. This thickness undulating effect can be lessened by the use of short arms in addition to long arms and especially by using deep spiral flights. A center annular spaded hopper can also help in a more continuous, dense sludge underflow. These four spades have to be extremely rugged.

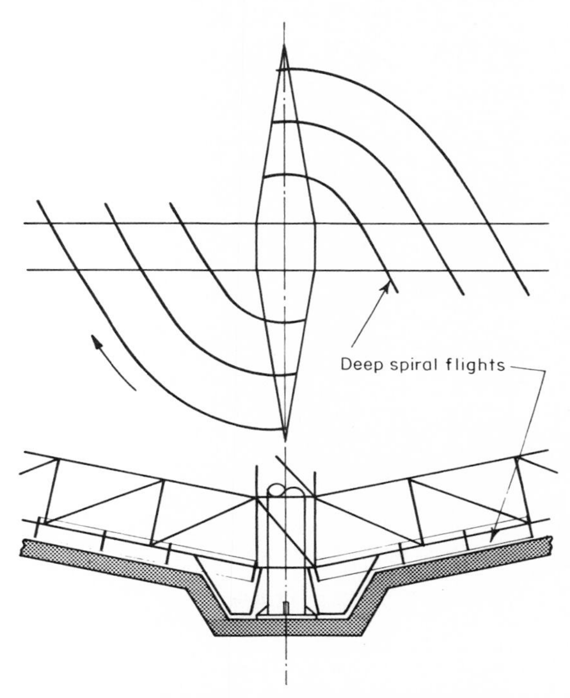

Fig. 6 Deep spiral flights. Effective to keep sludge progressively moving in the center region.

The flights (straight plows) are installed along the bottom of the trusses on about a 30° attack angle and should *always* be installed with an overlap so that the scraping effect on all arms will yield full coverage of the floor. Some faulty designs have been tried staggering the plows between the two arms resulting in poor sludge movement toward the hopper.

Deep Spiral Flights. When used in the center region, deep spiral flights run 18 to 24 in. deep and connect between the inner parts of the long and short arms. These special plows are effective for moving heavy compacted sludge loads in the center area where ordinary plows are nearly useless because of the very slow rotary motion (Fig. 6). Deep spiral flights will, generally, eliminate the necessity for mechanical arm raising.

At a plant in central Illinois which principally handles soybean mill waste (with domestic sewage), the two plow arms in the 110-ft-diameter primary clarifiers were specified with *staggered* plows. The putrescible sludge did not get scraped into the center hopper fast enough and considerable amounts of troublesome, gassy sludge blanket floated to the surface and over the effluent weir. The sludge removal operation was improved by adding the intermediate flights. Later, the operation was completely improved by adding a pair of short arms and deep spiral flights in the center area.

A few years ago, both a board mill and a pulp mill experienced considerable benefit from adding deep spiral flights. The pulp mill used a 190-ft-diameter primary clarifier having two long and two short arms with a full complement of plows (not staggered). Pumping to remove the accumulated sludge failed because the sludge did not get pushed into the hopper, and piled deep in the clarifier. Then serious overloads on the presumably adequate gear drive caused its failure on several occasions. After study, a solution was effected by the addition of auxiliary short arms and 18-in. deep spiral flights. The sludge-pumping troubles and the collector overload trouble vanished! Dependable ability to effectively pump the sludge underflow came only with the addition of deep spiral flights.

The board mill with a 135-ft-diameter clarifier was much the same story. The sludge could not be properly pumped from the tank and piled up to great depths on the floor causing drive overloads that literally ruptured the seemingly massive double-pinion-gear turntable drive. Then 18-in. deep spiral flights were added between the long and the short pairs of arms. Immediately it became possible to pump the inventory of sludge as it occurred; it was pumped at between 1 and 10 percent. At the same time, the torque load on the turntable drive was diminished from the serious overload condition to about one-quarter of the design running torque. No more trouble!

Bottom Thrust Bearings. These bearings are advisable on all pier drive rethickeners and on collector assemblies larger than 100-ft diameter which handle thick sludges. Sludge viscosity increases in the collector center region and the drive cage may try to escape laterally. Such lateral movement brings the plows to bear on the floor or "cocks" the turntable, with a resulting overload. The bearing surface should be cast-iron shoes attached to the cage and a wide, adjustable steel ring ruggedly attached to the bottom of the center pier.

Skimming. A squeegee, supported from the rotating collector arm, pushes floating scum (trapped inside a peripheral baffle) up a ramp and into a radially disposed scum trough. This squeegee means should move in and out laterally several inches to conform to any inexact roundness of the scum baffle; a spring means holds the squeegee in contact with the circular baffle. On large clarifiers, to avoid capriciousness of wind direction, two scum ramps and troughs are used, set diametrically opposite to each other.

In some special situations involving great amounts of floating oil or scum removal, the scum ramps should project 8 ft rather than 4 ft. This will provide a more efficient system.

In all cases, it is best to support the short 45° skimmer boom and squeegees directly from the collector arm rather than to depend on letting the outboard end of the skimmer means ride (on wheels) on the circular scum baffle. A radial skimming boom, running contiguously between the feed well and squeegee, is discouraged because of its extremely slow rotation.

Design details and problems

Classification. Classification of heavy, gritlike solids into a packed central mass on the bottom is the major cause of arm stoppage and digging parties. When the thick plowed sludges converge on the center region, there is a slowing in progressive radial movement of the heavier particles. If the most plowable fractions are not progressively moved and pumped out through the hopper, they compact into a deep ring formation. A small part of these packed larger particles are pushed through the drawdown profile into the hopper outlet, but the major part builds into a deep, toruslike mass of classified, densely packed particles. The scraper arms slowly rotate this mass as long as they can, but eventually the friction against the bottom is too great and arm rotation stops from overload. When the tank is drained and digging commences, this classified torus is found to be rigid enough to walk on, and the outlying, dammed up sludge is very fluid.

On down days or when the thick underflow sludge cannot be transported to the next step in disposal, the sludge pumps are best kept operating, and the sludge is discharged back into the clarifier feed well. This keeps the sludge progressively moving along the clarifier bottom and out, and avoids classification that would occur were the collector arms kept turning and no underflow sludge pumped.

Bottom and Hopper Considerations. Some plants are blessed with or have subsequently added grit separators ahead of their clarifiers to avoid most of the classification trouble at the source. However, grit separation is never 100 percent, and even with it, some attention should be given to center-area bottom slope, number of arms, and center-area scraper blade design in order to avoid trouble.

A *two-slope bottom* should be applied where hard-to-move sludges are involved. The two-slope bottom not only increases (doubles) the important bottom slope in the center half of the bottom diameter (25 percent of the area), but also acts to increase the thick sludge storage pool and provides thick sludge freeboard above the hopper discharge to avoid postholing. This center region having the increased slope is also where the deep spiral flights can be effective for moving thick sludge into the hopper as fast as it is sucked out by the sludge pumps. Such a bottom design provides better sludge storage than employing too deep or too large a center hopper depression (Fig. 7).

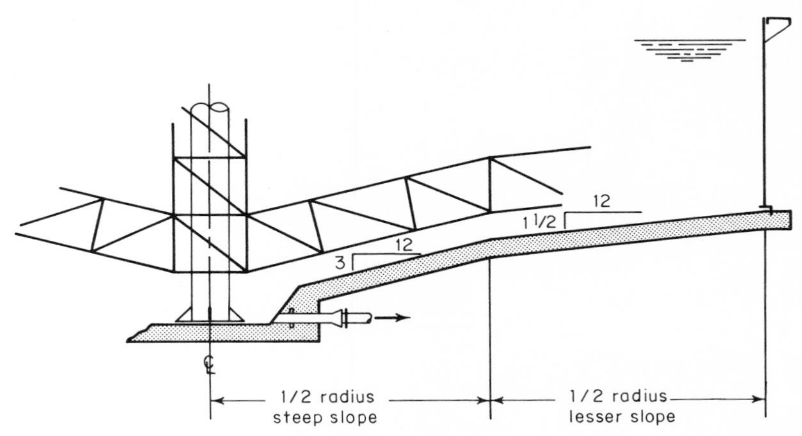

Fig. 7 Double-sloped bottom. The inner quarter of the floor area is where the sludge becomes the most viscous. The speed of arm rotation is almost nil.

The *center hopper* design is important to avoid operating problems. With pier drives, the hopper may be offset near the center or may surround the center pier circumferentially. When the scraper means is bridge-supported, the hopper is centerline located with very heavy stirrups (four at 90°) attached to the rotating arms and protruding into the small center hopper to spade it clear of adhesions and also to act as a rough steady bearing, particularly in the case of mechanical thickeners.

Offset hoppers cannot be spaded and usually should not be used. Offset hoppers are best applied when placing the hopper out away from the feed-well skirt and "water fall" effect as when dealing with influents carrying a flocculant high-suspended-solids load.

The *concentric hopper* surrounding the center pier is the most usual (Fig. 8). This hopper should be spaded with very rugged stirrups which will keep it clean of adhesions. The concentric hopper is sizable enough to discharge from two sludge lines. The hopper should be not much greater than 18 to 24 in. deep and not greater than about 4 sq ft cross section to avoid cementacious growth of lingering, rocklike lumps. Ample slurry-pool depth near the center and controlled pumping without postholing are better accomplished with a two-slope bottom than by making the concentric hopper too deep or wide.

Sludge pumps handling abrasive sludges should be rubber lined or made of hard manganese alloy construction. The pump should be designed with a full-diameter impeller and for relatively slow speed to achieve small capacity and should be belt-driven for speed and capacity choice. Controls should allow for repeating, intermittent pump operation over short cycles. This allows time, during the pump off-cycle, for sludge to be pushed into the center region and into the hopper by the very slowly rotating scraper means and can avoid excessive drawdown in the thick sludge pool and consequent breaking through the sludge blanket, i.e., postholing.

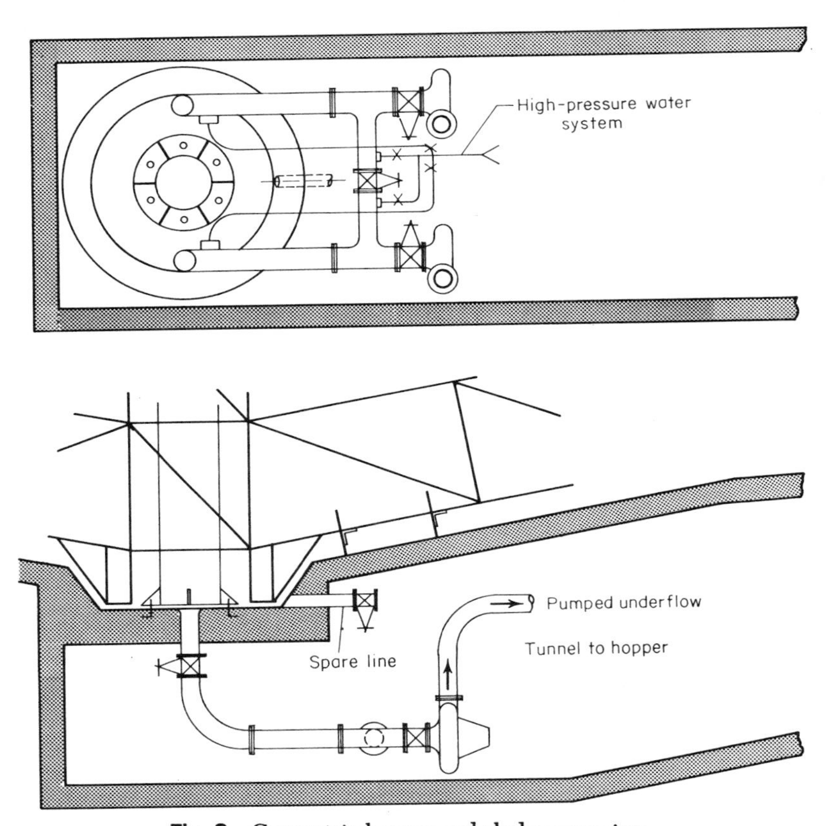

Fig. 8 Concentric hopper and sludge pumping.

Once the thick sludge interfacial profile lowers, by drawdown from overpumping, thick sludge fill-in from the plows is often too slow, and continuous pump operation will then draw mostly water with a little thick sludge added. This extreme drawdown condition abandons the mass of thickened sludge to build up on the bottom in the center region and *classify* causing severe overloads and stoppage of the rake means. Short, intermittent pumping cycles also allow for higher velocities (if necessary) in the suction lines during pumping.

Feed Well. The feed well is important in *large-diameter* clarifiers inasmuch as, properly designed, it starts the (hopefully) uniform, expanding, radial displacement through the clarifiers with a minimum of short circuiting. The relative size and hydraulic design of the feed well can make or break displacement stability through any medium to large circular clarifier. In many cases an outsized clarifier has to be employed to do the work that otherwise could have been done by a well-designed smaller one with an adequate feed well.

An adequate feed well for a large-diameter skirt reaching down to about middepth is shown in Fig. 10.

An inner diffusion chamber receives influent flow and uniformly distributes this flow (by means of about 4-in. head loss) inside of the large-diameter feed-well skirt. If this primary distribution and rotating homogeneity within the large skirt is not effected, the influent flow may well short-circuit inside of the large-diameter skirt as though it were not there, thereby losing the effectiveness of a large-diameter feed well. An acceptable guideline is to use approximately 3 percent of the clarifier surface area for the feed well. Using such a parameter, a guideline for feed-well design would be as shown in Table 2.

Some designers will ponder that perhaps the stress on large, functional feed wells is overaccentuated. This is a moot point and hard to prove except in actual parallel practice. The large homogenized feed-well point is not too important in tanks much less than 60-ft diameter. However, when tanks reach 80 ft and over, the feed well becomes *very* important, especially in those greater than 100-ft diameter. Instability and short-circuiting are silent robbers of sedimentation efficiency. Tanks larger than 100-ft diameter without good feed wells do well to exhibit a flow-through efficiency of even 35 percent!

TABLE 2 Diffusion Control Feed-Well Suggestions

(For plain primary sedimentation basins, clarifying without aid of coagulants)

Tank diameter (plain primary sedimentation), ft	Outer skirt size, ft	Inner diffuser size, ft	Side-water depth, ft
80	15 diameter × 7 side	8 diameter × 5 deep	11
100	18 diameter × 7 side	10 diameter × 6 deep	12
125	24 diameter × 8 side	12 diameter × 6 deep	13
150 (maximum)	26 diameter × 8 side	14 diameter × 6 deep	14

Note: These approximations assume the surface-loading rate in the region of 1,000 gpd/sq ft surface at maximum overflow. These feed-well sizes occupy about 3 percent of the tank surface. The inner, multiple tangential-gate diffuser is a way of achieving stirring and homogeneity within the entire feed-well volume to minimize short-circuiting.

Peripheral Feed. Occasionally, peripheral feed means are used on ordinary-sized clarifiers, the advantage being that the better influent distribution yields better hydraulic stability and that a basin can thereby carry a greater throughput. Peripheral feeds worthy of note consist of an annular feed trough discharging (hopefully uniformly) through nozzles spaced at about 20-ft intervals all around the periphery. These multiple nozzles feed either through horizontal projections or under a contiguous peripheral skirt. The flow is presumed to travel to the center and then displace back to the peripheral weir system. With this feed system, heavy solids are dumped at the periphery instead of near to the center hopper. These units are also very tender to even slight temperature increases—rising peripheral influent mass short-circuiting into the peripheral weir when there is even a small temperature rise.

Effluent Weir. The effluent weir is most often attached to the peripheral wall of the primary sedimentation basin. When concrete walls are used, they are cast to form an outboard, circumferential effluent-collecting trough, which receives effluent spilling over a circular, V-notch weir attached to the tank wall proper (Fig. 9).

When tanks are built with much greater than 150-ft diameter, part of the peripheral effluent region starts to become overloaded because of serious short-circuiting. Using an inboard weir trough, or otherwise increasing the weir length, can do little to correct this type of regional overloading. Even though the actual weir overflow may be about equal all around, it is not necessarily true that radial displacement through an out-sized tank is stable and free of rampant short-circuiting.

Parameters

Surface Loading Rate. This important sizing parameter (see Table 3), based mostly on effluent overflow, results from empirical experience. Criteria gathered from jar tests or small test units, corrected with an empirical factor, brings the art back to field experience. Unfortunately, data gained in the operation of a 205-ft-diameter groundwood pulp primary, say, at 300 gpd/sq ft surface rate does not signify that a smaller diameter and more stable (less short-circuiting) tank, say, 125-ft diameter would not have effected equal clarification at 600 to 800 gpd/sq ft. In fact, operating experience bears out that the smaller clarifier would have performed the best;

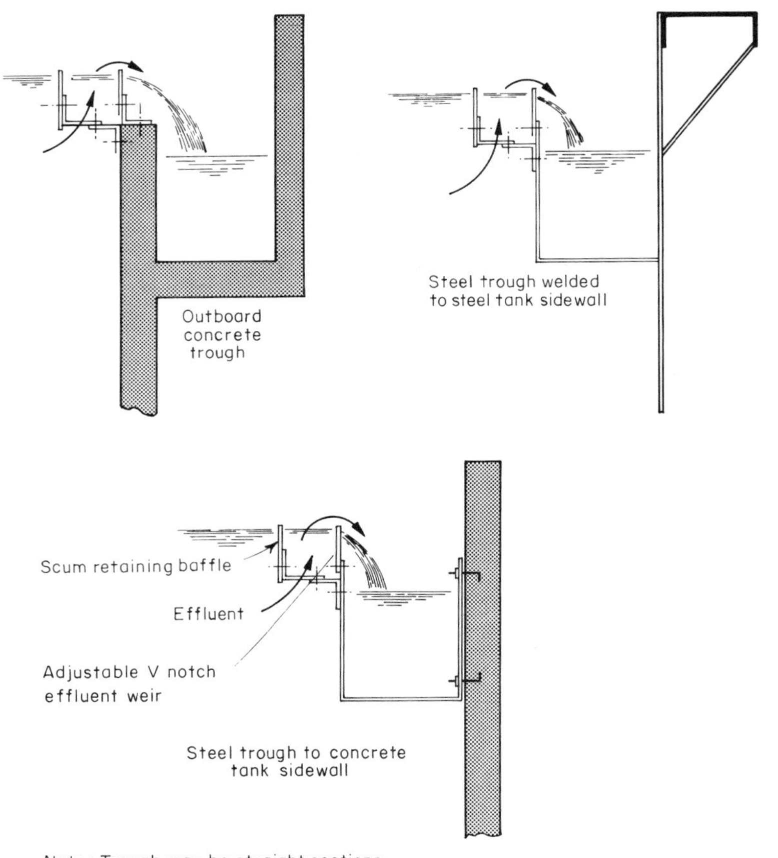

Fig. 9 Plain primary overflow weir arrangements.

still better performance can be achieved with two 80-ft units at 1,000 or more gpd/sq ft surface rate.

Size Limitation. An important factor with plain sedimentation basins is size limitation. When basins approach diameters of 200 ft, they are too large and any radial diffusion is apt to be unbalanced. Wind action often produces waves contributing to hydraulic instability and, in extremes, causing a hydraulic slope on the surface so that perhaps less than half of the peripheral weir system is effective.

A smaller tank, an 80-ft-diameter sedimentation unit, was tested in parallel for comparison with a 200-ft-diameter clarifier treating a blast furnace flue-dust waste

TABLE 3 Suggested Surface-loading Rates
(Circular clarifier overflow rates)

Sedimentation application	Suggested surface rates, gpd/sq ft*
Plain primary sedimentation	1,000
Lime coagulation:	
Primary sedimentation	1,200
Tertiary sedimentation (upflow)	1,500
Secondary biodegradable sludge (suction pipe):	
MLSS 2,000 to 5,000 mg/l:	
SVI 50–100	800–1,000
SVI 200–300	500–700
SVI 350–400	500
MLSS 10,000 mg/l†	400
Alum/iron-coagulation-sedimentation	900
Upflow/solids contact	1,000–1,200‡
Flue dust:	
Primary, plain	1,200
Primary, with coagulation	800
BOF dust:	
Primary, plain	1,000
Primary, with coagulation	800
Rolling mill wastes	1,200
Pulp mill "thickeners"	700–800
White water sedimentation	1,000
River water desilting basins	1,500

* Suggested surface-loading rates are for clarifiers not exceeding 125-ft diameter and for solids-contact basins not exceeding 100-ft diameter. For large clarifiers (exceeding 125-ft diameter) it is suggested that the rates be reduced 15 to 25 percent or more, depending on the size selected.

† All activated sludge clarifiers, especially those handling high MLSS, are further subject to solids-loading limits. See Fig. 13.

‡ Rates are for tertiary. Water treatment rates increase up to 25 percent.

produced by an Eastern steel mill. The smaller tank had, on a corrected basis by handling one-half of the split flow, only one-third of the area and volume of the 200-ft unit, but out-performed it by consistently producing a superior effluent.

Side-water Depth. The side-water depth parameter is not too important when dealing with plain sedimentation; but if chemicals might be added, the side-water depth should be increased in conformity with floc-settling primary clarifiers.

Chemical Primary Sedimentation

Plain clarification does not remove the range of solids (colloids, suspensoids) that can be precipitated by properly applied coagulants. By coagulating and flocculating ahead of clarification, not only is the clarifier effluent rendered relatively clear, but additional COD is removed. Also, some types of wastewaters (such as pulp mill wastes) clarify so well on a plain primary basis that it would be unnecessary to consider coagulant addition to this step, except for very special reasons.

With the addition of coagulants, and the important ensuing floc aggregation, the primary clarifier design details take on an added importance in order to take full advantage of the coagulant effect. Some of the sedimentation basin design parameters are changed as follows.

Flocculating feed wells There has to be some form of floc aggregation (flocculation) to get the most meaningful response out of the coagulant. This can be done in a 15- to 30-min slow-mix tank preceding the clarifier. However, with most industrial primary wastes, flocculation is best done either in a large flocculating feed well (see Fig. 10) or in a large, bottomless flocculation container nested inside the clarifier so that any heavy particles can settle through this flocculation chamber into the control of the scraper mechanism.

Flocculation clarifier The other system is a large, slow-mix bottomless chamber in the center of the clarifier and is used on wastes where the dwell time must be 30 to 45 min for effective flocculation.

The bottomless chamber is suspended, much like a feed well, in the center of the clarifier basin and extends down through three-fourths of the water depth. The rotating scrapers operate under this section, as well as in the clarifier annular portion. Sludge is plowed (both ways) to an offset hopper just outside the center chamber.

Slow-speed axial-flow turbines are used to create a *well-distributed* fine-scale turbulence inside this flocculation region, G value* of 25 to 50 sec^{-1} (selectively variable). More than one mixer is used, depending on the volume of the chamber, and they are strategically arranged so that, although they uniformly slow-stir the

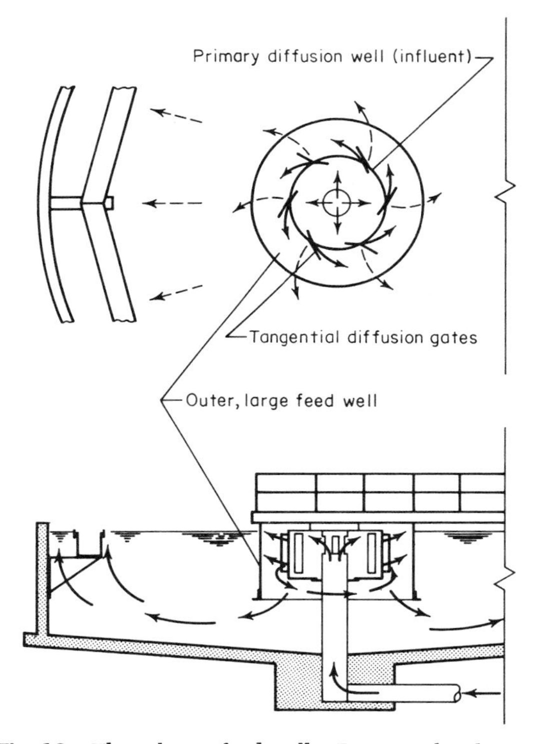

Fig. 10 Flocculating feed well. Bottom inlet shown.

volume inside the skirt, there is no induced instability in the annular clarification compartment.

The detention period for any of the internal flocculation systems is properly calculated as the entire center volume included inside the large-diameter skirt from surface to about 2 ft above the center depth.

Inboard Weir Troughs. Inboard weir troughs now become more important because of the increased settleable suspended solids caused by coagulation. Because of the heavier floc load, there may be a density current problem—the larger the tank diameter, the greater the possibility. Density current flows radially along the floor and up the peripheral wall and may carry solids over a peripheral overflow located on the wall.

* G value is a measure of the velocity gradient. The driving force creates uniformly distributed, fine-scale turbulence for flocculation effect.

Clarifier depth. This too now becomes more important, and somewhat deeper tanks should be used than for plain primary clarifiers. Because of some density current and a deeper hindered zone blanket, the side-water depths should be increased about 30 percent over those of plain sedimentation depths to about that employed with secondary flocculent solids sedimentation.

General Multiple-suction-type sludge removers are not recommended here because of the relatively low sludge volume and the possibility of precipitated chemical sludge adhering to the pipes. A well-designed plow system, working on a good slope, can adequately move the precipitated sludge into an annular center hopper for underflow pumping.

There may or may not be a grit problem involved here. If grits or heavy solids are present, auxiliary short arms, deep spiral flights, and even two-slope bottoms may be involved to expedite classifiable sludges especially in large-diameter clarifiers where center region scraper speeds are almost nil.

Flocculent Solids Sedimentation

Circular secondary clarifiers Sedimentation of activated sludge solids involves gravity floc separation and solids recycling of voluminous amounts of vital floc aggregates. The rapid settling, discrete solids present an additional sedimentation problem, namely, density currents contributing to dynamic instability and possibly high solids contributing to the overflow. In these clarifiers, the feed well should be more sophisticated than that required for plain or primary sedimentation both to avoid some of the density current and instability effect and to reduce radial short-circuiting.

In most secondary applications, floating scum will be encountered, so a scum baffle and skimmer system usually will be employed.

A general design distinction should be made between sedimentation of aggregated chemical primary or tertiary floc and activated sludge. The amount of solids to be settled in the case of chemical coagulation may amount to somewhat less than 1,000 mg/l, requiring a relatively small underflow to remove it. The multiple-plow-type scraper, combined with adequate bottom slope, can control the blowdown of chemical sludge through a single center hopper. However, in the case of voluminous biomass sludge (3,000 mg/l, more or less) from an activated sludge system, not only are the large flocculating feed well and the inboard weir trough strongly indicated but also the multiple-suction-pipe sludge underflow collector system. The latter type of secondary design will now be discussed.

Another flocculent sludge type, the *solids-contact upflow basin,* is applied principally to potable water supply and to tertiary polishing. It is a chemical precipitation–floc aggregation system nested inside a hydraulically stable upflow clarifier basin.

Circular activated sludge clarifiers Evidently the best way to separate and pump back large quantities of biomass seed sludge attendant to the activated sludge process is by means of a gravity sedimentation process—a clarifier. In such clarifiers, the sludges are drawn continuously, at less than terminal thickness, to avoid degradation that would occur were the basin to be operated with a deep sludge blanket (long sludge dwell time) to achieve maximum thickness.

Equipment

Multiple-suction-pipe Sludge Collectors. The mechanical collector unit consists of a very slowly rotating turntable gear drive mounted on a central hollow steel pier which resists the drive torque and feed influent into the feed well. The turntable rotates a cage which, in turn, rotates the two full radial sludge collector arms. In very large basins (greater than 150-ft diameter), there should be four radial collector arms because of the very slow speed of rotation. (The turntable gear is shown in Fig. 4.)

In the case of clarifiers greater than about 60-ft diameter, biomass sludge underflow (return) should be effected by a multiple-pipe "suction" device rather than by reliance on "plowing" to a single underflow hopper. The great mass of relatively thin activated sludge solids to be blown down as underflow cannot be pumped from a center hopper without encountering unfortunate blanket drawdown breakthrough. The multiple-suction-pipe collector is tantamount to a slowly rotating system of multiple (upside down), low-entrance velocity hoppers and can effect the return of settled activated sludge (RAS), no matter how great the percentage of flow rate or sludge thickness.

The arms carry several polyvinylchloride (PVC) suction pipes (spaced at, roughly, 6- to 10-ft intervals along the arms) which slurp up all the thick sludge from the immediate floor region. Each pipe conveys sludge from the apex of a V plow. The pipe sizes and spacing are varied to accommodate the relative floor area served and to equalize pipeline head losses. This system balance does not need to be precise since movement of these thin sludges (laterally along the arm from one suction region to an adjacent one) is easily possible (Fig. 11).

The total suction effect is caused by the pipes discharging, as a gang from each arm, into the observation box which has an inside water level a few inches (about 6 to 12 in., viscosity-dependent) lower than the clarifier water level. This combined sludge flow then egresses through a center sludge downcomer pipe running down through the core of the center pier. The level in these observation boxes (below

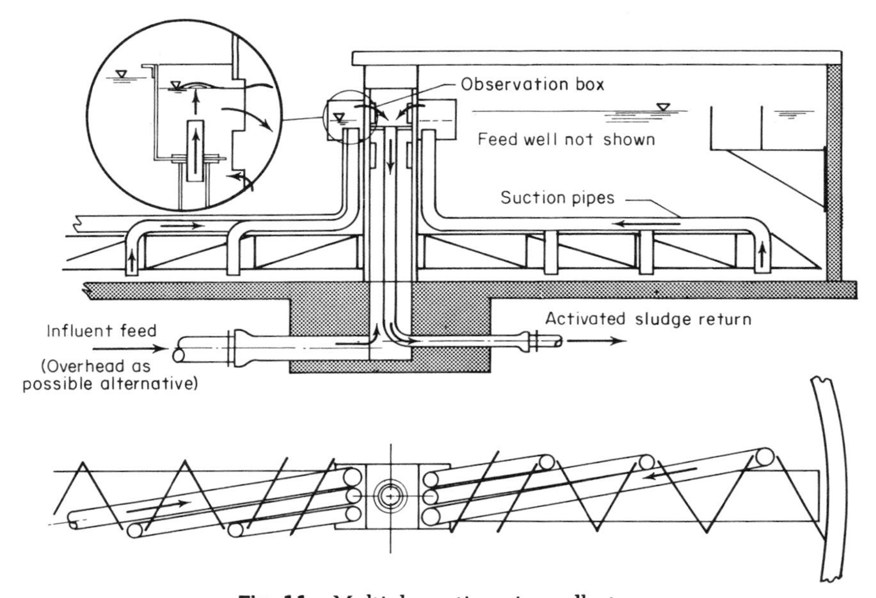

Fig. 11 Multiple-suction-pipe collector.

the clarifier surface) is kept lowered, as required, by subsequent pumping to satisfy the rate of total underflow RAS. It is this rate, the resulting thickness of removed sludge, and the depth of the sludge blanket in the clarifier that the operator monitors.

Because of the radial "washout" effect immediately under the feed well, the plows in this region all plow outwardly; no suction pipe is employed here because it would only withdraw thin influent liquor.

Arms. Two full arms, with each arm removing sludge from the entire bottom at each revolution, are mandatory on all suction clarifiers. Using one radial suction arm (and a counterweight radial plow arm) lengthens the time between sludge pickups to the detriment of the highly putrescible, thickened floc.

Corner Sweeps. Corner sweeps are used on all square tanks and on long rectangular tanks scraped by two or more center-drive collectors. The corner sweeps eliminate large corner fillets and make possible designing two or more circular collectors in series to clean a long rectangular basin.

The corner sweep is a long, retractile flight which is cantilevered from the end of each collector arm. (The sweeps are *always* used in pairs.) A counterweight or spring forces the corner sweep to follow the contour of the wall and "hook out" any sludge on the corner floor area. This area must be flat to accommodate the pantograph motion. The outer end of the corner sweep carries a semipneumatic tire wheel (about 18-in. diameter) which rolls along the wall and forces the boom back during retraction. A skid or skidding wheel of hard material should be discouraged. A steel curb is used at the corner to form the path of the corner sweep; the path has to describe a small radius in the corner. This curb should be a minimum of

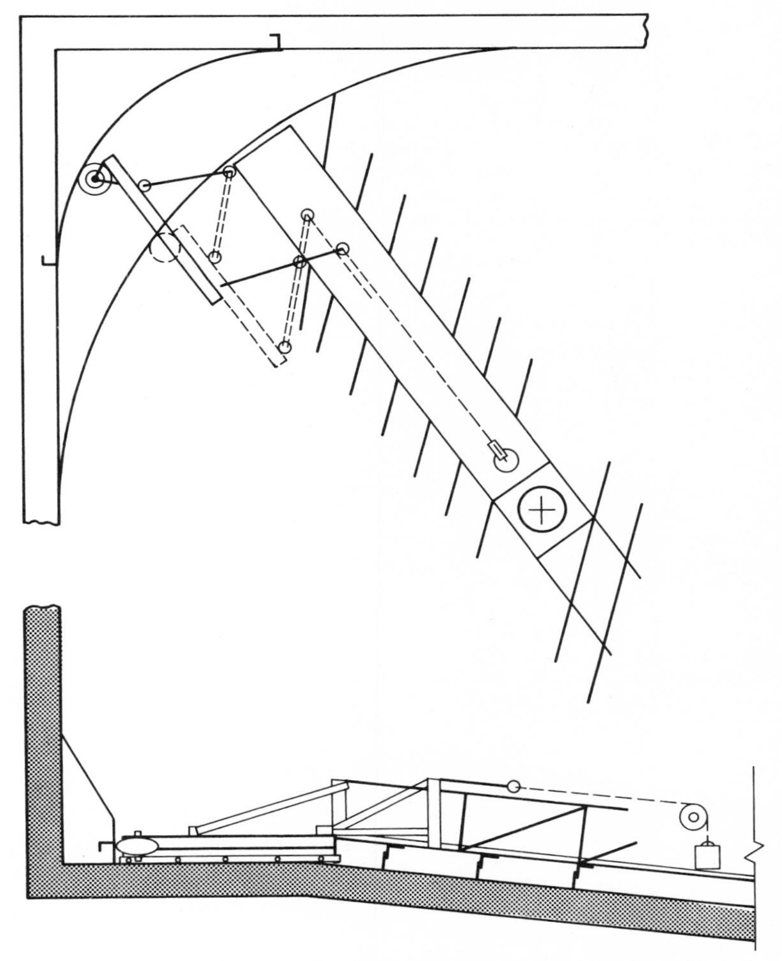

Fig. 12 Corner sweep. Retracted position is shown dashed.

18 in. high, so that the end guide will not climb over it where it starts the retraction phase (Fig. 12).

When corner sweeps are used in conjunction with multiple-suction units, the sweep is always used as a single flight (blade) and should never be complicated by attempting suction in these corner areas.

Influent Line. Feed to the clarifier is ordinarily brought in under the tank bottom and up through the steel center column to be discharged into an influent diffusion well. Whereas industrial primary grit-bearing influents are often brought in over the water surface, activated sludge influents bearing flocculent solids and no grits present no danger of clogging a bottom-entry influent line even at operating velocities of around 4 ft/sec or less.

Sometimes it is desired to bring the influent line through the sidewall above the bottom and under the effluent weir trough. This side entry into a large diffusion well when properly designed is hydraulically satisfactory, but does mechanically interfere with the skimmer support means, and skimming is generally mandatory.

Feed Well. One of the most important elements in any circular clarifier is the feed well. An adequate feed well is particularly important in a floc sedimentation clarifier; the greater the suspension of floc and the greater the clarifier diameter, the more important it becomes.

The traditional small feed well is too often inadequate for four reasons. First, it is very small in diameter—too small to direct orderly, radial departures toward the periphery. A simple increase in diameter would be meaningless because the lack of well-directed influent energy will not keep the displacing mass homogenous within the larger well, resulting in rapid, uncontrolled fallout. Second, it is generally too shallow—scarcely deep enough to control the radial streaming direction taken by a strongly flowing influent vector. Often a telltale, floc-bearing streak slanting from the feed well along one radius of the tank forbodes serious short-circuiting. Third, there is no way to control and uniformly diffuse the influent energy. Fourth, the discrete floc particulates are allowed to fall, uncontrolled, from surface to bottom of the clarifier, like a waterfall, causing a strong radial density current and peripheral wall climb, especially at a high solids-loading rate.

A reasonable solution to these problems is to employ a better feed well. One version is the combination of an influent diffusion well equipped with multiple tangential gates, dissipating about 4 in. of head loss, and an outer flocculation chamber reaching to middepth. The biased gates deflect the outflow to set up an equal streaming velocity through each port which, in turn, sets up an overall rotating action in the annular flocculation chamber feed well. The nicety of design is to proportion the inner diffusion well to the large flocculating feed-well diameter so that the balanced energy dissipation completely fills the outer skirt with flocculation turbulence. In this way, discrete floc particles are kept in rolling homogenized suspension nearly to the bottom of the tank, thereby considerably reducing the free fall distance and the ensuing density current.

The slowly rotating mass inside the feed well produces slightly biased, uniform displacement under the skirt and into the hindered zone which minimizes jet streaming (see Fig. 12).

Floc Aggregation. In the activated sludge process, some floc particles may end up in a diffuse phase, partly because of shearing action from long period or violent aeration ("over-aeration"), and will not clarify unless there is some meaningful slow mixing, before or within the influent feed, to cause floc aggregation (employing existing, naturally secreted polyelectrolytes). The flocculating feed well described can assist in this flocculation or aid in aggregation where a small amount of coagulant, say polyelectrolyte, is added. Table 4 describes suggested diffusion well and outer feed-well sizes along with percent of the surface area and presumed flocculation retentions.

Skimming. Skimming secondary clarifiers is nearly a must. Sometimes when no primary sedimentation is employed, or with some trade wastes, scum occurrence at the surface is so voluminous as to require double squeegee and double scum ramp units. On large circular clarifiers greater than 100-ft diameter, and in all persistently windy locations, it is best to use two diametrically opposite scum ramp units anyway. The wind blows the scum to one side and the squeegee takes it around the inner periphery of the baffle and dumps it into the leeward scum trough. Sometimes automatic trough flushing is provided to aid the scum in flowing by gravity into an accumulating well.

In order to strengthen the otherwise weak circular skimmer system, it is far better to considerably elongate the gate means (say to 8 or 9 ft) to increase the captive grease mass that will be pushed up the shallow ramp. Both the lead edge of the ramp and the immediate scum baffle need to be low enough to prevent underflow (escape) and overflow of thick scum. Shallow dishlike, hydraulic drawdown skimmer systems are not efficient except when good skimming was not required in the first place.

TABLE 4 Diffusion Control (Flocculating) Feed Well Recommendations
(For secondary sedimentation basins handling chemically precipitated solids or activated sludge mixed liquor)

Tank diameter, ft, MLSS sedimentation	Outer skirt size, ft (diam × side D)	Percent of area (approx.)	Flocculation time, (approx. min)*	Inner diffuser size, ft	Tank side-water depth, ft†
80	16 × 8	4	14	8 × 5	14–16
100	20 × 9	4	15	12 × 6	15–17
125	25 × 10	4	16	13 × 7	16–18
150	30 × 12	4	16	16 × 7	18–20

* Surface (overflow) rate is assumed to be 500 gpd/sq ft and full center depth under the outer skirt is assumed as the floc aggregation volume.

† When dealing with flocculant solids clarification, ample side-water depth is a buffer between blanket disturbances and clear overflows.

Recommended side-water depth range. Increasing MLSS content requires greater side-water depth.

Scum and other floating influent particles tend to pop up to the surface immediately after displacing from beneath the feed-well skirt. Accordingly, the scum baffle will be efficient when it encloses about one-third to one-half of the central area (or influent end, in the case of long rectangular basins). The circular scum baffle is supported from the most inboard side of the weir trough(s). Scum pop-up adjacent to the overflow weir system may become a problem with rim-feed clarifier modes.

The use of a full radial surface baffle, slowly rotating with the squeegee, does nothing to propel the scum toward the periphery and may even be detrimental by holding scum masses anchored to this creeping radial member. A short boom projecting 45° inward (5 to 8 ft) from the squeegee assembly is sufficient.

Design details

Basin Size Limitation. Limiting the size of the basin is important because, in addition to reasons of wind stirring and flow-through instability discussed in connection with primary sedimentation, density current is accentuated as the basin size becomes greater and as the mixed liquor suspended solids become greater.

Floor Slopes. Unlike the slopes required for arms plowing to a primary basin center hopper, floor slopes for suction units may be relatively flat since radial movement of thickened sludge along the arm is minimal. If steep floor slopes are used, the multiple-suction collector will function just as well, providing that the plant operator is mindful that the sludge blanket interface is essentially level. Accordingly, in order for the most remote and largest suction tube to be covered and operate in thick sludge, the thick blanket must be at least up to that height. This then results in a deeper than necessary blanket mass toward the center, unnecessarily increasing the sludge residence time.

Effluent Weir Trough. The position of the effluent weir trough now becomes important because of substantial residual density current effect when dealing with a high mixed liquor solids influent. The greater the aerator solids content and the tank diameter, the more substantial the effect. The double-sided weir trough should be spaced inboard from the peripheral wall (at the brackets) by at least 15 to 20 percent of the tank radius. This will provide spatial distance to avoid overflowing "blowup" floc from the wall region when there is modest density current activity up the wall. This placement, generally in the region of surface dividing line, assists in the hydraulic stability of flow-through displacement by avoiding local high rise rate.

This inboard trough system generally is composed of multiple *straight* sections, 15 to 20 ft long, installed in chordlike geometry on a like number of cantilever brackets. A drop box section is used at the connection point of the effluent pipe so as to inundate that entry against vortex. About 2½ pipe diameters of inundation is required (based on 4 ft/sec velocity in the pipe).

The 12-in.-wide scum baffle is cantilevered from the inboard side of these trough sections, in a circle so the rotating skimmer can work against it. This baffle must be made twice as deep and higher above the water level at all scum ramps to avoid direct forcing of skimmings into the effluent.

The greatest working stresses on inboard troughs occur during tank filling (buoyancy) and during emptying (trough hanging full). Large relief holes (1-in. diameter, spaced at about 20 ft) in the trough bottom can alleviate these abnormal stresses. Assuming the tank to be deep enough, these open relief holes do not contribute additional solids to the effluent.

Square Tanks. Square tanks, operated with centerfeed, like circular clarifiers, can be nested for common wall and area economy, and corner sweeps are used to push sludge out of the corners. The inboard weir trough should partially parallel each wall (say inboard 7½ to 10 percent of the tank dimension), and then cut across the corners to form an octagon, as regular as possible consistent with practicability. The corners should be avoided for drawoff because radial throughput vectors intercept the tank sidewalls at varying angles, accumulating toward the corners. This produces a *corner effect,* resulting in rising settleable solids in these unstable corner regions, which will pour solids over any weir that is too close.

Underflow control Activated sludge underflow control may be effected in several ways. The problem is to continuously allow the sludge to compact to a desired thickness, and then to *progressively* remove all of the compacting sludge and not break through the thick sludge blanket. When the underflow withdrawal rate from one hopper is too great, the drawdown profile of the thick sludge becomes excessive and, if continuous withdrawal is not arrested (temporarily), thin overlying liquor breaks through the sludge blanket. Underflow, after breakthrough, then persists as a combination of a small amount of thick sludge flow and thinner ambient liquor. One-hopper, plow-type operation will not effectively remove settled activated sludge from tanks larger than 60- or 70-ft diameter.

Design parameters

Surface-loading Rates. These should be designed in the order of 800 to 1,000 gpd/sq ft for heavy sludges of SVI (sludge volume index) 50 to 100 and 500 to 700 gpd/sq ft for lighter sludges of SVI 200 to 300, but not bulked—subject to the *limitation* of the solids-loading rate. Conservative surface overflow rates for any given type of floc are decreased as the basin exceeds 125- to 150-ft diameter and as the MLSS increase, especially when these reactor solids approach the unusual content of 1 percent (10,000 mg/l) or greater (see Table 3).

Solids-loading rates. Based on clarifier floor area, the solids-loading rate is determined by the weight of suspended solids in the total influent feed, including return activated sludge flow, and should not exceed certain empirical limits, or else the density current may prove to be so strong that it converts into vertical rise at the peripheral wall causing deterioration of the effluent clarity. Too high a solids-loading rate can also disrupt sludge masses and increase pinpoint in the overflow (effluent). When this is the case, the clarifier has to be made larger than required by the surface rate simply to accommodate the limiting solids-loading rate. The limit can be extended by employing any feed well means that partially eliminates some of the density current energy and increases throughput displacement hydraulic stability.

Although safe limits of solids-loading rates may be oversimplified, as exhibited by Fig. 13, these rates have proven practical in applied usage. These limits are also modified by many geometrical criteria. It is of importance whether the tank is square, round, or long rectangular; the limits being slightly greater in that order. The size of the basin also has an effect with the out-sized circular basins being more unstable and subject to lessened limits.

So, as the reactor MLSS and the RAS rate increase, depending on the type of center feed well used, the solids loading (not the surface rate) may control the final clarifier tank diameter (see Fig. 13).

Blade Load. Blade load resulting from the V plows (and corner sweeps) slowly pushing the thick sludge over the bottom determines the continuous operating torque of the turntable drive train. Table 5 relating to sludge plowing load shows the application of this factor which controls the expected continuous operating torque of the drive and the design of the arm trusses.

Tip Operating Speed Selection. The operating speed of the tip determines the speed or arm rotation. The choice of this speed largely depends on experience and is subject to considerable latitude. Unlike tip speeds in primary sedimentation where too great a speed may result in local sludge stirring and disturbed particle rise in the region of the effluent weir, there is more latitude here because the heavy concentration of suction-pipe drawoff will draw in any ambient disturbed floc. Tip speeds as great as 24 ft/min may be acceptable, although speeds of 10 to 12 ft/min are commonly used.

Weir Overflow. This parameter, in gallons per day per foot, involves the rate of weir edge overflow (or submerged orifice trough rate) and is not too important. Experimentally, in at least two full-sized plants involving a range of tank geometry, it was determined that the old regulatory agency figure of 20,000 gpd/ft (of weir) is far too conservative and that rates five times that amount do not cause effluent deterioration, providing that the weir location is well balanced over the working effluent surface. This traditional rate did, hopefully, enforce the use of inboard weir troughs. The *placement* of effluent weirs should be done carefully.

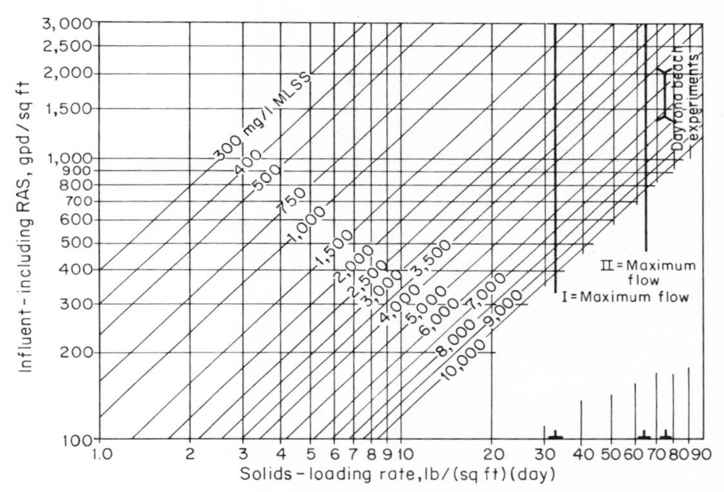

Fig. 13 Solids-loading rate. The vertical bars I and II show safe design floor loading (to the left) at maximum flow plus maximum return activated sludge (RAS). I is for traditional feed well and limits to 32 lb. II is for a large flocculating feed well and limits to 64 lb/(sq ft)(day)(rate). The vertical bar labeled "Daytona Beach Experiments" shows the 1969 performance of that 80-ft diameter x 18-ft WD final clarifier with a large, flocculating feed well clarifying 5,000 mg/l MLSS. The region at the bar is the maximum influent flow beyond which the density current rolled up with remarkable uniformity all around the periphery, and poured solids over the outer weir of the inboard trough. Simultaneously the inner weir drew clear effluent. The effect increased with the rate.

Side-water Depth. Sometimes, for construction or cost reasons, side-water depth is sacrificed to the detriment of good final clarifier performance. When dealing with sedimentation of flocculent solids, good tank performance will depend to some degree on water depth. Depth is required to insulate the overflow weirs from ambient floc above the blanket resulting from omnipresent unstable jet streaming (short-circuiting) and density current stirring.

The greater the MLSS content in the influent, the greater the water depth needs to be. The side-water depths indicated in Table 5 reflect a choice in the tank diameters indicated. Modern activated sludge modification design tends toward higher space loading which results in greater MLSS concentrations. Accordingly, the depths are selected for MLSS in the order of 3,000 to 5,000 mg/l. Since the design engineer does not *really* know just what amount of suspended solids will be selected, either by design or through neglect, it is more prudent to select the greater depth.

Greater tank liquid depth does suggest two possible disadvantages that require explanation. Presumably the greater *falling distance* of discrete floc particles from the surface to the floor might produce greater density current with its deleterious effect. This is not valid if a type of feed well is employed which keeps the influent contents homogenized within a large feed well until throughput displacement nearly reaches the bottom.

Presumably, overall *detention* period, being longer at greater water depth (volume), may result in anaerobic degradation and/or denitrification of activated sludge. This is not valid since, as stated before, the sludge residence time is independent of the water depth and detention period. After leaving the control of the feed well, discrete particulates pack together on the floor to form the sludge blanket. This thickening sludge mass exhibits a substantially level interface between the sludge blanket

TABLE 5

Type of sludge settled	Load factor, lb/ft arm
Hydroseparators:	
Grit	25
Plain primary sedimentation—degritted	10
Plain primary sedimentation—with grit	13
Lime coagulation:	
Primary solids sedimentation	30
Tertiary sedimentation	15
Water softening (cold)	15
Secondary biodegradable sludge (suction with V plows)	8
Alum/iron coagulation:	
Low turbidity sedimentation	6
Tertiary sedimentation	7
Chemical primary sedimentation	13
Rethickening (sludge):	
Lime	40–60
Plain primary sedimentation	60
Primary sludge day tank	80
Secondary sludge	40
Eleutriation tank	70

Clarifier drive—torque calculation

The maximum continuous operating torque T required by the turnable drive can be found by applying the arm load, factors LF in the formula:

$$T, \text{ft-lb} = 0.25(\text{diameter})^2(LF)$$

When calculating the continuous operating torque requirements for clarifiers with more than two radial (one full diameter) scraper arms, treat as two systems. In the case of corner sweeps, the tank diameter is considered including fully extended sweeps.

Scraper blade working loads are apt to continuously operate near to the overload shutoff point because of the propensity for operators to "thicken" settled sludge on the clarifier floor. Accordingly, the "load factor" values anticipate this maximum continuous collector drive resistance.

and the clarified liquor riding above it. Therefore, the sludge residence time is a function only of the mass of thick sludge on the tank floor and the rate of effective withdrawal as underflow.

Actual RAS residence time can be measured by ORP technique. The operator runs an ORP curve on a sludge sample, millivolts versus time curve, then fits a grab return sludge sample reading (5-min ORP value) to the total ORP curve to approximate the residence time.

Mechanical Thickeners

Plain gravity thickeners This type of thickener is used to increase sludge thickness after it is drawn as underflow from clarifiers. This increased thickness may result from simply decanting excess free water pumped with the underflow sludge, or possibly from "stirring" the thick sludge blanket with pickets to mechanically release the surface-bound water. This latter function is of doubtful effect. Often excess free water is included in the pumped sludge underflow, either accidentally through careless operation or by design, as with the *cascade system* and in secondary return activated sludge (RAS) practice. In a cascade operation, the pumps are deliberately set to draw a thin sludge to keep the thickened primary sludge layer moving to avoid classification and arm stalling.

The sludge loading on gravity thickeners is, roughly, around 30 lb/(day)(sq ft) of surface for primary sludges. Chemical and waste activated sludge (WAS) types operate at loadings around one-third of this (see Table 6). This loading is moot, and sometimes the thickener is employed as a sludge storage unit. When the freeboard depth above the hindered zone (sludge blanket interface) to the overflow is less than one-third the side-water depth, the loading (or storage) should be reduced. Thickeners should be quite deep, at least 18 to 20 ft center water depth. The bottom is sloped at about 2½ to 3 in./ft of radius. The slope may seem steep, but steepness is important as it aids the progressive movement of thick sludge into the hopper. Sometimes, as an aid to sludge movement to the hopper, the rake arms are

TABLE 6 Gravity Thickener Design Parameters
(Rough guide for circular units)

Type of sludge	Solids loadings, lb/(sq ft)(day)	Possible thickness, percent
Plain primary sludge:		
About 75% volatile	10–20	6–8
About 60% volatile	20–30	8–15
About 40% volatile	30–40	10–20
Alum sludge	45–55	10–12
Lime sludge	50–60	15–20
Plain WAS	5–8	2–3
Primary sludge + WAS—plain	8–15	4–5
Chemical WAS sludge (poly)	10–12	3–4
General parameters:		
Water depth at center, ft	18–20	
Bottom slope, in./ft of radius	2½–3	

Note: The data shown above are rough approximations to be used as a guide. Test procedures, employing water-depth length plastic tubes, can be set up to determine rough quantitative criteria for designing thickener loadings and predicting results. The test tubes should be at least 6-in. diameter and 20 ft high. See also Refs. 1 & 2.

(later) adjusted to a steeper slope than the poured bottom, leaving the inert particles to form an effective, steeper sloping bottom. Thickener rakes should be designed with this adjustment capability.

Equipment In terms of equipment, the basins and mechanical equipment are essentially the same as for plain primary clarification, except skimming may be omitted and the plows are often offset below the arms to reduce the added lateral resistance of the truss proper and deep spiral flights may be used. The slow, turntable drives on these units are relatively rugged for the size of the tank (see Table 1).

Pickets. The two rotating plow arms are sometimes equipped with *picket fences,* vertical "stirring" members attached to the arm trusses, spaced (staggered) about 24 in. c.c. These stirring members are of questionable value when applied to plain thickening application.

Hopper. A conical, steel-lined center hopper, spaded by heavy stirrup extensions from the center drive column to keep the hopper from bridging, also acts as a side-thrust bearing.

Offset Flights. The thickest sludge offering the greatest resistance lies along the floor in a viscous mass 1 to 3 ft deep. Considerable resistance to plow arm (lower chord, etc.) rotation can be eliminated by offsetting the flights about 2 to 3 ft below the lower chord of the truss (Fig. 14).

Speeds. Peripheral tangential speeds are on the order of 12 to 24 ft/min, a two-speed motor or other means of changing the drive speed being desirable. The gear and motor should be capable of handling the greatest speed of rotation.

Under some conditions, especially where the underflow is properly removed, the increased rotating speed may better move the thick sludge along the slope and actually decrease resistance.

Retractable Collector Systems. Vertical lifting of the collector arms to avoid overload, unfortunately, also lifts the important spading means out of the hopper and abandons the advantage of the plow system for moving previously compacted sludge mass into the hopper.

Larger diameter thickeners, especially large-diameter clarifiers used like thickeners, are prone to hard packing by classification in the center region unless special center deep spiral flights and steep (center region) bottom slopes are used along with proper pumping of the underflow. The use of these special deep spiral center flights along with offset flights may offer a better mode of uninterrupted operation than designing the mechanism for vertical lifting.

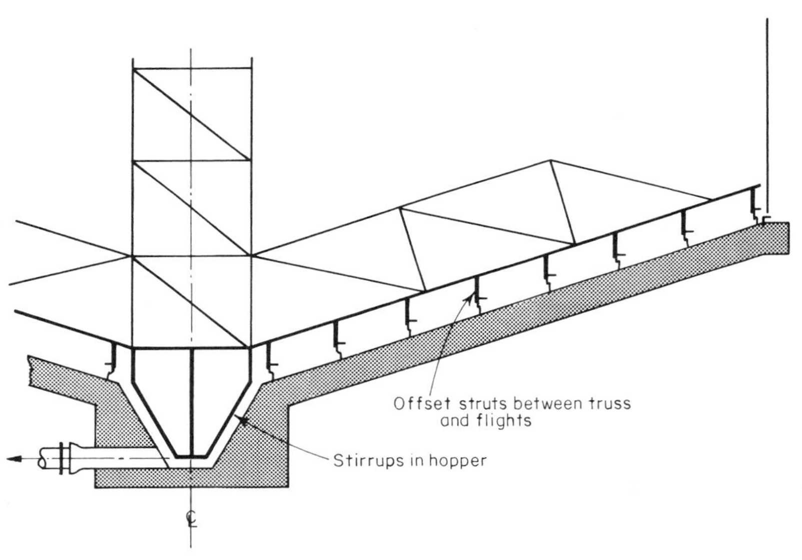

Fig. 14 Offset flights.

Air Blow-up. When thickening sludges that may pack hard (sludges treated with 10 to 15 percent of lime, etc.), one successful system uses compressed air nozzles located along each arm, near the floor, at about 3- to 5-ft intervals. Sequential application of air pressure to these nozzles will literally blow out the hard packed sludge and allow the scrapers to function without overload.

Sludge Pumping. It is important not to break through the thickened sludge layer (posthole). Although postholing is less apt to happen with rethickeners than with large primaries, care still has to be taken in the form of pump speeds (capacity) and intermittency of operation.

When, for unusual reasons, the underflow sludge cannot be pumped to the usual receiver, the sludge pumps and rakes should be *kept operating* and the sludge pump should discharge back into the thickener. This will avoid classification and an almost certain digging party if the sludge contains grits.

Solids-contact Upflow Basins

The solids-contact basin could be characterized as a combination mixing-flocculation-sedimentation system nested into one tank and often serving the secondary effluent polishing function of tertiary coagulation-clarification. Reactions in the solids-contact system are nucleated with admixture of previous (fresh) precipitate, and often, considerable mass recycle (3:1) from second-stage flocculation back through first stage.

The clarifier section has excellent sedimentation characteristics because of uniform displacement into the lower sedimentation region from under the rim of the large-diameter-center flocculation well. The clarified water displaces mostly upwardly to a weir trough system strategically well distributed over the entire surface. This upflow hydraulic displacement is quite stable, so the tank can accomplish good clarification in a relatively small basin.

The space used by these solids-contact basins is considerably smaller than an aggregation of separate rapid-mix, slow flocculation, and clarification units of equal effectiveness, and the system is cheaper to build. These solids-contact basins are either round or square, but if they are made too large (larger than 125-ft diameter), they lose much of their excellent upflow hydraulic properties.

System operation The system consists of displacement through three stages: rapid mix (rapid flocculation), slow mix (floc aggregation), and upflow clarification. The inner stages are built of steel, and the outside clarifier either of steel or concrete. The inner chambers are nested in a frustroconical shape, with a small center diameter at the surface and inclined circular wall to provide the flocculation volume required. By using a radial weir system, most of the surface area within the outer tank diameter is efficiently worked for settled effluent collection.

The rapid-mix chamber is agitated to the extent of a velocity gradient of 200 sec^{-1} or more, in a short retention period of a minute or so. The mixing may take place through a number of different arrangements: circulation by air lift, axial-flow turbine, or plate turbine.

Actual coagulant *blending* should be effected before this stage in the influent line by means of some local turbulence—a lift pump (shell turbulence, if any), in-line blender, etc. Some discretion has to be used when blending polyelectrolyte. It must be blended to avoid molecular underfeed-overfeed, but after becoming fully diluted, the hydrolyzed polyelectrolyte will not tolerate too much agitation.

The recirculated slurry and any recycle, along with chemical feed for pH adjustment, are well mixed here for first-phase coagulation. This rapid-mixing-recycle function is always made adjustable so that the operator may select the best level of velocity gradient.

The slow-mix chamber is within an open-bottom skirt, frustroconical in shape with sloping sides that spread out into the annular clarification section more or less on a 45° slope. This provides volume for 15 to 30 min (as designed) of floc aggregation under the skirt. The slow-mix volume is agitated by uniform fine-scale turbulence to about 35 to 50 sec^{-1} of velocity gradient. The modus operandi for recycle mixing is by various means, but all must have the common quality of providing the energy whose decay results in well-distributed fine-scale turbulence. The flow-through from this chamber must be hydraulically balanced so as to minimize short-circuiting into the clarifier (upflow) section.

Mass recycle is often employed from the core of the flocculation chamber back through the rapid-mix chamber, further minimizing short-circuiting. This recycle is selectably variable and is often designed on a 3:1 (maximum 5:1) basis—three volumes of recycle for each volume of influent.

The upflow clarifier portion surrounds and overrides the central mixing chambers. The clarifier section utilizes a system of overflow weir troughs well distributed at the surface, either with V-notch weirs or with submerged orifices. Each is equally effective and neither causes more floc breakup than the other. Where surface skimming is not required, multiple radial-weir troughs are used with their outside ends spaced 25 to 28 ft apart. In the case of square basins, the weir troughs are radiated to each side of the corner, so as not to take surface overflow under the influence of the rising "corner floc" effect.

Where surface skimming is required, as with tertiary waste treatment, the weir trough system is supported well inboard by cantilevered brackets. The inboard distance should be a minimum of 7 ft from the wall with basins around 80-ft diameter, and around 10 to 13 ft with basins around 100- to 125-ft diameter. In the case of square tanks, these inboard weir troughs are eight-sided and cut across the corners to avoid the corner effect.

Sludge (slurry) collecting means used in these basins is quite similar to the multi-plow scrapers used in chemical or plain primary sedimentation. There is not enough precipitated sludge to warrant multiple-suction-pipe units and, in the case of high lime coagulation, the excess lime hydroxides would plate out in the pipes and cause operating troubles.

Sludge blowdown is automatically regulated so that a deep contact sludge blanket is not carried. In fact, the sludge blanket hindered zone should never be allowed to rise higher than the bottom of the flocculation skirt or else instability and blowups will occur carrying floc to the surface. The usual manner of blowdown is by means of timer controlled valves blowing down small amounts at spaced, frequent intervals so as not to break through the thick sludge blanket.

Recycle sludge is often effected on a controlled basis adjusting the sludge blanket to ride closer to the skirt bottom rim and thereby sucking up sludge, as desired, with the recycle flow. Operators find that controlling the amount of recycled slurry to be carried is best done by measuring the volume that settles in 5 min in a test cylinder rather than by sampling and weighing the suspended solids. The contact function is volume (area) oriented.

Surface rates, where apropos for industrial wastewaters, are shown in Table 3. Tank side-water depths are the same as those used for clarifiers handling chemical coagulant floc.

DISSOLVED AIR FLOTATION

Dissolved air flotation technique is used to cause flocculent or fibrous particles to become attached to tiny air bubbles and float out of suspension and up to a collection surface. In this case, the suspended particles form a thick sludge blanket on the surface instead of settling to the bottom of the vessel. Tiny air bubbles attach to the particle by surface phenomena and buoy it up. In this manner, very light or small particulates that otherwise settle slowly can be removed from suspension in a very short time and in a very small basin. The tiny bubbles are formed by semi-saturating the flotation tank influent liquor with dissolved air in a contact tank under high pressure, and then flowing them through a control orifice where the pressure is suddenly reduced as the influent liquor flows into the flotation tank. When the pressure is reduced, the air leaves the solution phase and appears as multitudinous minute bubbles. Sometimes the influent flow is not pressurized, but a recycle stream taken from the effluent is saturated with dissolved air in a pressure tank, and blended into the influent flow just as the pressure relief takes place.

Floated scum is taken off the flotation cell as a product, and the subnatant is decanted under a baffle-trap as an effluent (Fig. 15).

Application

Flotation cells are used either as sludge thickeners or as clarification units. When flotation is employed as a sludge thickening means, the clarity of the subnatant is not too important providing that only a small percentage of the suspended solids in the substrate is not floated and recycled through the plant.

When flotation is used to replace a wastewater gravity sedimentation step, the effluent (subnatant) clarity is important. Conditioning by coagulants, carefully selected by trial-and-error studies on *representative* samples, is required to produce relatively clear effluents at a reasonable chemical cost.

Chemical Conditioning

To create a surface or flocculent structure that can more easily adsorb or entrap the minute air bubbles, conditioning chemicals are often employed. Metal salts of aluminum or iron and polyelectrolytes are used both to flocculate and bind the finer particles and to effect a better union between the bubbles and the particulates. The selection of the best and proper polymer often requires infinite jar testing. Like all other coagulation problems, the intimate dispersion and instantaneous blending of the coagulant to avoid overfeeding-underfeeding are most important. The blending of these two mistakes does not effect an average. Many a good conditioning chemical or feed concentration has been condemned because of lack of understanding on this point of instant meaningful blending.

Shapes of Units

Flotation tanks are both round and rectangular and rather shallow. Both types have top-acting scum removal equipment, and some have bottom-acting settled solids removal equipment as well.

For industry, the rectangular tanks are often superior to the round tanks since the rectangular geometry may better fit the space available.

Rectangular units The length and width of rectangular tanks are important. If the flotation tank is wider than about 10 or 12 ft, multiple means to distribute the feed should be provided, because of limited lateral diffusion effectiveness. The air mass rises within the first 20 ft from the diffusion inlet so that tanks much longer than 40 ft may not be too effective in the last several feet of length.

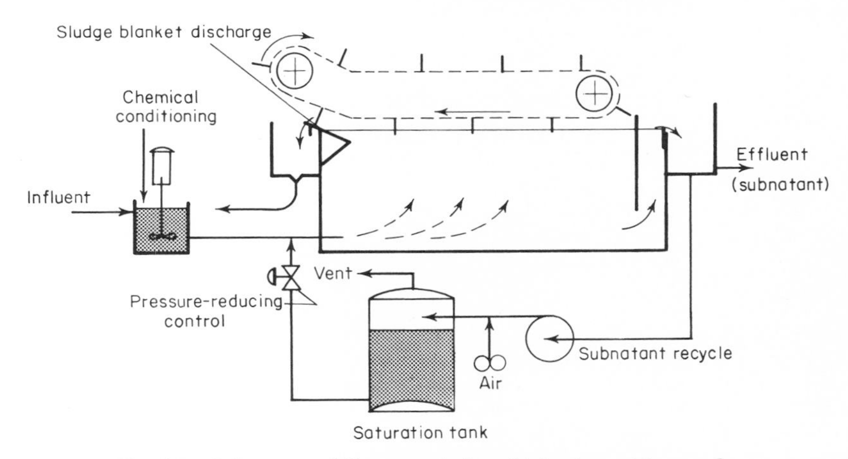

Fig. 15 Schematic of flotation sludge thickening with recycle.

The flotation unit had better be designed to a maximum surface area of around 400 sq ft as a reasonable limit for a single-diffusion inlet mode. Units have been built as long as 90 ft, mostly for thickening of waste activated sludge, but for industrial clarification work that size may be too big for one unit. In the case of such a long tank, an auxiliary pipe diffusing fine-air-bubble-laden flow is often employed midway along the tank to boost the declining flotation effect.

Circular units Circular units release the air-saturated influent in the center of the tank so that diameters as great as 50 to 80 ft (employing 5,000 sq ft of flotation area) have an advantage of a small radial spatial distance of about 20 to 30 ft to the periphery.

The circular unit has an advantage that it can better process wastes bearing some readily settleable, nonfloatable solids. The drive propelling the skimmer arms is extended to propel a pair of bottom plow arms. These arms plow any settled sludge to a sump for underflow.

Parameters and Details

Tank water depth This is not too important a detail. Depth is usually 6 to 8 ft, with a headroom requirement of another 6 to 8 ft. The saturation tanks (vertical attitude) require about 12 to 14 ft headroom.

Floating sludge blanket The sludge blanket is squeegeed up a ramp and into a discharge trough by the skimmer flight means and must not be too roughly propelled or else the floating blanket will partially break up and some particles will partially settle to join the effluent subnatant. Time is important too. Too long a residence time on the surface will allow some of the floated sludge blanket to lose its air and start to settle to the bottom.

Surface rate For clarification application, the surface rate is best designed at a conservative 1½ gpm/sq ft with a 2-gal rate as the extreme, except for free oil flotation which is an easy job where the rate can run higher.

For flocculent organic sludge thickening, the flotation surface rate is around a maximum of 2 lb/(sq ft)(hr) with emphasis on providing enough bubbles to actually float and thicken that load. In round numbers, this will result in a liquid rate of about 0.8 gpm/sq ft for average WAS conditions. See Table 7.

The fine bubble rate should be as much as 0.030 lb of fine air per pound of (dry) solids floated. Some designs attempt to apply as little as 0.006 lb of air per pound of solids, but should be considered substandard. The number of fine bubbles might be increased by increasing the saturation tank pressure or efficiency (or both) and/or by increasing the rate of liquid flow through the saturator (perhaps from recycle) provided the saturator tank is large enough to handle the increased throughput. All such practice is costly both in vessel size and in pumping pressure.

TABLE 7 Dissolved Air Flotation Loadings (Guide)

Service	lb/(sq ft)(day)	gpm/sq ft
WAS	15–45	0.3–2.0
Primary sludge:		
Stale	45–40	
Fresh	60	

Skimmer flights Dipping a few inches into the floating sludge blanket, skimmer flights are used to move the float gently to a ramp and discharge trough for disposing of the floated sludge.

Rectangular units use transverse flights spaced a few feet apart and drawn slowly by two strands of chain. The flights push the float up a ramp and into a transverse-end discharge trough. The flights must not disturb the float blanket too much or be too slow, otherwise the blanket will partially break up and settle. Separate sets of conveying flights may pull settled sludge, if any, along the floor to an underflow sump.

Circular tanks use rotating skimmers that push the float blanket over one or more long radial (often two-thirds of the radius) ramps and collection troughs. The center drive most often carries bottom arms and plows to push the settled sludge fraction into an underflow hopper.

Sludge transfer pumps These pumps must be carefully selected. The bubble-laden flotage is easy to pump, from a clogging standpoint, but if not properly handled, will easily gas-lock a pump, sometimes even under positive suction head. Progressing cavity pumps, full-diameter, very slow speed centrifugal pumps, or plunger pumps can handle the flotage provided there is absolutely no suction lift.

Saturation or "dwell" tanks These pressure tanks are, perhaps, the heart of the flotation process. Some or all of the throughput is pumped into this tank under pressure along with compressed air so that the air substantially dissolves and nearly saturates the throughput. This saturated flow leaves the dwell tank and enters the flotation cell proper through a pressure relief control, which releases the high pressure so that the saturated air "blooms" as tiny bubbles which can attach to ambient particulates.

The pressure-reducing device is of considerable importance in that if the pressure-reducing control (sometimes two valves in series) is released too far from the actual skimming tank entry, there may be some deleterious coalescing of air in the connecting pipe. Also, it is best to release this great amount of energy in the presence of the substrate so that microscopic bubbles detraining from the saturation tank throughput are homogenized with the solids to be floated.

The pressure in this tank is carried at from 50 to 90 psig (70 psig being common) and uses plant air supply. Higher pressures are sometimes indicated as a matter of increasing fine bubble power (total number of bubbles) without increasing dwell-tank throughput, but this should be approached with caution.

Dissolution above 90 percent of theoretical saturation has nearly become a fetish, with at least one proprietary design promoted to accomplish this. Less than 90 percent (theoretical) air dissolution means that proportionally more bubble-carrying liquor has to be pumped through the saturator; but if the dissolution efficiency is not too low, it is not disastrous to an ample design. Or perhaps this amount of air saturation is not required for the service in the first place. This is particularly evident when dealing with the many flotation situations (other than waste activated sludge thickening) which do not require nearly as high an air/solids (A/S) ratio as 0.020 or 0.030.

The air added to the pressurized saturation tank does not go into 100 percent dissolution. The unsaturated air (5 to 20 percent) has to be well separated before admittance into the flotation cell, otherwise it will bubble up and "boil" under the floating sludge blanket and break it up. Effective, large air separation is a matter of the saturation tank design, that is, how the undissolved free air is channeled, and not an attempt to push too much flow volume through the tank. Pushing more flow than was intended through a minimum-sized saturator may carry some bubbles along with the influent instead of being exhaused through the vent.

A relatively small dwell tank can save equipment cost, but ampleness in the saturation tank allows for some latitude in increasing throughput, if desired. As a guide, up to 2 min of residence time within the saturation tank is quite ample, although many commercial designs only use 1 to 1½ min, leaving little or no leeway for future operation changes or change in dissolution effectiveness.

Operation and Analysis

Operation of the flotation unit can be critical. Besides careful jar testing to determine the type and proper quantity of coagulant for optimum performance, other conditions have to be met. The influent feed needs to be a constant flow. This may require effluent recycle back to a pump well to maintain constant flow or a waste-flow-equalizing supply tank. Any recycle to achieve constant throughput, in turn, requires the surface rate to be designed low enough to accommodate the total flow. The flotation operation should be protected from shots or large solids; this may require scalping screens.

Both for original design and for major changes in operation, small rental test units of 1 or 2 sq ft of surface can be employed to get reliable qualitative-quantitative design and operation information.

ACTIVATED SLUDGE AND AERATION (SECONDARY TREATMENT)

Wastes containing biodegradable carbonaceous organic matter can be synthesized into settleable activated sludge flocs and a relatively clear effluent by the modern activated sludge process. Further, for advanced waste treatment, wastes can be oxidized to complete nitrification (nitrates). If properly designed, the process reliably handles a wide array of organic wastes, both industrial and domestic.

Two ingredients are important to this continuously seeded process: good mixing and interchange and well-distributed oxygenation. Dissolved oxygen to support the aerobic biomass can be supplied either by air dissolution or by direct oxygen dissolution. This section deals with operating a reliable activated sludge process by air dissolution.

Aeration by atmospheric air, either by air diffusion or by mechanical surface film exposure, is still the backbone of activated sludge application. Although direct oxygen has started to trace an operating history, the simplicity and ease of maintenance and overall low cost of air oxygenation systems tend to perpetuate the use of air except in cases of high-soluble, high-BOD substrates. Considering the small- to medium-sized waste treatment plants, amortization and operating labor costs seem to be less with air oxygenation notwithstanding direct oxygen claims for thicker waste sludge, less covered reactor space requirements, and other fringe benefits. Looking toward the near future, better mixed regimes and better process modifications can further improve the position of air activated sludge regarding ability to maintain aerobic conditions throughout the reactor at all times. A possible trend toward raw or settled waste flow equalization would be a further aid, accentuating the operation cost advantages of air oxygenation.

Unfortunately, some diffused air designs have long followed traditional system concepts that have been proven not to be the best, at least in some cases. At Milwaukee, for example, a "modern" spiral-roll system when compared with the original cross-roll (ridge-and-furrow) system showed considerable lackluster.[3] Following study and experimentation, the error was corrected by abandoning spiral roll and replacing it with closely spaced (about 5 ft) longitudinal rows of diffusers. During the last decade many other plants have changed from spiral roll to some form of cross roll, considerably improving dynamic mixing, oxygenation, and process response. Spiral-roll circulation has been measured to kill over one-third of the air-lift streaming flow needed for turbulence and mixing, as compared to circulation realized from forms of cross roll. Accordingly, it well may be that some operating complaints lodged against air use (lack of critical mixing and spotty anaerobiosis) have been due to design errors. This is of particular importance at the commencement of process where return seed sludge and substrate are first mixed and good interchange and oxygenation are so important to support the elevated uptake rate. Better blending and mixing here actually further increase the demand for direct oxygenation (DO).

System Considerations

Modifications of the original plug-flow activated sludge system and more attention to mixing have made it practical to handle waste combinations and strengths that used to be considered untreatable. Along with these system modifications, several techniques have been developed that assist in the efficiency and success of air activated sludge.

Reaeration One of the modifications, complete mixing, has advantages of blending out high strength, high soluble BOD-COD within the reactor. However, it has been observed that the return seed sludge often requires substantial reaeration to avoid a sludge-bulking problem and consequent solids loss to the effluent. The extent of the reaeration should be substantial (about one-fifth to one-fourth of the detention period) even in plants having high space loadings. Contact stabilization and step feed (both with substantial return activated sludge reaeration) are examples of application of meaningful reaeration. Some plants have converted part of their reactor volume to return sludge reaeration to a considerable advantage.

Blending Rapid blending (after reaeration, if any) of the activated seed sludge with the substrate is of great advantage in immediately catalyzing the synthesis process. Plain aeration of part of the substrate waiting for sludge enzyme contact will have a deleterious effect on the process. Good blending requires a great deal of mixing applied at this critical time, which may amount to more intense air diffusion at the commencement point, or intense mechanical mixing. Good immediate blending will increase the local uptake rate (oxygen demand), so enough stirring and oxygenation have to be introduced *throughout* the mass at this point to avoid partial anaerobiosis. This is no place to endure the "dead core" effect of a spiral-roll regime.

Getting away from traditional placement of air diffusers along one wall allows the air-lift mass to stream naturally in both directions above the header. This results in a measured pumping (circulation) increase of well over one-third. This increased mixing, alone, creates a better dynamic condition for metabolic reactions. "Dead" regions and spotty anaerobiosis no longer exist.

Cross roll A well-tried system of diffuser placement is cross roll (Fig. 16). In such a system, the rows of diffusers are placed across the width of the reactor at intervals of about twice the water depth or closer, depending on the rate of air diffused per thousand cubic feet. Such an arrangement, besides allowing wider reactors, is very efficient for creating more uniformly distributed medium-scale turbulence.

These crossrows do not act as air curtain walls or "baffles," and uncontacted short-circuiting through long reactors has to be avoided by employing a series of solid walls.

Clumping tendency The viable activated sludge floc, developed in a good regime employing 3 to 4 days mean cell residence time (MCRT), is encapsulated in a sticky slime layer of extracellular natural polymers. This creates a strong natural clumping tendency, which resists penetration of substrate and DO into the core of the floc unit—a process contradiction. Medium-scale turbulence (a result of good mixing) can break up this clumping tendency so that the floc now consists of many subdivided floc masses. This not only exposes more microorganisms to the substrate but also allows DO to penetrate the floc and maintain aerobic conditions throughout.

Equipment Equipment for air oxygenation is considerably varied, but the major types used to treat industrial and municipal wastewaters are: mechanical surface aeration, diffused air, and sparged turbine aeration.

Mechanical surface aeration is over one-third cheaper (power) than diffused air. Also "coarse" bubble aeration is about as cheap, in terms of power, as "fine" bubble diffusion considering "half-clogged" diffusers and difference in air pressure.

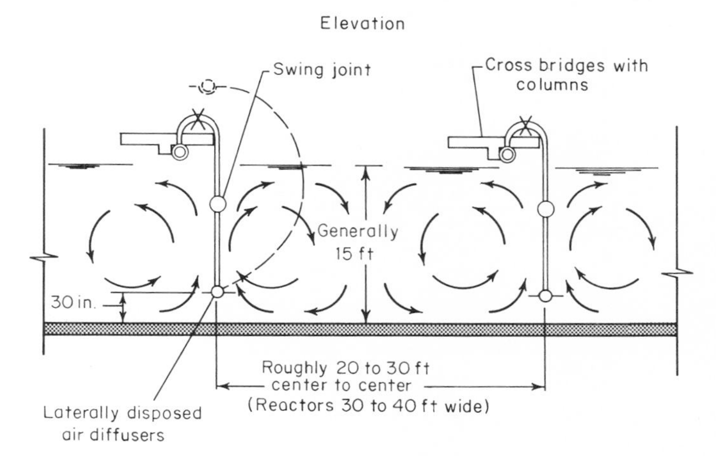

Fig. 16 Cross-roll regime.

Mechanical Surface Aeration (Vertical Axis—Radial Pumping)

There has been a movement, especially in industry, to reduce energy, equipment, and construction costs by employing large slow-speed mechanical surface aerators often installed in large earth-banked flat-bottom reactors. Mechanical aerator units have been increasing in size until they are now regularly installed as large as 150 hp, thereby decreasing their installed cost and aiding overall mixing. Today the slow-speed mechanical aerator is the cheapest means for activated sludge oxygenation.

Mechanical surface aeration is performed by two major vertical-axis types: gear-drive, slow-speed turbine units and direct-drive, medium-speed axial-flow units. Either type can be mounted on floats, on pier-supported platforms, or on bridges. However, the slow-speed aerators generally are pier-mounted, and the direct-drive units ring-float-mounted, the latter primarily used in aerated lagoons.

Gear-drive units Gear-drive units rotate a slow-speed surface turbine at between 47 and 56 rpm (about 15 to 25 ft/sec impeller-tangential speed) by means of a very-heavy-duty helical-type gear-drive unit designed to easily withstand the overhung load of the large surface turbine (Fig. 17). Figure 18 is a handy quick reference for selecting sizes of gear-drive aerators and reactor mixing response.

The impeller design exhibits a nearly linear oxygenation, pumping (mixing), and power response to change in submergence. Change is effected by an operation-controlled change in water level employing a motor-driven, variable-height overflow weir. This allows the operator safely to vary the oxygenation (and power) at will between full load and about 60 percent of full load, a handy, simple way to vary power and dissolved oxygen.

Direct-drive units Direct-drive units are driven by a vertical, direct-connected, totally enclosed motor, generally 880 rpm. Liquid is pumped through a controlled passage by a stainless-steel three-bladed impeller that discharges radially over the

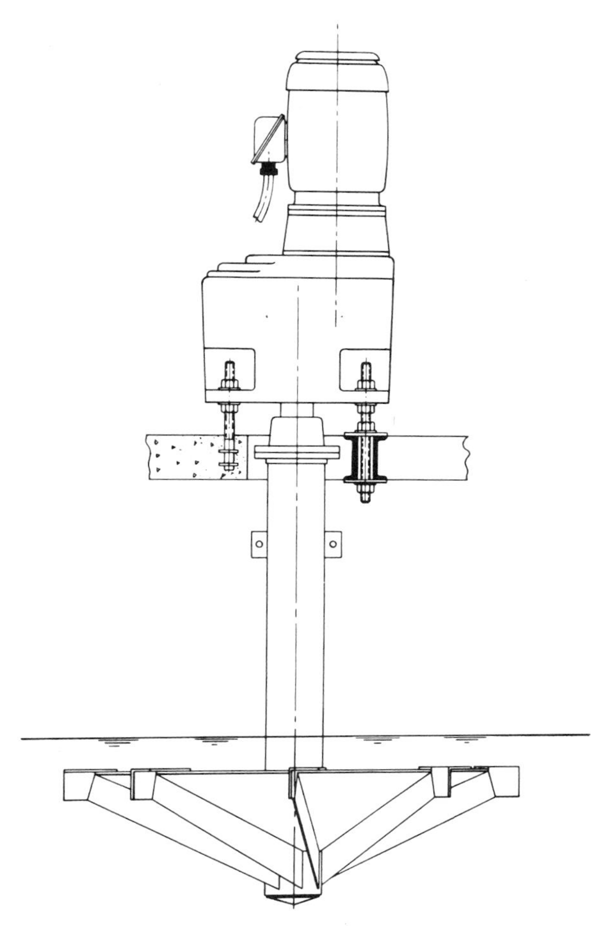

Fig. 17 Gear drive mechanical surface aerator. (*Peabody Welles.*)

annular float at a velocity of about 15 to 20 ft/sec and impinges on the basin surface at a small angle, thereby generating considerable induced flow for mixing. The radial discharge mixes and oxygenates a very large region surrounding this unit.

These axial-flow units are mounted on circular floats surrounding the impeller housing and are moored in position by radiating lines and the power cable (see Fig. 2).

Turndown on these units is possible by admitting air to the low-pressure region of the impeller, thus reducing its pumping and power load. Power turndown, oxygenation, and mixing are all about linear.

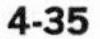

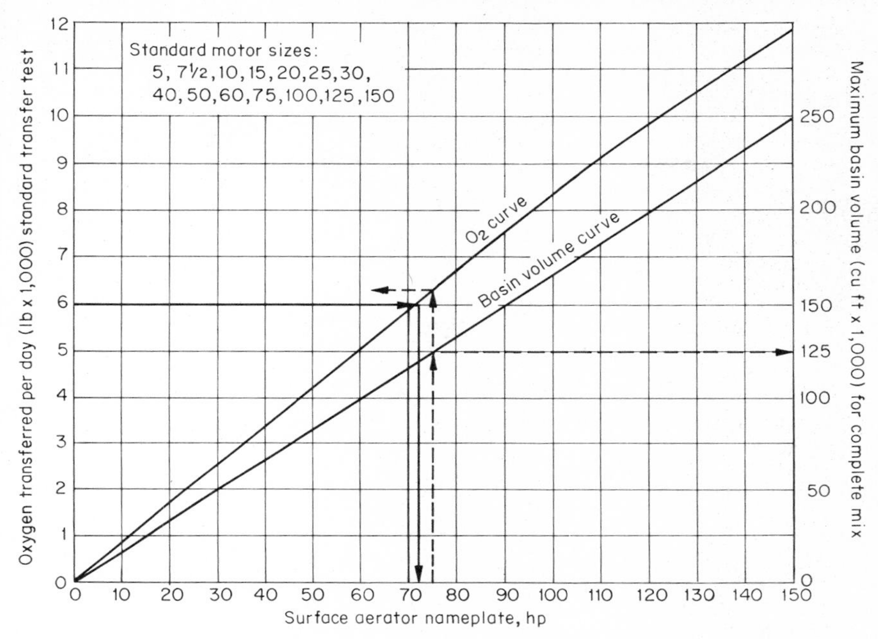

An example using this quick reference chart to size gear-drive surface aerator units(s) to satisfy given criteria is given below.

Required: 4,000 lb 0_2/day (in MLSS; $\alpha = 0.90$; $\beta = 0.95$; DO $= 2.0$)

$$N = N_o \left[\frac{\beta(C_{SW} - C_L)}{9.17}\right] \alpha = N_o \left[\frac{0.95(9.17-2) \times 0.9}{9.17}\right] = 0.668\ N_o$$

$$\frac{4{,}000\ N}{0.67} = 5{,}978 \text{ lb/day } 0_2 \text{ (standard tap water conditions)}$$

Enter Fig. 18. From 6 (oxygen transfer per day) cross horizontally to the oxygen curve and down to the horsepower, intercepting at about 72 hp (nameplate or water hp). (*Note:* hp $\times$ 1.17 = electrical input hp.) Since next motor size is 75 hp, move vertically, ascertaining the resulting (standard) oxygen response to be 6,300 lb 0_2 (standard conditions).

Also, intercepting the basin volume curve, read that 125,000 cu ft is the largest practical reactor size that a 75-hp aerator can adequately mix completely.

The chart indicates response from slow-speed integral-motor gear-drive units. For 860-rpm direct-drive units, discount performance as follows: oxygen exchange, 5 to 6 percent; mixing effect, about 20 percent.

Fig. 18 Oxygenation and mixing performance of mechanical surface aerators.

Operation and analysis Some engineering qualities peculiar to all mechanical surface aerators need to be examined for purposes of evaluating the application of this mechanical equipment.

Fine Aerosol Spray and Cold-climate Operation. A quality that the surface aerator has been condemned for is the attendant fine ambient spray. Adding a horizontal-plate shield can eliminate any local aerosol pollution with little or no loss in efficiency.

With wastes of cooler temperatures (around 20°C), the dissipation of heat in cold winter climates will lower the culture temperature only slightly, but there will be some ice formation on walls and walkways if ice shields are not used over the aerators. Ice shielding consists of a circumferential skirt hanging from the deck, midway to the liquid level, and will reduce the oxygen transfer efficiency about 6 percent; the mixing remaining unimpaired.

Floc breakup. Another argument used against surface aerators is floc breakup. In activated sludge practice, viable biofloc bound by natural, continuous polymer secretions does not permanently break up except under extenuating circumstances. *Overaeration* (which is unusual floc overshearing causing breakup into a partial diffuse phase) can come from any form of aeration (diffused air or surface aeration) and is not necessarily a by-product of mechanical aeration.

Mass Rotation. There is a desirable strong vertical-approach rotation, induced by the impeller blades, extending from the floor to the impeller. To a degree, this vortex aids to sweep the floor and sustain good tank bottom mixing, even in deep geometry. However, this vortex in some geometries possibly could build to a strong, destructive, overall rotation of the basin contents and might cause deleterious surging and reduction in pumping, oxygenation, and mixing. Baffling may be required to correct overall rotation, and its use is a matter of experience.

Diffused Air

Compressed air diffusion in activated sludge reactors is achieved by two major types of units: fine air diffusers and "coarse (air) bubble" orifice diffusers. The operator can increase or decrease oxygenation (and mixing) by changing the air-blower output. Changes greater than 50 percent, however, are better effected by changes in the number of diffusers to maintain efficiency.

Air is carried from the blowers to the diffusion equipment through mains, and then through control valves and downcomers into the tanks, and laterally through the diffusion headers. The weak point for piping corrosion is the air/water interface on the downcomer.

Fine air diffuser Diffused fine air is blown through fine-pore ceramic media (plates or tubes), or through woven cloth media "tubes" having very fine-pore openings. There should be a preparatory baghouse filter stage to remove dust from the air or else it will cause internal clogging in the fine-pore diffusers.

A fine air diffuser system requires a system blower pressure of about 7¼ psig when the diffusion media is suspended 30 in. off the floor of a typical 15-ft WD tank, and 8 psig or more when the media are located on the floor. Any media clogging is reflected directly in additional air pressure, cost, and loss of oxygen transfer efficiency.

Coarse air diffuser Coarse air is diffused at a system pressure of about 6½ psig (in typical 15-ft WD tanks) from closely spaced multiple plastic diffuser units attached along horizontal pipe headers. Each plastic unit diffuses air through groups of orifices about ¼ to ⅜ in.

Actually, the coarse air is converted into smaller bubbles either by "spoiler" film-shear surfaces at the diffuser or by act of the rising, roiling turbulence. Good orifice bubble systems actually effect more pumping (mixing) per unit of air volume than do fine air systems. Where mixing is important, as with strong, highly soluble wastes, these systems have an advantage (Fig. 19).

The net effect in an activated sludge reactor is that both types of diffusion systems are about equally efficient in oxygen dissolution when comparing the relative power *actually used* by the blower motors. Orifice bubble units do not require frequent cleaning to maintain low back-pressure and high process efficiency and represent an important labor-saving advantage.

Air headers Air headers, feeding from the air mains, are either designed in a fixed position or, better, in a removable mode, and generally are arranged about 30 in. off the bottom of a 15-ft WD reactor. Mounting the diffusers above the bottom not only saves air compression energy but also enhances air-lift pumping and mixing in the case of orifice bubble units. Individual air headers are from 15 to 20 ft long.

Sparged Turbines

The sparged-turbine mechanically diffused air unit operates at about middepth in the reactor and is a combination of diffused air and an axial-flow turbine (Fig. 20). Air is broken into very fine particles when it encounters the large-scale turbulence resulting from velocity gradient created by the downward discharge from the turbine

Fig. 19 Diffuser in underwater operation. (*Peabody Welles.*)

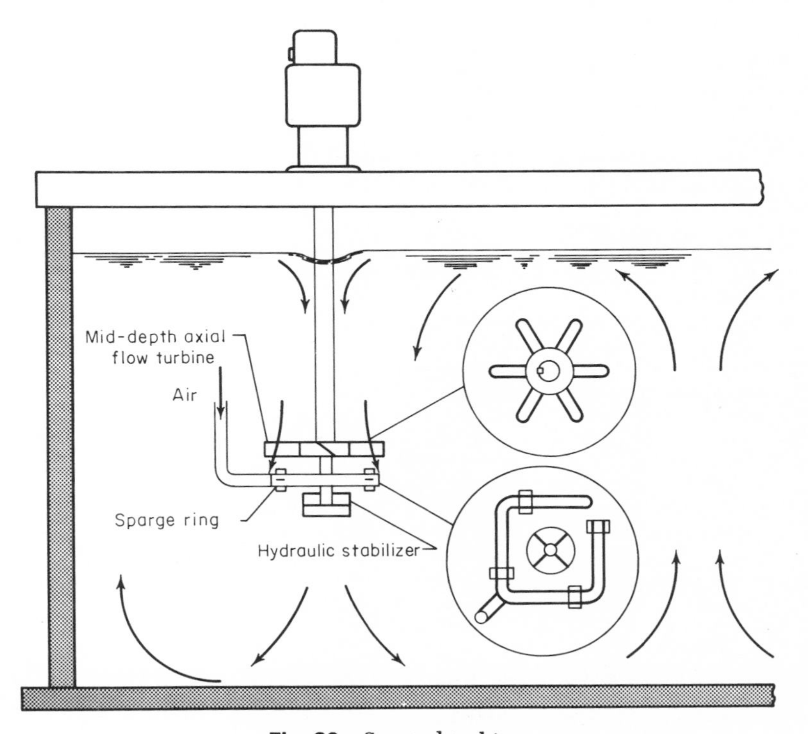

Fig. 20 Sparged turbine.

blades. This form of diffused air is much finer than even the small bubbles which release from unclogged fine porous media. The fine air, being continuously under the influence of considerable local turbulence, benefits from improved gas transfer kinetics. A very high oxygen transfer efficiency, on the order of 20 to 35 percent, is realized. The extent of oxygen transfer efficiency depends on the ratio of compressed air energy to the turbine water horsepower. By and large, however, the sparged turbine is not quite as efficient in oxygen transfer rate as is the mechanical surface aerator, but it does have several operating advantages.

The *drive* is a slow-output-speed gearbox, 50 to 70 rpm, much the same as the surface aerator except that the gearbox has a long shaft extending to about tank middepth. Since it is most desirable not to employ an underwater steady bearing, a high service rating is required (around 2.0 or greater) for the gearbox to have bearings that can take the long overhang. A large hydraulic ring stabilizer, attached below the impeller, nearly eliminates side thrust and makes the long shaft overhang practicable.

Unfiltered, compressed air is discharged into the primary sparge ring mounted just below the impeller and is acted on by the strong downdraft velocity gradients discharged by the impeller. The air bubbles are further divided and swept radially across the floor and upwards through the tank.

Aeration Blowers

Diffused air plants use air blowers to supply the air for diffusion. These blowers compress the air to 6 to 8 psig (infrequently 9 psig), depending on the submergence of the diffuser and the system back pressure resulting from head loss through the snubbers, air filters, mains, balancing valves. and air diffusion equipment. The greater the back pressure at the blowers above that required to overcome submergence of the diffusers, plus a reasonable amount for transmission and system losses, the greater the waste of diffused air in terms of kilowatthours. In some operations, this waste averages 1½ psig, or over 20 percent of the ordinary cost of power!

Heat of compression runs about 6°C/psig increase over ambient temperature. Recognizing that this will be a varying temperature condition, the air mains have to be designed for considerable expansion and contraction. This heat is variably dissipated through the air mains (depending on design) and, finally, when the air is diffused.

Noise pollution is becoming more of an industrial problem, so all rotary positive blowers should be equipped with noise attenuators both on the air intake and on the outlet. Additional noise abatement is achieved with massive, well-isolated blower foundations with efficient vibration dampers under the blower base, especially in the case of large, rotary positive blower installations. Small, multistage centrifugals do not require more than base vibration dampers. In general, air-discharge piping should be connected by flexible rubber connectors to reduce telegraphed noise and avert misalignment.

Blowers used primarily for wastewater treatment air supply can be classified in two general categories: rotary positive and centrifugal. The centrifugals can be broken down into two classes: multistage and single stage.

Rotary positive blowers The rotary blowers are generally the two-lobe type rotating in a cast-iron case with the close-meshing lobes pushing air through the case in a series of rapid pulsations. The two lobes are synchronized by timing gears, which require careful monitoring for lubrication. These blowers are used for 7- to 8-psig air deliveries up to about 15,000 scfm (their practical upper limit) but, in general, not often applied to a single-unit delivery of over 10,000 scfm. The speeds run from 500 to 1,200 rpm with the larger units usually running at the higher range of 1,000 to 1,200 rpm. These units must be protected against shutoff pressure by ample relief blowoff means, carefully adjusted so that the relief will truly work when called on, otherwise the timing gears will fail.

Centrifugal blowers The discharge rate of all centrifugal blowers can be modulated by adjusting a suction-valvelike damper. The capacity and power essentially vary linearly. The maximum safe turndown is on the order of 50 percent for multistage blowers and 40 percent for single-stage blowers designed with inlet guide vanes. The centrifugal blower head-capacity characteristic is like a flat arch, and too much turndown will cause the blower to hunt on both sides of the summit, possibly going into surge that could be disastrous. Accordingly, an *antisurge* protective device should be used to protect each centrifugal blower against inadvertent excessive turndown (such as when a diffusion system suddenly clogs and back pressures the air system). Any protective device should be purchased with the blower.

One major disadvantage of the centrifugal blower is that when operating with hot (greater than 38°C) ambient air temperature, the blower, if not designed for that (hot) suction air operating point, will not be able to produce the required pressure for underwater diffusion especially when any diffuser clogging has increased back pressure. It is advisable always to specify that the blowers be designed to deliver the maximum expected (specified) pressure when the ambient air temperature is 38°C (or 43°C, etc., as the case may be). Then, in the wintertime, the blower can be throttled to deliver the desired air volume at lower ambient suction air temperatures.

Multistage Centrifugal Blowers. The multistage blowers all run at 3,600 rpm and are direct-connected to the motor. The shaft bearings are mounted outboard to avoid the heat of the centrifugal shell, but they still require vigilant care to hold alignment and maintain lubrication. Some form of screening or crude air filtering is required to prevent birds and debris from entering the suction.

These blowers are manufactured from about 1,000 to 18,000 scfm and, provided the delivery pressure is not required to exceed 8 psig, their efficiency is good. This makes them particularly suitable for plants using coarse bubble or turbine air diffusers.

Single-stage Centrifugal Blowers. The single-stage blower is the giant of the business, running at about 5,600 rpm and delivering 7- to 8-psig air from 20,000 to 60,000 scfm. The 60,000-scfm unit will use about 2,500 connected horsepower driven through a speed increaser. These single-stage blowers require careful attention to bearing lubrication, i.e., the temperature of the lubricating oil must be raised to safe operating temperature before the blower is brought up to operating speed and pressurized.

Wherever applicable, the single-stage blower is probably a good choice of air supply except that, like all centrifugals, the critical hot weather temperature-pressure point has to be designed carefully.

Pressure-swing Oxygen Generators

The application of semipure oxygen to oxygenate activated sludge is a newcomer in practice, made practicable by newly developed small, on-site, pressure-swing oxygen generators. Semipure oxygen, like oxygen in air, is very difficult to dissolve. Unlike air, however, oxygen is expensive and the nicety of application is to get at least 85 to 95 percent dissolution efficiency. The high partial-pressure oxygen driving force can maintain very great MLSS contents (10,000 mg/l or greater) in a completely aerobic condition. This makes activated sludge crowding (high MLSS content) in the reactor a practicable way to save reactor tank volume or to upgrade existing operation. The high oxygenation driving force per se may be beneficial to treatment of high-strength, highly soluble BOD-COD industrial wastes.

Direct oxygen One company has a broad patent covering the application of direct oxygen to wastewater treatment by the activated sludge process in covered reactors.

The high DO tension approach seems well suited to very strong, highly soluble organic substrates and eventually may work out to supplant most other forms of oxygenation mixing where the organic COD is very great and where aeration reactors necessarily must be of small geometry because of site limitations. At present, the entire direct oxygen regime is in the early operation and development stage and management and operation problems and costs are unspecific so far. Also, on-site pressure-swing oxygen generators may require extensive mechanical development.

Oxygen boosting Many industrial wastewaters are subject to dumps or periods of very high organic content having unusually great oxygen demand. Even with blending tanks, the temporary inroads may be too great to blend and equalize. Also, a given waste treatment plant may have become overloaded because of industry expansion or in-plant manufacturing causing a change in wastewater strength. At such times, the ability to augment the DO supply in the aeration reactors by oxygen boosting would save the process.

The oxygen-boosting idea employing an efficient oxygen-dissolution mechanism in open tanks is new in practice and remains to be proven in industrial wastewater treatment. An advantage of the oxygen-boosting system is that (if proven) it can be added to existing traditional air-supplied aeration regimes to upgrade their ability. Another advantage is that higher MLSS can be carried, increasing the sludge age and resulting in less and a more inert waste sludge, similar to direct oxygen preliminary experience.

Aeration Basins

The geometry of both aeration tanks and secondary clarifiers is closely connected with equipment design and application. Whereas in municipal waste treatment works, design engineers are compelled by circumstances to build with everlasting concrete and also to produce eye-pleasing structures and surroundings, in industrial work imagination can be used to reduce construction costs without sacrificing performance.

Where available site area is limited, deep, nested steel tanks have been employed, even two-story layouts have been used where required. Many heavy industrial plants do have land available and here ponds have been employed advantageously. By making the ponds reasonably deep, say 15 to 18 ft, both aeration and clarification can be operated in the ponds. The side slopes are often 2:1, and the walls (at least at the air/water interface) are stabilized inexpensively with crushed rock, sheet plastic, or cheap bank-run cement grout. By making the aeration reactors quite wide

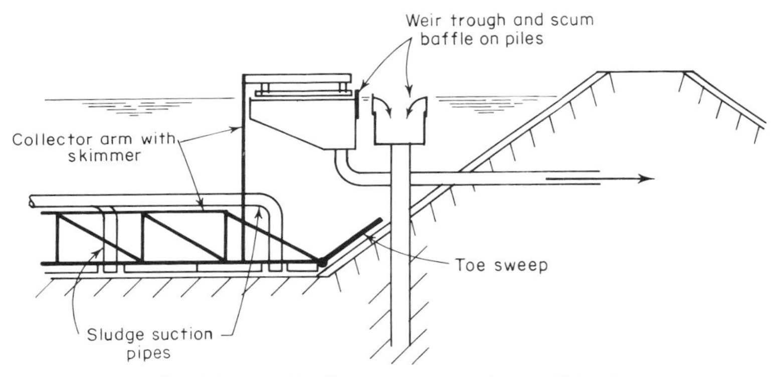

Fig. 21 Final sedimentation earthen-wall basin.

and employing complete mix regimes, such ponds are ordinarily much less expensive than reinforced concrete tanks or even steel. The ponds are well suited to equipment placement: either widely distributed platform-mounted large hp surface aerators or pile-mounted crossrows of light bridges and swing-up air diffuser headers. If plug flow is required, say, in a series of three completely mixed reactors, sheet piling (nonhydraulic) can be driven longitudinally along the wide pond to split it into three (or more) long passes. Sluiceways can be used to distribute influent and collect effluent and also to effect the all-important function of rapidly, completely blending the RAS with the substrate influent.

The secondary clarifier designed as a deep pond can also be expertly treated as to influent control and effluent drawoff. Here, piles driven around the periphery will hold a weir trough and scum baffle system rather ideally positioned. The weirs will be well inboard from the "wall" because of the slope. A heavy concrete foundation in the center will carry the collector equipment and a well-designed, diffusing and homogenizing feed well. The light access bridge can carry the overhead influent line or trough. A pivot-connected end flight is used to scrape out the peripheral intersection of the sidewall slope with the bottom where sludge would otherwise "hang up." Such a design has been in successful operation for many years in a large industry in Michigan (Fig. 21).

Unfortunately, many ponds have been designed needlessly shallow, with little attention paid to short-circuiting or good process requirements. An earthen basin should be as well designed, in terms of process, as any formal concrete structure system.

Return Activated Sludge Pumping

The return activated sludge system (RAS) which catalyzes and seeds the activated sludge process is an inseparable and vital part of any suspended biomass process. Return activated sludge well blended with the influent substrate causes the plain aeration lag phase to be skipped entirely, and immediately starts the process on the efficient log growth phase. Since settled sludge is no longer stored in the final clarifier, in order to obtain the thickest sludge possible, all of the activated sludge is returned as it settles into the compression zone blanket on the floor of the clarifier. When there is a change in substrate flow (gallons per minute) through the reactor, more RAS (by weight) is required to blend with this flow to maintain a semblance of a constant food/microorganism ratio. The required MLSS content is satisfied in one of two modes:

1. The return sludge pumping rate during average flows is of such a volume that the sludge blanket on the clarifier floor has not reached terminal thickness. Then, when more tonnage of sludge (by increased flow) comes to the final clarifier, there is enough latitude in sludge potential thickness that the same RAS rate is sufficient to include the additional weight in the, now thicker, return sludge.

2. The return sludge underflow pumping rate can be increased when there is an increase in sludge settling into the blanket.

Simply, the entire operation-management of a RAS system is to keep the sludge blanket from building up on the clarifier floor. If it does, RAS has to be increased in one way or another to maintain the steady-state blanket depth. Any change in the total weight (a function of MLSS and volume) of activated sludge carried in the system is controlled only by the net growth and sludge wasting. The percentage of return has no effect on the MLSS, presuming a very minimum of inventory on the final clarifier bottom.

Rate of return sludge The rate of return sludge may vary from 35 to 50 percent in systems carrying a thin MLSS content (around 2,000 mg/l) and from 75 to 100 percent in systems carrying higher MLSS content. Regimes carrying extremely high MLSS content may have to use up to 200 percent RAS. The thickness to which the sludge will concentrate in the final clarifier also affects the RAS rate. The following formulas apply to the RAS thickness and return rate.

Sludge Volume Index. The determination of the sludge volume index (SVI) is one of the useful aids in determining whether the aeration process is being operated properly. The SVI (by Mohlman[4]), as applied to mixed liquor (MLSS), is quite widely used and can be defined by either of the two ratios

$$\text{SVI} = \frac{\text{percent settleable solids (in 30 min)*}}{\text{percent suspended solids}} \tag{1}$$

or

$$\text{SVI} = \frac{\text{percent settleable solids} \times 10{,}000}{\text{suspended solids, mg/l}} \tag{2}$$

Return Activated Sludge (RAS). The percentage (of the influent flow) of sludge return can be calculated from the following equations:

$$\text{Sludge return, percent} = \frac{\text{mgd of RAS} \times 100}{\text{mgd of waste feed}} \tag{3}$$

$$\text{Sludge return, percent} = \frac{100Sa}{Sr - Sa} \tag{4}$$

where

Sa = mixed liquor suspended solids, mg/l
Sr = return sludge suspended solids, mg/l

Note: At 100 percent RAS, $Sr = 2Sa$ (approximately), at 50 percent RAS, $Sr = 3Sa$ (approximately), and at 33 percent RAS, $Sr = 4Sa$ (approximately).

* In a 1,000-ml cylinder. When MLSS is greater than 5,000 mg/l, dilute with clear water and judge accordingly.

Sludge loading Sludge loading in an aeration reactor is of considerable importance in selecting the size of a reactor. The amount of sludge carried in the process has marked influence on proper functioning of the process. The sludge loading can be defined as the ratio of the pounds of 5-day BOD added per day to the pounds of MLSS in the tank [lb BOD/(day)(lb MLSS]. The reciprocal of the sludge loading is the *sludge age* (actually, sludge displacement time). For conventional activated sludge processes, a sludge age of at least 3 days is considered necessary, with 4 days more desirable. Some difficult operations will require a more endogenous (8- to 10-day) sludge. For very-high-rate modifications, the sludge age may be less than 1 day.

Figure 22 shows the relationship between MLSS concentration, space loading [lb BOD_5/(day) 1,000 cu ft of reactor] and sludge loading [lb BOD_5/(day)(lb MLSS].

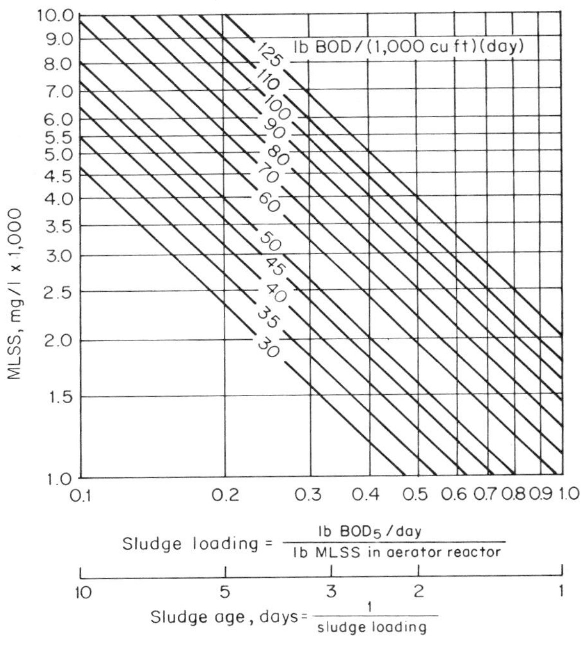

Fig. 22 Mixed liquor solids vs. BOD loading. The concentration of solids required in the aerator for a given 5-day BOD space loading [lb/(day)(1,000 cu ft reactor)] to provide a given sludge loading or sludge age. From these data the characteristics of the aerator tanks can be calculated. *Note:* "Sludge age" is actually the mean new cell displacement time in days. ⊥ symbol is a common operation point for a stable process just emerging from the exogenous respiration state into the endogenous, i.e., a sludge loading of 0.33 or 3-day sludge age. More strictly, sludge age = Xv(lb)/ ΔXv (lb/day), where Xv = vol. MLSS and ΔXv = vol. solids accumulation rate.

PHYSICAL-CHEMICAL SYSTEMS

Physical-chemical organic waste treatment (P-C), a system of granular activated carbon adsorption following primary chemical precipitation, although now in the pilot-plant and early installation stages, may hold considerable promise for application to industrial wastewaters in the future. After the practical application and operating problems have been worked out, the system's operating costs can be evaluated properly. Even though the installation cost of P-C is cheaper, the 10-year overall cost for P-C is considerably greater than for activated sludge. Such a system requires on-site regeneration of the granular carbon in a furnace. This, in general, involves the functions of after-incineration of the volatilized organics and steam reactivation of the granules. The regenerated activated carbon is returned to the adsorber towers, along with makeup carbon, by means of a complex materials handling system.

In the future, it is possible that P-C may, in some fields, replace[5,6] activated sludge as an industrial wastewater treatment system, particularly when dealing with heavy chemical wastewater treatment problems. Unfortunately, P-C does not adsorb nitrogen forms (NH_3, etc.); however, in many industrial cases this will be of no importance.

Refractory Contaminants

Certain contaminants, termed *refractory,* are not capable of being removed in conventional biological water and waste treatment plants. These refractory contaminants range from simple inorganic salts and organics (such as tannins and lignins) through an increasing number of highly complex synthetic organic chemicals (such as a variety of substituted benzenes).

Refractory contaminants can kill fish and other aquatic life, cause taste and odor problems in drinking water, and create foaming and corrosion or scale in recycle distribution systems. They can adversely affect coagulation and settling rates in tertiary treatment.

Of the processes capable of removing refractory organic materials from wastewater, adsorption on activated carbon appears to be the best method at this time. However, wastewater is a biological fluid and adsorbed organics become substrates for biological synthesis activity; hence overall removals often exceed removal due to adsorption only. This can lead to problems such as loss of adsorption efficiency and odors, and the necessity for early regeneration. Backwashing carbon columns is not efficient for the removal of these slimes.

Carbon Regeneration

For granular carbon adsorption to be economically feasible, the spent carbon must be regenerated and reused. Makeup carbon is routinely added to the system to replace that lost during hydraulic transport and regeneration. These losses include both attrition loss due to physical deterioration and burning losses during the actual regeneration process. The overall losses from thermal regeneration by multiple-hearth furnaces vary from 5 to 10 percent per cycle.

Figure 23 illustrates the carbon regeneration flow scheme in use at Lake Tahoe. Spent carbon, taken in slurry form from the adsorption columns, passes to the drain and feed tanks. The water drains through screens near tank bottom to about 50 percent moisture in about 15 min and is then discharged to the furnace by a variable-speed metering-screw conveyor. The six-hearth 54-in.-diameter furnace has a capacity range of 1,000 to 6,000 lb/day of dry carbon. In the furnace, the carbon is heated to 1600 to 1700°F in a controlled atmosphere which volatizes and oxidizes the adsorbed impurities. About 1 lb of steam is added per pound of dry carbon to reactivate the granules.

The off-gases pass through a 1200°F afterburner and a wet scrubber. The regenerated carbon discharges into a small quench tank and is pumped as a slurry to the defining (backwashing) and storage tanks. The wash tank is pressurized and the carbon slurry forced through a 2-in. line to the top of the adsorption columns.

Typical Flowsheet

Figure 24 illustrates a typical flowsheet being used for design of complete physical-chemical treatment systems. Chemical clarification and filtration are used to achieve almost complete suspended and colloidal solids removal before carbon adsorption. Outside of a little NH_3 diffusion into the air, this system does not remove ammonia. Screening, grit removal, and final disinfection are provided. The filtration step is usually provided before the carbon adsorbers with downflow packed beds, or following the carbon if they are upflow expanded bed units. Some systems use filters on both sides of an upflow adsorber layout.

Sludge Disposal

Sludge disposal plays a dominant role in the economics of any chemical clarification system. Only limited data on the characteristics of sludges resulting from the chemical treatment of wastewater are available. These data indicate that with iron or aluminum salts as coagulants

1. The resulting sludge volume sometimes exceeds and sometimes is less than primary sludge from the same waste.
2. The chemical sludge is more difficult to dewater in a vacuum filter than the corresponding primary sludge.

With lime as the coagulant, the sludge should thicken well, but the full effectiveness of reclaiming lime from a mixture with raw sludge still remains to be demonstrated.

Operation

In these systems the waste is passed either upward or downward through columns containing granular carbon. Downflow columns function as packed beds and ac-

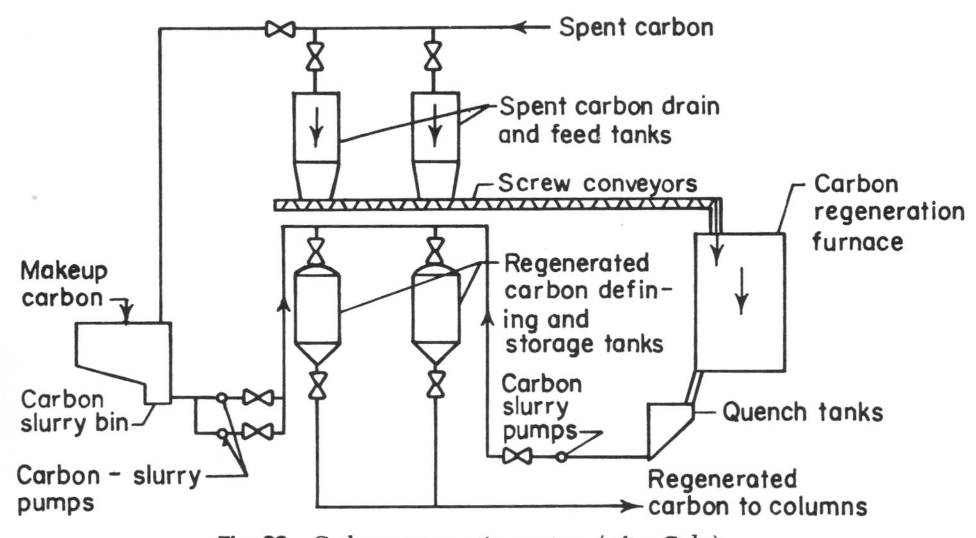

Fig. 23 Carbon regeneration system (*after Culp*).

complish filtration of the wastewater. Flow rates of 2 to 8 gpm/sq ft have been employed. In this flow range essentially equivalent adsorption efficiency is obtained provided the same contact time is employed. At flow rates below 2 gpm/sq ft, adsorption efficiency is reduced because of short-circuiting. At flow rates above 8 gpm/sq ft, rapid clogging may take place. Contact time employed is in the range of 30 min (empty bed basis). Contact time beyond 30 min yields less increase in sorption efficiency; at about 60 min contact, increase becomes negligible.

Carbon beds designed for gravity flow are expected to operate at the lower application rates. Systems designed for the higher flow rates employ pressure vessels. A pressure vessel is more expensive to construct than a gravity-flow vessel, but it requires less land area, and provides greater ability to handle fluctuations in flow rate.

Downflow carbon beds, even if they are preceded by a filter, gradually collect suspended solids and require backwashing. Biological growth takes place on the carbon granules and tends to clog the bed, and it may be advisable to include air scour to achieve some removal of the gelatinous slimes.

Backwash of the carbon beds satisfactorily relieves clogging head loss but does not completely remove the slimes. Biological activity is manifest in the carbon beds at most times, which leads to anaerobic conditions in the carbon bed and perhaps serious operating problems.

An upflow semifluidized (10 percent) contact system may be used to help overcome anaerobic conditions. Care must be exercised to avoid hydraulic surges which could wash carbon out of the system. A filtration unit must follow the carbon contact when the fluid-bed system is used.

Note: If this expanded system is allowed to operate as packed bed upflow during low flows, suspended solids (*mud balls*) may accumulate near the bottom and would be very difficult to remove. This should be carefully avoided. Also, during fluid-bed operation, slimes may grow and permanently clog the bottom strainer system, indicating the necessity to provide operating access to the bottom strainer without complete medium removal.

FILTERING

There are many situations in wastewater treatment where sand filtering for maximum suspended solids and included COD removal is indicated either to prepare a flow

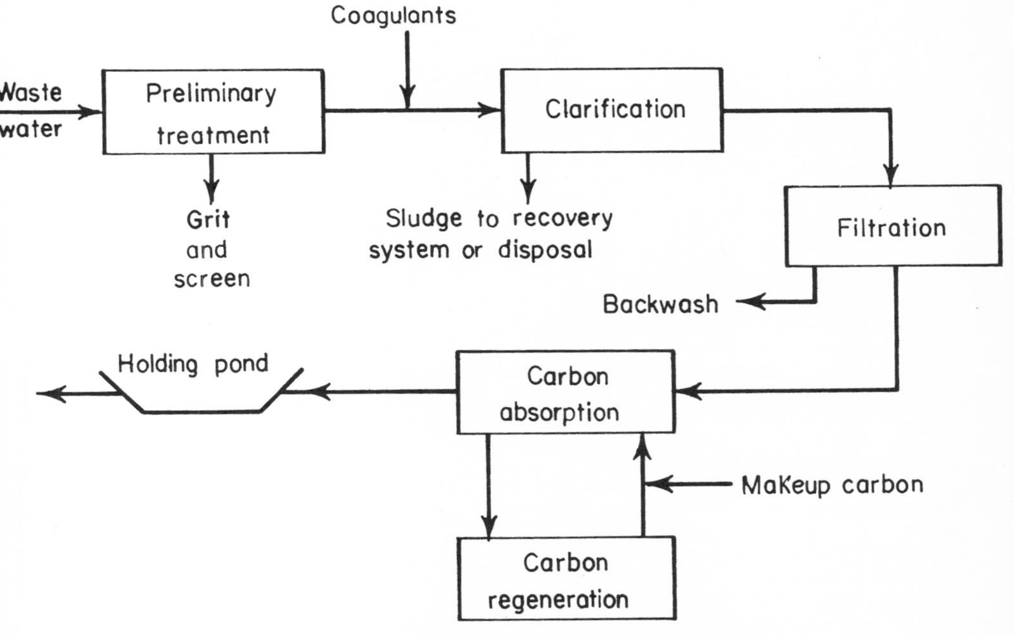

Fig. 24 Flow diagram of a physical-chemical treatment system.

stream by filtration for a subsequent contact media (such as carbon granules or zeolite) or in tertiary application to polish an effluent.

Where a somewhat lesser degree of suspended solids removal is required, microstraining can be applied.

The tertiary sand filter, employing a practical 0.8-mm effective size medium, can remove roughly 85 to 95 percent of the suspended solids. A micromesh filter employing a screen with 25-micron openings can remove about 50 to 70 percent of the suspended solids. A deep-bed filter using 6 to 8 ft of relatively coarse, 2.0-mm sand size can remove certain kinds of solids and free oil.

The various forms of filtering as applied to industrial wastewater will now be discussed.

Sand Filters

There are several modern versions of the traditional rapid sand filter, a reliable performer long used in process and potable water treatment. However, except for the use of multiple media and air-and-water backwash, the mechanics of operation and performance have remained much the same through the years. A prime disadvantage inherent in the *rapid sand (packed bed) filter* is the necessity for sporadic backwash with large quantities of water—sometimes aggregating a sizable portion of the filtered product water, especially in wastewater tertiary straining where the filter is apt to encounter slimes and a relatively high suspended solids feed load. There are some corollary problems associated with the sporadic backwash: sudden, increased loading on the remaining filter units while backwashing one and the necessity to handle the large quantities of backwash water back through the plant.

Packed bed sand filters will remove about 85 to 95 percent of the suspended solids presented to them provided good operating conditions exist. Filters should not be kept in operation for too long a cycle (not past the early breakthrough point), change in operating rate should be slow, and backwashing must be with filtered water.

Modern controls, such as effluent turbidity meters, have been developed which monitor early breakthrough and substantially aid in filter operation. Automatic control panels take a backwash starting signal, and sequentially go step-by-step through the entire program of removing the unit from service, backwashing and placing it back into service.

Dual media are often used (and perhaps three or four media sizes) to lengthen the filter runs by utilizing a larger, hard coal medium on top of the filter sand layer. The greater interstitial voids in the larger medium act to collect and store solids avoiding early head loss and breakthrough. By intercepting a large amount of the applied suspended solids in this larger medium, the total suspended solids applied to the filter sand proper is reduced, increasing the removal efficiency of the sand.

Air can be used to scour the media, followed by a backwash water rinse and reclassification. Especially in the case of wastewater tertiary filtration, air wash not only effects good scour to release zoogleal growths from both the coal and the sand but also saves considerable backwash water, not in rate, but in quantity. Air assist in backwash makes practical the use of the coarse coal layer.

Modern packed bed filter design The packed bed (rapid sand) filter is an inundated straining device consisting of a false bottom equipped with slotted strainers, which holds the layer of filter sand. Above the sand is the layer (or layers) of hard coal media somewhat coarser and containing more voids than the sand. A wash-water gutter lies a couple of feet above the media layers and serves to overflow the backwash rinse water to sewer. Backwashing is repeated every time the media attains a substantial head loss during operation.

In operation, dirty water flows into the filter and slowly percolates through the media, through the underdrain strainers, and out to the filtered water storage. From time to time, as required by head-loss increase, the filtering cycle is interrupted and the filter media is backwashed by pumping a supply of *filtered* water backwards through the media. Air may also be used in the backwash operation to break loose slimes clinging to the media. The air is uniformly distributed through the strainers ahead of the backwash–water-rinse cycle (Fig. 25).

Filter Media. Most of the packed bed filters use substantially the same media size and type combinations, delineated as follows.

The filter sand (bottom 15- to 18-in. layer) is a special, filter-grade quartz sand with a specific gravity of 2.65, graded to a uniformity coefficient of not less than 1.3 nor greater than 1.7. The sand is sized approximately like this: 0.5-mm effective size for low solids content wastewater (or water supply) and 0.8-mm effective size for tertiary straining service.

The coal-medium layer (15- to 18-in. layer above the filter sand) is a specially selected anthracite of medium filter grade with a specific gravity of 1.5. The effective size of the coal is selected from a commercially available size to expand compatibly with the filter sand to about 22 percent. The coal medium sizes run roughly about 1.2 mm to team with the 0.5-mm sand, and about 2.4 mm to team with the 0.8-mm sand. Sometimes two sizes of coal are used in the coarse layer, each having different density to keep the largest size predominantly on top.

Backwash-water Design. When the filter attains a head loss of between 5 and 8 ft of water column (WC), or whenever early breakthrough shows up, the unit is backwashed to purge the solids accumulated in the interstices.

Small filters, less than 15-ft diameter, are ordinarily backwashed directly by wash water pumped from filtered storage. Filters larger than 15-ft diameter are backwashed by gravity from an elevated filtered water storage tank.

Backwash Air. Backwash of multimedia units is commonly inaugurated with an air scour, designed at about 4 scfm/sq ft of filter. The air scour quickly loosens slimes, breaks up mud balls, and saves considerably on the total quantity of backwash water that would otherwise be required with a long water-wash period.

To be effective, the air scour must be applied quite uniformly over the entire filter bottom, otherwise it can be a disaster. The air generally is applied through the false bottom strainers and is controlled by orifices in the plunge pipes extending down from the strainers through the false bottom.

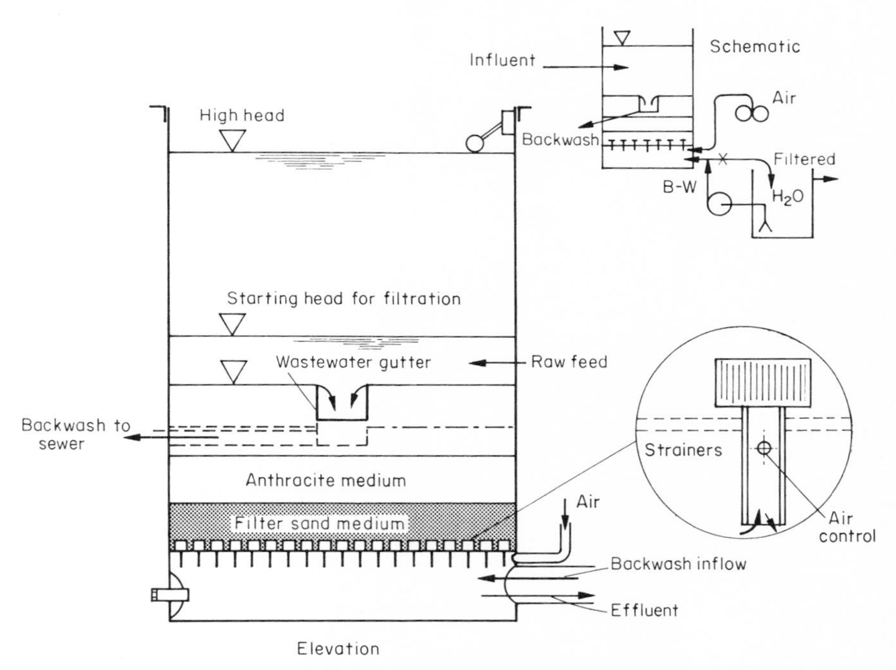

Fig. 25 Schematic dual-media filter, air-and-water wash.

Backwash following the air scour fluidizes the media and both rinses out dislocated particulates from the expanded interstitial voids and also reclassifies the layers of media. The desired media expansion is about 22 percent, down from the older practice of 50 percent which tended to jet stream through the fluidized media. The quantity of water required to effect this 22 percent expansion depends on the absolute viscosity of the water (temperature), and will run in the order of 20 to 24 gpm/sq ft. The entire sequence is automated.

Surface Wash. Filter backwash is sometimes aided by surface wash units, generally rotary arms driven through the expanded media by water jet propulsion. Surface wash, when used with dual media, takes the place of the air scour, and is not used in addition to air scour. Surface wash may not be as effective as air scour to dislodge slimes attached throughout the media, especially in tertiary use following secondary activated sludge carbonaceous treatment. Following complete nitrification, slimes may not be such a problem, and surface wash may suffice. However, air scour does save backwash-water quantity and may be desirable for that reason.

Filter Bottoms. These are commonly made of either steel plate or precast concrete beams supported above the false bottom space. Strainers are mounted on 8-in. centers on these bottoms. The strainers, which eliminate the graded gravel underlayment, are designed with fine slots to retain the smallest sieve-size sand particle and with just enough slots to effect a backwash distribution head loss through the strainer of 3 or 4 ft of water column at 20 gpm/sq ft (20°C). For air-wash assist, the strainers have plunge pipes equipped with orifices to meter an air rate of 4 cfm/sq ft at a 4-in. WC air-pressure loss. The air blower operates against a 5-psig back pressure.

Sometimes the underdrains use perforated, hollow tiles covered with layers of graded gravel to support the filter sand in place. In such cases, air wash is not used, and surface-wash units aid in scouring slimes from the coal medium.

Wash-water Troughs. Wash-water troughs are designed about 18 to 24 in. above the coarse media surface, so that when the media are partially fluidized and expanded (about 22 percent) during the water backwash, the overflow lip will be 12 to 15 in. above the interface. In this way the turbulent rinsing will carry dislodged organic particles (but not the media) into the trough and to the sewer.

These troughs and the egress piping must be designed large enough to discharge free, and not flood out the wash-water gutters during backwashing. The safest design is to use a drop-forebay from the troughs so there will be ample head above the very turbulent entry into the gravity-flow sewer pipe.

The spacing of these troughs is moot and not too important but should probably not be greater than 5 or 6 ft.

Types of filters

Small, Open Gravity Steel Filters. These units have two main advantages: the media and backwash operation can be observed through the open top and they afford easy access.

The filters are shipped completely fabricated in sizes through 12-ft diameter by 15 ft high and are field-erected in larger diameters. Multiple units are used to cut down backwash rate and the overload on remaining units during backwash.

Steel Pressure Filters. Pressure filters are commonly built in sizes up through 12-ft diameter and are shipped fabricated. The strainer systems and backwashing are the same as for open shell filters.

In vertical units, the steel bottom is supported above the dished head, allowing just enough room for backwash space and plunge pipe clearance. In the horizontal units, the bottom is supported in the lower third of the diameter.

The combined inlet diffuser and wash-water discharge is effected by a large diffuser plate disposed a few inches below the inlet (and/or outlet) piping through the top head in a vertical unit and a horizontal, drilled pipe (or multiple-plate diffusers) running longitudinally just under the top of a horizontal unit.

Advantages of the pressure unit are that head loss through the filter media can run somewhat in excess of 8 ft (but cannot exceed early breakthrough) and that the system can be piped irrespective of the gravity-flow hydraulic grade line. Since all piping is under pressure, smaller piping can be used at the expense of additional head loss during the backwash operation.

Disadvantages are that the inner filter is not accessible and media cannot be observed during backwash. Also, operating service (such as breaking up cementation or mud balls) is, unfortunately, only poorly accomplished through an upper manhole.

Steel Self-backwash Filters. These units are designed in many styles. The most commonly applied style in the industrial wastewater field consists of two compartments, one built above the other. The closed bottom compartment contains the filter media, strainer bottom, and inlet-outlet means, and the open upper compartment stores the filtered backwash water. An interconnected, standing overflow forces the filtered water leaving the bottom to flow through a riser which communicates with the upper storage compartment. Only when this compartment is filled can the filtered water overflow to the filtered water storage.

When the time comes for backwashing, opening a valve inaugurates reversal of the flow from storage into the lower filter unit for the backwash and rinse functions. The diminishing available head in the storage tank enforces declining rate backwash which, under some circumstances, may not be desirable.

The cost of self-stored units is a small advantage; but as insurance for protracted or double-backwash requirement (to overcome upsets in clarification), the separate backwash from storage is to be recommended.

Rectangular Open Filters. Rectangular concrete construction is applied to large filter units in excess of a 2-mgd rate for each unit. Even the filter bottoms may be poured-in-place or precast concrete, using plastic inserts into which the strainers are screwed.

Otherwise, the arrangement of media and strainers, wash-water gutters, inlet and outlet are generally the same as for the small, open gravity filters.

Backwash piping is arranged so that each half of each filter unit can be washed separately, one at a time. This reduces the wash-water rate, but the filter operates as one single unit when in the filtering mode.

Deep-bed Filters. The deep-bed filter is sometimes applied to industrial wastes involving substantial quantities of suspended, nonflocculent, solids, such as fine rolling mill scale, tramp oil, or silts. Slime-forming, organic solids–bearing wastewaters are not candidates for this type of filtration. This filter is designed with deeper, coarser media layers than is the polishing sand filter. Polyelectrolyte feed to the filter influent should be available.

The deep-bed industrial filter, treating primary clarified wastewater, sometimes may take the place of a secondary chemical coagulation and clarifier operation and has the advantage of requiring considerably less space with about the same installation cost.

Surface-loading rates of 20 gpm/sq ft and higher have been suggested. However, operation demonstrates that loading should not ordinarily exceed 10 to 12 gpm/sq ft if cycles between backwashing are to be kept within reasonable limits (12 to 20 hr). These units are designed only as pressure filters and operate at a high pressure loss, as much as 20 psig or more, before they are backwashed.

Deep-bed filters usually employ a quartz sand of 1.9 mm (range of 1.3 to 2.5 mm). Because of the large filter-sand size and the great media depth, a top, coarse coal layer has not ordinarily been employed.

The sand media is supported directly on a false bottom equipped with strong plastic strainers having slots fine enough to retain the filter sand. These strainers are installed on 8-in. centers, both ways, and have plunger pipes to control the distribution of the air-and-water backwash.

Backwash air (a must) is at a 5 cfm/sq ft rate, and water wash at a 35 to 40 gpm/sq ft rate at 20°C. Mandatory operation is at about a 10 percent expansion of the media—sufficient for the air to scour out the heavy interstitial clogging. Since there is no danger in washing this large media into the wash-water sewer system, air wash is admitted simultaneously with the wash water during the entire wash cycle.

Moving-bed Filters. To avoid sporadic shutdown and backwashing and to keep the filtering operation in continuous service, several modes of tertiary filters have been designed to move the sand media countercurrent to the intrusion of solids interception and clogging. These units are actually moving, packed bed (rapid sand) filters.

The dirty sand is removed and washed as a sidearm function, and then returned to the cleanest part of the advancing media. Sand media of a single size is used because there is no reason or possibility for employing multiple media.

In one of these designs, packed filter sand media is pushed forward in pulses through inclined modules, countercurrent to the influent flow. The extruded sand mass emitting from the upper, influent end of the module moves out a few inches from each pulse, and is then mechanically cut off to fall into a hopper. From here, the sand is moved and washed externally, and returned to the lower end of the moving filter sand column.

There have been some functional and developmental problems, but eventually these problems will be worked out and the continuous filters will compete with the cyclic, packed bed filter units, at least for tertiary application.

Micromesh Filtering

An intermediate filtering (straining) operation, performing with somewhat less efficiency than a multimedium filter, may be characterized as a continuous backwash strainer. This micromesh strainer system incorporates a specially woven stainless-steel wire cloth, or monofilament nylon cloth, with free openings on the order of 15 to 60 microns in size, mounted on the periphery of a revolving drum arranged for continuous backwashing. The drum operates submerged in the flowing waste to approximately 70 percent of its depth. Raw water enters through an open end of the drum and flows radially outwards through the microfabric leaving behind much of its suspended solids content. The strained-out solids are carried around on the inside of the fabric and underneath rows of wash-water jets. The jet rows, spanning the full width of the fabric, flush the solids for disposal into a receiving hopper mounted on the hollow axle of the drum. Filtered water for back flushing is drawn from the downstream side of the unit and pumped through high-pressure jets.

Applications Applications are varied, the unit sometimes being somewhat misapplied (in the place of a polishing sand filter) because of its desirable lesser installation cost and continuous backwash characteristics. Ordinarily it is used following the physical-chemical clarification step before carbon contact; following secondary sedimentation where the total suspended solids (TSS) load is not too great and where 60 to 70 percent removal of suspended solids is expected; following flotation cells to remove some solids from the subnatant directly to product water as a save-all or fine scalping unit (with larger mesh size); or most any TSS removal application where efficiencies of 60 to 70 percent are acceptable and where there are a few gross settleable solids in the influent.

Equipment The equipment is most often made of epoxy-coated steel, and the rotating drum is equipped with removable stainless-steel micromesh panels. The drum is mounted in a steel open-top shell in small (shippable) package units and

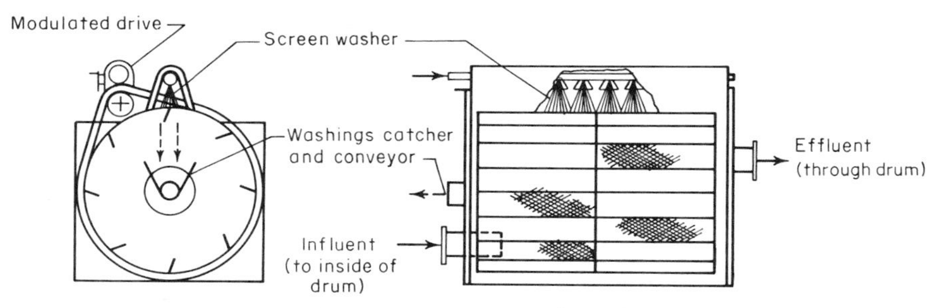

Fig. 26 Sketch of a micromesh drum filter unit.

in a concrete shell in large units. There is a neoprene seal means between the open (influent) drum end and the shell, and the drums are rotated by peripheral, outside drive gears, chain belts, or rubber V belts. A variable-speed drive, automatically controlled by the head loss, is used. The high-pressure wash-water spray header lies in axial juxtaposition with the top of the drum (Fig. 26).

The screen sections are bolted in place and have a coarse stainless-steel mesh affixed outside of the stainless-steel wire cloth, or nylon micromesh cloth, to retain it. The woven cloth medium has apertures of 60, 35, and 25 microns with 60,000, 80,000, and 165,000 openings per sq in. respectively. Stainless-steel cloths as fine as 10 to 15 microns have been tried, but do not seem practical. Nylon cloth seems to have advantages in retaining smaller suspended solids for the same mesh size with less head loss and in being easier to backwash. Thus, nylon cloth is coming into increasing use in these strainers.

Drum speed Drum speed runs 25 to 150 ft/min (tangential peripheral). The speed is increased to reduce head loss through the micromesh medium, but too fast a peripheral speed may cause gross loss of solids to the effluent. A surface mat accumulation is required for better performance in filtering efficiency. Running the drum too fast results in skin turbulence, loosening of the filter mat, and loss in efficiency.

The peripheral drum speed is automatically, progressively increased to respond to increases in head loss, sensed by a bubbler control. Sometimes, the backwash spray pressure is also increased automatically with increasing head loss to effect better cleaning (reduction in head loss) to avoid as much drum speed increase as possible.

Surface area This is often confusing. The gross surface area is calculated from the drum submergence, generally 60 to 70 percent. The net micromedium area is calculated after deducting frame area, which runs about 15 percent. As a practical matter, filter rates are calculated on the basis of gross submerged cylindrical area—70 percent submergence on large units and 60 percent on small ones.

Throughput rates These rates run from between 7½ gpm/sq ft with 3-in. head loss to about 20 gpm/sq ft with 12-in. head loss. Of course, as the head loss increases, the drum speed will increase and the filter efficiency will degenerate. Accordingly, the design throughput should be on the basis of 7 to 8 gpm/sq ft with the higher rates employed only as a reserve.

Backwash rate The backwash rate will run about 3 to 5 percent of the throughput, depending on the quantity and type of influent TSS solids. The backwash rate is continuous with the pressure running at a nominal 25 psig—with an increase possible to increase the backwash effectiveness and avoid excessive drum speeds.

Backwash supply is drawn from the strainer effluent before any chlorination. The continuous use of a chlorinated supply will be deleterious to the longevity of the mechanical parts.

Operation Operation is relatively inexpensive from a labor and maintenance standpoint, with most of the modulations being automatic. However, there are a few services for the operator to perform.

Desliming is done superficially by an ultraviolet lamp installation along the length of the drum. The tube *must* be of the type that screens out ozone or else oxidation destruction will take place on the drum. The lamp desliming system is generally inadequate anyway and, according to need, the operator has to shock-treat the drum surface with a strong hypochlorite solution. Application is by a perforated shower means applied to the slowly rotating drum. This operation, if not automated, may take several hours. Where iron, manganese, calcite, etc., encrust on the screens, they need to be treated by inhibited acid using the same technique.

When the unit is not in continuous operation, it should be drained and hosed to prevent solids from settling inside and anchoring on the screen.

Grease and oil have to be avoided in the influent. Unlike the packed bed sand filter, these units do not tolerate free oil.

Some types of suspended wastewater solids do not respond to microscreening, the removals being of such a low efficiency as to preclude the application. The use of two micromesh screening units placed in series does not, ordinarily, effect any substantial improvement in solids removal.

Unknown applications have to be checked out by renting available field-trial units having about 1 sq ft of filter area.

SMALL TREATMENT WORKS

Industrial waste treatment for small operations often poses some additional difficult problems. Whereas large industries can better afford the sometimes high construction costs involved, smaller operations have to pay disproportionately more when following traditional designs, and full-time operation is a greater problem. The best solution involving waste streams around 100,000 gpd or so is apt to follow a path quite different from the large plant design, perhaps using membrane or ion-exchange technology for the removal of dissolved solids, or tube or plate settlers for clarification, or a complete system made up of prefabricated modules.

Membrane Techniques

Although membrane technology–reverse osmosis, electrodialysis, ultrafiltration, and ion-exchange reaction have been successfully applied to many in-plant recovery operations, application to large-volume industrial water treatment has been limited because of high equipment and operating costs. Other processes such as biomass contact and perhaps even physical-chemical seem to be cheaper and better understood and are more often applied to large waste treatment plants. However, their application to small waste flows, often on a leasing arrangement, or small, isolated sections of large industries may be to advantage.

Reverse osmosis (RO) using specially processed cellulose acetate or noncellulosic membrane for phase separation, consists of a relatively simple pumped system producing a continuous permeate stream relatively free of dissolved solids and ions. Operation is critical but not too complicated, and the system may be capable of treating a wide range of feed waste streams. Pilot-plant testing is advisable for each specific waste, along with a guarantee of performance from the manufacturer.

Electrodialysis (ED) is an electrical method of reducing the dissolved salt content of wastewater by a system of rectified high voltage and considerable amperage and membrane stacks. An ED membrane stack is a complicated mechanical structure requiring disassembly for cleaning. Reassembly requires some skill in arranging the exact proper sequence of alternate anion and cation membranes with spacers placed in exact positions depending on the membrane sequence. ED membranes are virtually ion-exchange resins in sheet form and subject to resin fouling even though protected by activated carbon pretreatment. ED removes ionizable salts except, perhaps, sulfates. Nonionizable substances (such as silica, organics, and bacteria) are not removed and remain in the product stream.

Ultrafiltration removes substances such as oils and suspensoids from dilute feeds, but does not remove submicron particulates or salts in true solution.

Ion exchange, generally mixed bed units, performs equally as well as RO, but apparently is a more expensive and complicated system to operate when treating industrial wastes. In small-scale operation, ion exchange is a batch process. The regeneration and eventual care to reduce media fouling makes operation of these units, perhaps, overly complicated for small-plant operation.

Of the above systems, RO seems the best suited to small waste flow application and will be delineated here.

Reverse osmosis The heart of the reverse osmosis system (RO) consists of a semipermeable modified cellulose acetate membrane module of either the spiral wound, large tube, or hollow fibers type providing a large amount of useful membrane surface area in a small pressure vessel. The driving force which extracts dissolved solids from the wastewater feed is the reverse osmosis pressure—the net difference between the applied pressure and the average osmotic pressure of the feed and the concentrate.

In most installations, a scale inhibitor and sometimes an acid is metered into the feed wastewater for the purpose of inhibiting precipitation of calcium and other slightly soluble salts on the membrane. The conditioned feed is then filtered, and the pressure continuously boosted with a multistage centrifugal pump. Operating pressures are normally in the range of 27 to 34 atm (400 to 500 psi). Product water freed of dissolved solids permeates through the membrane. The operating pressure on the RO unit is regulated by a valve which restricts the egress of the concentrate stream rejected by the membrane.

The RO unit operates continuously or intermittently, as required by supply, but will require attention to relieving fouling of the membrane. Occasional replacement of the membrane module will also be required when it eventually fails from organic fouling and breakdown (see Fig. 27).

Application. Many small industries may well consider RO, particularly, where zero discharge effluents may eventually be required. Chemical industries could recover glycerol, or phenols, etc. from waste streams. Small plating operations can treat rinse water for reuse and recover nickel, copper, and other metals but cannot recover cyanide.

The cyanide ion cannot be separated since at the pH required it exists as HCN and passes through both streams but can be treated with chlorine (first stage only) and then follow with RO as a separation stage.

Equipment. A typical RO unit is a package assembly of cartridge, filter, pumps, instruments, fail-safe controls, pressure vessels, valves, fittings, and chemical feed equipment. The filter may be a microporous membrane unit ($\frac{1}{10}$-micron retention). The multistage high-pressure pumps are designed to operate in parallel with one complete standby. The tubular pressure vessels, mounted on a steel frame, are of 4-in. standard epoxy-lined pipe about 20 ft long, each containing about 65 sq ft of membrane area. All high-pressure valves, fittings, and piping are stainless steel.

The pressure control valve automatically maintains a steady applied pressure of any selected amount. A pressure of 400 to 500 psi is regarded as normal operation. The ability to range up to an absolute maximum of 600 psi to handle extraordinary circumstances must be designed in. Too high a pressure (550 to 600 psi, more or less) results in rapid compaction and destruction of the cellulosic cell and the irreversible loss of flow rate.

A scale inhibitor (often sodium hexametaphosphate) is recommended to help prevent precipitation of calcium sulfate or carbonate from saturated solutions (at the membrane boundary layer). This generally consists of a solution tank and a metering feeder injecting into the line ahead of the cartridge filter.

Acid is injected similarly, as required, to reduce the pH to a range of 6.0 to 6.5. Sulfuric or any convenient acid is used. Sometimes a caustic is required to increase the pH.

Disinfection is practiced to kill biogrowth which can foul membranes. Chlorine injection to a residual of 0.5 to 1.0 mg/l in the feedwater is recommended. Sometimes the chlorine solution is added (proportionally) to the scale-inhibitor chemical solution tank. Ozone may also be used where chlorine cannot be tolerated in the treated water.

No suspended solids (SS) can be tolerated in the membrane module feedwater or the membrane will rapidly clog and production will cease. The filter just ahead

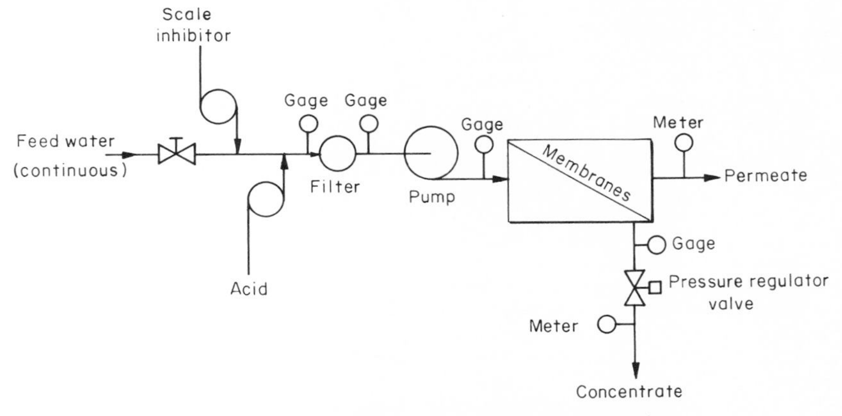

Fig. 27 Schematic diagram of reverse osmosis plant.

of the membrane will not accept too great a SS load without clogging and back-pressuring.

Suspended solids should be removed by a system of chemical coagulation, flocculation, and sedimentation and sand filtration. This pretreatment, ideally, should produce an inflow stream of a maximum of one Jackson turbidity unity (JTU).

The RO system operating pressure is very important as discussed in the section on pressure control valves.

pH range can vary between 3 and 7.5, but ordinary operation should be controlled between pH 6 to 6.5. This can be done by controlled feeding of any acid (or caustic) as discussed earlier.

Feed strength is important in that leakage of dissolved solids into the permeate will be a constant percentage of the feed concentration. This sometimes indicates a series of RO units (for zero discharge, especially with high-strength wastes).

When the RO unit is to be shut down for more than about a week's time, the system has to be flooded with a 0.1 percent formaldehyde solution treated to a pH between 4.5 and 5.0. The waste feed is closed and the formaldehyde solution pumped in, displacing the existing solution. The pressure control valve is then closed, the permeate line remaining open. The system should be flushed thoroughly before start-up.

Fouling of the membrane by deposition of SS, precipitation of slightly soluble salts, or biogrowth will seriously reduce the RO production rate. There are steps to take to attempt alleviation of such fouling.

Acid flushing should be done at pH 2.0 to 2.5 for 30 min. Chlorine flushing should be done at 10 mg/l for 30 min.

Once anchored to membrane sites, slimes are difficult to dislodge. An organic slime cleaner should be tried.

Direct osmosis can be tried by closing the feed line, opening the pressure valve and connecting the permeate line to the treated water source for reverse flow (ordinary, *direct* osmosis) for 15 to 30 min. The permeate line must *never be pressurized* because the membrane module will be damaged.

High-Rate Settlers

Many informed operators and investigators fully realize the shortcomings of a surprising number of settling basins. Rampant short-circuiting and hydroinstability continue to plague many clarifiers.

Better effluent results have been achieved in several unsatisfactory industrial wastewater clarifiers by adding flow-straightening devices in the form of short, *tube settler* modules.

This suggests that perhaps the same clarification job can be done in a much smaller unit of considerably shorter detention (15 min versus 120 to 180 min) and higher "surface" loading rate. This may well be true, especially in the small-flow applications, and in particular where slime-forming propensities are small or nil. However, there are problems to be considered before jumping to conclusions. Where concentrated suspensions of flocculant solids are to be settled, the tube or plate modular separators may not be able to handle the voluminous thick sludge masses (deposited between the plates or tubes). In such cases, the thick sludge mass may even back up from an accumulating (lower) sludge blanket and clog the passages that are expected to shed the settled sludge. Occasional bulking of biological sludge could pose an operating impasse at such times. Slimes and algae, too, may grow on and impede sludge flow down the inclined smooth plastic surfaces. Better designed clarifiers, even though larger, may be considerably cheaper than high-rate modules, or combinations of shallow clarifiers equipped with secondary-effect tube modules.

However, small flows may well be served by a mode of these high-rate, tube- or plate-module settlers because of both their expense and their performance. Many high-rate-settler designs have been patented and by and large, they are variations of either inclined small-dimension (roughly 2 in.) tube forms, or inclined lamellae closely positioned (2- to 4-in. spacing). The feed mode is either downflow or upflow, and soon after the flow enters the inclined narrow space, discrete particles will fall a very short distance to the lower plate or tube surface and the sludge quickly compacts and slides down the inclined plastic surface to discharge at the bottom.

Only two of the most experienced types will be delineated here. For further reference please be directed to Yao[7] and Culp et al.[8]

Lamellae sedimentation These multiple-plate-type, high-rate sedimentation units may be downflow, upflow, or medial flow (with flows both up and down). The most common commercial form is a downflow application having the settled sludge, which slides down smooth plastic plates, traveling the same direction as the flow through.

The effluent is derived through a header system which also maintains equal flow through each of the spaces. This separator consists of inclined (about 45°) parallel plates spaced 1 or 2 in. apart. Dividers are provided along the width of the plates to arrest lateral short-circuiting.

The operation is simple. The solids-bearing proportional flow enters the top of each space at an application rate about two to three times the rate used for small- to medium-sized plain clarifiers to achieve 90 percent or greater removal of *settleable* solids. Of course, various particles will require different application rates consistent with their different theoretical subsidence rates; viz., the laboratory subsidence rate of alum or iron flocs from nonorganic water turbidity settles at approximately 2 in./min (20°C). Ideally, a 1,795 gpd/sq ft of surface overflow rate. A 100-ft-diameter circular clarifier having a well-designed diffusing inlet would be designed at about 800 gpd/sq ft; one having a poor inlet, at 400 to 600. (A large 150-ft-diameter clarifier perhaps at 400 gpm/sq ft or less.) A lamellae separator would be safely designed at close to the theoretical subsidence point (about 1,500 gpd/sq ft) because the laminar, equal flow-through condition would be ideal. The liquid depth would also be approximately one-half of that for the 100-ft-diameter clarifier.

The surface loading rate at close to the theoretical particle subsidence rate is safer than that in most large clarifiers; even with a factor of safety of 3:1. Herein lie the charm and space saving of the high-rate settler, but for large flows the cost is apt to be prohibitive, assuming there is enough room for the less efficient deep plain settler.

Transport of sludge down the inclined lamallae is claimed to be aided by the concurrent downflow. However, the streaming flow velocity is so low, especially at the deposited sludge boundary layer (about 2 to 3 in./min), that this claim does not appear too valid. This seems particularly so since countercurrent, upflow designs seem to enjoy the same measure of hydraulic success as do the concurrent, downflow designs. Figure 28 suggests a system of flocculation–high-rate-settling filtration.

Tube sedimentation There are several configurations of tube shapes and sizes, generally all applied in an upflow mode. The most common commercial form is a system of 2 × 2 in. cross-sectional tubes inclined at 60° to the horizontal and formed into 10 ft × 30 in. wide × 21 in. deep modules. The tubes are inclined, alternately, both ways in this module and are made up of PVC and ABS smooth plastic.

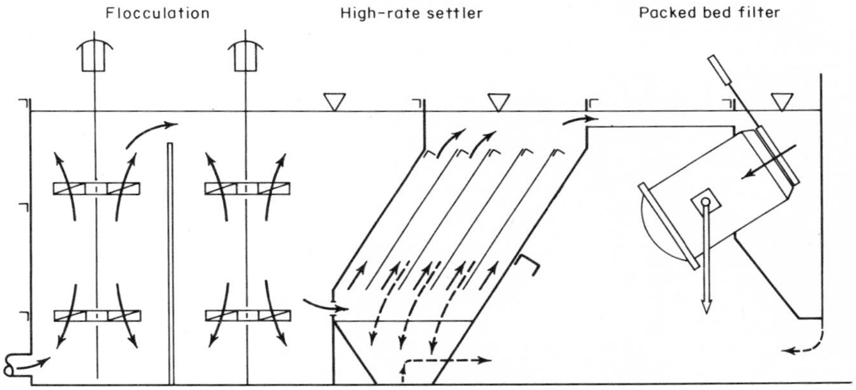

Fig. 28 Combination filtration system.

At ordinary rates of application, the head loss through the tubes suffices to balance the throughput for good hydraulic response.

The laminar flow and Reynolds number characteristics are quite similar to that outlined in the section on Lamellae Sedimentation as are the clarification results.

Evidently because of the superior hydraulic stability, the application rates in terms of gallons per day per square foot of tube horizontal surface can be expected to be about two times, and perhaps three times, the rates applied to standard clarifiers. This presumes that the rate never exceeds about 85 percent of the theoretical subsidence rate of the discrete particle to be settled when more than 90 to 95 percent removal performance is expected.

Module Treatment Units

This discussion pertains mostly to small manufacturing operations generating wastes containing oil, metals, and suspended solids such as those from metal finishing, plating and pickling operations, etc. Unfortunately, small operations may have too much waste to tank-truck to a disposal site but not enough waste to feasibly pump the flow to a remote site for normal waste treatment. The same may be true of small waste streams from large industrial plants which are too isolated from the large treatment works. In these cases it may be best to use a small treatment operation close to the source.

For these situations, an on-site package-type operation can probably handle the problem with a series of two or more module treatment units. Such units are often "turn-keyed" by the engineer-manufacturer and can be removed or added to if they do not entirely solve the problem. Also, expert operation assistance from the manufacturing company is invaluable for getting started properly and for training the operating staff.

Installation of these systems is often inside the mill and operation is by mill staff. In very small systems, the operation is on a batch basis; larger ones operate on continuous flow for most of the day.

These systems may embrace one or two coordinated steps acting as preliminary treatment to disposal into a large municipal sewer or industrial park combination system. They may also be quite complex—either recycling the treated waste for plant water supply or removing all of the objectionable dissolved solids and ions.

Sludge treatment for small operations is not economical or practicable. The oils are, in general, not reclaimable or refinable because of tax rulings and labeling adversity, additives and synthetic lubricants transportation costs and lack of specialists. The metal sludges, particularly iron, are not economically reclaimed from small operations. The same is true of acids and coagulants. The alternative is to arrange exporting of the sludges by organized waste haulers.

Equipment These layouts consist of several steps arranged in many combinations: holding and blending, neutralization or pH adjustment; grit removal, sedimentation and sludge storage; emulsion breaking; oil separation and storage; oil flotation (by dissolved air technique); and filtration.

Holding tank. A tank to receive flows and dumps from the manufacturing process is required to blend the varying constituents and to enable steady-state operation through the treatment units by constant-rate pumping. Often blending and homogeneity within this holding tank are effected by an air-lift eductor tube, especially in a deep tank. The layout may be, say, a 20- or 24-ft-deep cylindrical holding tank, having an eductor tube and air diffusion means (to the extent of 25 cfm/1,000 cu ft) operating near middepth at 7 psig. The eductor tube would extend from 2 ft above the air diffusion means to 4 ft from the bottom. As the liquid level lowers, one or two auxiliary systems of external sparge rings automatically cut in to maintain a continuous state of agitation, even to as low as 2 or 3 ft of waste depth.

Neutralization. Neutralization to the desired pH takes place in plastic or rubber-lined tanks. Either a caustic or acid is added by transfer pumps from storage. Batch operations are run on a fill-and-draw basis, and continuous operations are controlled automatically by pH-monitoring equipment. A top-mounted mixer is provided to agitate the tank for blending. In the case of fill-and-draw operation, duplicate lines of tanks should be provided in order to fill one while the other is going through its cycle.

When a heavy precipitate is expected, in the case of batch treatment, a sludge blowdown means is provided as well as a sludge storage tank to contain the blowdown. Such an operation can be automated for any full cycle to save operator attention.

For continuous-flow plants, a clarifier stage is provided to follow the neutralizing step, and a mechanical scraper unit should be provided on all tanks greater than 15-ft diameter. A hopper bottom can be used on smaller tanks. Since neutralization has taken place, this tank and mechanism do not require corrosion protection other than shop-applied epoxy paint. In the case of nonorganic sludges, the bottom of the clarifier can generally be used for sludge storage awaiting export or a storage tank may be provided. High-rate settlers may also be used (see Fig. 28).

Grit removal. Grit removal is required on operations containing large grit contents (such as foundry wastes, etc.). Otherwise, any grits will lodge either in the holding tank or in the neutralization stage (if used). An effective grit-removal module is illustrated in Fig. 1.

Skimming and sedimentation. Many problems involve oil-bearing wastes which also contain settleables. In such cases, the mode of oil removal often is to use a coagulant (such as alum) and precipitate the colloidals and some oil, and skim free oil from the surface. The operation may be either continuous or on a batch basis. The equipment consists of a clarifier and skimming means along with chemical feeding and mixing equipment, and both sludge and oily scum storage has to be provided. The surface overflow rate should be low—about 300 gpd/sq ft. for continuous, or a 3-hr detention period in the case of batch operation.

Such a system can also provide for emulsion breaking by chemical addition in an agitated, short-detention-period tank before the sedimentation step.

Dissolved air flotation. This method is sometimes used in lieu of sedimentation when there are no settleable solids involved (see Fig. 16). Air flotation is particularly effective for separating oils after the waste flow has been properly conditioned with chemicals. This technique is applied to continuous-flow operations only.

Filtering. Sand filters (see Fig. 25) or micromesh drum filters (see Fig. 26) are used to remove most of the last traces of suspended solids where this polishing step is a requirement.

Where all of the ions and dissolved solids removal is required, reverse osmosis is applied (see Fig. 27).

Expected sources of wastes Many small industrial operations have oily wastes or wastes containing metals and suspended solids (SS). Typical situations are:

Industry	*Source of oily, metal, and SS wastes*
Textiles	Wool and cotton scouring
Tanning	Animal skin soaking, liming, and washing
Metal finishing[9]	Cutting, grinding, heat treating, cleaning/plating, paint spray
Pickling	Cleaning metals preparatory to painting
Railroads and airlines	Engine, tank car, aircraft steam, and detergent cleaning
Food processing	Meats, dairy, and vegetable oil processing
Metal plating	Pickling—chrome, copper, nickel, etc.

Each of the above sources produces wastes requiring treatment to remove or reduce the content of suspended solids, COD, heavy metals, greases, oils, soaps, caustics, acids, paint over-spray, and many pollutional dissolved solids. Removal techniques also produce objectionable sludges which have to be disposed of separately.

The module or turnkey approach can generally solve the problem for the small operation on a safe venture and reasonably economical basis. Often such module/turnkey operations can be leased advantageously, and supervision of the operation can be included, if advantageous to the industry.

SLUDGE DISPOSAL

Waste sludges are derived in a number of ways both from manufacturing processes and wastewater treatment systems. Wastewater sludges requiring processing for disposal are generated mainly from primary sedimentation, either plain or chemical, and biological metabolism processes such as activated sludge. The manufacturing process sludges, considerably varied, are waste oils, barks, white water, waste pickle liquor, etc., many of which can best be lagooned or incinerated or which are small enough in volume to be wet-hauled. Such sludges can sometimes be batched with those from wastewater treatment operations, but often should be disposed of separately. For instance, some sludges can be incinerated, but would poison anaerobic digestion used for the wastewater sludge. Others, like neutralized pickle liquor sludges, require special processing to produce a ferric hydroxide sludge which is filterable, producing a disposable cake.

Disposal of wastewater sludges is one of the most troublesome and expensive parts of the entire operation. Disposal by lagooning or by flooding furrowed land is by far the cheapest and easiest disposal system, if such is practicable. Smaller treatment operations can often best afford to export liquid sludge to land disposal sites; larger ones may best dewater to form a cake to haul. One strong point in favor of land disposal is the lack of human waste (infectious pathogenic bacteria) in the sludge so that there are no public health aspects clouding the operation. This factor may influence the exclusion of shift load and cafeteria sewers from the main industrial waste plant. The human excrement load can sometimes be treated separately to advantage to make land disposal of the major sludge load practicable.

One alternative to wet disposal may well be to dewater the sludges (to considerably reduce the water content) and haul the sludge cake to land disposal sites. Such sites might be strip mines, waste lands, or sanitary (covered) landfill.

Sludge Dewatering

The water content of waste treatment sludges can be decreased by a number of machines designed for the purpose. The equipment most frequently employed is vacuum filters, centrifuges, and filter presses. In order to effectively dewater the sludge, it must first be preconditioned by chemicals, as part of the dewatering system, so that the otherwise discrete, amorphous sludge particles are agglomerated into

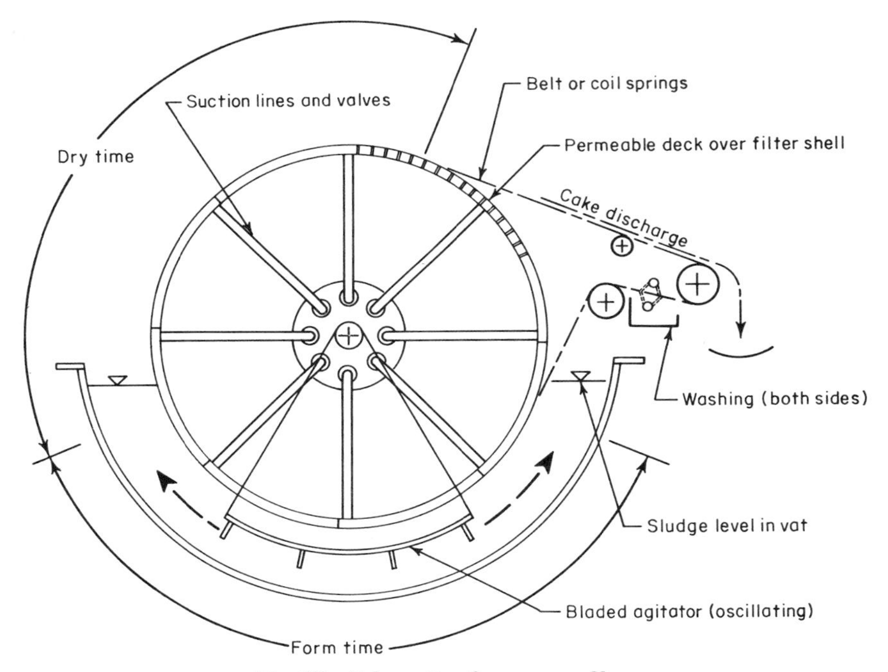

Fig. 29 Schematic of a vacuum filter.

a tough floc structure which has the rigidity to maintain a permeable or dewaterable mass under the vacuum or pressure forces.

Vacuum filter The vacuum filter is one of the most universally applied continuous sludge dewatering devices for wastewater sludge especially in medium- to small-sized installations. It is used to dewater a wide range of conditioned waste sludges—chemical, primary, or biological. In general, the system will handle sludges of 3 to 10 percent solids content and render a dewatered cake of about 20 to perhaps 30 percent solids (80 to 70 percent moisture).

The filter will form a continuous cake of about ¼ in. thick which drops onto a conveyor belt. When inclined conveyor belts are used to transport the cake, the inclination should be kept to recommended maximums and cleated belts are to be discouraged. The cake can be pumped short distances (say, into a furnace) through pipelines by progressing cavity pumps equipped with a special inlet feed hopper. Such lines should be glass or plastic lined. The cake is mostly thixotropic, i.e., will mold into a solid mass when transported long distances by truck (see Fig. 29).

Equipment. The filter proper is a slowly revolving cylindrical filter shell encircled with attached, slotted plastic decks which apply vacuum through the medium and drain off the filtrate. The shell rotates with the lower part submerged in a shallow, agitated vat into which the conditioned sludge flows. The continuous-belt (or coil springs) filter medium is in contact with the shell during the inundated cycle, and then runs off on outboard rollers, discharges the cake, and returns to the shell.

The *chemical conditioning* system is an important step ahead of the vacuum filter. The sludge is mixed with chemicals (sometimes lime and ferric chloride, and sometimes polyelectrolyte). The coagulant blended with the sludge is agitated a few minutes for floc aggregation, and flowed into the vat where a slow-moving bladed agitator furthers flocculation and maintains heterogeneity of the conditioned sludge awaiting pickup onto the filter medium.

The proper coagulants and blending are determined first by bench testing with filter leafs—a small laboratory unit which emulates the act of vacuum filtration and allows an estimate as to sludge pickup ability and cake yield. It can also aid in selecting the proper filter cloth weave with which to operate (refer to Table 9).

For estimating purposes, Table 8 estimates the amount of $FeCl_3$ and CaO that may be used to condition some sludges. Chemicals are stated in percent of dry sludge solids.

The cylindrical shell is either of stainless steel, for acid sludges, or carbon steel, for neutral or caustic sludges. It is variable-speed driven to effect a choice of from 1 to 10 ft/min peripheral speed and is furnished with a surface area of from 50 to 300 sq ft, each unit being from 4 to 12 ft in diameter and up to 25 ft long. Inside, the drum is divided into narrow longitudinal sections, each piped to a rotary manifold, connecting with the suction/blower system. This manifold has adjustable bridge blocks which can vary the duration of the vacuum cycle.

TABLE 8 Chemical Dosage Estimate

	Raw sludge		Digested sludge	
Source	$FeCl_3$	CaO	$FeCl_3$	CaO
Primary	1.5–2.5	6–8	2–3.5	6–10
Primary + WAS	1.5–3	6–10	1.5–4	6–11
WAS alone	3–6	1–5		

The *vat* under the lower half of the shell provides a sludge reservoir of variable capacity. It carries the end bearings and a slow-oscillating bladed agitator driven by a separate variable-speed system.

The *vacuum pump* should be capable of 26 in. Hg but in operation it is adjusted between about 20 to 26 in. Hg.

The *filter medium* is either a synthetic tightly woven filter cloth medium, or a very long, tightly wound coil spring-mounted in the form of a belt. The endless-belt cloth medium generally is woven from monofilament yarn of nylon or Dacron, etc., about halfway around the rotating shell, then travels outboard over a series of outboard rollers, and back to the shell, completing the circuit. The arrangement is such that the belt is always in close, airtight contact with the drainage deck on the shell while the assembly is passing through the vat.

The outboard arrangement is used for better cake disengagement (onto the conveyor) and for better medium washing. Not only can the cloth medium be washed by high-pressure jets on *both* sides, but more wash water and higher pressures can be used since the wash water is *diverted* and does not enter and dilute the conditioned sludge in the vat. This outboard arrangement, however, requires special attention to keep the long belt medium from creeping sidewise (poor tracking). Signal means should be provided to warn the operator when the belt moves sidewise out of position by more than ½ in.

The older cloth medium arrangement was to attach the filter cloth directly to the drum deck by wire-wrapping. Here the high-pressure spray washing was limited to one side and entered the vat. This arrangement may be advantageous with some types of sludge cakes (those with, say, great specific gravity) or where product washing is essential.

When small-diameter coil springs are used, the tightly coiled continuous spring wraps around the rotating shell and the outboard roller system in a unique double-layer arrangement which forms interstices similar in general effect to the cloth medium.

The part of the cycle when the medium (cloth or coil spring) is inundated and picking up sludge as a cake on the lower face of the shell is called *form time.* As the cake leaves the vat and vacuum is still applied sucking air and moisture through the cake, the cycle is called *dry time*—all adjustable by bridge block arrangement inside of the rotary manifold.

Filtrate quality and cake yield are important and somewhat interrelated. In general, the woven cloths will produce the cleanest (less solids) filtrate, and the coil spring the dirtiest. The coil spring medium, in general, will produce a cake yield under conditions (such as thin feed, etc.) that may prove to be impractical for fine-weave cloth media. In such cases, a slightly "dirtier" filtrate may well be the best alternative. Nevertheless, the suspended solids in the filtrate with either type of filter are quite low and very easy to treat.

Cake yields for common applications, assuming proper conditioning, can be estimated as outlined in Table 9. More factual criteria result from filter leaf studies.

TABLE 9 Vacuum Filter Yields Estimated

Sludge filtered	Cake, lb/(sq ft)(hr)
Raw primary sludge	5–14
Raw primary + activated sludge	4–5
Raw activated sludge	2–3
Digested primary sludge	4–10
Digested primary + activated sludge	3–5

For estimating purposes, a yield of about 4 lb/(sq ft)(hr) can be used, but this is subject to wide fluctuations.

Adjustments can be made to affect filter mechanical performance, presuming that the chemical conditioning is proper.

The net vacuum pulled through the filter medium can be adjusted. Normal range will be between 20 and 26 in. Hg. The use of a higher partial vacuum is probably futile and suggests that another combination of adjustments might be more practical.

Filter shell peripheral speed can be changed through a smooth transitional wide range between 2 to 10 ft/min for purposes for increasing the form time and the dry time.

The liquid sludge depth in the vat can be varied a couple of feet, perhaps to change the form time while holding a given tangential speed. Vat depth also may be lowered to avoid classification and *sand locking* of the agitator.

The bridge blocks in the rotary manifold valve can be changed to vary the duration of form time and dry time by activating more or less separate longitudinal sections for each function.

Operating Trouble Several problems may arise such as inability to pick up cake on the medium or a cake too wet or too thin. Change in chemical conditioning is suggested along with the usual mechanical adjustments.

When the sludge contains classifiable grits, they may detrain in the vat and accumulate so as to stop the agitator or mechanically rub cake off the medium. When such grits are expected, the vat can be specially equipped to convey this "sand" out of the vat.

Sometimes the cake will not discharge at the turn point and a shearing strip has to be added to cut the cake off as the belt rounds the outboard roller. Too thin a cake or too wet a cake is troublesome in this respect.

Some thick and well "dried" cakes may fall off the outboard end in great sheets, falling off the cross-conveyor belt and causing trouble. A power-driven rotating shaft equipped with short knives spaced a few inches apart and operating in juxtaposition with the outboard roller will cut the cake into pieces and avoid the problem.

Costs Costs per ton of sludge (dry basis) will run about \$10 for operating cost and \$3 for capital cost, about \$13 annual costs, based on \$3.50 per hour labor and 0.015 cents/kwh.

Centrifuge The centrifuge is increasing in use, as compared to vacuum filtration, because of improved designs and the totally enclosed construction. If used without

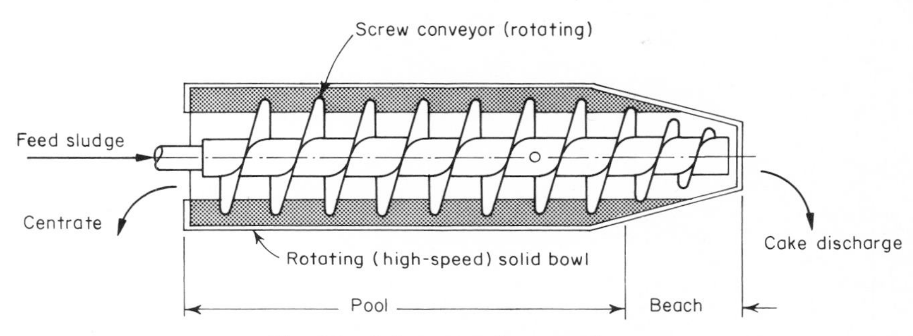

Fig. 30 Schematic of a centrifuge.

chemical conditioning, it uses less space than a vacuum filter system, but if conditioning is required, the space saving is not significant.

The unit mechanically dewaters sludge by use of high centrifugal force to accelerate sedimentation. The continuous function consists, progressively, of sludge concentration, dewatering, and cake discharge. There is a separate centrate discharge, inclined to be very "dirty." The machines used usually consist of a high-speed rotating solid bowl with an electric motor drive. There is also a screw conveyor motor driven at slightly different speed inside of the rotating bowl. This screw discharges the cake from a frustoconical area near the end (beach), where it is further dewatered before discharge. Supernatant liquid (centrate) is discharged continuously from the core

TABLE 10 Estimated Recovery and Cake Solids

Sludge	Recovery percent		Solids, percent
	No chemical	Chemical conditioning	
Raw primary	75–80	90–96	25–35
Digested primary	65–80	85–90	25–40
Primary + WAS	60–75	60–80	18–25

over an adjustable weir system at the opposite end from the cake discharge. Most units may be characterized by centrifugal forces of greater than 3,000 *g's,* and a length to diameter ratio of 2½ to 3½ (see Fig. 30).

Power draw is relatively large, and demands heavy electrical circuiting and starter gear. Because of the speed and large motors, there is apt to be a vibration-noise problem that must be dealt with in the installation.

Capture of solids in the sludge feed depends on sludge feed type and thickness, preconditioning, and machine adjustments. Without conditioning, the capture may run 75 to 80 percent; and with adequate chemical conditioning may increase to 90 to 95 percent (see Table 10).

Cake dryness offers considerable problems in deciding the balance between a drier cake and a better centrate (more clarification and capture). Bowl speed and pool volume are the principal machine operating variables. Greater clarification (and cleaner centrate) is obtained at increased bowl speeds. This greater speed may also produce a drier cake but the increased G pressure on the beach makes cake discharge difficult and may seriously increase abrasion if grits are present. A drier cake can also be achieved by lowering the pool depth, i.e., increasing the beach length. However, when detention is decreased by lowering the pool depth, clarification and capture decrease and the centrate fines increase.

Often, chemical conditioning increases the capture (less fines in the centrate) but yields a wetter cake.

Chemical conditioning. Chemical conditioning is required with most waste treatment sludges, particularly if the content of colloidal fines carried by the centrate are of concern. These fines, when recycled back through the treatment plant, can build up to equilibrium and cause waste treatment troubles. Otherwise the fines would require expensive, tertiary chemical precipitation or lagooning. Wherever possible, small, laboratory-sized centrifuges should be rented to determine operating variables and feasibility and, in particular, the chemical conditioning required. For chemical rough estimating purposes see Table 8.

Feed rates. These will vary, in general, between about 1 and 3 gpm/sq ft and depend on the thickness of feed. The gpm/hp ratio is held between 0.5 and 2.0 for reasonable solids capture.

The feed rate is a selective variable, and increase in the volumetric rate results in a higher overflow rate and increase in fines in the centrate, and less fines in the cake; hence, a drier cake. Increase in thickness of feed lowers the volumetric flow and decreases the fines in the centrate.

Operation. Operator adjustments are bowl speed, pool volume, and feed rate. The relative velocity of the screw can also be altered, generally by change in gears.

Grit can cause serious bowl abrasion. Sometimes reducing the relative speed difference between the bowl and the screw can reduce abrasion.

Fines in the centrate can be a serious back-load hindrance to the waste treatment operation. Obtaining a dry cake at the expense of increasing the centrate fines is often unworkable.

Too wet a cake has been further dried by employing another centrifuge (say a basket type) in series. This could salvage an otherwise impractical situation.

Cost. The centrifuge is less in first cost but carries a higher operating and maintenance cost than the vacuum filter. All in all, the centrifuge installation comes out to the *same cost* per ton of dry solids as does the vacuum filter, about $13. However, there is an advantage if the cake can be satisfactorily centrifuged without the cost and nuisance of chemical conditioning, even if a polymer has to be added.

Pressure filtration The filter press is one of the least applied units for wastewater sludge dewatering. The plate and frame press has long been applied to industry manufacturing processes but, in United States practice, has not been applied much to sludge drying. One disadvantage is the installed cost—probably twice the cost of vacuum filters—and the intermittancy of operation. A newer type of continuous-belt press is being introduced but experience on the scale of waste sludge plant is lacking. Continuous pressing has long been applied to industrial manufacturing such as to waste bark, etc.; but relatively thin, amorphous waste sludge may be a different matter.

The pressure filters with the most experience applied to waste sludge dewatering are the recessed-plate filters and the cloth-and-plate filters. The latter compresses a protruding filter cloth medium between successive stages of plates (having a cake cavity). The protruding cloths drip (and may even squirt if folds are compressed) and have not become too popular in the United States. The recessed-plate unit is tightly closed by gasketing between the frames, and the filter medium is caulked into each corrugated face. By and large, these high-pressure presses require a lot of attention and hand work. Mostly, they are applied in certain situations where other systems cannot form a dry cake.

Recessed-plate Filters. The unit consists of a heavy main frame having a bulkhead on one end and a heavy hydraulic ram on the other. Filter plates from 2 to about 4 ft square or round are held together by the ram when under internal pressure. These plates are recessed, forming a pocket about 1¼ in. to as much as 1½ to 2 in. deep. The filter cloth bears against a shallow fluted deck through which the filtrate runs and escapes from each plate. Each plate is slid along the heavy frame, one at a time, either opening or closing, by a mechanical carrying device. The ram clamps the frames together so that they will not leak when under the up to 200-psig filtering pressure used. Conditioned sludge is pumped under pressure into conduits formed through the closed frames, and filtrate is collected in separate channels.

Sludge Conditioning. The sludge conditioning is done on a double batch basis, one being pumped into the press and the other, meanwhile, being prepared for the next cycle.

Press Operating Sequence. The press is charged rapidly with conditioned sludge, sometimes by a pressurized blow-pot, or by pumping. The high pressure for pressing is then held (by slow pumping) at the operating pressure for the duration of the press time, which may be about 2 to 3 hr and sometimes longer.

At the end of the pressure cycle, the liquid sludge cores are first blown out and the press is automatically opened by withdrawing the ram and moving each plate about 3 ft to allow the cake to drop. The large cake is partially broken up by falling onto *breaker bars* which lie between the bottom of the press and the conveyor belt. If the cake sticks to the medium and does not drop, an operator has to be agile with a "canoe" paddle to pry the cake out of the recess. After all of the cakes are removed, the cloths are hosed down and the press closed for another cycle. Elapsed cycle time is from 4 to 8 hr, allowing, conservatively, about 3 cycles/day for each press. Large presses have as many as 20 to 80 plates, running up to 4½ ft square or 5-ft diameter.

Feed Rate and Cake Thickness. The rate of sludge feed for estimating purposes is about 2 lb/sq ft (dry basis), depending on the sludge thickness and characteristics. The recess in the plates ranges from 1¼ to 2 in. deep to form a cake of that thickness. Some designs feed conditioned sludge through the center of the plates, and others feed through the top corners.

Advantages. Cake dryness is the outstanding feature of these presses. The cakes attain a dryness of 35 to 60 percent solids under conditions that with vacuum filters or centrifuges would produce a cake of only one-half to two-thirds that dryness.

The *filtrate* is very clear and low in colloidal fines.

Filter medium surface aids are employed to help pressing, and mostly, to aid disengagement of the pressed cake. These aids also prolong cloth life, but are relatively expensive to use. When used, the cycle first charges filter aid and precoats the media, then the sludge is applied. Precoating materials are commonly diatomaceous earth or carefully sized fly ash.

Operating Troubles. Often the cakes do not drop when the press is opened, especially when filter aid is not used, and they have to be pried out manually.

When edge-sealing gaskets wear, sludge squirts slidewise under high pressure requiring gasket maintenance.

If the grid below the press fails to break up the cakes, they have to be broken by hand and shoveled onto the belt conveyor.

Sometimes wet cores do not blow out, or lower regions in the cavity are wet and come out when the press is opened to join and add unwanted moisture to the rest of the cake parts.

Synthetic cloth media replacement is a chore. The units, in general, lack an efficient means of cleaning the cloths in place—only one side can be flushed.

The discharge of the press is sporadic, and if there needs to be a continuous supply of the dry cake (as in an incinerator system), it must be ground and stored in a live-bottom hopper for continuous discharge.

Costs. The operating and capital costs of a pressure filter system are nearly double those of a vacuum filter or centrifuge system. If a filter precoat aid is used, an additional $2 to $4 per ton is added.

Sludge Treatment

One scheme to "dispose" of organic sludge is to treat it by one of the digestion paths: anaerobic fermentation, aerobic digestion, or high-pressure wet oxidation. The solid end product of these biochemical and oxidation processes is a humuslike sludge of very low organic content which is resistant to further biodegradation. This product is readily drainable on sand beds, filters, etc., about one-half or more reduced in net mass, and two to three times increased in potential thickness. The humus so produced, either in the wet or dried form, may be recycled to the land, especially where barren or waste land can be benefited.

These processes are all relatively easy to operate and require little maintenance, with the exception of wet oxidation which may require a great deal of maintenance because of the high operating pressure involved.

These processes more or less solubilize organic matter. The first, anaerobic fermentation, solubilizes to a minimum degree, probably less than around 5 percent to be recycled back through the plant. The second, aerobic digestion, solubilizes almost not at all. Wet oxidation solubilizes to a great degree recycling from 15 to perhaps 30 percent of the organic matter in the sludge. This colloidal, high COD liquor is difficult to handle in any bioprocess and requires considerable extra energy use to re-treat it.

Anaerobic fermentation Anaerobic digestion is a completely mixed, constant-temperature system contained in a covered and mixed reactor. Biodegradation proceeds rapidly under the action of two major groups of anaerobic microorganisms. The first group liquefies and breaks down the organic sludge, primarily to volatile acids; and the second group breaks down the acids into methane gas and carbon dioxide. The anaerobically degraded sludge is relatively stable to further rapid degradation, and drains well when dewatered by sand beds, filters, or centrifuges. The fermentation process handles most types of organic sludge (those having a BOD) with very few operating problems. The problems that might occur (such as metal poisoning from accumulation of chromes, nickels, etc., and cyanides or from extremes in feed pH) can readily be evaluated before design. The process works in a wide mesophilic range (all the way from 50 to 100°F) and in the thermophilic range (110 to 130°F). It can be effected in deep lagoons (in warm climates) or in heated cylindrical vessels (insulated in cold climates). When anaerobic lagoons are used, there should be two or three, so that one can be eventually retired to muck out the humus. The succeeding lagoon can be seeded from the first while starting to feed (see Fig. 31).

There is no temperature "no-man's land" where methane digestion ceases. A reactor can be operated at a wide range of temperatures if temperature variation is slow. New methane formers grow at any established temperature.

Equipment. Equipment consists of steel-walled cylindrical tanks with shallow hoppered (1½- to 12-in.) concrete floors. The tank will be from 25 to 30 ft high, sidewall, and has either a floating cover or, preferably, a fixed steel cover. The tank and cover should be insulated in cold climates. This reactor is, preferably, mixed by an eductor-tube unit, compressing the generated gas to effect the gas-lift torroidal stirring. The stirring should be sufficient to effect a completely mixed reactor requiring about ⅓ bhp in the gas compressor (or 7 scfm) per 1,000 cu ft of reactor volume and resulting in a G value* of about 100 sec^{-1}. The evolution of gas within the digester, especially with a modern high-rate loading, does a great amount of natural stirring but, unfortunately, stratifies the contents by gas flotation. This stratification is deleterious to good, steady-state operation, and the contents must be redistributed for better control. The gas-lift torroidal mixing will effect this purpose.

The organic sludge loading on a well-designed digester should run about 10 to 12 days or around 200 lbs of volatile matter per 1,000 cu ft, whichever gives the larger reactor. (See Table 11.)

The *digester system* requires a thickener, a storage tank which accumulates waste sludge and decants as much water as possible under gravity conditions. Feed sludge is pumped, either continuously or about once an hour, into the reactor to effect continuous feeding. Overflow of mixed liquor from the reactor is stored and later dewatered.

* G value is a quantitative expression which delineates the velocity gradient and relative state of uniform turbulence. G value is the relative amount of energy dissipated in completely mixing a unit volume of a liquid and is expressed as the square root function of foot pounds per second per cubic foot (dissipated) divided by the absolute viscosity.

Volatile solids (mass) reduction during digestion should amount to from 60 to about 80 percent, depending on the proportion of inerts and nonbiodegradables making up the feed sludge.

The longer the MCRT, the greater the reduction in the mass of solids under fermentation. Gasification accounts for the balance of the mass; the gas being principally methane and carbon dioxide.

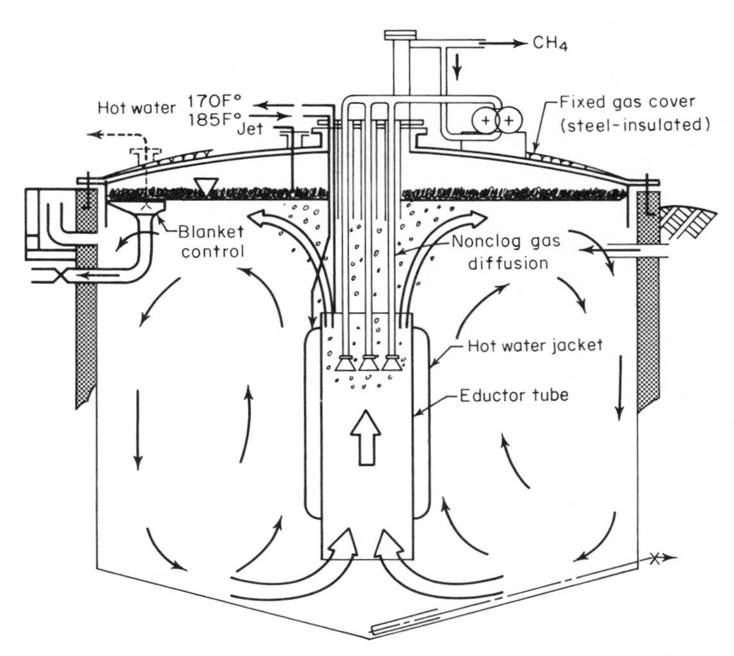

Fig. 31 Eductomix. Anaerobic fermentation digester gas mixed with an eductor tube. Jacketed for hot water heating. (*Peabody Welles.*)

Methane gas is produced during anaerobic digestion. The total gas evolved is about 8 to 12 cu ft/lb of volatile sludge fed. The gas is, roughly, 65 percent CH_4 and has an approximate net heating value of 600 Btu/cu ft of gas. This is considerably in excess of the heat required for a well-run digester unit.

Operating Problems. Operating troubles are few (excepting poisoning) unless the unit is grossly abused or poorly designed. Sludge recycle (from the humus storage unit) for increased MCRT helps to even out operations as does continuous feed.

Rapid changes in temperature of 2°C will suppress the methane formers (bacteria)

TABLE 11 Digester Loading Relationships

Hydraulic displacement time, days	Digester volume solids loading, lb/(1,000 cu ft)(day) (assuming 75% volatiles)					
	Sludge thickness, percent					
	2	4	5	6	8	10
10	95	191	232	277	381	476
15	64	127	159	191	254	318
20	58	96	119	143	191	238

and might even kill off the process. The methane formers can operate at any one of a large spectrum of steady-state temperatures but cannot tolerate rapid changes of any magnitude. Temperature pockets within the reactor or elevated, stratified temperature in the upper mass can hinder orderly methane digestion. One of the prime reasons for auxiliary gas-lift stirring is to break up heat pockets and stratas and keep the catalytic enzyme and new feed well distributed.

Grit, if present, will fall to the floor and gradually accumulate, requiring subsequent costly entry and removal to restore reactor volume.

Mineral oils, greases, and other nonbiodegradable flotables will accumulate at the surface in an increasing depth of blanket. This accumulation should be withdrawn on a weekly or monthly basis, if the cover is properly designed for this function.

About 50 grains/100 cu ft of hydrogen sulfide (H_2S) in the gas will cause serious deterioration in boilers and engines. If sulfur is present in the sludge, H_2S will be generated in the digester and may require removal by an *iron sponge* when in excess of 50 grains. The iron sponge consists of a mixture of ferric oxide and an inert filler which, in general, will remove about 4 lb of sulfur per cubic foot of sponge. When spent, the vile sponge material is wasted.

Costs. Operating cost is minimal. Very little electrical energy or maintenance is required. All in all, the cost may run less than $1 per ton (dry) of feed sludge treated.

Aerobic digestion Organic sludge, especially sludges produced from biosynthesis processes, can be stabilized in an extended aeration process called *aerobic digestion* or *autooxidation.* The operation range is from 60 to perhaps 90°F. The process is an autooxidation or lysing process where, since the available supply of new food is absent, the microorganisms begin to consume their own protoplasm for energy. The cell tissue is oxidized to carbon dioxide, water, and ammonia; and the ammonia is subsequently oxidized to nitrate. Some of the cell tissue is nonbiodegradable and remains as a stable end product, a humus.

Aerobic digestion is time related, and the longer the residence time of the digesting sludge proper (mean cell residence time, MCRT) the better the endogenous digestion. That is why decantation of the reactor is practiced routinely—to separate excess water resulting both from thin WAS feed and from bound water released from the digesting sludge. Decantation allows the sludge to remain in the reactor for an actual dwell (residence) period of up to 2 or 3 months, or longer. Sometimes, in lieu of reactor decantation, a clarifier is used to separate the sludge and decant the reasonably clear supernatant on a continuous-flow basis. This sludge is all returned to the digester to lengthen the mean cell residence time; a portion of it being disposed of from time to time.

It is not necessary for this decant to be absolutely clear since it is not a product and is returned to the works. When continuous decant clarifiers are used, the surface-rate overflow is held to around 100 to 150 gpd/sq ft in order to obtain a practical over flow clear liquor depth when the digesting sludge attains 4 to 6 percent thickness.

Aerobic digestion is nearly always carried out in open aeration tanks, similar in geometry and equipment to activated sludge reactors. Existing deep tanks are sometimes converted for use as aerobic digesters by adding air diffusion or mechanical aerators as mixing means. In the case of diffused air, where the digesters are deeper than 17 ft water depth, a submerged air-lift eductor tube is used to completely mix the deep tank. Reactors of any depth may be used, and the educator tubes may be circular or rectangular. Air is most often diffused at either 8 or 12 ft submergence within these eductor tubes, which run to within a few feet of the bottom.

Sludge drying is done easily on sand drying beds (in mild climate), on vacuum filters, and in centrifuges. Disposal can be on the land or as fill, etc.

Operating Problems. Operation troubles are minor, and the process is relatively easy to run. Infrequently, as the result of too much aeration, the pH may drop to as low as 5.0 because of air-stripping the buffering capacity. Reducing aeration and working on a practical low excess DO can control the situation, or it may be necessary to resort to addition of a caustic.

Using aerobic digestion for primary solids is probably a misapplication. The process is at its best handling waste sludges from aerobic synthesis processes, viz, waste activated sludge.

There is a large connected horsepower required, and the process will run around \$5 per ton of dry sludge (1.5 cents/kWh) based on digesting a waste activated sludge.

Wet oxidation Rapid oxidation of organic matter cooked in a reactor under high pressure and elevated temperature in the presence of oxygen (from air pumped into the pressurized sludge) is called the *wet oxidation process.* The process was originally developed for pulp-mill wastes and has been attempted on high COD waste treatment sludges. The oxidation, mostly chemical, averages 75 to 90 percent completion leaving some organic matter and ammonia in the end product. Unfortunately, solubilization during cooking forms, besides a relatively stable humus, a thick, high COD-carrying stream containing from 15 to 30 percent of the original COD. This soluble organic load has to be recycled through the works for retreatment. The wet humus from the process is separated from this stream and drains well and can easily be formed into a cake by vacuum filtration, etc.

Equipment. Raw sludge is ground and pumped through the system at a pressure of from 2,000 to 3,000 psig. Air is added at an amount of supply oxygen to the process about equal to the COD value in the sludge. This pressurized throughput is pumped through a series of heat exchanges and into a tall reactor vessel for the contact period. The discharge from the reactor backflows through the heat exchanges. Steam is added for makeup heat when sludges lack the required Btu to generate the heat required.

This stabilization process has met with variable success and has not become too generally used in sludge stabilization.

A lower pressure variation of the process has been used to pretreat sludge by low-pressure cooking for 30 min (around 150 to 300 psig at 270 to 390°F) to condition the sludge for dewatering before incineration. This process has been more widespread. The operation does a good job of breaking down the bound water so that a relatively dry cake can easily be formed on a vacuum filter or centrifuge. Here, too, considerable solubilization takes place so that from 15 to 20 percent of the COD has to be recycled for retreatment.

Sludge Incineration

Most organic sludges and many chemical sludges are amenable to incineration by combustion at temperatures ranging from 1250 to 1800°F. The total operating costs are relatively high, considering dewatering, incinerator operation and stack gas air pollution control, but the final ash is relatively easy to dispose of, being sterile and of very little organic content. Incineration can be used to dispose of obnoxious sludges generated from oil-related process, cake ovens, and many processes related to paper manufacturing such as pulp and kraft mills, chemical recovery in many types of mills, etc.

Although most wastewater sludges are amenable to incineration, compounds with low boiling points tend to be corrosive in the furnace or to require special air pollution control equipment. Chloride compounds are a danger to the firebrick lining.

Too high a water content in the feed sludge can cause furnace-operating problems because of the amount of vapor generated and can also increase operating expense by makeup fuel demand. Accordingly, all sludges should be prepared as autogenous as possible by removing as much water as possible. The pretreatment generally is effected through chemical conditioning and vacuum filtration (or centrifugation) to produce a cake low in water content. Roughly speaking, organic sludges may contain about 3 lb of water for each pound of dry solids, and the heat requirement for evaporation, hopefully, about balances with the heat available from sludge combustion.

Although there are many special incinerators used in manufacturing furnace and drying work, the furnaces most commonly used for waste sludge incineration are the multiple-hearth type and the fluid-bed type.

Multiple-hearth type The multiple-hearth incinerator has one of the best long-time operating records for waste sludge incineration. This furnace has the advantage of using waste heat to pass over the first (top) hearths. This acts as a water-drying phase and conserves considerable heat. Screenings, detritus, and scalpings can also be loaded onto this hearth to dry, and subsequently to incinerate. The furnace is not under pressure, so sludge cake can simply be dropped from a feed belt onto the top hearth (see Fig. 32).

Equipment. There is a steel cylindrical shell, free-standing and covered, about 20 to 25 ft high. The shell is lined with insulation and firebrick, and has several circular hearths stacked in close proximity to each other. The usual installation for waste sludge will use six hearths, built of firebrick as shallow arches. A motor-driven, slowly rotating, hollow shaft passes through the center to which are attached cantilevered rabble arms to stir and rake the burning sludge in or out, as the case may be, from one hearth to the next lower hearth. The arms are of alloy steel and are air-cooled by air supplied through the hollow shaft. Ash is discharged out of the bottom hearth and stack gasses out of the top. The stack gasses, running 500 to 700°F, are cooled and scrubbed as they pass through an air pollution control unit.

The air circulation system is designed to conserve the greatest amount of heat. Preheated air is admitted to the lowest hearth and is further heated by the burning sludge as it rises past the middle (hottest) hearths. The air then cools as it gives up its heat to dry the feed sludge on the upper hearths. Air, in general, passes

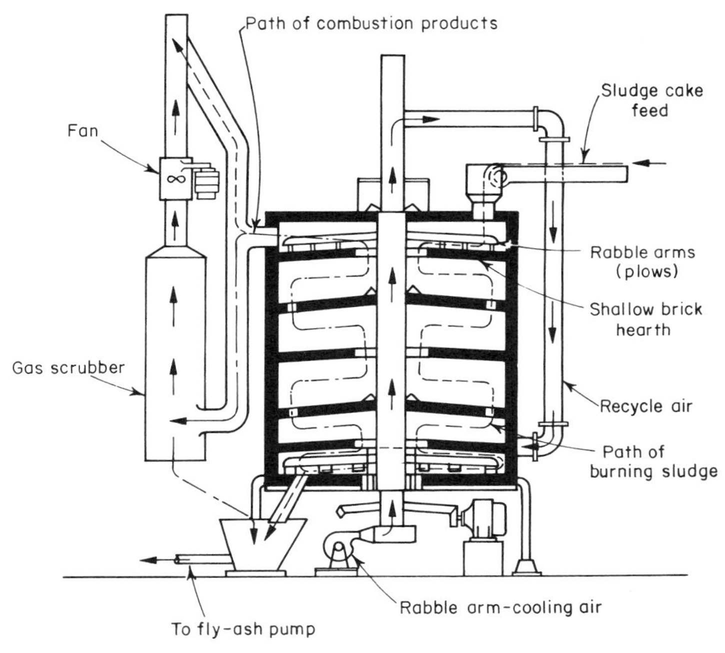

Fig. 32 Schematic of a multiple-hearth furnace.

twice through the furnace. Cooling air is blown into the central hollow shaft and hollow rabble arms for their preservation, and much of this warmed air is then recirculated to the lowest hearth (see Fig. 32).

Pretreatment. Sludge is pretreated to remove water, rendering the feed as autogenous as possible. The process generally consists of centrifugation or vacuum filtration. In the case of vacuum filtration, the dryness of the cake can sometimes be increased by squeezing it in a secondary pressure roller operation. In the case of vacuum filtration, dryness can be increased by employing double centrifugation, perhaps horizontal solid bowl followed by a basket type. The dewatered cake can be transported to the furnace by horizontal belt conveyor or, perhaps, by progressing cavity pump to achieve elevation where the layout requires considerable lift.

Heat required is about 1800 to 2500 Btu to evaporate each pound of water from the sludge as charged into a furnace operating at about 1500°F. The heat value available in various sludges varies, but a few are given in Table 12.

TABLE 12 Heat Value in Waste Sludges

Material incinerated	Btu
Waste sulfite liquor	8,000
Semichemical pulp (primary)	6,000
Newsprint	7,800
Activated sludge	6,500

When a representative sludge sample is available, a calorimeter test should be run to determine the exact heat available.

Stack gases will always require scrubbing to remove particulates before releasing to the atmosphere and, in some regions, will require cooling to remove the steam plume. A variable-throat, venturi wet scrubber made of stainless steel is quite efficient for this. A high stack is not required.

Ash disposal of the wet slurry discharged from the scrubber and the quenched solid ash discharged from the bottom hearth are best handled by ponding if the land is available. The ash is relatively inert and will not cause odor nuisance. It can also be dewatered sufficiently for hauling by feeding the wet ash to a grit classifier operated at about 6 gpm/sq ft surface rate. The classifier should have a long beach and a double pitch screw with a variable-speed drive.

Costs. Annual costs of incineration are varied depending on the building structure and difficulty of sludge dewatering, but, including preconditioning, dewatering, makeup fuel, and air pollution control they will run about as follows:

	Annual operating costs	*Capital costs*
Vacuum filtration	$12.50	$2.50
Incineration	$16.00	$10.00

Total annualized cost—about $41 per ton of dry solids.

Fluidized-bed type The fluidized-bed incinerator is applied to many industrial process fields for incineration, drying, lime burning, granular carbon activation, waste chemical recovery, etc.

Preheated air is blown through a false bottom-and-nozzle system supporting a bed of sand medium (or reclaimed material). This hot air expands the medium into a fluid mass. The dewatered waste sludge is fed onto (or into) the expanded bed and immediately ignites in the turbulent, grinding, hot fluid bed. Combustion products, water vapor, and gases pass through the freeboard and out of the top, then through a dry centrifugal separator. The combustion products then pass through the air pollution control scrubber which cools the gas and removes the particulates.

The air pollution control aspects and ash disposal are similar to the multiple-hearth unit, except that the off-gases from the fluid bed are hotter (about 1600 to 1800°F), and also carry all or most of the ash, depending on the efficiency of dry separator removals.

Sometimes, but not often, in waste sludge incineration the hot combustion gases are passed through a sludge heat exchanger or a waste-heat boiler for conservation of heat. The sludge heat exchanger is apt to give operating problems from plugging with fly ash.

When makeup heat is required, it is either supplied by a gas or an oil-gun-type burner, discharging through the sidewall and impinging on the sand bed, or by circumferential oil nozzles discharging into the fluid bed.

Equipment. The fluid bed proper is a tall and very-well-insulated cylinder, lined with insulating brick and firebrick and having a tight cover. An advantage is that this unit is gastight and does not leak vapors into the ambiency. The height runs about 20 to 25 ft, and the diameters from 4 to about 25 ft.

Air is blown by a centrifugal blower at 5-psig pressure through an inlet wind box where it is heated temporarily to 1400°F before each start-up of sludge feed. After start-up, the preheat burners are cut out. Nozzles in the false bottom uniformly distribute the fluidizing air and also retain the 4- to 5-ft bed depth of fine silica sand.

Hot vapor exits from the top of the freeboard carrying with it all of the products of combustion.

Sludge feed to the furnace is either by multiple sludge nozzles entering the side and discharging cake into the mass of the fluid bed or by a spray feed onto the surface of the sand bed from a nozzle protruding through the center of the roof. The

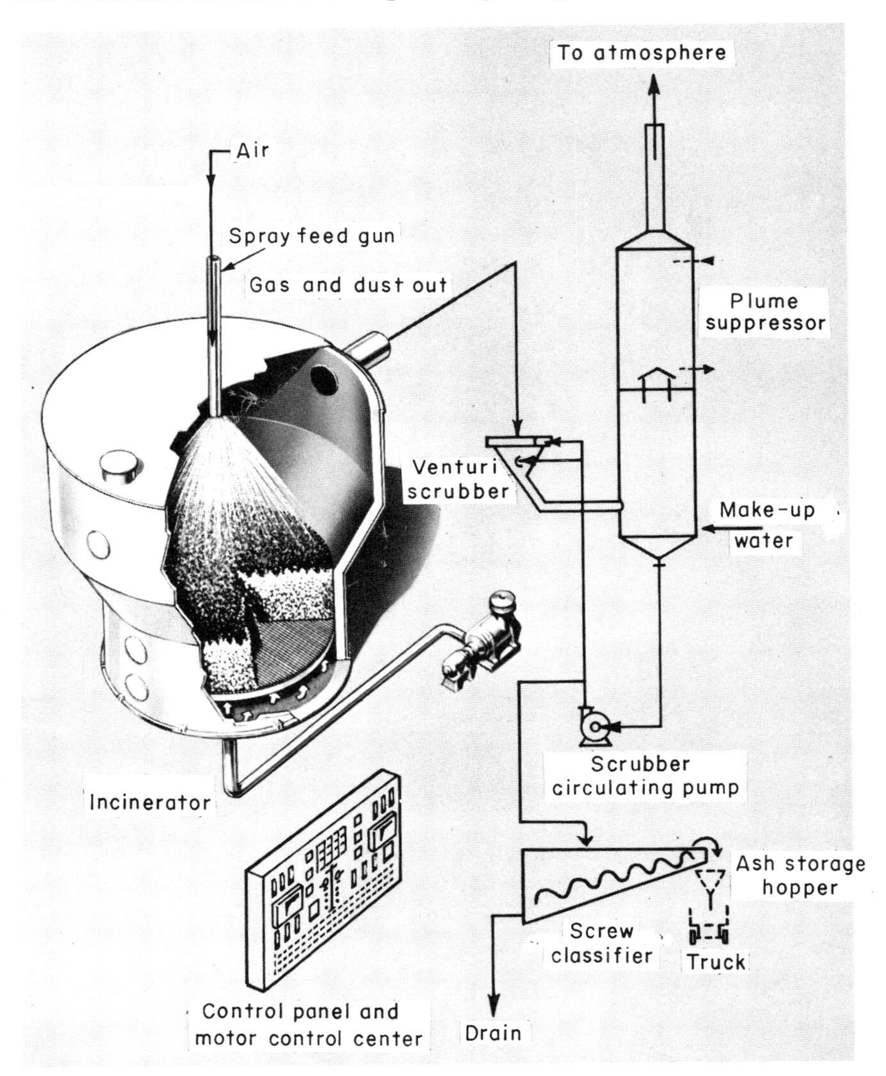

Fig. 33 Schematic of a fluidized bed incinerator system.

spray-nozzle type uses a sand bed diameter smaller than the upper furnace freeboard diameter because the gaseous products are generated above the fluid-bed medium (see Fig. 33).

Shutdown and start-up are important advantages unique to fluid-bed units. Since they are so well insulated and tight against ambient air circulation, they can be shut down and restarted at will. The furnace loses less than 200°F/day. For several days downtime, a small amount of auxiliary heat can easily keep the unit from cooling. Cooling and reheating is very hard on incinerator firebrick and insulation, so this is an important advantage when a unit cannot be fired continuously.

Operating Troubles. When shutting down, the sludge pressure feed lines must *not* be purged with water. The cold water contacts the hot sand bed with explosive force and drives sand into the wind box through the nozzles. If feed line and nozzle purging is required, it has to be done with air. When the feed line is looped sufficiently high above the roof, gravity will pull the last sludge out of the gun to prevent any baking in the line entering the furnace. Accordingly, single downdays do not require feed-line purging when using the spray-feed mode.

Pretreatment, heat required, stack gases and ash disposal are all, in general, the same as discussed for the multiple-hearth-type furnace.

Annual Costs. Incineration costs will, in general, run the same as for the multiple-hearth type except that in cases where the feed sludge cannot be dewatered to where it is autogenous, the fluid-bed type will require some extra makeup heat fuel expense.

REFERENCES

1. Newton, Donald: Thickening by Gravity and Mechanical Means, *University of Michigan Symp.*, January 1963.
2. Sparr, A., and V. Grippi: Gravity Thickeners, *J. Water Pollution Control Federation,* vol. 41, no. 1, part 1, p. 1886, November 1969.
3. Leary, Raymond D., et al.: Effect of Oxygen Transfer Capabilities on Wastewater Treatment Plant Performance, *J. Water Pollution Control Federation,* vol. 40, no. 7, pp. 2198–1310, July 1968.
4. "Standard Methods for the Examination of Water and Wastewater," 13th ed., Water Pollution Control Federation, 1971.
5. Cohen, Jesse M., and J. Irwin: Annual Literature Review—Physical-Chemical Treatment, *J. Water Pollution Control Federation,* vol. 45, no. 6, pp. 1027–1037, June 1973.
6. P-C Treatment Gets Industrial Trial, *Environmental Sci. & Tech.,* vol. 7, p. 200, March 1973.
7. Yao Kuan, M.: Design of High-Rate Settlers, *ASCE J.,* vol. EE5, pp. 621–637, October 1973.
8. Culp, Gordon L., Kou-yng Hsiung, and Walter R. Conley: Tube Clarification Process, Operating Experiences, *ASCE J.* vol. SA5, pp. 829–847, October 1959.
9. Lancy, L. E., et al.: Upgrading Metal—Finishing Facilities to Reduce Pollution, *EPA Technology Transfer,* no. 2, July 1973.

Section 2

Specific Industries

Chapter 5

Water Pollution Control in the Food Industry

L. C. GILDE

Director, Environmental Engineering,
Campbell Soup Company, Camden, New Jersey

and

OSMAN M. ALY

Manager, Environmental Quality,
Campbell Soup Company, Camden, N.J.

INTRODUCTION

The increased national awareness of the need to halt the progressive deterioration of the environment coupled with the realization that water supplies are not unlimited has prompted governmental bodies at both state and federal levels to promulgate and enforce more stringent water quality standards. To supply an urgent need for solutions to the nationwide problems, the food industry has been actively engaged in intensive research efforts toward the effective minimizing of the pollutional loads by changing process technology and evaluating water conservation, reclamation, and reuse methods.

This chapter discusses the water pollution problems and treatment methods of the food processing industry as a whole. The wastewater sources and characteristics and the water conservation practices of some selected food industries which contribute significant amounts of pollutional loads are discussed in more detail. The Standard Industrial Classification (SIC) numbers of these industries include the following:

SIC Code	*Industry*
20331 through 20334	Canned fruits and vegetables
20371 through 20372	Frozen fruits and vegetables
206	Sugar beet
2011	Meat packing
2015	Poultry and small game

The discussion, however, does not include the effects of solid wastes generated during the manufacturing processes or those resulting from the eventual discard of containers used for food packaging.

THE INDUSTRY PROFILE

There are approximately 50,000 establishments in the total food processing industry in the United States. Food processing is a low profit margin, highly competitive industry. Food processing profits as a percentage of sales average about 2.5 percent compared with well over 5 percent in all manufacturing industries. The value of food and kindred products shipped in 1970 is estimated to total $97.5 billion[1] as shown in Table 1.

The growth in food consumption is determined largely by population growth. While total manufacturing output grew 74 percent during the past decade, the food processing activities expanded at about half that rate. The relatively modest sales/profit ratios in the food processing industry reflect the intensity of competition. Measured in terms of the number of brand labels seeking the consumers' favor, the food processing industry is the most competitive of the nation's businesses. About 8.9 percent (1,794,000 workers) of the total manufacturing work force were employed in the food processing industry in 1969. Expenditures for plant and equipment in 1969 were $2.59 billion, or about 3.2 percent of the total spent by all manufacturing industries.

The contribution of the industry to the nation's economy has been significant. The raw product value of all domestic farm food items in 1969 was $32 billion. The value added in processing these commodities was $63 billion, leading to a finished product value of nearly three times that of the raw product.[2]

WATER USE AND WASTEWATER DISCHARGES

The food processing industry as a whole uses large quantities of water, but this is not a consumptive use. The water is required for washing all forms of food, blanching, pasteurization, cleaning of process equipment, and cooling of final product. The widespread and increasing use of hydraulic systems for in-plant conveying of raw foods has contributed greatly to the overall use of water. The quality of the water that comes in contact with the product is of extreme importance. The Food and Drug Administration's regulations for "Good Manufacturing Practice" state that "water used for washing, rinsing, or conveying of food products shall be of potable quality and shall not be recirculated unless suitably treated to assure its potability." This requirement puts a limitation on the utilization of water reuse and recirculation programs and contributes to the overall excessive use of water by the industry.

Since water comes in direct contact with the raw materials during the various food processing procedures, significant amounts of organic and inorganic materials in the soluble, colloidal, or particulate form are discharged in the wastewater. Generally, food processing wastes are characterized by high BOD (biological oxygen demand) content, particularly in the soluble form. The amounts of wastes and the quantity of organics and solids discharged from the processing operations depend a great deal on the type of individual processing steps and water use and reuse in each plant. There is a great variation in waste load from plant to plant, depending on the layout of the plant and the manner in which foods are handled. In general, waste loads from specific products fall into more or less generalized categories.

TABLE 1 Food Manufacturers' Shipments, 1970[1]

Dairy (cheese, milk, ice cream, evaporated milk)	$13,548 million dollars
Canned and frozen	9,672
Candy and chocolate	2,711
Coffee	2,070
Other foods	12,174
Meat and poultry	25,489
Beverages (including sugar)	12,465
Grain-based (including oils)	19,384
Total shipments	$97,513 million dollars

During the past 20 years, there has been a constant consolidation of smaller operations into larger, more centralized process operations, resulting in greater usage of water and more discharge of wastes per operation. Thus, during the highly seasonal periods of operation in the industry, it is not unusual for a process operation to utilize much more water and to generate more waste than the community in which the operation is located. The waste loads in many food industries are generated within a relatively small harvest period during the year; treatment systems must be geared to prevent pollution at periods when rainfall and streamflow are at a minimum. Further, where the wastes are channeled into municipal systems, these systems are often already overtaxed in capacity and inadequate for the community requirements.

It has been reported[3] that food and kindred products manufacturing was about one-tenth of all United States manufacturing as measured by value added. This segment of the economy used about 5.4 percent of the total water but produced 20 percent of the total BOD. The annual BOD loading of the same industry was estimated[4] to be approximately equivalent to four times the sewered population of the United States. These estimates reflect the relatively high-strength wastewater discharged by food manufacturing. Most of the wastewater generated by the industry is nontoxic to microorganisms and amenable to biological degradation.

FRUIT AND VEGETABLE FREEZING AND CANNING INDUSTRY

The National Canners Association in a recent publication[5] estimated that the fruit and vegetable canning and freezing industry includes operations in 1,838 plants employing 167,000 persons. The industry utilizes an estimated 99 billion gal of intake water, recirculating about 64 percent and discharging about 96 billion gal. The percentages of these values compared to those for all United States manufacturing and for all food and kindred products are, respectively:

Number of plants	0.6 and 5.6%
Number of employees	0.9 and 10.1%
Value added	0.8 and 8.3%
Intake water	0.6 and 12.2%
Recirculated water	0.3 and 12.4%
Discharged water	0.7 and 12.8%

Table 2 also gives estimated raw product tonnages, and BOD, suspended solids (SS), and solid residuals generated. Estimated totals for the United States in 1968 are:

26 million tons of raw product
83 billion gallons of wastewater discharged
800 million pounds of BOD generated
392 million pounds of suspended solids generated
8 million tons of solid residuals

Citrus, tomatoes, corn, and white potatoes (excluding dehydrated potatoes) account for 67 percent of the raw tonnage, 57 percent of the wastewater, 52 percent of the BOD, 62 percent of the suspended solids, and 72 percent of the solid residuals.

TABLE 2 Total Wastes from Canned and Frozen Fruits and Vegetables[5]

Product	Raw product	Wastewater		BOD		Suspended solids		Solids residuals	
	1,000 tons	10^3 gal/ton	Million gal	lb/ton	Million lb	lb/ton	Million lb	lb/ton	1,000 tons
Fruit:									
Apples	1,050	2.1	2,200	36	38	6	6	580	290
Apricots	120	8.7	1,000	71	9	16	2	240	16
Cherries	190	2.4	400	26	5	5	1	280	26
Citrus	7,800	1.8	19,000	16	125	3	23	790	2,080
Peaches	1,100	5.6	6,200	62	68	13	14	530	290
Pears	410	3.0	1,200	42	17	12	5	660	140
Pineapples	900	0.5	500	20	18	8	7	890	400
Other fruit	460	8.0	3,700	20	9	10	5		70
Fruit Subtotal	12,030		34,200		289		63		4,312
Vegetables:									
Asparagus	120	13.3	1,300	7	1	8	1	700	42
Beans, lima	120	9.0	1,100	25	3	80	10	320	19
Beans, snap	630	7.6	4,800	22	14	15	9	420	130
Beets	270	3.8	1,000	135	26	53	14	670	90
Carrots	280	3.7	1,000	50	14	29	8	1,000	140
Corn	2,480	2.2	5,500	44	110	22	55	1,310	1,620
Peas	580	5.3	3,100	61	35	22	13	260	74
Pumpkins, squash	220	1.5	300	41	9	11	2	500	55
Sauerkraut	230	0.4	100	14	3	1	0	660	76
Spinach, greens	240	8.4	2,000	28	7	18	4	280	33
Sweet potatoes	150	2.6	400	98	15	39	6	(In other vegetables)	
Tomatoes	5,000	2.7	14,500	14	70	7	35	180	400
White potatoes	2,400	3.4	8,200	47	110	53	130	760	910
Other vegetables	1,400	4.0	5,600	60	84	30	42		460
Vegetable Subtotal	14,120		48,900		511		329		4,049
Totals	26,150		83,100		800		392		8,561

The U.S. Department of the Interior report, "The Cost of Clean Water,"[6] estimated the following total waste loads, in millions of pounds, for the canned and frozen foods and vegetables industry:

Year	*1963*	*1968*	*1972*	*1977*
BOD	660	785	845	905
SS	750	890	960	1035
TDS	710	845	910	980

All these figures are for the raw wastewater prior to any treatment. Although these wastes represent a small part of the total national industrial load, they pose significant disposal problems. Because of the fact that this industry is highly seasonal, the waste loads are generated within a relatively short harvest period. The waste treatment system must have sufficient capacity to handle the peak loads which occur only during this seasonal short period and must be designed to prevent discharge of relatively strong effluents during periods of dry weather flows in the receiving streams.

Waste Sources and Characteristics

There is a wide variation in the liquid waste volumes and characteristics generated by fruit and vegetable plants. These variations are due to differences in the type of raw commodity, its condition upon arrival at the plant, tonnage processed per unit of time, processing machinery used, and in-plant transportation methods. Another important factor is the extent of water recirculation and reuse. Although the industry at large has made great strides in conservation and water reuse, there is not a great potential at the present time for a diminution of water requirements because of food quality improvements and more rigid definitions of cleanliness. Under today's economic conditions, there is a tendency toward development of large bulk handling methods which require hydraulic transportation of the produce from one piece of equipment to the next, in addition to the large amounts of water required for washing and cleaning of the produce. There is a limit on the amount of recirculation that can be used since the microbial counts for food in the can are influenced by the sanitary conditions as the produce is flumed or pumped.

The sources and characteristics of wastewater generated during the processing of some commodities have been investigated by the National Canners Association.[5] The major steps where water is used and solids and dissolved residuals are generated are washing and sorting, peeling, blanching, and processing. The washing and rinsing operations of the new product constitute a major source of wastewater. These treatments are applied for removal of soils, microbial contamination, extraneous matter (such as leaves or stems), and the removal of occluded solubles and insolubles after cutting, coring, peeling, or blanching. The volume of water used in washing and rinsing operations may be as much as 50 percent of the total usage in process operations. Table 3 summarizes the quantities and characteristics of water used for washing and rinsing fruits and vegetables.

Other sources of wastewater come from the peeling operations and contain large quantities of suspended matter primarily organic in nature. The amount of suspended solids varies with the type of peeling. The most extensively used procedures for peeling root crops include steam/abrasion, immersion in lye solution/hydraulic or abrasion, and abrasion. Peeling of fruits is frequently achieved by mechanical knives, immersion in lye solution, and rammers and corers. The strength of the waste is dependent on whether the vegetables have been blanched or lye-treated prior to peeling. In the latter cases, the liquid waste contains considerable amounts of dissolved and colloidal organic matter. Table 4 is a compilation by the National Canners Association of the characteristics of wastewaters from peeling fruits and vegetables. The caustic peeling solutions also constitute a serious disposal problem. The use of hot caustic is usually confined to a recirculated system where the strength of the caustic is kept up to normal by the continual addition of concentrated sodium hydroxide. The food is thoroughly washed after the caustic bath, thus imparting a high alkaline waste load to the plant discharge. In addition, periodic discharge of the entire caustic bath into the wastewater streams creates undesirable wastewater characteristics.

TABLE 3 The Use of Water in Washing Fruits and Vegetables[5]

Product	Function	Water used, gal/ton	Effluent load, lb/ton BOD	Effluent load, lb/ton SS
Beans, green	Tank and spray	52		
	Flume	108		
Beets	Primary wash flume	100	0.8	20.0
Carrots	Primary wash flume	90	0.5	2.0
Corn	Husked corn washer	103	2.5	1.0
	Washer and silker	212	15.0	4.0
Cranberries	Skimmer and washer	1,440	36.5	15.0
Fruits	Spray	385		
Peaches	Spray	360 gal/min		
	Lye peel rinser	707 gal/min		
	Flume	1,028 gal/min		
Peas	Wash and flume	1,200		
	Clipper mill and wash	706	12.0	5.5
	Wash	432	4.0	0.5
Potatoes	Spray	2,500	20.0	30.0
	Spray and soak	640	10.7	21.0
	Peel and wash	468	2.2	2.2
	Spray	960	5.1	2.7
	Primary wash flume	70	0.5	2.0
Potatoes (dehydrated)	Slicer-washer	1,540	40.0	49.7
Tomatoes	Wash	1,320		
	Rinse after dump	1,186		
	Lye peel removal	504		

Blanching of raw foods is commonly practiced in order to expel air and gases from vegetables, to whiten beans and rice as well as to soften and precook them, to inactivate enzymes that cause undesirable flavor or color changes in food, and to prepare products so that they are easily filled into cans. Little freshwater is added to the blanching operation over a normal 8-hr shift, and therefore, the concentration of organic materials becomes high because of leaching out of sugars, starches, and other soluble materials from the product that is blanched. Although small in volume, the blanch water becomes a highly concentrated solution that frequently represents the largest portion of the soluble components in the liquid wastes of an entire food processing operation. The actual amount of dissolved and colloidal organic matter varies depending on the type of equipment used. Table 5 shows examples of the pollution loads in effluents from water blanching of vegetables.

TABLE 4 Characteristics of Wastewater from Peeling Fruits and Vegetables[5]

Product	BOD lb/ton	BOD % of plant waste stream	SS rate
Apricots	5–10		
Beets (blancher/peeler)	194	84	220 lb/hr
Carrots (blancher/peeler)	97	65	163 lb/hr
Peaches (rinse after peeling)		40	
Peaches	8–12		5–9 lb/ton
Pears	12–18		10–15 lb/ton
Potatoes (peeler)	20		90 lb/ton
Potatoes (peeler, chips)	2.3		4 lb/ton
Potatoes (peeler/dehydration)	20		
Potatoes (lye peel)	186	89	
Potatoes (dry caustic peel)	26	80	
Potatoes (lye peel)	376		
Potatoes (infrared peel)	260		
Potatoes (steam peel)	260		

TABLE 5 Pollution Loads in Effluents from Water Blanching of Vegetables[5]

Vegetable	Effluent flow, gph	BOD, lb/ton	COD, lb/ton	SS, lb/ton
Beets (and peeler)	13,100	194 (85)*	323 (83)	239 (55)
Carrots (and peeler)	8,420	97.6 (65)	196 (67)	338 (64)
Corn	270	610 lb/day	860 lb/day	144 lb/day
	2,272	24.6 (16)	30.1 (18)	6.0 (12)
Peas	1,280	3,500 ppm in effluent		
	1,280	3,500 ppm in effluent		
Potatoes	2,520	52	58	37
	2,310	22	32	25
Potatoes (and peeler)	9,210	186 (89)	279 (86)	181 (37)

* Numbers in parentheses are percentages of total amount.

The final major sources of liquid wastes are from washing equipment, utensils, cookers, etc., as well as washing of floors and general food preparation areas. Cleanup periods after production will normally alter the characteristics of the waste in that a great deal of caustic is used, thus increasing the pH considerably above the normal character obtained when the plant is in regular operation.

After the product has been placed in cans and is cooked, it is cooled—an operation requiring a large volume of water. The water used for cooling is relatively high in temperature but has essentially no pollution load. Normally this cooling water is reused in washing vegetables. Where the cooling water cannot be reused, it can be sent directly to a stream without further treatment. In the latter case, it is important to keep this water segregated from the other liquid waste in the plant because diluting this liquid waste with the cooling water will not normally help to provide better treatment but will simply compound the problems. Table 6 shows estimates of waste-water quantities, BOD or COD and suspended solids from different steps in processing fruits and vegetables as percentages of the total amounts generated.

TABLE 6 Waste Generation (Percentages) from Unit Processing Operations on Fruits and Vegetables[5]

Fruits	Clean*	Peel*	Cut,* pit	Pulp	Fill, ht, syrup	Exhaust, seal, cook
Apple:						
Water	20–30	5–20	10–25	10	40–65	
BOD/COD	5–20	10–40	5–40	70	10–80	
SS	2–15	15–40	3–35	85	10–80	
Apricot:						
Water	20–95		5–40		15–15	25–40
BOD/COD	20–20		40–55		15–30	10–10
SS	30		40		20	10
Cherry:						
Water	30–60		3–6		35–65	
BOD/COD	10		80		10	
SS	35		60		5	
Peach:						
Water	15–20	25–50	15–35		10	10–20
BOD/COD	5–10	35–50	30–50		5–10	2–5
SS	5–10	30–60	25–55		5	2–5
Pear:						
Water	30–60		7–30		10–13	30–40
BOD/COD	50–78		10–40		5–10	2–5
SS	45–83		10–45		5–5	2–5

TABLE 6 Waste Generation (Percentages) from Unit Processing Operations on Fruits and Vegetables[5] (Continued)

Vegetables	Clean*	Peel*	Cut*	Blanch*	Fill, brine, seal, cook	Fill, freeze
Asparagus:						
Water	20–40		10–20	25–30	15–40	5
BOD/COD	20		10	60	10	5
SS	50		10	30	10	5
Beans, snap:						
Water	30–40		0–40	10–45	20–50	5–10
BOD/COD	10–60		0–20	40–60	0–20	5
SS	30–80		0–30	20–30	0–10	5
Beet:						
Water	10–30	30–40	20–26		20–24	
BOD/COD	15–20	50–60	20–20		5–10	
SS	15–30	50–70	10–20		0–5	
Carrot:						
Water	12–30	30–40	20–28	0–5	15–20	
BOD/COD	16–20	50–60	20–21	0–10	0–3	
SS	10–18	40–65	15–40	0–10	0–2	
Corn, canned:						
Water	30–40		40–41		20–29	
BOD/COD	20–30		50–75		5–20	
SS	10–15		70–80		5–20	
Corn, frozen:						
Water	19–40		26–30	25–50		5–5
BOD/COD	10–18		30–68	13–55		1–5
SS	10–15		70–80	5–15		0–5
Peas:						
Water	50–60			10–30	20–40	5–10
BOD/COD	45–55			40–45	5–10	5
SS	55–65			30–35	5–10	5
Potato, sweet:						
Water	30	35	15		20	
BOD/COD	25	50	20		5	
SS	25	40	30		5	
Pumpkin, squash:						
Water	10	20†	20	20	30	
BOD/COD	15	30†	35	10	10	
SS	10	25†	50	10	5	
Spinach, greens:						
Water	20–60		0–10	10–40	15–55	5–10
BOD/COD	15–30		10–30	30–60	10–20	5
SS	30–60		10–40	20–20	10–10	5
Tomato, whole:						
Water	50–80	10–40			10–10	
BOD/COD	60	35			5	
SS	70	30			0	
Tomato, pulped:						
Water	30–85	5–30			10–60	
BOD/COD	95	5			0	
SS	95	5			5	

* "Clean" includes washing, sorting, shaking, blowing, etc.; "peel" and "blanch" include related steps such as rinsing; "cut" includes slicing and dicing.
† Pulping operation (not peeling).

The total volumes and characteristics of wastewaters generated by some fruit and vegetable processing plants are shown in Table 7. It can be seen that the waste loads are commodity-specific. Even different plants processing the same commodity vary widely in the raw waste loads. Some of this strength variation is attributable to the volume of water used. In general, the larger the volume of water used, the weaker the waste. However, there are a number of factors which greatly increase the concentration of the waste, such as fluming of the waste, screening solids, trims, and rejects, dewatering of waste solids in presses or cyclones without separate disposal of the liquor so created, and comminution of solids in grinders.

Generally, the wastewaters generated by this industry can be treated successfully by the physical and biological methods used for domestic sewage treatment to achieve substantial reductions in organic pollution loads. The treatment of cannery wastes will be discussed in more detail in a later section of this book.

Since World War II, there has been a tremendous mushrooming of the freezing industry with the advent of the home freezer. The freezing of products originated in canning plants, and in some cases both canning and freezing are still performed in the same plant. Except for the final step of preservation, the preparation of foods for freezing, starting with the planting of seeds, harvesting of crops, washing, blanching, and all other preparatory procedures, is the same as for canning. In the latter case, the final preservation step is accomplished by heat sterilization, whereas in the former, freezing techniques are utilized.

TABLE 7 Summary of Statistical Analysis of Reported Raw Waste Loads[53]

(Total plant effluents)

			BOD				Suspended solids			
	Volume, gal/ton		lb/ton		ppm		lb/ton		ppm	
Product	Mean	Std. dev.	Mean	Std. dev.	Mean	Std. dev.	Mean	Std. dev.	Mean	Std. dev.
Apples	1,440		50		2,320		4		320	
Apricots	8,720	1,970	71	26	1,060	380	16	5	211	64
Asparagus	13,300	7,450	7	3	45	15	8	3	48	20
Beets	4,270		133		4,760		46		1,750	
Carrots	3,860		47		1,875		20		1,380	
Cherries	1,800		28		1,140		4		271	
Citrus	1,720	1,130	14	12	1,370	460	3	3	163	
Corn	2,150	1,330	26	11	2,270	1,640	20		1,170	
Peas	5,320	1,910	72	33	1,390	840	14	6	500	430
Peaches	5,620	1,710	62	17	1,490	440	13	7	360	190
Pears	4,935		82		2,060				333	
Potatoes	3,420	1,590	47	19	1,800	940	53	27	1,990	970
Pumpkins/squash	1,580		46		3,350	730	10		670	
Sauerkraut	630		18		3,400		2		420	
Snap beans	7,820	5,040	28	24	380	180	17		148	
Spinach	8,390	3,420	28	16	340	96	18	13	193	77
Sweet potatoes	3,500		104		3,560		42		1,450	
Tomatoes	2,740	1,780	14	11	810	660	7	7	350	300

Water Conservation

The reduction of the pollution load in cannery effluents depends on the identification of sources and characteristics of the wastewater. As pointed out previously, this industry uses large volumes of water during the various stages of processing. Historically, water has been considered the cheapest commodity available in comparison with the processing equipment and labor; therefore, water conservation procedures have not been practiced successfully.

Food processors have become increasingly aware of the importance of water conservation because of current national interest in pollution control. This has been the stimulus for research programs directed toward equipment modifications and changes that reduce water usage during processing. More research programs are needed for the improvement of the quality of raw product brought to the cannery for processing. Mercer et al.[7] have suggested the need for the evaluation of the feasibility of use of water at site of harvest to prewash the crop on site, to reduce the transport of nonedible material and facilitate the transport of crops from the field to the plant. The economic benefits of such water conservation have to be established in order to be widely accepted by the food processors.

Water Reuse

Wastewater loads can effectively be reduced by segregation of the waste streams for the possible reuse of less-polluted water for certain phases of the operations. Can-cooling water has been used and reused successfully in tomato processing operations. The recycled water is used for primary washing of the product and is later used for fluming the waste material. Maximum utilization of recirculated water is achieved in counterflow systems for vegetable washing. Figure 1 shows a counterflow system for reuse of water in a pea cannery. At the top of the system, freshwater is used for the final product wash before the peas are canned and from this point the water is reused and carried back in successive stages for each preceding washing and fluming operation. Since the water flows countercurrent to the product, the washing and fluming water becomes progressively contaminated and, therefore, chlorine is added in order to maintain satisfactory bacteriological conditions in each phase of the operation.

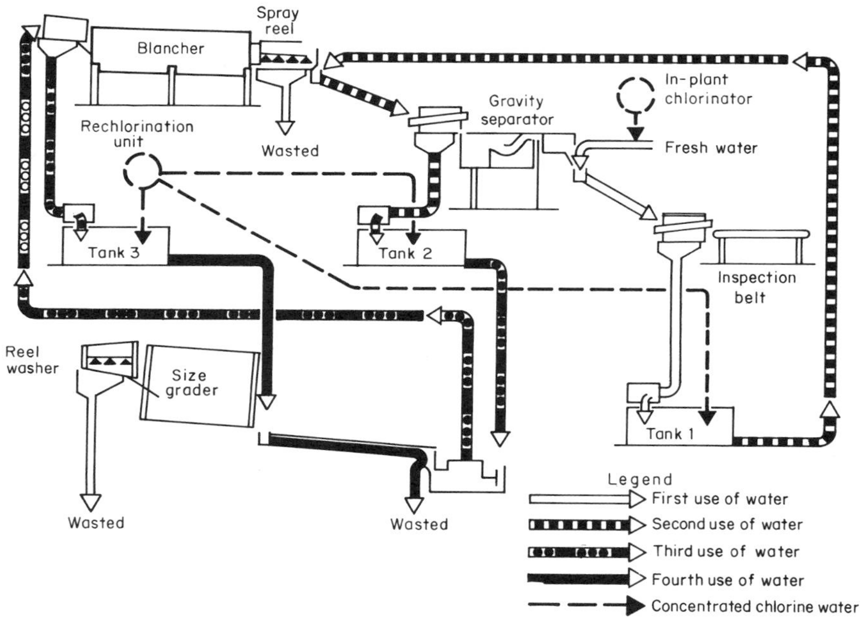

Fig. 1 Diagram of four-stage counterflow system for reuse of water in a pea cannery.

A unique example of water recirculation and reuse is encountered in one of the Campbell Soup Company's plants, located in Napoleon, Ohio. At this site, the company owns and operates its own water treatment plant. The raw water is withdrawn from the Maumee River, which is characterized as a slightly polluted river with water of high hardness content. The treatment system consists of chemical oxidation of organic matter, lime-soda softening, mixed-media filtration, disinfection, and activated carbon filtration. During the winter months, the river water temperature drops to about 33°F and the chemical reactions in the softening step decrease sharply, thus resulting in reduction in the efficiency and capacity of the system. During this period, all the cooling water with an average temperature of 120°F is recirculated and combined with influent water to the treatment plant. This results in raising the raw water temperature to about 45°F where better efficiency of the softening processes is achieved. During the tomato season, however, this cooling water is recirculated to the tomato fluming and primary washing system. The cooling water, therefore, is recirculated and reused about 8 months each year.

Recently, the water reuse in two food processing plants in England was reported[8] where strict water pollution control regulations and high cost of process water justified the reuse of the reclaimed wastewater. The first case is a potato processing plant which handles 150 tons/day of potatoes and produces about 720,000 gal of wastewater containing 12,000 lb BOD. The wastewater treatment system consists of primary settling biological treatment by two plastic-media filters followed by activated sludge systems. The settled effluent is further subjected to tertiary treatment consisting of sand filtration and chlorination. The treated water which has a BOD of 2.5 mg/l and negligible suspended solids is reused for makeup water for the fluming system, washdown, and nonprocess uses. The second example of reuse of treated wastewater involves a fruit juice bottling plant. The caustic wash of the bottles contained all the BOD load of the plant (1,200 lb BOD/day). The wastewater treatment system consisted of neutralization, biological treatment by trickling filters, followed by tertiary treatment consisting of sand filtration and activated carbon treatment. The treated effluent having no measurable BOD is reused in the washing of the bottles and first rinse.

The reuse of reclaimed wastewater for nonprocess uses has never been fully practiced in the canning industry in the United States but in the light of the newly enacted Federal Water Pollution Control Act recommendation of zero discharge of pollutants in 1983, this approach merits serious consideration by the industry at the present time.

Reduction of total pollution load from a canning plant can be achieved by segregation and separate treatment of strong process wastes. The effluents from the blanching of vegetables and/or fruits, for example, which are low in volume but contribute significantly to the total waste load, can be segregated and treated separately by concentration and drying or anaerobic digestion, thus achieving a considerable reduction in the waste load.

During tomato processing, the rejected tomatoes and trimmings are pressed and centrifuged to separate the skins and seeds. The resulting liquid waste called *press liquor* has a BOD of 10,000 to 15,000 mg/l and suspended solids content of 4,000 to 8,000 mg/l. The discharge of this waste stream with the other process wastes results in a final effluent to 700 to 900 mg/l BOD. In one of Campbell Soup Company's plants, the press liquor is segregated from the other waste streams and disposed of by spray irrigation on land. This practice results in reduction of the total plant raw wastewater effluent to about 450 mg/l, which is less costly to treat in a wastewater treatment system especially if the wastewater is to be discharged to a municipal system.

Process Equipment Changes

It has been realized in recent years that water pollution abatement can be achieved efficiently by changing processing technology. The research efforts of the Engineering and Development Division, Agricultural Research Service, U.S. Department of Agriculture,[9] have resulted in the development of the dry caustic peeling system for potatoes in an effort to reduce the volume and strength of the wastewater generated in peeling of potatoes. This system has been worked into an industrial process by Magnuson Engineers, Inc., San Jose, California and utilizes infrared energy at 1650°F to condition the surfaces of potatoes treated with strong sodium hydroxide solution. The peel can then be removed mechanically by soft rubber rolls rather than by water as is done in conventional caustic peeling. The new process has demonstrated substantial reduction in water usage (about 75 percent) and waste strength (40 percent) in comparison with the conventional peeler. This process has been modified and used on a commercial scale for peeling tree fruits (mainly cling peaches) by Del Monte Corporation.[10] The results of their application of the dry caustic peeling system demonstrated reductions of almost 90 percent of freshwater requirement and 60 percent in BOD load in comparison with the conventional peeling process (Table 8).

Other technological process changes aimed at reducing pollution loads are the recent developments of new blanching techniques. As pointed out previously, the conventional blanching processes generate an average of 40 percent of the total BOD in the cannery wastes. Any reduction in the liquid waste volume and/or strength from this process is certainly a distinct wastewater management improvement. The

TABLE 8 Comparison of Waste Effluent Strength for Dry Caustic and Conventional Peeling of Cling Peaches[10]

	Range, ppm	Average, ppm
COD:		
Dry caustic	2,670–11,300	5,600
Conventional	910–3,275	1,520
BOD_5:		
Dry caustic	2,150–8,650	3,750
Conventional	700–1,260	940
Suspended solids:		
Dry caustic	1,150–3,630	2,430
Conventional	200–1,700	780
Total solids:		
Dry caustic	3,900–8,450	5,400
Conventional	1,910–4,130	2,510
Total nitrogen:		
Dry caustic	86.16–156.91	110.32
Conventional	22.42–47.63	35.14
Total phosphate:		
Dry caustic	2.32–15.39	6.98
Conventional	0.69–9.25	2.88
Alkalinity:		
Dry caustic	372–619	514
Conventional	374–488	430
pH:		
Dry caustic	4.35–5.85	4.90
Conventional	5.70–8.90	6.85
Water use, gal/ton:		
Dry caustic		170
Conventional		2,800 (80% recirc.)

newly developed processes are the individual quick blanching (IQB),[11] microwave blanching,[12] and hot-air blanching.[13] The details of these processes are described elsewhere. Field studies conducted by Lund[14] demonstrated that the IQB process results in reduction of the blancher effluent by 68 to 99 percent while maintaining product quality. Table 9 shows the characteristics of wastewater from pea blanching by the IQB and the conventional pipe method. The National Canners Association reported[13] the results of a recent comparative study of four different blanching methods using simulators of possible commercial units. The comparison included the microwave, hot-air, steam and hot-water blanching methods of several vegetable commodities. Table 10 shows comparison of the wastewater characteristics generated in the blanching of green beans. The results show a substantial reduction in volume and strength of the wastewater resulting from the hot-air blanching and the microwave methods.

These recent developments in process technology discussed above offer some solutions to reduction of the total waste loads generated in the cannery. However, the same concept needs to be extended to other unit processing operations. For example, substitutions of hydraulic fluming by pneumatic or other conveying methods that

TABLE 9 Characterization of Wastewater from Pea Blanching by IQB and Pipe Method[14]

Percent drying (IQB)	Water flow gal/case	TS, %	BOD, ppm	Can loss, %
0	0.32	2.33	16,700	2.1
6.5	0.09	2.92	15,600	1.1
17.2	0.06	3.32	19,600	1.0
Pipe	0.76	2.31	15,100	4.8

TABLE 10 Comparison of Wastewater Characteristics for Green Bean Blanching by Four Different Methods[13]

Unit	Wastewater, gal/ton	COD, lb/ton	SS, lb/ton
Microwave	48.0	0.59	1.8×10^{-2}
Hot air	0.25	2×10^{-3}	2×10^{-4}
Steam	47.0	2.1	4×10^{-2}
Hot water	1,710.0	4.7	0.11

require less water should be evaluated. The feasibility of washing and peeling the vegetables in the field and disposal on land before the transport of the raw materials to the processing plant merits serious consideration.

SUGAR BEET INDUSTRY

A recent state-of-art study of the sugar beet industry[15] revealed that the total production in 1968 was 3.5 million tons of sugar processed from 25 million tons of sugar beet roots in 58 processing plants located in 18 different states. Table 11 shows the location of sugar beet plants by states and their rated, actual, and projected capacities within a 10-year period. These plants are located in different climatic conditions ranging from hot, arid conditions to very cold climates. These climatic conditions influence the physical handling processes of beets prior to processing and the methods of handling the by-products and wastes generated in the plants. Basically, the processes used in all phases of the operation are the same within the different plants. The differences in waste loads and in freshwater use and reuse result from differences in operating practices and equipment. Most of the water used in sugar beet processing plants is used for condensing vapors from evaporators and for conveying and washing beets. These uses do not require high quality water; therefore, considerable recirculation is possible. The quantity and quality of wastes discharged are affected by differences in freshwater use and recirculation practices.

TABLE 11 Present and Projected Processing Capacity of Sugarbeet Factories by States[15]

State	Number of factories	Rated capacity (1968), tons beets/day	Actual capacity (1968), tons beets/day	Projected capacity (within 10 years)
California	10	39,800	37,825	40,000
Colorado	10	25,400	26,500	29,300
Michigan	5	10,900	10,324	11,800
Idaho	4	20,000	20,169	24,950
Minnesota	4	12,800	11,830	14,750
Nebraska	4	9,510	9,974	10,000
Montana	3	8,720	8,450	11,450
Ohio	3	5,000	5,130	5,130
Utah	3	6,350	5,972	6,350
Wyoming	3	7,200	6,817	7,550
Washington	2	10,525	10,250	13,800
Arizona	1	4,200	4,200	4,200
Iowa	1	2,400	1,881	2,400
Kansas	1	3,200	2,605	3,600
Maine	1	4,000	4,000	4,000
North Dakota	1	5,000	3,915	5,000
Oregon	1	6,650	6,600	7,200
Texas	1	6,500	6,500	6,500
Totals	58	188,155	182,942	207,980

Wastewater discharges from the sugar beet processing industry are extremely high in dissolved organic matter, approximately 2,200 gal containing an average of 4 to 8 lb BOD per ton of beets processed. The total discharge to streams from the entire sugar beet industry in the United States in 1968 was estimated to be about 57 billion gal containing about 87 million lb BOD. The seasonal nature of the industry and the concentration of most of the processing plants in semiarid areas where the streams are relatively small cause significant water pollution problems.

The processing of the beet sugar begins with fluming of the beets from piles or cars into the plant. The beets are lifted from the flume to a washer and then subjected to a final wash by sprays. The washed beets are sliced into thin strips, called *cossettes*, and fed into a diffuser. The diffuser is the first step in the beet sugar process. It extracts sugar and other soluble solids from the cossettes under a countercurrent flow of water. The liquor containing the sugar and other soluble solids is drawn off the diffuser and pumped to the purification stations. The exhausted cossettes are usually conveyed to pulp presses which reduce the water content of the pulp to about 80 percent before the cossettes are fed into a pulp drier. The pulp-press water usually returns to the diffuser as a part of the diffuser supply. If the pulp is not dried, it is usually separated from the transport water by screening and then discharged into a silo. The juice from the diffuser is treated with lime or calcium saccharate (from Steffen process) and the mixture is gassed with carbon dioxide to precipitate the lime. The calcium carbonate thus formed carries with it the suspended impurities in the juice. The lime precipitate is separated from the mixture by means of thickeners and filters and is then pumped into a waste pond. The juice, after further treatment with CO_2 and filtration, is concentrated in a multiple-effect evaporator to 65 percent solids and is then boiled in a single-effect evaporator to crystallize the sugar. The sugar is separated by centrifugation and then dried in a granulator system and stored. The syrup is further concentrated to yield additional crystalline sugar and, finally, molasses. The molasses may be sold as such or desugarized by the Steffen process. In this process, the molasses is diluted and treated by lime to precipitate the sugar as calcium saccharate. The latter is separated by filtration and recycled to first carbonation. The Steffen filtrate may be discharged as waste, or after precipitation and removal of calcium carbonate evaporated to a thick liquor, called *concentrated Steffen filtrate*, and dried on beet pulp.

The largest single usage of water is for the flume, washer, and sprays and ranges from 1,200 to 4,000 gal/ton of beets averaging about 2,340 gal. Large quantities of cold water are also required for the barometric condensers of the evaporators. The amount of condenser water used varies from 1,300 to 4,500 gal/ton of beets averaging about 2,210 gal/ton of beets processed. A much smaller volume of water is used to extract the sugar from the beets averaging about 270 gal/ton and even smaller amounts, about 50 gal/ton, are used to slurry the filtered lime for pumping into storage ponds.

Sources and Characteristics of Wastewater

The major sources of wastes in the sugar beet plants are flume water, barometric condenser water, lime mud, general wastes from washing floors and equipment, and Steffen wastes.

The flume and wash waters contribute the largest amount of wastewater and contain considerable amounts of soil, suspended beet fragments, stems, leaves, and dissolved solids which have diffused from the beets. The amount of soil depends on the harvesting conditions and generally averages 5 to 6 percent of the beet weight. The BOD of this wastewater is about 200 mg/l and may be considerably higher if the beets had decomposed during storage.

The barometric condenser and cooling waters have a low BOD content, about 40 mg/l, however. The condenser water picks up ammonia from the evaporating juices and therefore is always alkaline, having a pH ranging between 8 and 10.

The lime mud is the slurried lime cake discharged from the filters. This waste is low in volume but it has high BOD, and the suspended solids content ranges from 4 to 6 percent of the beets, which is approximately the same as the flume sediment.

Some plants do not dry the exhausted pulp; in these cases the cossettes are flushed out from the diffuser and the effluent is screened. This waste contains sugar, other dissolved organics, and finely divided suspended pulp. The volume of this waste is relatively small, but the BOD and suspended solids are relatively high. The screened pulp is usually discharged into a silo. Drainage from the wet pulp silo constitutes one of the main sources of BOD in the plant effluent.

The Steffen wastes constitute one of the most serious disposal problems in the sugar beet industry. The wastewater is extremely high in BOD and consists principally of sodium and potassium salts of nitrogenous compounds. Several plants had to partly discontinue the Steffen operations because of the waste disposal problem. Table 12 shows the unit loadings of beet wastes from various operations.

Water Conservation

Water reuse has been used to a considerable extent in the sugar beet industry in order to eliminate most of the wastewater. The amount of water reuse varies greatly among the plants; at most plants raw water intake constitutes one-third to one-half of the total usage. The reduction in freshwater usage has been achieved by recirculation of the flume water and by the reuse of condenser water. Maximum

TABLE 12 Representative Values of Unit Process Wastes from Sugar Beet Manufacture

Source of waste	Flow/ton beets, gal	BOD, ppm	Suspended solids, ppm	BOD/ton sliced beets, lb
Flume water	2,600	210	800–4,300	4.5
Pulp screen water:				
Bottom dump cell	240	980	530	2.0
Side dump cell	1,420	500	620	5.9
Continuous*	400	910	1,020	3.0
Pulp press water	180	1,710	420	2.6
Pulp silo drainage	210	7,000	270	12.3
Lime cake slurry	90	8,600	120,000	6.5
Lime cake lagoon effluent	75	1,420	450	0.89
Barometric condenser waste	2,000	40		0.67
Steffen's waste	2,640†	10,500	100–700	231(3)

* Pulp transported by water.
† Per ton molasses processed on a 50 percent sucrose basis.
SOURCE: Adapted from Tables 2 and 3 in "Beet Sugar—An Industrial Waste Guide to the Beet Sugar Industry," Federal Security Agency, U.S. Public Health Service, 1950.

recirculation and reuse of water should be practiced in order to conserve freshwater and to reduce the wastewater volume. The following is a flow pattern where considerable reuse of water can be achieved.

The freshwater is used only in the evaporators and condensers and other cooling processes and for dilution of molasses at the Steffen plants. Flume water is screened and the suspended solids are removed in a pond or clarifier, and then the effluent is recycled back to the flume. The water from the evaporators and barometric condensers is reused as makeup water in the diffuser, the beet washers, and the sprays. Pulp water and pulp-press water are returned to the diffuser as a part of its supply, thus eliminating a considerable portion of wastewater discharge. Lime mud is pumped to a separate lime pond as the overflow is discharged to the waste treatment system. The lime cake which contains 50 percent solids can be hauled away for disposal instead of pumping this slurry, but this practice has never been utilized. Only two plants in the United States regenerate the lime from the lime cake in special kilns, thus eliminating completely the disposal problem of the lime mud. Cooling towers or spray ponds are used for cooling most of the condenser water for recycling. The Steffen wastes are evaporated to concentrated Steffen filtrate which can be dried on the beet pulp. Figure 2 shows a flow pattern of a sugar beet plant involving considerable reuse of water.

Recently full-scale, closed-loop water recirculation systems have been used in only three plants in the United States. A schematic diagram of such a system is shown in Fig. 3. At the end of the processing campaign (16 weeks), the system and surplus waters are discharged into anaerobic lagoons and stored for almost 31 weeks until the water quality meets the discharge standards. The BOD of the wastewater discharged into the ponds is reduced from 3,000 to about 50 mg/l. In one plant, the ponded water is not discharged at all but is used to fill the fluming-washing system for the following season.[16] This water recirculation approach represents the only total water reuse in the food processing industry and fulfills the zero-discharge goal of the Federal Water Pollution Control Act of 1972.

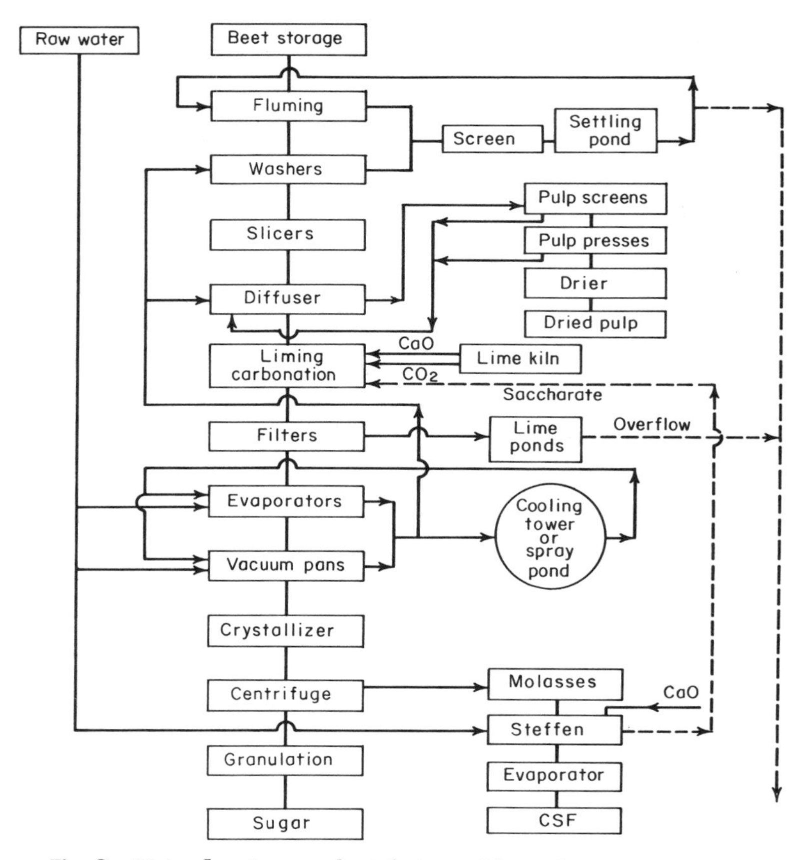

Fig. 2 Water flow in sugar beet factory with maximum water reuse.

POULTRY PROCESSING INDUSTRY

The poultry processing industry is engaged in slaughtering, eviscerating, cutting up, and packing young chickens (broilers, fryers), mature chickens, turkeys, and other poultry. During the past decade, the industry has achieved a high degree of vertical integration by coordinating the successive stages of production from the hatchery through the feed mill, processing plant, and contract production. The total production in federally inspected plants (90 percent of total United States production) increased from 8.1 to 12.9 billion lb live weight between 1961 and 1970.[17] Whole turkeys and young chickens account for 93 percent of the total production in 1970. The South Atlantic region (Delaware, Maryland, Virginia, North Carolina, South Carolina, Georgia, and Florida) and the South Central region (Kentucky, Tennessee,

Alabama, Mississippi, Arkansas, Louisiana, Oklahoma, and Texas) accounted for 86.8 percent of turkey production in 1970. The total value of shipment of the poultry industry increased from $2,241 million in 1963 to $2,936 million in 1967.

Water Usage and Waste Production

A large volume of water is used in poultry processing operations for scalding, product preparation, cooling whole birds and parts, transporting wastes, and general cleanup. Significant amounts of soluble and suspended organic matter are picked up by the

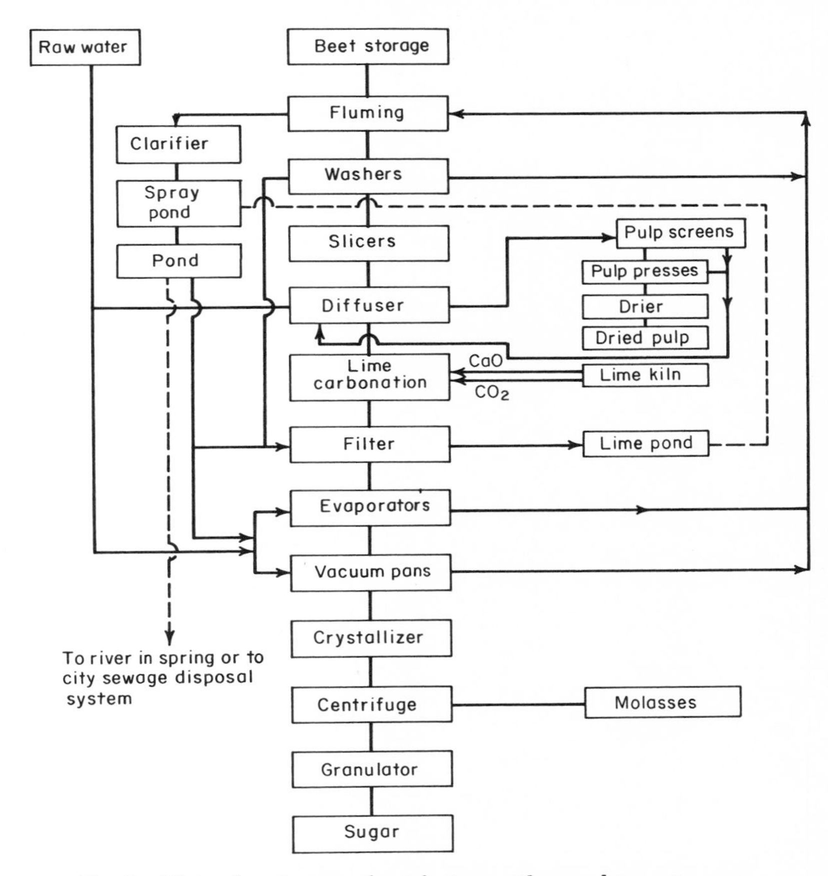

Fig. 3 Water flow in sugar beet factory with complete water reuse.

water, resulting in high-strength, biologically degradable waste. A 1970 survey of federally inspected plants revealed that the total volume of water used by 368 surveyed plants was estimated to be 27.3 billion gal with an annual average for all plants of 70.8 million gal. The wastewater loadings were estimated to be 7.1 billion gal containing 26.1 million lb BOD, and 19.4 million lb SS discharged to private treatment systems, compared with 18.4 billion gal containing 68.9 million lb BOD and 50.5 million lb SS discharged to municipal treatment, and 1.8 billion gal containing 6.8 million lb BOD and 5.0 million lb SS discharged without treatment. These estimates were based on actual volumes of poultry slaughtered in plants in 1970 using water use and standard raw waste loads shown in Table 13.

TABLE 13 Coefficients Used in Estimating By-products, Water Use, and Waste Loads of Poultry Slaughtering Plants

Variable	Unit	Value per 1,000 lb*
By-products:		
Blood:		
Young chickens		70
Mature chickens	Pounds	70
Turkeys		70
Other poultry		70
Offal:		
Young chickens		175
Mature chickens	Pounds	170
Turkeys		125
Other poultry		140
Feathers:		
Young chickens		70
Mature chickens	Pounds	70
Turkeys		70
Water use:		
Young chickens		2,198
Mature chickens		2,173
Turkeys	Gallons	1,700
Other poultry		2,100
Cut-up		500
Further processing		500
Wasteloads:		
BOD:		
Young chickens		8.2
Mature chickens	Pounds	8.7
Turkeys		8.0
Other poultry		8.0
Suspended solids:		
Young chickens		6.3
Mature chickens	Pounds	5.4
Turkeys		5.0
Other poultry		5.0
Time span of operation:†		
Young chicken, mature chicken, and other poultry plants	Days	234
Turkey plants	Days	130

* Live weight except for cut-up and further processed coefficients which are ready-to-cook weight.

† These coefficients are based on a maximum of 260 operating days per year. We assumed that the chicken and other poultry plants operated at 90 percent capacity: 0.90 × 260 = 234. Turkey plants were assumed to operate at 50 percent of capacity: 0.50 × 260 = 130.

SOURCE: U.S. Environmental Protection Agency, Industrial Waste Study of the Meat Products Industry, 1971; U.S. Department of Agriculture, Processing Poultry Byproducts in Poultry Slaughtering Plants, *Marketing Res. Rept.* 181, 1957; and industry contacts.

Sources and Characteristics of Wastewater

Poultry processing wastes are characterized as high-strength organic wastes with high suspended solids and grease content. The manufacturing processes in plants with flow-away systems consist of receiving, killing, defeathering, eviscerating, chilling, packing, and further processing (Fig. 4). The wastewater is generated from these processes in addition to the subprocess of scalding, washing, offal and blood handling, and cleanup.

It is a common practice to store the live poultry after delivery to the plant for a short period of time in the receiving area. The feathers, manure, and dirt accumulated in this area may contribute 32 to 36 lb BOD/(1,000 birds) (day). The wastewater generated from daily wet wash varies greatly in quantity and strength among the different plants. This waste load can be substantially reduced by dry cleaning the solid wastes and disposing of them as refuse or by loading them onto offal trucks. High-pressure sprays for final washing can further reduce the volume of wastewater generated. Dry cleaning and low water volume usage can reduce the waste load in the receiving area to 5 lb BOD/1,000 birds.

The first major processing operation is the killing of the live poultry. This is usually done by manual severance of the jugular vein or by mechanical means while the birds are hanging by their feet from a moving conveyor. The drained blood constitutes the most significant pollution source in the process plant. The chicken

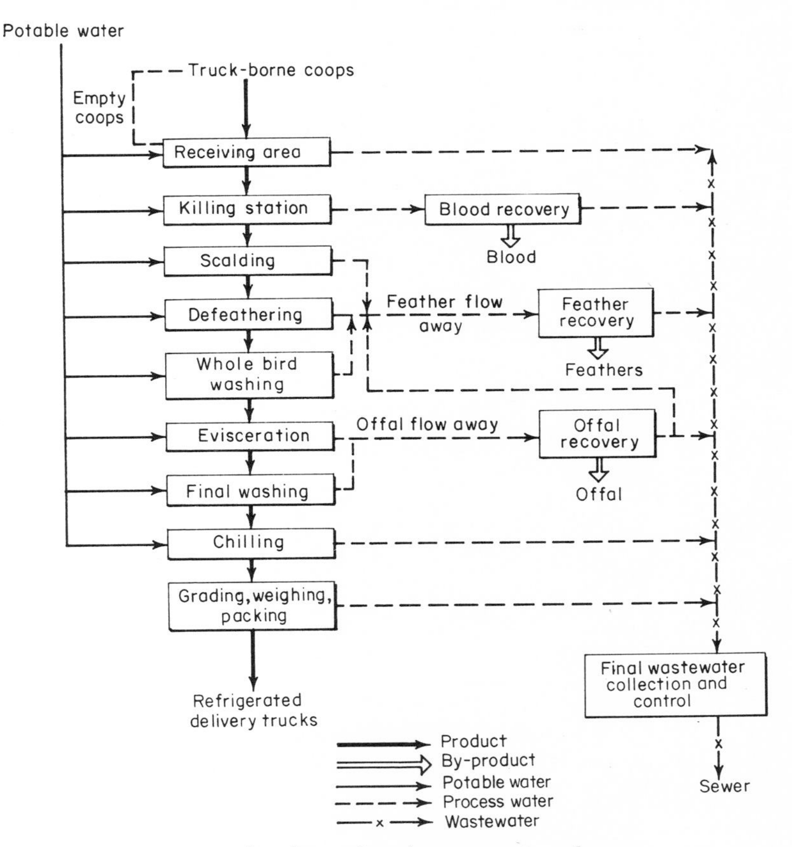

Fig. 4 Flowchart of poultry processing plant.

blood has an approximate BOD of 92,000 mg/l and may contribute an organic loading of 17 lb BOD/1,000 chickens. In modern plants, as much as possible of the free-draining blood is collected in collection troughs under the conveyor lines in a well-contained area to prevent drainage and splattering onto the floors. The blood is allowed to congeal and is removed as a semisolid to be mixed with the feathers and offal on the offal truck or it is put into a separate receiving tank attached to the offal truck to be sold to a rendering plant. Thus, final cleanup of the killing area requires much less water and a substantial waste-load reduction can be achieved. Collection of the blood may reduce the total wastewater strength by 35 to 40 percent.[17]

After bleeding, the birds are scalded to loosen the body feathers and to provide a first wash to the carcasses. The scalding operation is carried out by the use of a spray or by immersion in a scald tank using hot water (approximately 130 to 140°F). The immersion process is the most commonly used. The water in the scalding tank is maintained at the desired temperature by continuous addition of hot water at a rate of ¼ gal/bird. Overflow wastewater from the tank contains significant amounts of blood, feathers, dirt, manure, fats, and grease. The BOD of the scalder water has been reported[18] to be 1,182 mg/l, with suspended solids and grease content of 682 and 350 mg/l, respectively. Table 14 shows wastewater characteristics generated in the different processes in a poultry plant.

Immediately following scalding the feathers are mechanically removed from the birds. The most common defeathering method is a continuous operation in which the birds are suspended from the conveyor and pass in front of rotating drums containing rubber fingers which beat the feathers off the birds. Continuous streams of water wash the feathers from the carcasses to a flume and then they are flushed away to a central facility. After defeathering, the remaining pinfeathers are removed by hand and an arc-gas flame is used to singe the fine hair and remaining pinfeathers. At this point, the birds are washed with an external fine spray. A considerable volume of wastewater is generated by the defeathering process and from washdown of floors and equipment during cleanup. Water usage has been estimated to be 11 percent of the total water supply[18] to the plant at a rate of 1.4 gal/bird for the mechanical feather removal, final body wash, and periodic area cleanup. Additional in-plant water reuse for the feather flume raises the total water usage for the defeathering process to 2.8 gal/bird which is also the waste discharge from the defeathering

TABLE 14 Wastewater Characteristics of Different Processes in a Poultry Plant[18]

			Solids			
	BOD	COD	Total	Dissolved	Suspended	Grease
Scalder entry	1,182	2,080	1,873	1,186	587	350
Scalder exit	490	986	1,053	580	473	200
Whole bird wash	108	243	266	185	81	150
Final bird wash	442	662	667	386	281	580
Giblet chiller	2,357	3,959	2,875	1,899	976	1,320
Chiller I	442	692	776	523	253	800
Chiller II	320	435	514	331	183	250
Feather flume	590	1,078	894	382	512	120
Eviscerating flume	233	514	534	232	302	430
Plant effluent	560	722	697	322	375	150

process. The wastewater contains feathers, blood, dirt, and grease with BOD content of 580 mg/l.[18] A considerable reduction in water usage can be achieved by screening the wastewater for removal of the feathers and reuse of the screened water in the feather flume where there is no direct contact with the poultry product. Screening of the defeathering process wastewater is very important in order to avoid overloading the waste disposal system with the high volume of feathers involved. It is estimated that 1,000 birds will yield approximately 70 lb of feathers.

After defeathering, the birds are moved into the evisceration area which is an enclosed room separated from the other operations of the plant to prevent cross contamination. The first step of evisceration is the removal of the feet and resuspension of the birds from the conveyor for easier access to the stomach cavity. Consequent operations consist of removal of the oil gland and opening the peritoneal cavity. The viscera are then pulled out and exposed for inspection by the USDA inspectors. The hearts, livers, and gizzards are separated from the inedible viscera for separate processing. Cleaning of the gizzards is a special subprocess of the evisceration operation which involves splitting, washing out the contents, peeling the inner lining, and a final wash. As the birds continue along the line, the lungs are removed by vacuum, the heads are cut off, and finally, the necks are removed and washed. A large volume of water is used to flush the inedible viscera and heads in a flow-away flume system.

The last step in the eviscerating area consists of thorough washing of the inside and outside of the birds before federal inspection.

A considerable volume of freshwater is used in the eviscerating process to clean the carcasses, to wash workers' hands, to wash recoverable viscera, and to transport waste heads, feet, and offal down a flume to a screening station. The water usage in the eviscerating flume was reported to account for 24 percent of the plant's freshwater supply.[18] A typical example of flume water has a flow of 3.1 gal water/bird, gizzard cleaning requires another 3 gal/bird, giving a combined flow of 6.1 gal/bird discharged into the viscera flow-away flume. The wastewater generated in this operation contains the inedible portions of the bird in addition to blood, flesh, fat, grease, sand and silt. The wastewater has to be screened to recover the by-products, but the screened effluent still contains considerable amounts of suspended and soluble organic matter. The wastewater has a BOD content of 230 mg/l but because of the large volumes of flushing water in this process, this represents 40 to 50 percent of the BOD load of the plant effluent.

The final step in poultry processing is chilling the birds before shipment. The removal of the body heat at this point is very important because rapid cooling prevents bacterial decomposition and thus lengthens the market life, and also ensures the proper flavor. The chilling operation is governed by federal rules and regulations. Large processing plants use mechanical chill tanks in series. Countercurrent flow is utilized through the series, so that the first chilling vat is warmer than the following ones. The body temperature is lowered to 65°F in the first chill tank. Ice or ice and water are added to the second and third chill tanks in sufficient quantities to keep the chilling media in all sections reasonably clean and in continuous overflow. The overflow from these tanks is used as makeup for the first tank. The amount of overflow is governed by federal regulations which specify continuous overflow of at least ½ gal per frying chicken in the first chill tank. The chilling operation lasts about 30 to 40 minutes where the body temperature reaches about 34°F. Smaller plants do not use mechanical equipment for quick chilling. Instead, the birds are placed in portable tubs containing ice and water. Giblets are usually cooled in a similar continuous or batch system that is smaller in size. The chilled birds and giblets are drained on a conveyor line, then sized, graded, and packaged.

The wastewater generated in the chilling operation contains fats, grease, blood, and meat tissue. This waste load accounts for 8 percent of the BOD load and contributes a major share of the grease load in the plant effluent. The BOD in a two-stage body chiller has been reported[18] to be 442 and 320 mg/l in the first and second chillers, respectively, while the BOD of giblet chill water was 2,357 mg/l with a grease content of 1,320 mg/l.

Water and Wastewater Management

Water conservation The introduction of flow-away systems in poultry plants to provide quicker and more automatic processing has resulted in a significant increase in water use. Further mechanization (such as continuous chillers and gizzard machines) has also added increased demand for freshwater. The use of water in most plants to transport by-products increases the probability of higher BOD levels in the plant effluent. Significant reduction of water usage by equipment modifications and water reuse has been demonstrated in a recent study conducted in the Gold Kist plant at Durham, N.C.[18] High-efficiency spray nozzles with quick shutoff valves were installed in the whole-bird washers, hand-wash outlets at the evisceration lines, and the final bird washers to improve the cleaning action while applying a smaller volume of water. Pressure control valves and pressure gages were installed on the water supply lines to these processes to regulate the flow and to smooth out fluctuation of air pressures due to varying water demands in the plant. Timed control valves were also installed for side pan wash at the eviscerating line where the full force of water was sufficient to clean the pan surface at timed intervals without the need of flowing water all the time. Mechanical improvements in the replacement of old free-running hoses by a high-pressure cleaning system using foam cleaners reduced daily cleaning water from 112,000 to 46,000 gpd. A significant reduction in freshwater was also achieved by reuse or multiple continued use of process water. USDA regulations require a continuous overflow of chiller water at a rate of 0.5 gal/chicken. In the

Gold Kist plant, freshwater is used in the final chiller and then it is pumped to the prechiller. The prechiller overflow is skimmed off and pumped to the scalder as make up water. As a scalder effluent, the same water discharges into the feather flow-away flume to assist in transporting the feathers to the by-product recovery screens before final discharge into the sewer. The reduction in water use achieved by these water conservation schemes is detailed in Table 15. The water use was reduced from 850,000 to 620,000 gpd with a reduction in the waste load from 4,000 to 1,500 lb BOD/day.

Waste-load reduction Pollutional load from poultry processing plants can be substantially reduced by utilization of effective by-product recovery methods. Removal of the by-products from the waste streams reduces the cost of waste treatment and, in addition, these materials in themselves have economic value. The major by-products of poultry processing are blood, feathers, and offal. Rendering plants convert these by-products into proteinaceous supplements for animal feeds. In 1972, blood, feathers, and offal were sold to renderers in Florida at the rate of $9 to $10 per 1,000 broilers processed.[17]

TABLE 15 Water Reduction Development Activities by Area of the Plant and Changes in Freshwater Use

Area of plant	Activity	Reduction in freshwater use, gpm	
		From	To
Evisceration	Use of improved nozzles		
	Final bird washers	50	30
	Hand washers	285	100
	Cycling of side-pan wash	90	30
	Rearrangement of giblet handling	360	320
Scalding and defeathering	Use of improved nozzles in whole bird washers	45	30
	Substitution of recirculated eviscerating flame water for freshwater and new design on feather flume	94	0
	Use of chiller water in scalder to replace freshwater	40	0
Cleanup	New high-pressure cleaning system with foam	112,000 gpd	46,000 gpd

SOURCE: W. M. Crosswhite, et al., Water and Waste Management in Poultry Processing, Proc. Second Natl. Symp. Food Processing Wastes, Denver, Colo., March 1971, p. 323.

Blood constitutes the major source of BOD in all the poultry processing operations. Blood recovery, therefore, is an important step in the reduction of the pollution load in the plant effluent. Stunning the birds before killing, installing collection troughs under the conveyors in a well-contained area, and dry handling of the blood will provide an efficient recovery operation. Only about 70 percent of the blood can be collected but this results in 40 percent BOD reduction in the plant wastewater.

Dry handling of the feathers and offal can also reduce water use and wastewater loads in the flow-away systems. The waste loads from the picking and eviscerating areas are primarily controlled by screening. The utilization of line defeathering with mechanical conveyance of the feathers from the picking area to a central dry storage or to a rendering truck can reduce freshwater usage and screening requirements.

Dry offal handling will also reduce water requirements and BOD loads in the flow-away systems. It has been reported[19] that if waste solids from evisceration are put directly into containers at the table, the effluent BOD will be reduced from 12.1 to 6 or 8 lb BOD/1,000 chickens.

Recently, an automatic dry offal handling system has been developed[20] by W. A. Nichols Company, Kansas City, Missouri, and is now operating in two turkey plants under an experimental permit from the USDA. The system, called *Dry-Vis*, mechanically moves edible products and waste products by a combination of food grade belt conveyors and augers. Giblets are also moved to chilling and wrapping by a small conveyor. Dry contents of the gizzards are dumped into containers to be moved away to the waste products area. The dry offal and other inedible wastes are transported by the belt conveyors to augers for final dumping into a truck. Water usage in the eviscerating area has been reduced by 75 to 80 percent resulting in low wastewater volumes and strength. Another dry offal handling system[20] has been developed by Stork Brabant Company in Holland. This system uses several stations to collect offal by vacuum to be transported in plastic piping to the rendering hopper.

The 1970 survey conducted by the USDA[17] revealed that nearly all offal and feathers were salvaged and kept out of the final wastewater of plants. However, 14 percent of the total blood was estimated to be unsalvaged and was discharged into the plants' wastewater streams. The major practice was to sell to renderers the salvaged by-products. About 71 percent of offal, 72 percent of feathers, and 55 percent of blood were sold to renderers and farmers. In-house rendering accounted for 27 percent of offal, 26 percent of feathers, and 22 percent of blood. Only 4 percent of all by-products were given away to renderers. The study also showed that 1 percent offal, 1.3 percent feathers, and 1.8 percent of blood were dumped or burned after collection.

MEAT PACKING INDUSTRY

The meat packing industry includes all plants engaged in slaughtering and/or processing of "red" meat animals. Over 4,000 plants are operating, producing 55 billion lb of fresh, canned, cured, smoked, and frozen meat products per year. These plants vary greatly in size, ranging from small plants where the annual live weight kill (LWK) is less than 25 million lb to medium-sized plants with annual live weight kill of approximately 100 million lb, and large plants with annual live weight kill of 200 million lb or more. Federally inspected meat packing plants[21] totaled 629 processing 46.5 billion lb of meat. Of these, 239 small plants contributed 5 percent of the total live weight killed, 325 medium-sized plants contributed 53 percent, while 55 large plants accounted for 42 percent of the total live weight killed.

Water Usage and Wastewater Production

The gross wastewater volume generated by the meat packing industry in 1967 was estimated[21] to be 75 billion gal/year, containing 1.03 billion lb BOD. Table 16 shows the total production, gross waste loads, and wastewater volumes for selected years between 1963 and 1967 as well as projections to 1977. These wastewater loads represent the raw wastewater loads prior to any treatment (precatch basin). The wastewater is generally characterized as highly organic with relatively high content of nitrogenous compounds, suspended and dissolved solids, and grease. Table 17 shows the approximate range of flows and wastewater characteristics from meat packing plants. The size of the plant and waste conservation practices affect the volume and characteristics of the wastewater.

Sources and Characteristics of Wastewater

The major meat packing processes are shown in Fig. 5. The cattle, hogs, sheep, and calves are held for a few hours in a holding area. The animals are immobilized by chemical, electrical, or mechanical means before entering the kill area. They are then suspended by their hind feet for sticking and bleeding. Blood is collected in a bleeding trough underneath the conveyor. The cattle hide is removed by mechanical hide removers. Hogs are not skinned but their hair is removed by scraping after scalding in water tanks at 140°F. The viscera are removed and separated into edible

TABLE 16 Production, Gross Waste Loads and Wastewater Volumes 1963, 1966, 1967 and Projections to 1977 (Pre-Catch Basin Wasteloads)[21]

Year	Total comm. slaughter, billion lb/year	Wasteload per unit, lb BOD/ 1,000 lb LWK	Wastewater per unit, gal/1,000 lb LWK	Total waste-load per year, million lb BOD	Total waste-water per year, million gal/ year
1963	50.8	21.32	1,531	1,083	77,806
1966	54.9	18.73	1,322	1,028	72,578
1967	57.0	18.73	1,322	1,068	75,354
1968	60.2	18.73	1,322	1,128	79,584
1969	61.4	18.73	1,322	1,151	81,171
1970	62.8	18.73	1,322	1,176	83,022
1971	63.9	18.73	1,322	1,197	84,476
1972	65.2	18.73	1,322	1,221	86,194
1977	71.6	17.13	1,205	1,227	86,278

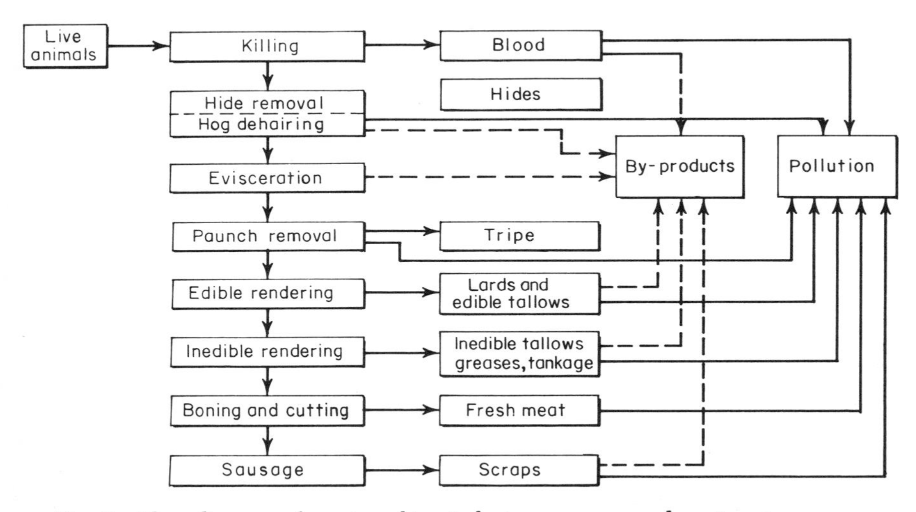

Fig. 5 Flow diagram of meat packing industry processes and wastewater sources.

TABLE 17 Approximate Range of Flows and Analyses for Slaughterhouses, Packinghouses, and Processing Plants

Operation	Waste flow, gal/1,000 lb LWK	Typical analysis, mg/l		
		BOD_5	Suspended solids	Grease
Slaughterhouse	500–2,000	650–2,200	930–3,000	200–1,000
Packinghouse	750–3,500	400–3,000	230–3,000	200–1,000
Processing plant	1,000–4,000*	200–800	200–800	100–300

* Per 1,000 lb finished product.

SOURCE: U.S. Public Health Service, "An Industrial Waste Guide to the Meat Industry," publication no. 386, p. 6, revised 1965.

and inedible products. The paunch or first stomach of ruminants (cattle, calves, and sheep) is opened and contents are removed. Washing the carcass and internal organs takes place throughout the meat packing process. The carcasses are further processed into different meat products. Meat packing plants also generally are engaged in the rendering of edible fats into lard and edible tallow and in the rendering of inedible fats into grease.

Blood constitutes one of the major sources of BOD in the meat packing process. The average weight of blood generated per beef (at 1,100 lb LWK) was shown[22] to be 32.5 lb with a mean BOD of 156,500 mg/l (Table 18). This results in a contribution of 4.67 lb BOD/1,000 LWK. Failure to recover the blood increases the plant effluent BOD by 72 percent.[21]

TABLE 18 Characteristics of Cattle Fresh Whole Blood[22]

	Mean	Std. dev.	No. of determinations
pH	7.34	0.14	37
Moisture, %	82.4	3.4	39
COD, ppm	218,300	35,700	70
BOD_5, ppm	156,500	58,000	35

Discharge of paunch contents into the plant waste stream also results in a substantial increase in solids and organic loadings. The paunch content of cattle is estimated at 40 to 60 lb with an average of 54 lb/animal and consists of partially digested hay, grass, and corn. The BOD of rumen was estimated at 50,200 mg/l which contributes 2.49 lb BOD/1,000 lb LWK.[22] Typical analysis of rumen is shown in Table 19. In older plants the paunch contents are discharged directly into the sewer. However, in most plants they are flushed into a flowing stream of water which passes over vibrating or rotating screens. The separated solids are then trucked away for land disposal. The screened effluent which contains significant amounts of suspended and dissolved solids passes into the plant effluent.

TABLE 19 Characteristics of Cattle Rumen[22]

	Mean	Std. dev.	No. of determinations
pH	6.54	0.56	57
Moisture, %	84.7	3.4	58
COD, ppm:			114
Liquid portion	51,940	12,800	
(Percent liquid)	(88.4)	(3.3)	
Solid portion	1,138,000	82,000	
(Percent solid)	(11.6)	(3.3)	
Total COD	177,300	38,500	
Percent COD from liquid	26.7		
Percent COD from solid	73.3		
BOD_5, ppm:			
Liquid portion	28,240	11,410	88
Solid portion	151,900	40,800	40
Total BOD_5	50,200	13,400	
Percent BOD from liquid	59.1		
Percent BOD from solid	40.9		

Another major source of organic loadings in plant effluent is the wet rendering process. The tank water which remains after the fats are drawn off and the suspended solids removed is discharged to the sewer. This tank water contains about 75 percent of the total protein content of rendering input and therefore is a major source of BOD. It has been estimated that the average BOD of tank water is 32,000 mg/l.

Some plants concentrate the tank water by evaporation to about 35 percent moisture to be sold as protein supplement. However, it is estimated that as much as 50 percent of the protein content will be lost to the sewer.

Wastewater Conservation and Management

The water conservation methods that will reduce the waste volume and strength in the meat packing industry are basically similar to those discussed for poultry processing plants, i.e., reduction of freshwater usage and efficient by-product recovery.

Mechanical conservation procedures can be applied in order to achieve reduction in water usage. These include installation of valves to regulate the flow in the washwater lines and changing from continuous-flow hoses to an interruptible-flow type. The latter can be regulated so that the water is turned off when the chain conveying the animals stops. Reuse of the plant wastewater for inedible purposes (such as condensing in the tank house and spray cleaning of mechanical screens) has been recommended.[23]

Reduction of wastewater strength can be achieved by recovery of by-products and by process changes in the rendering operations. Blood recovery and dry cleaning of the kill area before wet wash can reduce the BOD load of the plant effluent by 42 percent.[21] A survey conducted in 1967 revealed that 80 percent of all the plants in the United States recover blood, and it is expected that all the plants will practice blood recovery by 1977.

Direct discharge of the paunch contents into the waste stream results in substantial increases in solids loads in the plant effluent. Dry handling of paunch material by dumping into a hopper to be hauled away by a truck for off-site disposal will eliminate this pollutional load completely. Paunch solids may be used as fertilizer or soil conditioner by farmers. Elimination of the paunch material by dry dumping results in reduction of the waste load by 10 percent. Recently, Bauman[24] demonstrated the economic feasibility of dehydration of cattle whole blood and rumen by gas-fired dryers as a means of elimination of water pollution by these by-products in packing house wastes. This approach was proved in a demonstration project[22] supported by the Environmental Protection Agency and conducted at the Beefland International, Inc., plant at Council Bluffs, Iowa. The return on the sale of dried blood alone was reported to be greater than the combined dehydration costs of the whole blood and rumen. Reduction in the plant waste strength was about 6.2 lb BOD/1,000 LWK.

Reduction of the pollution loads can also be achieved by recovery of the grease in air flotation or gravity separation units. The recovered grease can be rendered with other inedible by-products.

The organic loading contributed by the direct discharge of the tank water can be reduced 50 percent by the installation of evaporation equipment. However, substitution of this wet rendering method by the dry rendering processes (low temperature and continuous rendering) will reduce the organic loading by about 60 percent.

WASTEWATER TREATMENT METHODS

In previous sections, it has been pointed out that the wastewaters generated by the food industry are organic in nature and can be successfully treated by physical and biological treatment methods. Generally, the treatment methods used for domestic sewage can be applied to food industry wastes after suitable modifications to compensate for the wastewater characteristic differences. These include physical suspended solids separation, chemical treatment, ponds and lagoons, biological filtration, activated sludge, various land disposal techniques, and anaerobic digestion. Selection of the type of treatment by the individual plants will depend on many factors such as disposal method, degree of treatment required, proximity to urban centers, capital and operating costs, and several other considerations.

Disposal of the wastewaters into municipal systems for joint treatment with domestic sewage is a common practice with many food processors. The 1967 Census of Manufacturers[25] showed that the food industries discharged a much higher proportion of their liquid wastes (35 percent) into municipal systems than did all the United States manufacturers (7 percent). Nearly all of cannery wastes,[5] 65 percent of poultry wastes,[17] and 70 percent of meat packing wastes[21] receive final treatment in municipal systems. The wastewaters are commonly subjected to screening only prior to discharge to the municipal sewer. Some few plants also provide primary treatment or some secondary treatment before discharge into the sewer. The newly enacted Federal Water Pollution Control Act Amendments of 1972 require the establishment of guidelines or regulations for pretreatment of wastewaters introduced into publicly owned treatment works. The act also requires the municipalities to adopt a system of charges to assure that industrial users will pay their proportionate share of the costs of construction, operation, and maintenance of the waste treatment system. These requirements will encourage the municipal users to adopt more effective water conservation and waste reduction techniques and in certain instances they may discourage the food processor from utilizing municipal treatment systems.

In the following sections, the wastewater treatment methods presently being used by the food industry are presented together with an analysis of the variables affecting the selection and performance of these methods.

Pretreatment Methods

Screening Screening is the most widely used method for the separation of coarse discrete suspended solids from effluent waste streams in the food industry. It is generally more advantageous to separate as much of the solids content as possible from the wastewater prior to discharge to any treatment system. Screening units usually occupy a small space and can effectively reduce the solids loading on the subsequent treatment systems. In addition, screened solids are easier to handle than sludge from primary settling tanks. Sludge is more difficult to dispose of or may occupy considerable valuable digestion tank space.

The removal efficiency of screening is affected by several factors including: (1) mechanical factors: screen-opening dimensions, ratio of open area to mesh area, type of screen, and screen motion; (2) effluent characteristics: flow rate, flow conditions, concentration of discrete materials, particle dimensions, and fibrous matter.

Where coarse screening is required, it is possible to use bar screens. The simplest type consists of evenly spaced bars installed at angles 30° to 60° away from the direction of flow so that the separated material will be forced up the screen. The normal spacing between the bars is ½ to 2 in. The screened materials can be racked manually or mechanically. One of the advantages of a mechanically operated bar rack is that it takes up very little space and can be installed "on-stream." The equipment can be installed in a small pit designed to maintain a minimum velocity of 1 ft/sec so that the solids do not settle out and also to avoid velocities of 3 ft/sec in order to prevent wedging of solids between the bars. The primary purpose of the bar screens is the protection of the pumps and the subsequent finer screens.

Fine-mesh screens are used for effective removal of smaller but discrete suspended materials. Three types of screens are generally used for screening food industry wastes: rotating, vibrating, and stationary screens. There are different types of *rotary screens*. The *drum screen* is a commonly used rotary screen consisting of a revolving cylinder frequently made of perforated metal or coarse wire mesh as a structural frame with the fine-mesh screen supported on the structure. One type of drum screen has the waste enter into the center chamber, pass through, and drop out the bottom. These solids are carried up and flushed away with a back-spray arrangement. Another arrangement for solids removal with this type of screen is an internal helix to screw the solids forward for removal in a relatively dry state. Another form of rotating drum screen has the wastewater coming from the outside, passing the screened water to the inside, removing the waste solids in a waterborne arrangement. Most drum screens are horizontal although a vertical arrangement drum screen is available. They vary in size from 2 to 8 ft in diameter and are 4 to 12 ft long.

Another type of screen is the *disk screen* which consists of a large circular disk submerged approximately one-third to one-half in the waste. As the screen rotates, the solids cling to the screen mesh or the collector arms. The screen is backwashed before it returns to the wastewater stream. The backwash water carries away the solids to be handled in a separate system. These screens vary in size from approximately 4 ft in diameter to in excess of 12 ft in diameter.

The *vibrating screen* has several arrangements. One is rectangular or square, set at a slight incline so that the waste is applied at the top and the solids are vibrated down to the end, where they fall off in a relatively dry manner with the water passing through the screen. Another type of screen available is circular and utilizes eccentric weights to give a three-way gyrating motion.

Both types of vibrating screens normally have a capability of discharging the solids in drier fashion than either the disk or rotating drum screen. The type of screen to be utilized clearly depends on the character of the waste to be screened and the degree of clogging encountered with the waste. Normally, waste with high grease content can be screened better with either the disk or rotating drum screen since high-pressure sprays can keep the screening continuously clean, although vibrating screens can be equipped with cleaning arrangements.

A number of other types of screens are available which are variations of the above types and are too numerous to comment on here. A new basic concept in screening has been introduced with a *stationary screen* made with triangular bars on a parabolic curve. This has the advantage of no moving parts but requires a higher head loss than with most other screens and may be subject to clogging with grease-bearing wastes, although it can be equipped with mechanical cleaners.

The size of screen openings used in the food industry varies from few meshes per linear inch to 150-mesh wire cloth, although the 10- to 40-mesh screens are the most commonly used. The most common size used for cannery wastes is the 20-mesh screen. The same size is also common for offal screening, while 36 × 40 mesh is used for feathers in the poultry industry. The loading rates on the screens also vary greatly; generally the vibrating screens can take higher loading rates than the rotary screens. The loading rate on the screens is a surface loading expressed as gallons per minute per square foot of the surface area. New York State[26] recommends a loading rate of 3.5 gpm/sq ft on rotary screens, whereas a loading rate of 20 to 70 gpm/sq ft is recommended for vibrating screens. A 4- by 7-ft vibrating screen with 20-mesh stainless-steel wire is reported able to handle 600 gpm of paunch manure wastewater. The same size vibrating screen with 30-mesh cloth has handled 700 gpm of sugar beet pulp waste. Vibrating screens have been reported to be the most commonly used screens for vegetable and fruit processing wastes.

The solids recovered from the screening operation will vary appreciably depending on the type of operation and the type of waste. The volume of solids collected and dependent on the aforementioned factors may vary from 15 to 80 lb/1,000 gal of waste screened. As previously indicated, vibrating screens produce the driest solids, and the moisture content of these solids may vary between 70 and 95 percent, depending on the product handled.

The efficiency of screening is affected by the distribution of large and small particles in the wastewater. A high proportion of finely dispersed or colloidal suspended solids effectively reduce the efficiency of even finer mesh screens. Only a slight reduction in BOD loads is achieved by screening since it does not remove soluble solids. Removal of particulate solids from the wastewater prevents subsequent dissolution which would otherwise contribute to the BOD content of the wastewater.

Grease removal The wastewaters from several food processing industries (e.g., poultry, meat packing and processing, and seafood) contain significant quantities of fats and greases. Removal of the grease from these wastewaters constitutes the first step in the treatment and disposal of the wastes. Most municipalities require some form of pretreatment for grease recovery prior to discharge into the sanitary sewer system. The main objections to large quantities of free grease in a municipal sewer are that it coats the sewer and reduces its flow capacity. Grease also becomes a problem in pumping stations because of the formation of a heavy sludge blanket on the surface or large grease balls which are a disposal problem.

There is an incentive for food processors to recover grease since it has a market value and can be sold as a by-product. Normally, the sale of this grease not only will pay toward the installation and operation of the necessary recovery equipment but frequently is capable of netting a profit.

Grease from food processing operations falls into two main categories depending on its physical state: free-floating and emulsified. As the name implies, *free-floating grease* is readily recovered and has the greatest economic value to the food processor. It is normally collected in a relatively clean state and is high in fat content which can readily be processed for by-product recovery. *Emulsified grease* in the wastewater is produced from processing operations such as cooking and pumping. This grease tends to remain in suspension and requires special treatment for its removal.

Grease-bearing wastes should be segregated from other waste streams to minimize the size of the recovery units. Generally, it is desirable to recover the grease as close as possible to the source in order to avoid pumping, which results in emulsifying of the grease, and to prevent clogging problems in the in-plant sewers. There are two basic types of grease recovery systems: gravity separation and air flotation. The most commonly used types in each system will be discussed next.

Gravity Separation. Grease removal by gravity separation depends on the difference under quiescent conditions between the specific gravity of the grease and that of water. This difference results in the separation of the grease from the carrying liquid in an upward direction. The separated grease floats on the surface of the water and can be removed by manual or mechanical skimming devices. The design of the units is based on an overflow rate of 700 gpd/sq ft, especially if the unit is utilized as a primary sedimentation basin as well as a grease-removal unit. Satisfactory removals have been reported in some grease-removal applications with surface loadings as high as 1,440 gpd/sq ft; however, many states will require rates not to exceed 700 gpm/sq ft. Rectangular or circular tanks may be used with a liquid depth of 6 to 7 ft and a detention time of 1 to 2 hr. In addition to skimming devices, the tanks are usually equipped with sludge-collection mechanisms to remove the settleable solids that settle out in the basins.

The efficiency of these systems depends primarily on the physical state of the grease. Removals of over 90 percent of free-floating grease have been reported, but removal of emulsified grease is on the order of 40 to 60 percent. Better removal of the emulsified grease is obtained by the addition of chemical coagulants. Grease gravity separation systems (catch basins) are used extensively by the meat packing plants. A study conducted by the Meat Packing Industry revealed[21] that the detention time which maximized the economic return of the use of catch basins was about 20 min. Catch basins designed on this basis do not result in the efficient waste-load reduction which can be achieved by properly designed systems as discussed above.

Air Flotation. Air flotation is considered one of the most effective methods for the removal of grease and other suspended solids from the food industry wastewaters. Basically, the air flotation process relies on the entrainment of minute air bubbles which upon attachment to a discrete particle reduces the effective specific gravity of the aggregate particle to less than that of water and thus causes its separation and rise to the liquid surface as foam or float. The various flotation processes used are divided into vacuum, dispersed air, or dissolved air flotation systems.

1. *Vacuum flotation.* In this process, the wastewater is generally subjected to a short period of aeration with 0.025 to 0.05 cu ft of air per gal of waste, then passed to a compartment for release of the large air bubbles, and finally, sent to a holding tank where it is subjected to a vacuum of about 8 to 10 in. Hg. Finely dispersed air bubbles are released which rise rapidly to the surface carrying the grease and other suspended solids attached to them. A relatively dense floating layer is formed which can be removed by mechanical skimmers.

Several meat processing plants utilize this process for grease recovery, but there is no available information on their efficiency. However, this process is successfully applied for oil recovery in oil refinery wastes. Application rates ranging between 1,650 and 6,600 gpd/sq ft are used with oil recoveries ranging between 99 and 63 percent. Nelson[27] reported 50 to 80 percent suspended solids removal from peach and tomato wastewater at hydraulic loadings up to 7,000 gpd/sq ft. Removals ranging between 77 and 99 percent of suspended solids have also been reported[28] for effluents of tomato, pear, asparagus, string beans, and spinach.

2. *Dissolved air flotation.* Dissolved air flotation is one of the most popular methods for grease and suspended solids removal in the food processing industry. In this process, a portion of the influent or recycled clarified effluent is introduced into a pressurization tank into which air is injected. This wastewater is pressurized to 40 to 60 psig and becomes completely saturated with air, then it flows through a pressure-reducing valve to mix with the incoming raw wastewater in the air flotation tank which is at ambient pressure. This pressure drop causes the pressurized flow to release its dissolved air in the form of tiny bubbles which float the grease and

suspended solids up to the surface. A skimming device is used to remove the floated solids from the tank. The units usually are supplied with bottom scraping devices for removal of the heavy solids that may settle to the bottom. The air flotation units are designed based on an overflow rate (rise rate) of 1 to 3 gpm/sq ft and a recycle ratio of 25 to 100 percent. The detention time is about 30 min. The addition of chemical coagulants or coagulant aids to the wastewater prior to the air flotation treatment improves the removal efficiency of emulsified grease and colloidal suspended particles. The chemicals neutralize the charges on the particles, thus resulting in the breaking of the emulsion and the formation of larger flocs which can easily be separated in the air flotation tank.

The removal efficiency of the air flotation system for grease removal from meat packing wastes has been reported[29] to range between 60 and 76 percent without chemical addition. Woodard et al.[30] reported that 97 to 99 percent grease removal from poultry processing wastewater was achieved by an air flotation system after the addition of aluminum sulfate at 75 mg/l and a cationic polymer at 2 mg/l.

The National Canners Association has recently reported the results of pilot-plant studies of air flotation for suspended solids removal from cannery wastes.[5] With peach-lye-peel rinse water, the suspended solids removal was about 93 percent at a hydraulic loading of 1.0 gpm/sq ft and 65 percent at 2.6 and 2.9 gpm/sq ft. With tomato processing waste, the suspended solids removal was 84 percent at 1.0 gpm/sq ft and 61 percent at 2.9 gpm/sq ft.

Biological Treatment Methods

Most of the wastewaters generated by the food processing industry are organic, nontoxic to microorganisms, and amenable to biological degradation. The stabilization of organic matter in biological treatment systems is brought about by the metabolic activities of mixed culture of heterotrophic microorganisms. In aerobic systems, oxygen is supplied to be utilized by the microorganisms in the oxidation of organic matter into end products (such as carbon dioxide and water) and to obtain energy for synthesis of new cells (biosolids or sludge). Efficient biological oxidation of organic wastes requires minimal quantities of nitrogen and phosphorus for the synthesis of new cells. Many food processing wastes are deficient in these nutrients, and they must be added as a supplement to the system. Optimum pH range has to be maintained also for efficient operation of biological treatment systems. Several food processing wastes are highly alkaline because of the utilization of caustic compounds either in certain processing steps (e.g., lye peeling) or in cleaning compounds. Neutralization of these wastes usually will be required. Biological treatment processes include trickling filters, activated sludge, aerated lagoons, stabilization basins, lagooning, spray irrigation, and anaerobic digestion. The selection of the biological treatment process to be used depends on the flow rate, the wastewater characteristics (organic and suspended solids loading), availability of land, and the effluent quality required. Process design is important in the selection of a biological treatment process. Laboratory or pilot-plant studies have to be conducted in order to determine the correct design parameters for each individual treatment process.

Trickling filters Trickling filters have commonly been used for the treatment of different food processing wastes because of their ability to handle shock loads and their ability to function satisfactorily after shutdown periods over weekends, etc. Conventional trickling filters normally consist of rock bed over an underdrainage system. The continuous application of organic wastes develops a gelatinous film of microorganisms on the filter-bed stones. The soluble and colloidal organics in the waste are adsorbed by the film as the waste trickles over the rocks where it is stabilized by the microorganisms. The filters slough, and the microbial cells and slimes readily settle out in settling tanks for removal of the major portion of the BOD. Conventional rock filter beds have been designed as either standard-rate or high-rate trickling filters. Properly designed low-rate trickling filters operate at hydraulic loads of 25 to 100 gpd/sq ft and organic loadings of 5 to 25 lb BOD/(1,000 cu ft) (day). High-rate filters employ recirculation in single-stage or two-stage units. Hydraulic loadings usually vary from 200 to 1,000 gpd/sq ft and organic loadings of 25 to 300 lb/(1,000 cu ft) (day).

The efficiency of properly designed trickling filters for the treatment of cannery wastes ranges from 75 to 85 percent BOD and suspended solids reduction. However, poor efficiency and poor performance have been encountered with several cannery wastes. This may be attributed to failure to provide a proper nutrient balance in the filter influent and to the existence of extremely high organic loadings as well as to the natural tendency of trickling filters to clog, unload solids spasmodically, and produce occasional objectionable odors. Experience with treatment of meat processing wastes by trickling filters proved to be unsatisfactory.[23] The high protein content of these wastes produces heavy biological growth that tends to clog the filters and other pretreatment methods are required to reduce the BOD loading before application to trickling filters.

Conventional trickling filters for complete secondary treatment of brewery wastes have been used in the past at several plants. The overall treatment efficiencies for a system utilizing two filters in series to handle combined domestic and pretreated brewery wastes were 60 to 70 percent for BOD and 35 to 60 percent for suspended solids. Generally, the performance of trickling filters handling brewery wastes has been unsatisfactory. Treatment efficiencies have been well below current acceptable levels, and offensive odors have compounded the problems.[31]

More recently, plastic-media filters have been used for trickling filters. The advantage of this type of construction is that the lightweight plastic pack can be stacked many times higher than the conventional rock filters, thus resulting in reduction of the land area required. Depths as great as 20 ft are not uncommon. The results of several pilot-plant studies with plastic-media filters have shown good performance under high BOD loading conditions which would generally not be tolerated by a conventional-type medium because of the clogging problems. In addition, these filters exhibit a high degree of resistance to shock loads and to sudden increases in BOD and hydraulic loadings without reduction in the purification efficiency. These characteristics indicate the potential use of plastic-media filters as roughing filters for organic-loading reduction of food processing wastes prior to conventional biological treatment or discharge into municipal systems. However, at high organic loadings severe odor problems may develop and it would be desirable to cover these filters or to install odor control equipment.

The performance of plastic-media filters can be evaluated from the following modified Velz expression[32]

$$\frac{L_e}{L_0} = e^{-KD/Q^n}$$

where L_e = effluent BOD, mg/l
L_0 = influent BOD, mg/l
K = BOD removal-rate constant or treatability factor
D = depth of filter, ft
Q = hydraulic application rate, gpm/sq ft
n = exponent, for Surfpac media = 0.5

The BOD removal-rate constants for different wastes using packed towers and media similar to Surfpac were found[33] to be:

Type of Waste	*K*
Domestic waste	0.088
Canning waste	0.021
Slaughterhouse waste	0.044
Whey	0.030

The National Canners Association has experimented with plastic-media trickling filters and determined that BOD removals up to 85 percent for cannery wastes can be achieved with proper control of hydraulic and organic loadings, pH shock, and nutrient ratios. Table 20 shows the performance of trickling filters for the treatment of cannery wastes.

Activated sludge The activated sludge process has been used successfully for the treatment of many food processing wastes. In this process, flocculant actively oxidizing microbial population is maintained as suspension in the wastewater. Air is supplied for mixing and to provide the microorganisms with the oxygen necessary for their metabolism. The aeration step is followed by a solids-liquid separation step where a portion of the settled sludge is recycled with influent waste to maintain a constant active solids concentration in the contact chamber. The overall performance of the activated sludge system depends on the ability of the final clarifier to separate and retain the solids from the effluent to be returned to the system or wasted. The principles and kinetics of the different phases of the activated sludge process have been formulated in mathematical expressions for the design and operation of the treatment plants.[34] Various modifications of the basic process have also been developed and are discussed elsewhere; only their application to food processing wastes is presented here.

For successful activated sludge treatment of food processing wastes, laboratory or pilot-plant studies have to be conducted in order to establish the necessary design

TABLE 20 Trickling Filter Performance in Treating Food Processing Wastes

Product	BOD loading, lb/(1,000 cu ft)(day)	BOD, % removed
Cannery	1,200*, †	80
	500*, †	50
	100*	80
Cannery, sewage	40	77–85
	60	63–78
	80	50–68
	100	35–57
	140	35
Fruit	640	53
	950	20
	1,200‡	39
	1,600‡	26
Peas	180–420	25–37
	220	50
Peas, sewage	250	45
	52	90
Peaches	2,900*, †	23
	2,400*, †, ‡	85
Potatoes	23	92
	46	77
	69	55
Specialties	600*	53
Vegetables	145	69

* Plastic medium.
† Pilot-plant studies.
‡ With added nutrients.

parameters for the individual waste. The most important parameters are:

1. The organic loading expressed as pounds of BOD applied per day per pounds of mixed liquor volatile suspended solids (MLVSS). This parameter is used to determine the optimum efficiency removal for sizing the aeration tank, the amounts of mixed liquor suspended solids (MLSS), and percent recycle.
2. The oxygen requirements expressed as pounds per day in order to determine the type and size of aeration equipment.
3. Biological growth or sludge yield in pounds per day to determine the quantity of excess sludge which requires disposal and the amount of solids to be recycled.
4. The settling characteristics of the sludge for efficient control of the process and the production of effluent of desired quality.
5. Nutrient requirements, mainly nitrogen and phosphorus, for efficient operation.

The organic loading for activated sludge systems treating food processing wastes ranges between 0.01 and 0.5 lb BOD/(day) (lb MLVSS) although values as high as 4 to 6 lb COD/lb MLVSS have been reported for the treatment of cannery wastes in the first stage of a two-stage system.[35] The mixed liquor suspended solids are usually maintained at 2,500 mg/l. The BOD removal efficiency of well-operated activated sludge systems usually exceeds 90 percent.

Most food processing wastes are deficient in nutrients and the addition of nitrogen and phosphorus usually is required to maintain a BOD/N/P ratio of 100:5:1 in the activated sludge system. The lack of nutrients results in reduced BOD removal rates and affects the flocculating and settling characteristics of the mixed liquor suspended solids.

Fruit processing wastes were treated in a completely mixed activated sludge system at a loading of 0.4 lb COD/(lb MLVSS) (day) with removals greater than 90 percent. Nutrient addition was necessary to achieve successful treatment. The biological sludge developed had slow settling characteristics and 90 percent volatile matter content.[36]

Foaming is one of the major problems in the treatment of citrus and potato processing wastes by the activated sludge process. This results in the reduction of the treatment efficiency and the carryover of biological solids into the final effluent. Foaming has been controlled in the treatment of potato wastes[35] by maintaining high mixed liquor volatile suspended solids in the aeration tanks of at least 2,000 mg/l.

TABLE 21 Performance of the Activated Sludge Process for the Treatment of Food Processing Wastes

Product	Flow	BOD, mg/l Influent	BOD, mg/l Effluent	MLVSS, mg/l	lb BOD/ lb MLVSS	% removal	Ref.
Citrus	1.1	1,198	29	3,800	0.14–0.40	98*	37
Peaches	2.5	860	20	1,000	0.40	97*	36
Pears	2.0	1,600	9	2,000–3,000	0.4	99*	36
Apples	0.5	1,190	5	2,000–2,500	0.4	99*	36
Cannery and sewage	1.0	635	8	2,200	0.05–0.4	98	39
Potatoes	1.12	3,830†	380†	3,500	6.0†	90*	35
Brewery	Pilot	1,260	38	2,500	0.25–0.3	97	31

* Nutrient addition.
† Expressed as COD.

The cause of foaming in citrus wastewaters[37] was attributed to the discharge of orange oil and peel press liquor into the treatment system. Elimination of this waste stream resulted in the control of the foaming problem. Excessive foaming has also been reported in the treatment of whey or whey wash water by the activated sludge process.[38] The foam has been shown to be a combination of microbial cells and major whey protein B-lactoglobulin.

Sludge bulking has been reported as one of the major problems encountered in the treatment of brewery and milk processing wastes by the activated sludge process. Filamentous growths which do not settle readily in the final clarifier develop in the aeration basins, resulting in an effluent high in suspended solids and BOD. Modification of the conventional activated sludge process into the contact stabilization process or the Kraus process (where high MLVSS are maintained in the aeration basins) minimizes the sludge-bulking problem in the treatment of brewery wastes. The sludge-bulking problem has been attributed to high organic loading (more than 0.4 lb BOD/lb MLVSS) and/or nutrient deficiency. Generally, sludge-bulking problems arise because of the frequent changes in the waste characteristics with variations in production schedules. This frequently results in high organic loadings to the conventional activated sludge systems. A properly designed and operated activated sludge plant achieves 90 percent or more BOD removal. Table 21 shows the performance of activated sludge treatment of some food processing wastes.

The *extended aeration process* which is a modification of the activated sludge treatment has demonstrated successful application for the treatment of food processing wastes. The popularity of the process is attributed to the low cost of installation and operation as well as to the high BOD removal efficiency possible. The process does not require extensive sludge-handling facilities since theoretically very little sludge has to be wasted. The basic theories and principles underlying the extended aeration are described in detail in the literature and will not be discussed here. Generally, the design is based on low organic loading of 0.05 to 0.15 lb BOD/lb MLSS or 10 to 20 lb BOD/1,000 cu ft of aeration tank capacity and a detention time of 24 hr based on an average daily flow. BOD removal efficiencies in the range of 94 to 99 percent have been reported for the treatment of citrus wastes,[40] cannery wastes,[35] and poultry processing wastes.[41] The extended aeration process has been recommended as the "best available control technology" (BATEA) for the treatment of meat and poultry processing wastes for achieving the requirements of the 1972 act.

Lagoon systems Lagoons have been used for the treatment of food processing wastes for a considerable number of years. The early lagoons were merely holding ponds or evaporation basins created at sites chosen as convenient as possible to the processing plant. As the physical and biological processes in lagoons became better understood and as application was varied, descriptive terms were assigned to distinguish types of lagoons. These include storage lagoons, oxidation ponds, aerated lagoons, and anaerobic lagoons. The application of the different types of lagoons for the treatment of food processing wastes will now be discussed.

TABLE 22 Middle West Storage Lagoon Operation, Seasonal Tomato Operation

Date	COD, ppm	BOD, ppm	SS, ppm
Waste strength to lagoon:			
9/6/61	1,980	760	664
9/22/61	2,430	800	806
9/28/61	1,194	1,127	1,374
Lagoon samples:			
12/18/61 (60 days after pack)	123	150	144
1/25/62 (90 days after pack)	127	135	122
4/12/62 (final lagoon drainage)	55	40	52

Storage Lagoons. Storage lagoons are utilized primarily for operations of a seasonal nature where it is possible to store the waste from an entire season's pack. Prior to discharge into the lagoon, the wastewater is screened to remove the gross solids and some suspended solids. Normally, the wastewater is stored for a period of 90 to 120 days and then discharged during high river flows. The discharge is regulated to avoid substantial increase in the BOD or reduction of the dissolved oxygen in the receiving stream. During storage, sedimentation of suspended solids and anaerobic decomposition of the organic matter take place. This type of lagoon is very common for the disposal of wastes from the sugar beet industry[15] and some seasonal operations of the canning industry.[42] A seasonal tomato operation in the Middle West utilizing a storage lagoon had peak daily loadings of 600 lb BOD/(acre) (day). Table 22 indicates the strength of the waste to a Middle Western storage lagoon and the strength of the waste in the lagoon after storage for 60 days, 90 days, and final lagoon drainage approximately 6 months later.

The major advantages of storage lagoons are low initial cost, minimal sludge-handling problems, and availability of storage for the entire season's operations with controllable discharge timing. However, severe odor problems usually are associated with these lagoons and frequently the reduction of the pollution load is low. In addition, the enforcement of more strict discharge requirements makes this type of lagoon unsuitable as the only method for treatment of food processing wastes.

Oxidation Ponds. Oxidation ponds or stabilization ponds have been utilized to a considerable extent for the treatment of food processing wastes. Applications vary from complete treatment to intermediate, secondary, or supplemental treatment.

These lagoons are generally shallow in depth and the waste is stabilized by aerobic and anaerobic biological processes. The oxygen necessary for the aerobic oxidation is provided by algal photosynthesis. Aerobic conditions are frequently maintained near the surface and sometimes through the depth of the pond. Settled sludge deposits are stabilized anaerobically. These lagoons, therefore, develop into a facultative system with two distinct zones: one aerobic and one anaerobic, and a balance between the two zones is essential to minimize odors. Several modifications of these lagoons have been developed for the treatment of the food processing wastes under high loading conditions. The aerobic zone can be maintained by mixing the lagoon(s) contents through recirculation of the pond effluent or by supplemental mechanical aeration. The oxidation ponds are designed based on organic loadings of 30 to 80 lb BOD/(acre) (day) and a detention period from 20 to 180 days depending on the local climatological conditions. Loadings as high as 800 lb BOD/(acre) (day) can be applied in aerated oxidation ponds.[43] The performance of stabilization lagoons in treating cannery wastes is shown in Table 23. BOD removals as high as 96 percent have been reported for multiple-pond operations. Oxidation ponds, however,

TABLE 23 Stabilization Lagoon Performance in Treating Food Processing Wastes[5]

Product	BOD, ppm		BOD, lb/(acre)(day)	Detention, days	BOD, % removed
	In	Out			
Apricots, peaches...	....	...	90	106	96*
			800	47	79*
			500	78	93*
			600	70	88*
Cannery...........	....	...	4,770	2.5	40
			786	72	90
Citrus.............	....	...	200	120	83*
Corn..............	2,760	...	...	42	84
	2,760	...	...	40	95*
	2,936	...	...	9.6	59
	774–3,700	11–56	(6 lb in series)		
Peas..............	337–1,050	17–58	(6 lb in series)		
Tomatoes..........	....	...	628	17	74–81*
			396	26	80–81*
	1,800	...	...	42	93
Tomatoes, citrus....	....	...	662	22	74–75*
			135	17	85–88*

* With added nutrient.

require large land area and their performance depends on the climatological conditions. Severe odor problems are sometimes associated with the operation of these lagoons, especially in colder climes after the ice melts in the spring. In addition, excessive amounts of blue-green algae are often discharged resulting in effluents of unacceptable quality. Subsequent treatment processes may be required in order to meet the strict effluent standards imposed in many states.

Aerated Lagoons. Aerated lagoons are a relatively new treatment process which has been applied to the treatment of food processing wastes to achieve high BOD reduction. Oxygen is supplied to the lagoon by means of a mechanical or diffused aeration unit and a high degree of mixing is provided in order to maintain the solids in suspension. The detention time required to attain the desired degree of BOD removal is significantly less than the facultative lagoons because a higher equilibrium level of biological solids is maintained. The aerobic lagoon is analogous to an activated sludge with extended aeration without sludge return. The effluent from the lagoon is identical to the liquid in the aeration basin and contains the biological solids and the remaining soluble BOD. Therefore, in order to remove these solids and reduce the suspended BOD, a settling tank would be required before final discharge of the effluent. The performance of aerated lagoons for the treatment of some food processing wastes is presented in Table 24.

Aerated lagoons are more sensitive to temperature variation than is the activated sludge process because of the lack of sludge recycle. Lower treatment efficiency is expected at temperatures below 55°F and design modifications have to be considered to minimize heat losses in colder climates. Aerated lagoons are usually operated at high organic loadings (food/microorganism ratio, F/M) because of the low biological solids maintained in the system. Application of excessively high loadings may result in sludge-bulking problems, and solids separation becomes a serious operational problem. In an aerated lagoon treating potato processing waste,[44] 90 percent BOD reduction was obtained at F/M between 0.22 and 0.34 lb BOD/lb volatile solids; however, at loadings between 0.5 and 1.0, severe sludge-bulking problems developed which affected the overall treatment efficiency of the system. The application of aerated lagoons for the treatment of food processing wastes offers several advantages; namely, low operating cost, ability to treat high-strength wastes, high degree of BOD

TABLE 24 Aerated Lagoon Performance in Treating Food Processing Wastes

Product	Influent BOD, ppm	Detention, days	BOD, % removed
Beets	4,236	1.1	98
	3,830	0.75	96
Cannery	360	4.5(17.2°C)	94
	920	4.5(6.3°C)	43
	980	13.0(8.5°C)	95
	1,650(COD)	2–5	50–80
Carrots	1,910	0.37	86
Peas	535–1,212	12.0	76–97
	970	0.39	94
	578	0.23	93
	820	5.6	78
Peas, carrots	1,260	0.25	81
Peaches	1,650	0.16	54
	1,100	0.6	60–70
Potatoes	1,000	82.0	97
Pumpkins	1,380	0.35	60
	1,380	6.0	77
	1,380	6.0	85
	1,380	6.0	88
	2,500	1.2	50–60
Tomatoes	....	5.0	68
	1,500		98
Tomatoes, corn	580	5.0 (lab.)	71
	550	4.0 (lab.)	61–70
	890	3.0 (lab.)	60
	840	2.0 (lab.)	59
	605	1.0 (lab.)	43

reduction after solids separation, stable solids at low loadings, and high buffering capacity.

Anaerobic Lagoons. Anaerobic lagoons are being used extensively for first-stage treatment of poultry and meat packing processing wastes. Successful application for the treatment of other food processing wastes has also been reported. Stabilization of the wastewater is achieved by microbial conversion of the organic matter, under anaerobic conditions, to methane and carbon dioxide. The anaerobic lagoons used for treating meat packing wastes are generally deep and provide an average detention time of 7 days. The raw wastewater flows directly to the lagoon where equalization, digestion, and sedimentation all take place. Excess grease floats on the surface forming a natural cover which provides insulation to prevent cooling of the liquid in the lagoon, maintains anaerobic conditions, and appears to suppress obnoxious odors. Usually two lagoons are operated in parallel, and in some installations, recirculation systems are provided.

BOD loading in operating lagoons ranges from less than 10 to greater than 30 lb BOD/(1,000 cu ft) (day) while detention times generally range from 4 to 10 days. The majority of states where anaerobic lagoons are located generally allow loadings in the range of 12 to 15 lb BOD/(1,000 cu ft) (day). BOD removal efficiencies range from 60 to 90 percent; however, lagoons loaded in excess of 15 lb BOD/(1,000 cut ft) (day) operated consistently at BOD removal efficiencies between 75 and 85 percent.[45] Table 25 shows the efficiency of anaerobic lagoons treating meat packing wastes.[46]

Anaerobic lagoons have also been successfully applied to the treatment of sugar

TABLE 25 Efficiency of Anaerobic Lagoons Treating Meat Packing Wastes[46]

Type of waste	Loading rate, lb BOD/1,000 cu ft	Efficiency, %
Beef	16.1	58
Beef	31.4	87
Beef and hogs	10.0	85*
Beef and hogs	12–15†	85
Hogs	13	65

* Recirculation provided.
† Average of all plants studied by Iowa State Health Department.

TABLE 26 Anaerobic Pond Performance on Screened Food Wastes[5]

Product	BOD ppm	BOD lb/(1,000 cu ft)/(day)	Detention days	BOD, % removed
Cannery	....	9.6–430	1/6–37 (pilot)	40–95
Citrus	4,600	214	1.3*	87
Corn	....	70–104	6–11.3	25–69
		70–104	6–11.3†	53
Fruit, sewage	360–1,200	110–430	1/6–1/4 (lab.)	50–70
Peas	....	81.5–159	2.8–3.9	22–29
		81.5–159	2.8–3.9†	47–49
Peas, blanch	30,000		10.0	90
Tomatoes	550	7.5	7.4	80
		5.1	9.25	82
		0.86	37.0	98
		2.5–9.9	7.5–10	70
Tomatoes, lima beans	....	1,975	2.53	40

* Contact anaerobic process.
† With added sodium nitrate.

beet,[47] cannery, and milk processing wastes.[48] Table 26 shows the performance of anaerobic lagoons for the treatment of cannery wastes. A unique application of anaerobic lagoons has been reported for the treatment of cannery wastes[49] in Shepparton, Australia. The cannery wastes are mixed with settled sewage, digested sludge, and digester supernatant and treated in two shallow lagoons. The sewage and supernatant helped to maintain the optimum nutrient balance in the system. The lagoons have consistently achieved a BOD reduction of 75 to 85 percent at loadings up to 400 lb BOD/(acre) (day). When the BOD/nutrient ratio exceeded 50:1, the performance was adversely affected. At a value of 50:1 or below, loadings of 600 lb/(acre) (day) did not affect the performance of the lagoons.

Anaerobic lagoon treatment is usually followed by aerobic treatment in oxidation ponds, oxidation ditches or aerated lagoons.[47–49] The anaerobic-aerobic lagoons have been used extensively for the treatment of food processing wastes and have been recommended by the EPA as the "best practicable control technology" (BPCTCA) for the treatment of poultry and meat processing wastes. Table 27 shows the results from a survey of the treatment methods currently used in the meat industry.[50] The anaerobic-aerobic lagoons consistently achieved BOD reductions higher than 95 percent.

Generally, anaerobic lagoons provide excellent treatment of wastes containing high organic and solids concentrations when designed and operated properly. The economics of construction and operation of these lagoons certainly make them appealing for those food processing wastes suitable for this type of treatment.

TABLE 27 Waste Treatment Methods in the Meat Packing Industry—Complete System[50]

Plant number	General type system	Percent Reduction						
		BOD	SS	Grease	ON*	Total K N	TP	SP
A-1	Anaerobic-aerated lagoons	98.0	95.5	95.5	93.5	26.4	16.2	Inc.
		98.5	99.3	99.5	95.3	46.3	49.1	34.4
		98.1	95.5	97.7	93.8	42.5	28.6	Inc.
A-3	Anaerobic-aerated-aerobic lagoons	96.8	87.8	96.6	78.0	Inc.†	Inc.	Inc.
		89.8	83.2	94.0	71.0	17.0	28.0	48.2
		97.0	91.5	98.9	85.7	Inc.	1.3	Inc.
A-6	(Same as A-3)	99.5	90.0	97.8	91.2	46.5	48.7	25.6
A-2	Anaerobic-aerobic lagoons	99.2	77.8	99.4	84.0		Inc.	Inc.
		82.6	94.1	99.8	90.0	32.5	56.5	72.8
		85.7	95.3	99.2		0.0	35	
A-5	(Same as A-2)	99.3	99.8	99.6	46.1		58.2	73.8
A-7	(Same as A-2)	98.2	94.4	87.0	90.8	57.7	26.4	Inc.
A-9	(Same as A-2)	88.9	92.5					40
A-12	Anaerobic contact–aerobic lagoon	90.8	80.2					
		98.2	97.6					
A-13	Anaerobic contact	97.4	92.4			17.3		
A-10	Activated sludge	95.0	84.0	96.0				
A-8	Combined treatment, two-stage trickling filter	95.9	91.8	96.0	86.1	55.6	29.3	11.1
A-14	Trickling filter	87.0	80.0	90.0				5.0
								14.5

* ON: organic nitrogen; Total K N: total Kjeldahl nitrogen; TP: total phosphorus; SP: soluble phosphorus.

† Inc.: increase.

Anaerobic contact process The anaerobic contact process was initially developed by the American Meat Institute to treat meat industry wastewaters. A schematic diagram of the process is shown in Fig. 6. The process is analogous to the activated sludge process where settled sludge is recycled to a reactor in which biological degradation of the organic matter takes place. The influent wastewater flow is equalized over a 24-hr period by storage in a tank. After preheating to 95°F, the wastewater is fed at a uniform rate to complete mixing digesters. Digester designs are based on BOD loadings of 0.15 to 0.2 lb/cu ft. Detention time in the digester is approximately 12 hr with a mixed liquor suspended solids concentration of 7,000 to 12,000 mg/l. The mixed liquor flows through vacuum degasifiers to strip off dissolved gases. The solids are removed from the degasified effluent in a gravity sludge separator with detention time of about 1 hr based on total flow. Settled sludge is removed by suction-type removal mechanisms and recycled at a rate approximately three volumes per volume of incoming raw wastewater. Excess sludge is wasted at a rate of about 2 percent of the raw waste volume into a disposal lagoon. BOD and suspended solids removal is in excess of 90 percent. The effluent from the anaerobic contact system is usually further treated in polishing ponds. The overall performance of this treatment process is in the range of 96 to 98 percent.[45] A full-scale anaerobic contact process is in operation at Albert Lea, Minnesota.[23] This plant is loaded at approximately 0.2 lb BOD/cu ft of digester capacity with 95 percent BOD removal.

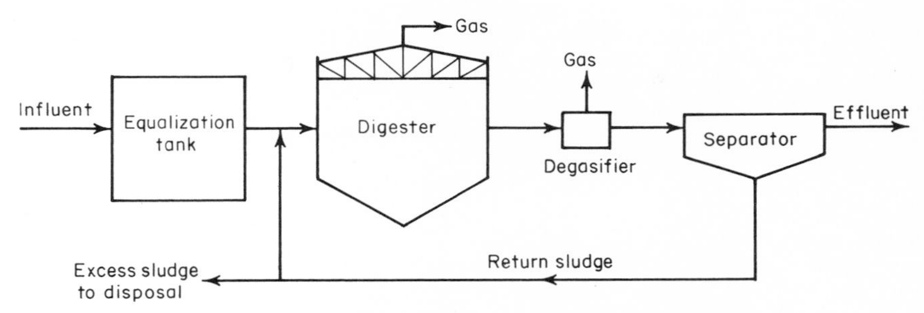

Fig. 6 Schematic diagram of the anaerobic contact process.

TABLE 28 Anaerobic Contact Process Treating Meat Packing Wastes, Albert Lea, Minn.

(Average operating data—all killing days in 1960)

	Raw waste	Anaerobic process effluent	Pond effluent	Loss, lb
Flow, gal	1,410,000	1,410,000	772,000	638,000

	Raw waste		Anaerobic process effluent		Pond effluent corrected for seepage	
	ppm	lb	ppm	lb	ppm	lb
BOD	1,381	16,220	129	1,517	26	304
Suspended solids	988	11,610	198	2,325	23	268

	Percent removal			
	Through anaerobic unit	Through ponds	Through entire plant	Digester loading, lb/(day)(cu ft)
BOD	90.8	79.8	98.2	0.156
Suspended solids	80.2	88.4	97.6	0.112

Table 28 shows the basic operating data through the anaerobic treatment system and following polishing ponds.

The advantages of anaerobic treatment in comparison to aerobic treatment for treatment of food processing wastes are: a high degree of waste stabilization, low production of waste biological sludge, low nutrient requirements, no oxygen requirements, resistance to shock loads, and the production of a useful end product, methane.

Land disposal The ability of soil systems to treat wastewaters has been widely utilized for the disposal of canning, diary, poultry, and other food processing wastes.

Land disposal methods include spray irrigation, ridge-and-furrow irrigation, and percolation or evaporation pond. Spray irrigation will be the only method discussed here since it is the most widely used of the land disposal methods. Survey of the disposal practices in the vegetable and fruit canning industry revealed that spray irrigation was the second most common method of waste disposal used.

Spray irrigation Conventional spray irrigation systems rely primarily on infiltration and are well documented in the literature. These systems require good site location in order to assure a high degree of infiltration into the ground. Therefore, the knowledge of local soil conditions is of paramount importance. Such systems on sandy loams that are well drained can tolerate in excess of 8 in. of water a day. As the water percolates through the soil, most of the biodegradable materials and nutrients are removed and the purified effluent recharges the groundwater. Table 29

TABLE 29 Land Disposal by Spray Irrigation (No Runoff)

Commodity processed	Region	Vegetation	Soil type	Area, acres	Volume, mgd	BOD, ppm	SS, ppm	Application: Rate, in./day	Application: Schedule
Asparagus and peas	Minnesota		Loam over clay	72	2.00	1,200		2.0	
Corn		Pasture and wooded	Loam	22	0.40			2.5–3.0	12–15 hr on 9–12 hr off
Corn and peas	Minnesota	Field crops	Sandy	110	8.00			8.00	8 hr on 16 hr off
Lima beans				6	0.60	76	54	0.38	
Peas	Upper Midwest	Grasses	Silt and clay	122	0.50			0.16	1–2 days on 6–7 days off
Peas	Washington	Grasses		20	1.80	5,000		4.00	5-day cycle time
Potatoes	Washington	Grasses and alfalfa	Loam, caliche and gravel	120	1.20	600+		0.35	1 day on 10 days off
Tomatoes	New Jersey	Honeysuckle and grasses	Sand, silt, clay, and loam	43	0.60+				1 day on 2 days off
Vegetables	Minnesota	Grasses and pasture	Loam over clay	90	0.10–0.70			5.00	8–12 hr on 12–16 hr off
Vegetables	New Jersey	Woods	Sandy; loam	84	5.00–10.00	210		6.40	8 hr on 24 hr off May–December

summarizes data reported for spray irrigation systems designed for no runoff. The land area required depends on the quantity and characteristics of the wastewater, climate, vegetation, soil conditions, and terrain.

A unique departure from the conventional spray irrigation disposal system is the *overland flow method.*[50] This technique is a highly effective substitute for conventional infiltration spray irrigation when the disposal field has relatively impervious soil structure. The system is laid out on land that is contoured so that the wastes flow in a thin sheet across the surface of the land and are collected in terraces to be conducted from the field. In both spray irrigation systems, a vegetative cover is essential in the disposal fields. Due to the relatively heavy application rates of wastewater, only water-tolerant grasses will grow in the spray irrigation areas. The grass serves multiple functions. First, it protects the soil surface from erosion and, in the overland flow systems, retards the flow of water across the slope. Next, it provides a protected habitat for microorganisms to grow and a vast surface area for adsorption of impurities contained in the wastewater. Finally, it provides an effective means for reclaiming nutrients which are released in soluble form when the organic waste material decomposes.

The spray irrigation technique depends almost exclusively on the soil microorganisms for the degradation of organic substances. The types of organisms are not different from those found in local, unirrigated soils. However, the oxidative activity of organisms on the spray fields is far greater. This indicates an acclimatization process whereby microbes specific for the wastewater develop in the treatment site.

It has long been recognized that a spray irrigation system will continue to purify water when temperatures drop to near freezing. Biological studies have shown that, although the respiration of microorganisms decreases as temperature decreases, the

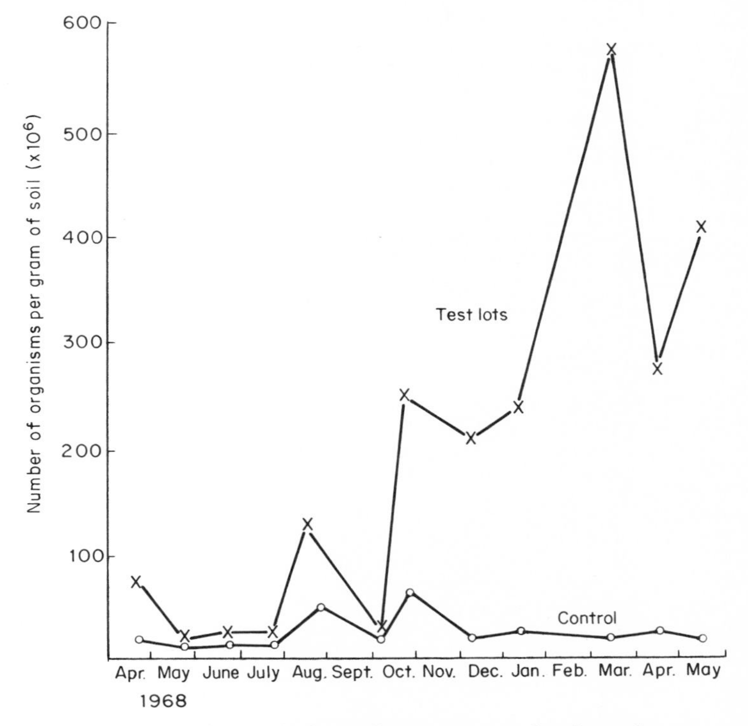

Fig. 7 Total microbial population on control and test lots.

number of organisms actually increases with falling temperatures, thereby maintaining a constant level of mass activity. Figure 7 shows the results of a study designed to demonstrate the changes in microbial population on the spray fields caused by seasonal temperature fluctuations.

Inorganic nutrients are removed from the wastewater by physical adsorption on the soil colloids. Phosphorus removal is primarily a soil phenomenon associated with aluminum and iron-containing clay minerals. Ammonium is also adsorbed on hydrated clay minerals and organic matter in the soil. The adsorbed ammonium ion, however, is not stable because it can be oxidized to nitrate ion by nitrifying bacteria.

An outstanding example of the overland flow method is the Campbell Soup Company's irrigation system in Paris, Texas. In this particular case, the site contained practically impervious soil, and it was not possible to obtain any significant infiltration into the ground. The overland flow method purifies water by flowing it over the surface in a thin uniform sheet. The system is laid out on land that is contoured so that the wastes flow in a thin sheet across the surface of the land and are collected in terraces to be conducted from the field. As many as four or five sprinkler lines are laid out on a hillside. The wastewater is applied approximately 0.6 in./day, and flows across the land where it is purified in its travel downslope. The application is made from 6 to 8 hr/day.

Detailed studies have shown that 175-ft lengths of slope will furnish effective purification. Basically, the downslope area requirement is 50 ft beyond the perimeter of the sprinklers. The main purpose of these sprinklers is to apply the waste on the slopes in uniform applications. The pitch of slope in Paris ranges from less than 1 to more than 12 percent. Studies led to the conclusion that a flat slope encourages puddling and subsequent anaerobic conditions while the retention time on a steep slope was insufficient for complete degradation at normal application rates. This established a design criterion of no more than 6 percent slope but not less than 2 percent. The area had been planted to Reed Canary Grass, Fescue, and Red Top. Basically any water-tolerant grass can be utilized, but it has been found that where the areas stay wetted Reed Canary Grass will predominate.

A complete water balance was obtained from the known quantity of water being applied and measurement of runoff, spray evaporation, evapotranspiration, and deep soil percolation. Water balance measurements accounted for 93 percent of the total liquid applied, runoff measurements accounted for about 61 percent, and the remaining 21 percent percolated through the soil.

TABLE 30 Treatment Efficiency of the Overland Flow System

Parameter	Mean concentration, mg/l		Percent removal	
	Wastewater	Section effluent	Concentration basis	Mass basis
Total suspended solids	263.0	16.0	93.5	98.2
Total organic carbon	264.0	23.0	90.8	
Biochemical oxygen demand	616.0	9.0	98.5	99.1
Total phosphorus	7.6	4.3	42.5	61.5
Total nitrogen	17.4	2.8	83.9	91.5

The actual treatment efficiency of the Paris overland flow system is shown in Table 30. While BOD and suspended solids removal efficiencies are known to remain extremely high through many different variations of operating procedures, nutrient removal efficiencies, particularly phosphorus, however, have been found to be much more dependent on the operational program of the system. It has been found that treatment efficiency can be improved by spreading the wastewater load over a greater fraction of the land area and by reducing the frequency of application. The greatest change is found in phosphorus removal, which can be increased to up to 88 percent by changing from the normal once-per-day application to a three-per-week schedule. The figures in Table 30 are yearly averages based on a once-per-day application rate.

Where food processing plants are located in rural areas, attempts should be made to utilize the natural environment. At a site in South Carolina,[52] the soil was of high infiltration for the first 5 to 7 ft and then encountered a denser clay structure. The entire field was underdrained at 200-ft spacing with perforated pipe wrapped in fiber-glass matting. This pipe conducted the drainage to a natural lagoon which is known locally as a Carolina bay or savannah. The concept was to have complete treatment with the spray system and to follow up with a polishing pond. In actual practice, the infiltration rate of the subsoil is sufficiently high to keep the drainage to the lagoon at less than 10 percent of the applied flow. Part of this is attributable to the fact that the drainage field acts as a French drain system so that, although in the immediate area of application the perforated pipe is quite active in carrying the water to the lagoon, the flow travels through so much unsaturated area it infiltrates into the subsoil.

The system has been highly efficient. The sprays are laid out on a permanent underground system; there is no aboveground piping. The sprays are on a 120-ft triangular spacing. The application rate reaches 1 in./day. The efficiency of the system is 99 percent on a total pound BOD removal basis because there is practically no effluent. The efficiency of the effluent going to the lagoon is in excess of 95 percent. The waste applied averages 635 ppm BOD with all samples of the effluent less than 10 ppm BOD (Table 31).

Food processors who are faced with seasonal operations can, if located in rural areas, rely on spray irrigation systems since they have the outstanding capability of handling shock loads on the one hand and periods of long shutdown and immediate start-up on the other, producing excellent results in either case. In addition, wide variations in effluent character (such as occur during night cleanup) produce no adverse effects.

Both federal and state water quality enforcement agencies are looking more and more to spray irrigation as a principal means of wastewater reclamation and an important part of the management of the total water resources. Land disposal methods have been recommended[53] to the EPA to be considered as the best available control technology (BATEA) for the disposal of cannery wastes.

TABLE 31 Efficiency of South Carolina Spray Irrigation System

Characteristic	Raw waste	Underground drain	Lagoon discharge
BOD, mg/l:			
Average	635	6.8	3.5
Maximum	1,490	10	6.8
Minimum	300	3	2
COD, mg/l			
Average	1,030	40	23
Maximum	3,270	68	47
Minimum	320	6	8

COST OF WASTEWATER TREATMENT

There is a considerable lack of information about the actual capital and operating costs of the treatment systems in the different segments of the food industry. However, in general the construction costs are associated with the design criteria of the unit facilities, but the unit facility cost is independent of the types of industries involved. The Federal Water Pollution Control Federation published a series of "Industrial Waste Profiles—The Cost of Clean Water,"[21] containing extensive data from surveys of waste strength and wastewater treatment cost for the different industries. The capital and operation and maintenance costs have been estimated for the meat products industry and are shown in Table 32. These data should be interpreted as only "ball park" estimates at the time of the survey. Adjustments of these cost estimates would be required due to inflation, variation between the plants, and the effects of geographic locations on the construction and labor costs.

Private and municipal wastewater treatment costs were estimated recently[17] for the poultry processing industry. Estimates of replacement value or required investment and operating and maintenance costs for 113 plants with private wastewater treatment facilities are shown in Table 33. The replacement values and operating and maintenance costs were converted to a cost per 100 lb LWK. On this basis, low, expected, and upper estimates of replacement value were 22.0, 38.0, and 64.0 cents/100 lb, while the similar levels of operating and maintenance costs estimates were 2.7, 4.5, and 7.3 cents/100 lb.

The cost of wastewater treatment of the 245 surveyed poultry plants discharging into municipal systems was estimated to be $46 million (Table 34). This estimate was based on 18.4 billion gal of wastewater treated by municipality at a charge of 25 cents/100 gal. The total live weight kill of the 245 plants was 8.4 billion lb at a cost of 5.5 cents/100 lb LWK was thereby derived. It must be pointed out that these cost estimates do not reflect the requirements of the Federal Water Pollution Control Act Amendments of 1972 whereby municipalities will be required to recover

TABLE 32 Cost of Waste Treatment Facilities[21]

Type of treatment facility	Small plant 20 million lb/year LWK 33 million gal/year wastewater 0.125 mgd wastewater		Medium plant 100 million lb/year LWK 143 million gal/year wastewater 0.54 mgd wastewater		Large plant 300 million lb/year LWK 444 million gal/year wastewater 1.68 mgd wastewater	
	Capital costs	Operating and maintenance costs	Capital costs	Operating and maintenance costs	Capital costs	Operating and maintenance costs
Catch basin only	$ 12,000	$ 1,000	$ 35,000	$10,000	$ 250,000	$ 18,000
Air flotation			$ 60,000	$13,000	$ 150,000	$ 30,000
Lagoon systems*			$215,000	$11,000	$ 415,000	$ 21,000
Trickling filter*	$ 70,000	$21,000	$700,000	$30,000	$ 900,000	$ 35,000
Activated sludge*	$275,000	$65,000			$1,900,000	$150,000
Anaerobic contact* (followed by lagoons, activated sludge, or trickling filter)			$410,000	$20,000	$ 630,000	$ 30,000
Channel aeration* (Pasveer process)			$ 15,000	$ 6,000	$ 350,000	$ 20,000

* It is assumed that a catch basin will precede this method of treatment.

TABLE 33 Estimates of Replacement Value and Annual Operating and Maintenance Costs of Waste Treatment Facilities for Surveyed Poultry Slaughtering Plants, 1970[17]

Item	Level of cost estimate		
	Low	Expected	Upper
	In thousands of dollars		
Replacement value:			
Total	7,108	12,036	20,341
Average per plant	62.9	106.5	180.0
Annual operating and maintenance costs:			
Total	86.2	1,424	2,350
Average per plant*	7.6	12.6	20.8
	In cents		
Average per 100 lb LWK:*			
Replacement value	22.0	38.0	64.0
Operating and maintenance costs	2.7	4.5	7.3

* 113 plants with private treatment and total live weight slaughter of 3.2 billion lb.

TABLE 34 Estimated Cost of Municipal Waste Treatment for Surveyed Poultry Slaughtering Plants, 1970[17]

Item	Cost
	In thousands of dollars
Total	4,600
Average per plant*	18.8
	In cents
Average per 100 lb LWK	5.5

* 245 plants with a total live weight slaughter of 8.4 billion lb.

the capital costs in addition to the operation and maintenance costs from the industrial dischargers. Enforcement of this act will result in considerably higher cost for wastewater treatment in municipal systems.

A recent questionnaire survey of liquid wastes generation and costs of their treatment was conducted by the National Canners Association, the American Frozen Food Institute, and cooperating processors. The survey covered canned, frozen, pickled, and dehydrated fruits and vegetables. The estimated costs for plants operating their own treatment systems are shown in Fig. 8, where the plant size is plotted against

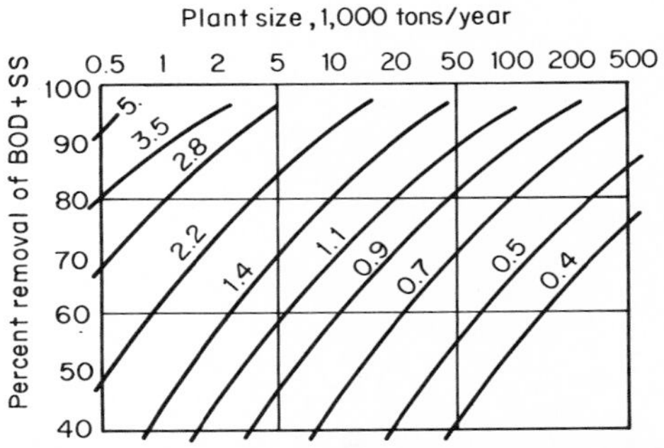

Fig. 8 Cost of company-operated treatment system.

the percent removal of BOD and suspended solids combined. Contour lines show smoothed average costs per year per ton of raw product. The treatment systems included lagooning, trickling filters, activated sludge, or any other biological systems. Economies of scale are quite evident in the results of this survey. For example, to remove 95 percent BOD, plants processing about 5,000 tons could expect costs per tons double those of 50,000-ton plants, or $2.8 versus $1.4.

An accurate estimate for the capital and operating costs of a specific wastewater treatment plant can better be obtained from the evaluation of costs associated with the unit facilities. The unit facility costs, as mentioned previously, are independent of the types of industries involved. It is not the objective of this author to discuss this subject here, but the reader is referred to the detailed reports by the EPA and the literature for the basic unit cost and the design criteria associated with it.

IMPACT OF ENVIRONMENTAL CONTROLS

Although generated pollutional loads have decreased during the last several years from food plants, the wastewater quantities and pollutional loads per unit of production still vary enormously among the industry's plants. Factors responsible for the variations include the process commodity, the product style, the percentage of the plant capacity utilized, the method of conveying the product and solids, the size of the plant, the location of the plant, and the actual length of the operating season per year. It can be seen that the natural and uncontrollable variations in the generation of wastes from food processing are large and require accommodation in any government controls.

The most severely impacted food processing plants will be the small operations, and especially the small seasonal operations. An example of this is the fruit and vegetable processing industry. This industry is characterized by a large number of small businesses and is highly competitive in the market place, operating on a relatively low profit margin. The before-taxes profit on sales for canning and freezing was 1.8 percent in the 1969 to 1970 year, and 48 percent of the industry's companies were reported to have no profit. These characteristics of the industry are the causes for its economic vulnerability to sudden imposition of excessively restrictive programs for environmental control.

The cost of treating wastes varies significantly based on the size of the operation and the degree of treatment required as indicated in Fig. 9. Basically, secondary sewage treatment has conventionally been considered able to remove BOD to approximately 85 to 87 percent. Unfortunately, EPA has taken the position that a pound of BOD coming from a food plant is not the same as a pound of BOD from a home garbage grinder or from a city system. The food processor, based on guidelines issued to date, is expected to achieve 95 to 97 percent BOD reduction in most instances and in some cases, as high as 99 percent removal. As seen in Fig. 8, the cost per unit of removing roughly 95 percent of the pollutants averages 2½ times as much as the cost of removing roughly 88 percent of the pollutants. Since the small processor must compete with large processors in the same marketplace, his disproportionate increase in cost means his economic death. This is shown dramatically in Table 35 developed by the National Canners Association showing the economic impact of proposed effluent guidelines. This table also clearly shows that the small food processor for the most part is located in relatively small communities and therefore the ripple effect of such a plant closing will be extremely detrimental in these areas. In this case, it is clear to see that all the segments which make up agribusiness are interdependent, and the forces that affect one affect all others. If the bell tolls for food processing, it tolls for agriculture and the entire community.

Although pollution by the food canning and freezing industry can be reduced to any arbitrarily established low level, the central question is whether or not the reduction is worth the impact on the nation's economy. The government and the public must balance the desirability of lower and lower pollution levels against the undesirability of food plant bankruptcy, higher prices for domestically processed food, and the use of natural resources for pollution abatement which may not be needed now or at any time in the future. It is in this realm that we have our most severe problems where the practical world of everyday living gets caught up in a numbers game established by lawyers who desire the more simplistic regulatory and enforcement approach. Unfortunately, nature is complex and our impacts and insults on nature are complex, and there is no simplistic numbers approach that will achieve our real goals or accommodate the crosscurrent effect or real benefits balancing achievements with energy conservation and realistic economics.

At the time of writing this article, it appears the EPA has opted for single numbers for effluent guidelines. What is desired and necessary to save the small food processor is flexibility to take into consideration the nature of the industry. Environmental control regulations should be designed to attain desirable cost benefit results to minimize adverse economic dislocations and to permit fair competition in the domestic and foreign marketplace.

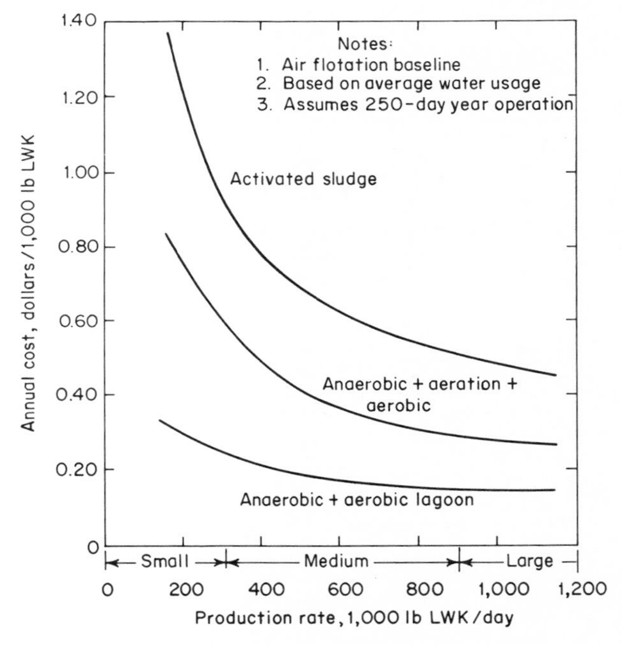

Fig. 9 Economy of scale: simple slaughterhouse.

TABLE 35 Economic Impact of Effluent Guidelines on Fruit and Vegetable Processing Industry

Total number of plants in United States	2,800
Number of small operations (less than 3,000 tons/year)	1,875
Estimated plant closings due to pollution control costs (over 25% of the small operations)	430
Economic losses due to 430 plant closings:	
27,000 jobs (full-time)	
31,000 jobs (part-time)	
14,000 outlets for farmers	
$300 million in local expenditures	
$600 million to $900 million in local economic activity	
Population of communities to be affected:	
More than half have less than 2,500 people	
About three-quarters have less than 5,000 people	

SOURCE: National Canners Association, Berkeley, Calif.

Table 36 shows an analysis of plants closed by treatment and at which level and degree of treatment the plant would theoretically be forced out of business. It is quite obvious that a plant which will be forced out of business at 60 percent reduction in BOD cannot be saved. However, where there are no adverse impacts on the receiving stream, it certainly should be possible for a large number of the plants achieving 80 to 90 percent BOD reduction to be allowed to stay in business and that most of the plants that can achieve more than 90 percent BOD reduction should be permitted to operate. A flexible system that considers cost in finally achieving the

TABLE 36 Plants with Own Treatment Closed by Pollution Control Costs

Required percent removal of BOD and SS	Plant size, 1,000 tons							
	0.5	1	2	5	10	20	50 up	Total
40								0
60	5	14						19
70	8	24						32
80	17	40		16				73
85	22	50	18	24	10			124
90	26	59	28	34	15			162
95	29	70	50	45	25	7		226

SOURCE: National Canners Association, Berkeley, Calif.

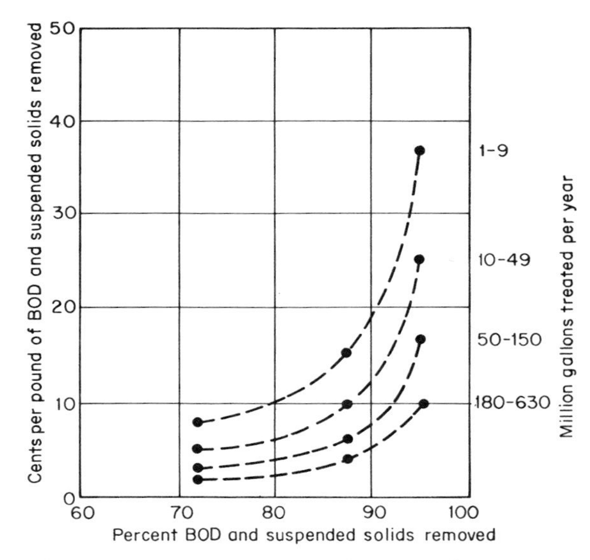

Fig. 10 Cost of treatment by percent of purification and size of treatment system.

reduction of pollution should be worked into a formula. At present no such formula exists, although the EPA Advisory Committee has recommended a matrix approach. The matrix system would take into account a number of factors and variables such as treatment technology, operational characteristics of the industry, geographic and climatic considerations as well as economic equity. An example of cost equity is shown in Fig. 10* referring to the cost of treating simple slaughterhouse wastes. In this case, one judgment factor might be to have very large plants treat their wastes

* Private communication, Dr. J. Roth, Vanderbilt University.

by activated sludge, therefore attaining a cost of approximately 45 cents/1,000 lb LWK. The small- and medium-sized plant might achieve the same cost of treatment utilizing an anaerobic-aeration-aerobic system with ponds.

An inevitable consequence of preparing and preserving foods is the large use of water and the generation of waste. Because raw foods must be rendered clean and wholesome for human consumption and because food processing plants must be sanitary at all times, relatively large volumes of clean water are used and discharged as wastewaters. Greater flexibility has to be incorporated in our regulatory program in order that food growing and food preservation can be protected and allowed to expand, otherwise the impact will not only be on the growers and processors but also on the consumers of our food supply.

REFERENCES

1. Pollution Problems in Selected Food Industries, *National Industrial Pollution Control Council, Sub-Council Report,* p. 9, May 1971.
2. U.S. Department of Agriculture: "Handbook of Agricultural Charts," Economic Research Service, Washington, D.C., 1970.
3. Powers, T. J., III, B. R. Sacks, and J. L. Holdaway: "National Industrial Wastewater Assessment Manufacturing Year 1963," U.S. Department of the Interior, Federal Water Pollution Control Administration, 1967.
4. Freeman, O., and I. C. Bennett, Jr.: "Control of Agriculture-Related Pollution," U.S. Department of Agriculture and U.S. Office of Science and Technology, 1969.
5. U.S. Environmental Protection Agency: "Liquid Wastes from Canning and Freezing Fruits and Vegetables," *Water Pollution Control Res. Ser.* 12060EDK, August 1971.
6. U.S. Department of the Interior: "The Cost of Clean Water, Vol. III, Industrial Profile No. 6—Canned and Frozen Fruits and Vegetables," Federal Water Pollution Control Administration, 1967.
7. Rose, W. W., W. A. Mercer, A. Katsuyama, R. W. Sternberg, G. V. Brauner, N. A. Olson, and K. G. Weckel: Production and Disposal Practices from Liquid Wastes from Cannery and Freezing Fruits and Vegetables, *Proc. Second Nat. Symp. on Food Processing Wastes,* Denver, Colo., p. 109, March 1971.
8. Allen, T. S.: Water Reuse in the Food Processing Industry, paper presented at ASME-EPA Water Quality Control and Food Industry Process Waste Conf., New Orleans, La., March 1972.
9. Graham, R. P., C. C. Huxsoll, M. R. Hart, M. L. Weaver, and A. D. Morgan, Jr.: Dry Caustic Peeling of Potatoes, *Food Technology,* vol. 23, pp. 61–66, 1969.
10. Stone, H. E.: Report on First Commercial Evaluation of Dry Caustic Peeling of Clingstone Peaches, *Proc. Third Nat. Symp. Food Processing Wastes,* New Orleans, La., *Environmental Protection Tech. Ser.* R2-72-018, p. 1, March 1972.
11. Lazar, M. E., D. B. Lund, and W. C. Dietrich: A New Concept in Blanching, *Food Technology,* vol. 25, p. 684, 1971.
12. Proctor, B. E., and S. A. Goldblith: Electromagnetic Radiation Fundamentals and Their Application in Food Technology, *Advances in Food Research,* vol. 3, p. 120, 1951.
13. Ralls, J. W., H. L. Maagdenberg, N. L. Yacomb, and W. A. Mercer: Reduced Waste Generation by Alternate Vegetable Blanching Systems, *Proc. Third Natl. Symp. Food Processing Wastes,* New Orleans, La., Environmental Protection Tech. Ser. R2-72-018, p. 25, March 1972.
14. Lund, D. B.: Field Study on the Application of Individual Quick Blanching, *Proc. Third Natl. Symp. Food Processing Wastes,* New Orelans, La., *Environmental Protection Tech. Ser.* R2-72-018, p. 71, March 1972.
15. U.S. Environmental Protection Agency: "State-of-Art, Sugarbeet Processing Waste Treatment," *Water Pollution Control Res. Ser.* 12060 DSI 07/71, July 1971.
16. Brenton, W. B., and J. H. Fischer: Concentration of Sugarbeet Wastes for Economic Treatment with Biological Systems, *Proc. First Natl. Symp. Food Processing Wastes,* Portland, Ore., p. 261, 1970.
17. U.S. Department of Agriculture: The Poultry Processing Industry: A Study of the Impact of Water Pollution Control Costs, *Marketing Res. Rept.* 965, June 1972.
18. "Upgrading Existing Poultry Processing Facilities to Meet the New Environmental Requirements In-Plant Water Management," Environmental Engineering, Inc., Gainesville, Fla., pp. 1-9 and 3-1, September 1972.
19. U.S. Public Health Service: Wastes from Poultry Processing Industry, *Tech. Rept.* W62–3, 1962.

20. Dry "Vis," Aerated Ponds Twin Keys to EPA Regulations, *Broiler Industry,* p. 45, January 1973.
21. U.S. Department of the Interior: "The Cost of Clean Water, Vol. III, Industrial Waste Profile No. 8—Meat Products," Federal Water Pollution Control Administration, September 1967.
22. U.S. Environmental Protection Agency: "Elimination of Water Pollution by Packinghouse Animal Paunch and Blood," *Water Pollution Control Res. Ser.* 12060-FDS-11/71, November 1971.
23. Steffen, A. J.: Waste Disposal in the Meat Industry—A Comprehensive Review, *Proc. Meat Industry Res. Conf.,* p. 115, March 1969.
24. Baumann, D. J.: Dehydration of Cattle Rumen and Whole Blood, *Proc. Second Natl. Symp. Food Processing Wastes,* Denver, Colo., p. 313, March 1971.
25. U.S. Bureau of the Census: *1967 Census of Manufacturers.*
26. Sanborn, N. H.: Treatment of Cannery Wastes, *Industrial and Engineering Chem.,* vol. 34, p. 911, 1942.
27. Nelson, F. G.: Pretreatment of Cannery Wastes, *Sewage and Industrial Wastes,* vol. 20, p. 530, 1948.
28. Fisher, W. W.: New Vacuum Flotation Process Aids Liquid Waste Disposal, *Food Ind.,* vol. 15, p. 87, 1943.
29. Dencker, D. O.: Some Solutions to Packinghouse Waste Problems, paper presented at 15th Ann. Waste Engrg. Conf., University of Minnesota, Minneapolis, Dec. 14, 1968.
30. Woodard, F. E., O. J. Sproul, M. W. Hall, and M. Ghosh: Abatement of Pollution from a Poultry Processing Plant, *J. Water Pollution Control Federation,* vol. 44, p. 1909, 1972.
31. Shwartz, H. G., Jr., and R. H. Jones: Characterization and Treatment of Brewery Wastes, *Proc. Third Natl. Symp. Food Processing Wastes,* New Orleans, La., p. 371, March 1972.
32. Germain, J. E.: Economic Treatment of Domestic Waste by Plastic Medium Trickling Filters, *J. Water Pollution Control Federation,* vol. 38, p. 192, 1966.
33. U.S. Environmental Protection Agency: "Whey Effluent Packed Tower Trickling Filtration," *Water Pollution Control Res. Ser.* 12130 DUJ 09/71, September 1971.
34. Eckenfelder, W. W., and D. L. Ford: "Water Pollution Control: Experimental Procedures for Process Design," Pemberton Press, Austin, Tex., 1970.
35. U.S. Environmental Protection Agency: "Demonstration of a Full-Scale Waste Treatment System for a Cannery," *Water Pollution Control Res. Ser.* 12060 DSB 09/71, September 1971.
36. U.S. Environmental Protection Agency: "Aerobic Treatment of Fruit Processing Wastes," *Water Pollution Control Res. Ser.* 12060 FAD 10/69.
37. U.S. Environmental Protection Agency: "Complete Mix Activated Sludge Treatment of Citrus Process Wastes," *Water Pollution Control Res. Ser.* 12060 EZY 08171, August 1971.
38. Harper, W. J., and J. L. Blaisdell: State of Art of Dairy Food Plant Wastes and Waste Treatment, *Proc. Second Natl. Symp. Food Processing Wastes,* Denver, Colo., p. 509, March 1971.
39. U.S. Environmental Protection Agency: "Combined Treatment of Domestic and Industrial Wastes by Activated Sludge," *Water Pollution Control Res. Ser.* 12/30 EZR 05/71, May 1971.
40. U.S. Environmental Protection Agency: "Treatment of Citrus Processing Wastes," *Water Pollution Control Res. Ser.* 12060-10/70, October 1970.
41. Platt, K. J.; Processing of Poultry Waste, *Industrial Wastes,* pp. 18–20, 1972.
42. Canham, R. A.: Stabilization Ponds in Canning Industry, "Advances in Water Quality Improvement, *Water Resources Symp. No. 1,*" p. 464, University of Texas Press, Austin, 1968.
43. Benjes, H., Jr.: Theory of Aerated Lagoons, *Second Intern. Symp. Waste Treatment Lagoons,* Kansas City, Mo., p. 210, June 1970.
44. U.S. Environmental Protection Agency, "Aerated Lagoon Treatment of Food Processing Wastes," *Water Pollution Control Res. Ser.* 1260-03/68, March 1968.
45. Hammer, M. J., and C. D. Jacobson: Anaerobic Lagoon Treatment of Packinghouse Wastewater, *Second Intern. Symp. Waste Treatment Lagoons,* Kansas City, Mo., p. 347, June 1970.
46. White, J. E.: Current Design Criteria for Anaerobic Lagoons, *Second Intern. Symp. Waste Treatment Lagoons,* Kansas City, Mo., p. 360, June 1970.
47. U.S. Environmental Protection Agency: "Anaerobic-Aerobic Ponds for Beet Sugar Waste Treatment," *Environmental Protection Tech. Ser.,* EPA-R2-73-025, February 1973.

48. Parker, C. D.: Experiences with Anaerobic Lagoons in Australia, *Second Intern. Symp. Waste Treatment Lagoons,* Kansas City, Mo., p. 334, June 1970.
49. U.S. Environmental Protection Agency: "Cannery Waste Treatment by Anaerobic Lagoons and Oxidation Ditch," *Environmental Protection Tech. Ser.* EPA-R2-73-017, February 1973.
50. Kerrigan, J. E., C. J. Crandall, and G. A. Rohlich: "The Significance of Wastewaters from the Meat Industry as Related to the Problems of Eutrophication," American Meat Institute, Chicago, Ill., November 1970.
51. Gilde, L. C.: Food Processing Waste Treatment by Surface Filtration, *First Natl. Symp. Food Processing Wastes,* Portland, Ore., p. 311, April 1970.
52. Gilde, L. C.: Waste Water Engineering Enhances Environment, *Mechanical Engrg.,* p. 43, 1971.
53. SCS Engineers: Industrial Waste Study Canned and Frozen Fruits and Vegetables, *Interim Rept.,* Contract No. 68-01-0021, U.S. Environmental Protection Agency, 1971.

Chapter 6

Water Pollution Control in the Paper and Allied Products Industry

MATTHEW GOULD

Corporate Director, Environmental Control, Georgia-Pacific Corporation, Portland, Oregon

INDUSTRY PROFILE

Definitions

Paper is a product manufactured in a continuous sheet formed by removing water from a slurry of cellulosic fiber called *pulp*. Pulp is produced by mechanically and/or chemically processing wood or other vegetative materials to extract usable cellulosic fibers as an aqueous slurry. The pulp slurry may be used directly in papermaking or may be dried and shipped elsewhere for processing into paper products.

The Standard Industrial Classification (SIC) definition of the pulp and paper industry includes the manufacture of pulps, primarily from wood, and from rags and other cellulose fibers; the conversion of these pulps into paper or board; and the manufacture of paper and paperboard into converted products such as coated paper, paper bags, paperboard boxes, and envelopes.

SIC Listing of Major Groups in the Pulp and Paper Industry

SIC Code	*Industry*
261	Pulpmills
262	Papermills, except building paper
263	Paperboard mills
264	Miscellaneous converted paper products
265	Paperboard containers and boxes
266	Building paper and board mills

Social and Economic Impact

The pulp and paper industry is the ninth largest industry in the United States, accounting for nearly 4 percent of the value of all manufacturing. (See Table 1). A regional distribution of the U.S. pulp and paper industry is shown in Table 2. The per capita consumption of paper is expected to continue to rise from the late 1969 value of 550 lb/year. The value of this industry is demonstrated in many ways.

1. Communication:
   - Correspondence to convey specific information and instruction
   - Public information: newspapers, journals, magazines, notices
   - Books: education, instruction, information, leisure
   - Data collection: statistics, accounting, financial and legal records
   - Technical plans: blueprints, manuals, records, computations
   - Arts: music publishing, painting and drawing, papercrafts
2. Packaging: from toothpaste to refrigerator containers for utility and product protection to transportation handling

TABLE 1 General Statistics for the United States Pulp and Paper Industry[1]

	1971	1967	1963	1958	1954
Operating plants:					
Total	6,087	5,890	5,713	5,259	5,004
with 20 or more employees	NA	3,813	3,552	3,214	3,277
Employees, thousands	664.6	638.9	588.0	551.3	527.7
Payroll, millions of dollars	5,536.8	4,436.2	3,508.2	2,759.4	2,204.7
Value added, millions of dollars	11,682.1	9,759.3	7,395.7	5,668.7	4,630.2
Cost of materials, millions of dollars	13,840.0	11,292.2	9,001.4	NA	NA
Value of shipments, millions of dollars	25,458.1	20,969.9	16,357.1	13,164.4	NA
Capital expenditures, millions of dollars	1,197.4	1,585.3	708.5	634.4	532.7
Production tonnage, tons					
Wood pulp	43,933	36,677	30,121	21,796	18,302
Paper and paperboard	55,092	46,925	39,230	30,823	26,876
Imports, tons					
Wood pulp	3,515	3,166	2,775	2,102	2,052
Paper and paperboard	7,617	7,115	5,825	5,149	5,190
Exports, tons					
Wood pulp	2,175	1,721	1,422	516	444
Paper and paperboard	3,146	2,096	1,341	853	687
Gross national product in 1958 prices, millions of dollars	7,866	6,735	5,163	4,061	3,331

NA = information not available.
All tons are 2,000-lb tons.

TABLE 2 Regional Statistics for the United States Pulp and Paper Industry

Area	Number of mills (end of 1971) Pulp	Number of mills (end of 1971) Board	Number of converting plants (1967)	Employees
Northeast totals:	46	255	2,077	219.4
New England	20	110	495	73.0
Middle Atlantic	26	145	1,582	146.4
North Central totals:	66	181	1,469	220.5
East North Central	51	158	1,169	171.3
West North Central	15	23	300	49.2
South totals:	121	180	933	183.6
South Atlantic	52	84	506	97.3
East South Central	35	46	174	44.0
West South Central	34	50	253	42.3
West totals:	56	84	619	66.5
Mountain	3	6	59	1.0
Pacific	53	78	560	65.5
Total	289	700	5,098	690.0

3. Substitutes: utensils, dishes, clothes, bedding, disposable products for hygienic or convenience purposes
4. World trade: 15 percent of wood pulp is exported from the origin country
   - Shipping logs and wood chips to countries deficient in fibrous resources for processing into pulp and paper products
   - Sale of dried pulp to other countries for local conversion into paper products
   - Sale of manufactured paper, paperboard, and other paper products to countries where consumption exceeds internal supply

Production Profile

The pulp and paper industry operated at peak levels in 1972 and at virtually maximum capacity. Production records were exceeded in all sectors of the industry. Exports rose to a new record, both in tonnage and in value. It is anticipated that the growth of the industry will closely parallel the gross national product.

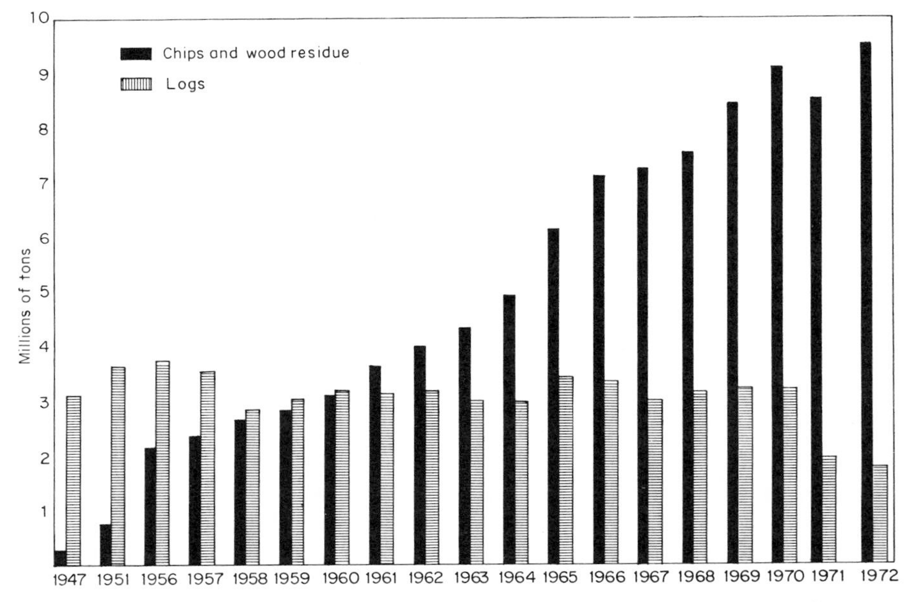

Fig. 1 Chips and wood residue raw material consumption by the pulp and paper industry in the Northwest.

MANUFACTURING PROCESS AND WASTEWATER DISCHARGE

In the Forest

Although wood chips, as a by-product of the lumber and plywood industries, have become an increasingly important raw material for the pulp and paper industry (Fig. 1), a significant amount of paper is still made from roundwood. It is not surprising then that the paper industry's pollution problems originate in the forest. Here there are three potential areas of concern; the first is the impact of logging activities on sediment entering small streams. Studies at Oregon State University[2] indicate that road building practices are the chief culprit, although logging itself can cause surface erosion under some circumstances. The second area of concern is the removal of vegetative cover on the banks of small streams which leads to a rise in water temperature. This may have a temporary adverse effect on fish propagation in the portions of the stream where gravel spawning areas are found. The third area of concern is the possibility of traces of forestry chemicals reaching the streams after infrequent fertilizer, herbicide, or pesticide applications. Environmental impacts from the forests belong under the *nonpoint sources* classification along with other vegetative and agricultural sources and, as such, it is expected they will be covered under a separate set of guidelines to be developed by the Environmental Protection Agency. Monitoring and control of these sources are an objective of the state *forest practice acts* which are presently being promulgated across the country to ensure the application of uniform, good forestry management practice.

TABLE 3 Analysis of Hydraulic Barking Effluents[3]

Mill	TSS, mg/l	Nonsettleable solids, mg/l	Percent ash of SS	BOD_5, mg/l	Color, APHA* units
1	2,362	141	27	85	<50
2	889	101	14	101	<50
3	1,391	180	17	64	<50
4	550	66	11	99	<50
5	521	53	13	121	<50
6	2,017	69	21	56	<50
7	2,000	200	19	97	
8	600	41	10	250	35
500	520–2,360	40–200	10–27	56–250	<50

* American Public Health Association.

Log Debarking

Although storage of logs at a mill site, in either a pond or river impoundment, can cause minor problems due to slight log leachate and bark deposits,[4] the first significant water contamination arises in the woodroom when bark is removed by a hydraulic process (Table 3). High-pressure hydraulic debarkers are the worst offenders as they tend to break up the bark into very finely divided particles which do not settle readily. Rotating wet drum debarkers, using only shower water, do not disintegrate the bark to the same extent and consequently yield a less objectionable effluent (Table 4). Some leaching of chemical constituents, including sugars, takes place during this debarking operation and tends to give rise to high bacterial counts in woodroom effluents. These bacteria, including coliforms of both animal and soil origin, gain access along with the logs. There is a current trend toward dry debarking in the industry using mechanical means. This process eliminates effluent due to debarking (other than wash water) if the logs are precleaned to remove sand and grit. Bark is disposed of by use as landfill or by burning as a fuel. If bark or wood chips are stored outside in piles, care is necessary to ensure that surface water or rainwater does not leach soluble organics and create a waste discharge. Logs stored in piles or decks are sometimes water sprayed to prevent deterioration. Here also, care is needed in disposing of this water.

TABLE 4 Characteristics of Woodwashing and Debarking Effluents[4]

	Effluent flow, 1,000 gal/ADT	BOD_5, lb/ADT	TSS, lb/ADT	Color, APHA units
Woodwashing	0.1–0.3	1–8	5–60	50
Hydraulic high-pressure debarking	5–9	1–10	6–60	50
Hydraulic drum, debarking	1–7.5	1–20	30–100	20–50

Major variables are wood species, type of equipment, screening, and recirculation.
ADT = air-dried ton of production.

Pulp Manufacture

Mechanical pulping The simplest form of pulp is a mechanically ground or macerated wood, chiefly hardwood, used in the manufacture of a low-grade paper called *newsprint*. The crushed wood fiber slurry is passed through a series of washing, screening (cleaning), and refining steps. After blending with a small amount of bleached Kraft pulp or selected recycled wastepaper, it is fed into a paper machine as a watery slurry where it is manufactured into rolls of newsprint (Fig. 2). Mechanically refined pulp produced by comminuting wood chips, sawdust, or shavings was introduced in 1960 (Fig. 3). Fourteen percent of the mechanical pulp is now produced from wood residues rather than from roundwood using grindstones. The principal effluents from such a mill would be contaminated wash waters and surplus filtrate or white water from the paper machine which will be dealt with later

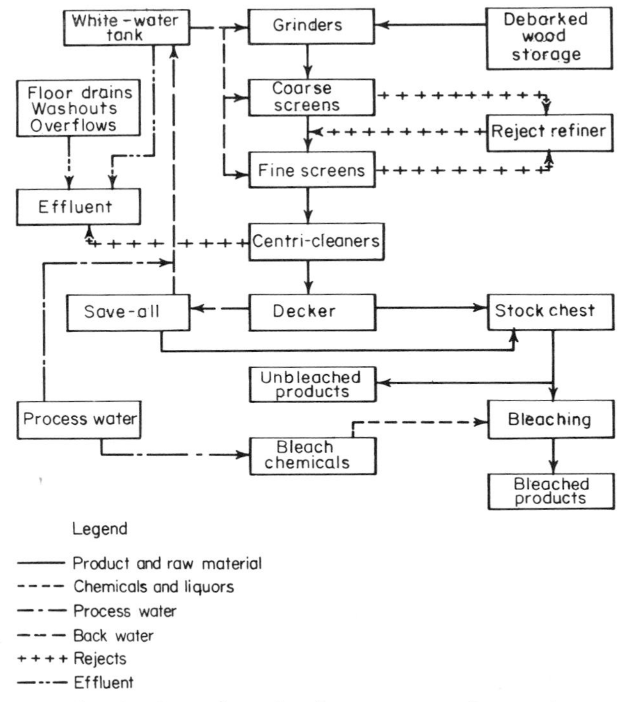

Fig. 2 Groundwood pulping process diagram.[3]

(Table 5). For some grades of newsprint, the groundwood pulp is lightly bleached with sodium or zinc hydrosulfite (or sometimes hydrogen peroxide) to produce a brighter pulp. High zinc levels (up to 10 ppm) have been reported in the effluent from those mills using zinc hydrosulfite, and in this country it is largely being replaced by sodium hydrosulfite. However, zinc hydrosulfite continues to be used extensively in Canada. As 70 to 80 percent of newsprint used in the United States is imported from Canada, high zinc levels are found in some American recycled wastepaper mill effluents.

Chemical pulping In chemical pulping, the object is to dissolve, with the help of steam under pressure, the natural lignin bonding materials that hold the cellulose fiber together in the wood. After pulping, the fibers are cleaned by screening and washing.

Kraft pulping The history of the pulp and paper industry in the last half century has seen the alkaline *Kraft* or *sulfate* process supercede the older acid *sulfite* process

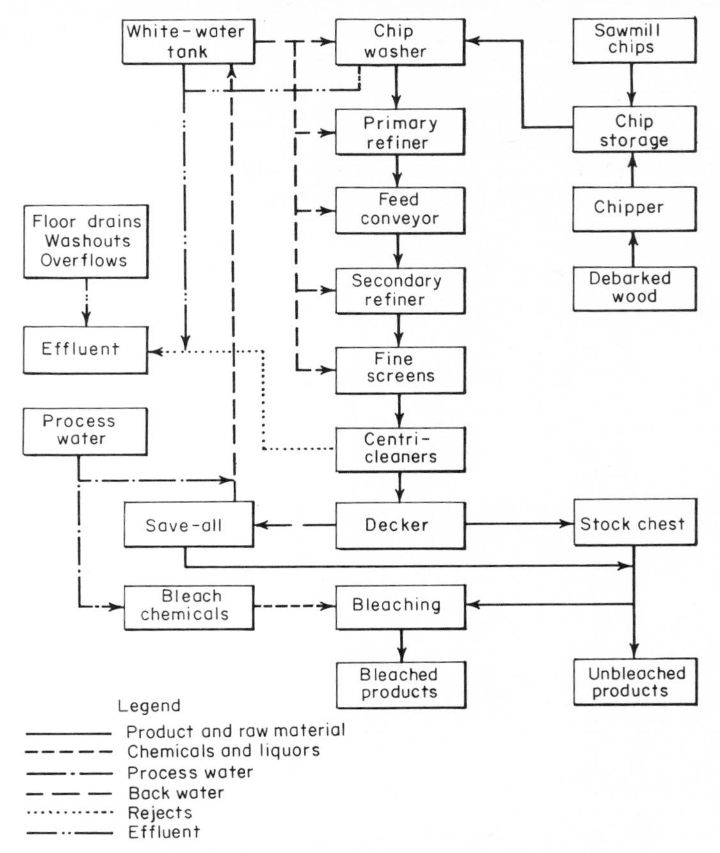

Fig. 3 Refiner groundwood process diagram.[3]

as the dominant method for the manufacture of wood pulp. A major attraction of the Kraft process is the ease with which spent cooking chemicals can be reclaimed and reused. Apart from the obvious economic benefits, a substantial reduction in waterborne pollutants is obtained. In the Kraft process, debarked logs from the woodroom are passed through a chipper and combined with any outside purchased chips before metering to a steam-heated pressure vessel where they are digested with cooking chemicals at 160 to 180°C. In the *sulfate* process, the cooking chemicals are a mixture of sodium sulfide and sodium hydroxide. The cast-iron or stainless-steel *digester* used may be of either the *batch*-type or the *continuous*-type operation. In the batch version, the mixture of chips and chemicals is heated with steam and

TABLE 5 Characteristics of Mechanical Pulping Effluents[4]

	Effluent flow, 1,000 gal/ADT	BOD_5, lb/ADT	TSS, lb/ADT
Grindstone pulping	2–10	4–20	10–50
Refined groundwood	1.5–7	15–120	30–110

Major variables are wood species, type of equipment, bleaching, and pulp washing, if any.

retained for a contact period of several hours before being discharged or *blown* from the digester (Fig. 4).

In a typical continuous digester, the chips are metered in at the top of a tall, vertical, cylindrical pressure vessel. Pulping chemicals are also added here and the chips are gradually displaced down the vessel passing through several heating zones as they are converted into wood fiber. Finally, a mixture of wood pulp and spent pulping chemicals is continuously extruded from the base of the digester.

Pulp from either the batch or the continuous digester is then washed in a series of stages to separate the usable wood fiber from the spent cooking liquor. Two or three stages of *brown-stock washing* are normal. The washed pulp is sent to a storage

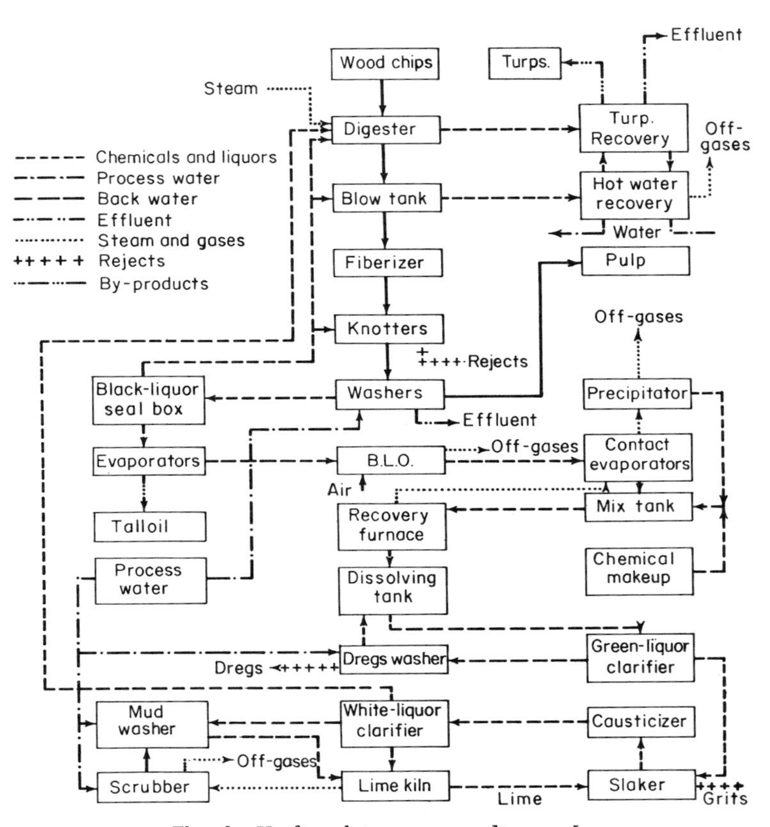

Fig. 4 Kraft pulping process diagram.[5]

chest and then on to the paper machine, if the characteristic tan-colored Kraft paper products are to be produced, or on to the bleach plant if white grades of pulp are to be produced.

The wash water from the brown-stock washers is sent to a series of multiple-effect evaporators followed by a second stage to raise the solids content to around 65 percent. The concentrated spent cooking liquor or *black liquor* is then sprayed into a *recovery* or reducing furnace where a melt of sodium sulfide and sodium carbonate is produced. This recovery furnace generates a substantial portion of the steam needed to run the pulp mill. The combustion process is largely self-supporting, being fueled by the nonfibrous organic extractives removed from the wood and concentrated in the black liquor. The hot *smelt* from the furnace is quenched and dissolved in water before treatment in a so-called *green-liquor* clarifier. Here carbon particles and siliceous material are settled out as green-liquor dregs and are disposed of by use as landfill. The clarified green liquor passes to a second clarifier where it is treated with slaked lime to form the cooking *white liquor* required for the Kraft pulping process ($Na_2CO_3 + Ca(OH)_2 \rightarrow 2NaOH + \downarrow CaCO_3$).

The final loop in the Kraft recovery process is reclaiming the lime. The heavy sludge drawn off from the bottom of the white-liquor clarifier consists of precipitated calcium carbonate or *lime mud.* The lime mud is then washed and thickened, with the wash water returned to the Kraft recovery cycle to reclaim its sodium values. The lime mud is then filtered to a 60 to 70 percent solids content before calcining in a kiln to regenerate the quicklime ($CaCO_3 \xrightarrow{heat} CaO + \uparrow CO_2$). The recovered lime is then slaked and returned to the white-liquor clarifier to causticize more green liquor. A small portion of the lime is lost on each cycle and purchased limestone or quicklime is added to the system to maintain the required levels. There are similar losses of chemical from the Kraft recovery or cooking cycle; purchased saltcake, a mixture of sodium sulfate and sodium carbonate that is a by-product of the alkali industry, is added ahead of the recovery furnace to replace this loss. Mills with low

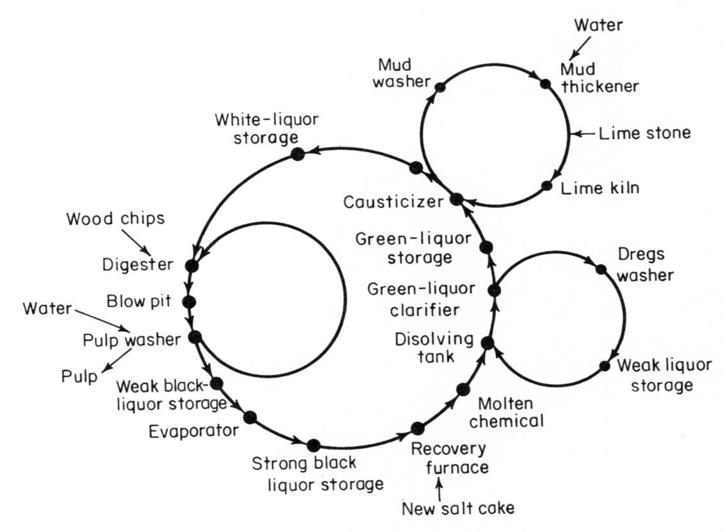

Fig. 5 Kraft pulping chemical recovery.[5]

chemical losses tend to develop a sulfur imbalance in the cooking chemicals, and in these cases, caustic soda is substituted for part of the saltcake makeup. Well-run, modern Kraft pulp mills need little in the way of freshwater makeup (Fig. 5). Most of their water requirements can be met by reclaiming wastewaters from other parts of the pulp mill with the balance being made up from excess paper machine *white water.* The black-liquor evaporator condensates are widely reused and their heat value is recovered at the same time.

Pulp bleaching Both sulfite and sulfate pulps are bleached for many applications. The bleaching imparts desired physical and chemical properties in addition to whiteness, or as it is called in the trade, *brightness,* to the pulp. The sequence of bleached chemicals will be determined by the product to be manufactured, the type of pulp, and the wood species from which it was derived. In the modern pulp mill, a multistage bleach plant based on chlorination is the norm. Many permutations and combinations of stages are possible. However, a typical sulfite mill might have four:

1. An initial chlorine bleach to oxidize residual lignin
2. A caustic soda extract stage to wash out solubilized material
3. An alkaline sodium hypochlorite stage to further oxidize the pulp
4. A chlorine dioxide stage as a polishing stage to increase brightness still further

To bleach Kraft pulp to the same degree of brightness as sulfite pulp requires more bleaching stages, particularly for softwoods typically high in lignin content. The chemistry of the bleaching process in alkaline Kraft pulp is quite different from that in acid sulfite pulp. However, essentially the same bleach sequence is usable. To produce fully bleached Kraft pulp, for example, the same initial four stages might be utilized, followed by a second caustic extract stage, final polishing, and second chlorine dioxide stage.

In the bleach plant, large volumes of water are utilized, volumes which may approach half of the total liquid discharge from a combined or *integrated* pulp and paper mill. Furthermore, because of the extractive nature of the bleaching process, the first- and second-stage effluents are very high in biological oxygen demand (BOD) and, in the case of the first stage in a sulfite bleach plant and the second stage in a Kraft bleach plant, highly colored as well. Much of the water use is derived from showers that wash the pulp thoroughly between each stage in the bleach plant. Freshwater use in the bleach plant can be minimized by recycling wash waters to an earlier stage or stages, i.e., *countercurrent washing*. For example, the second chlorine dioxide stage to the first chlorine dioxide stage and then to the initial chlorination stage; also the second caustic extract stage to the first caustic extract stage. Reuse of the early stages is limited because of the high dissolved solids content, in particular chlorides, which build up in the system and cause corrosion problems. In some mills, the effluent from the caustic extract stages is reused in the woodroom in place of freshwater for debarking operations since its alkaline nature is beneficial in this instance.

The sodium hypochlorite used in the bleach plant is manufactured on site from chlorine and caustic; similarly the chlorine dioxide used is manufactured from sodium chlorate by one of several available processes. Some Kraft pulp is also utilized in a *semibleached* form in which case the bleaching sequence is usually terminated at the third or hypochlorite stage. On the other hand, very pure chemical or *dissolving pulps* used in the manufacture of rayon may have seven or more bleaching stages to reach the desired quality.

A recent development in the bleaching field has been the introduction of oxygen bleaching. Very little has been published as yet on this process, but it holds promise for reducing the color and difficulty in handling bleach plant effluents because the absence of chlorides permits use of a recovery-type process. The pulp is treated with molecular oxygen, under pressure and alkaline conditions, to replace a portion of the initial bleaching stages. Oxygen bleaching was pioneered in South Africa and the first production facilities in North America are being watched with great interest by the entire pulp and paper industry.

WATER NEEDS AND WASTEWATER DISCHARGES

Water Supply

Pulp and paper manufacture by its very nature is a water-intensive industry. Annual water usage in the United States is approximately 2 trillion gpd. The principal function of water in the pulping process is to carry away the soluble extractions from the desired cellulose fiber. In the papermaking and bleaching processes, the function of the water is to act as a transport medium for the fiber during its manufacture into paper products. Important secondary uses of water are for cooling, boiler feed, vacuum seals, and housekeeping purposes. Water usage in the industry varies widely with the type and age of the mill from a low of around 10,000 gal/ton of product for an unbleached Kraft pulp mill, to around 40,000 gal/ton for a fully bleached, integrated pulp and paper mill.

In the absence of any real incentive to conserve water, most mills were built near large bodies of freshwater since requirements for a large mill could be in excess of 40 million gpd. In the early part of this century, however, smaller rivers were utilized by creating upstream impoundments and building one or more dams. These dams were often for hydroelectric generation to provide cheap power for the mill. Also, upstream waters were utilized in some cases for log transportation into the mill. Very few new dams for pulp and paper mills have been constructed in recent years and log transportation is gradually being phased out; although ponds for storage of logs at mill sites are still fairly common. Some mills also use wood flumes for transporting logs from storage areas to debarking facilities and, on occasion, for transporting debarked logs to the pulping area of the mill.

Water Quality

Raw water quality needs vary with the type of mill. Where white, bleached grades are produced, a color less than 5 APHA units and a turbidity of less than 2 ppm (JTU) are desired. Most other water quality criteria are not critical although low dissolved solids waters are preferred, particularly in mills where a high degree of water reuse is practiced. Many mills in the northeastern and northwestern United States and Canada have mountain runoff waters which are soft and largely free of turbidity and color for most of the year. These can be used without pretreatment much of the time. Where pretreatment is required, conventional alum coagulation in an upflow clarifier is usually followed by mechanical filtration for some, if not all, of the clarified water. Occasionally, small doses of chlorine will be used as a pretreatment to control biological growths in the water treatment and distribution system. Chlorine residuals are kept low to minimize corrosion and prolong demineralizer resin life. Very few large mills use groundwater as a supply; however, a significant number of small mills do use wells or municipal sources. In these instances, additional treatment such as iron or manganese removal or lime softening may be needed to provide adequate water quality. Boiler feedwaters generally receive supplemental treatment, usually sodium zeolite for low-pressure boilers and demineralizers for around 900 psig on up.

Wastewaters

On balance, the industry uses but does not consume water. The effluent volume discharged then is approximately equal to the total intake into the mill. The principal pollutants in pulp and paper mill effluents are biological oxygen demand (5-day BOD or BOD_5) and suspended solids (SS). Other potential problem areas are color, pH, temperature, dissolved solids, and coliforms. These contaminants originate in various parts of the mill and the quantities vary enormously from one type of mill to the next. Even in mills of the same type and size there are significant variations in concentrations and flow of contaminants.

As indicated previously, the two principal problems in pulp and paper mill effluents are high suspended solids and high 5-day BOD. The suspended solids are largely organic in nature; they consist of bark particles, wood fibers, and other cellular fragments. These solids settle well in a conventional upflow primary clarifier without the need for preflocculation or the addition of chemical flocculents. Most United States mills now have these units in operation and the efficiency of suspended solids removal is of the order of 90 percent, with virtually complete removal of settleable solids. The underflow from the primary clarifier is dewatered, usually mechanically, and the solids disposed of by incineration or by use as landfill. Those paper mills manufacturing printing papers that contain large amounts of added clay fillers, or titanium dioxide brighteners, may yield turbid primary effluents and give rise to high-ash clarifier sludges.

WASTEWATER TREATMENT STATUS

Secondary Treatment

With the possible exception of a few mills with saltwater outfalls, all United States pulp mills will have secondary, biological treatment by 1977, either in their own treatment facilities or connected to a municipal sewage treatment plant. The majority of these mills already have their secondary facilities on-stream or under construction at the present time. Aerated stabilization lagoons, with from 5- to 12-day retention, appear to be the most favored form of biological, secondary treatment. There are also a number of activated sludge systems and a few hybrid combinations of these two basic approaches. No operating physiochemical-type treatment plants capable of meeting the Environmental Protection Agency's 5-day BOD removal guidelines for industry have been reported at this time. There are, however, a handful of physiochemical treatment plants for color removal in operation using large doses of lime, and in one case alum, but the technology is not sufficiently far along to be applicable under 1977 guidelines. The characteristic dark brown color of Kraft mill effluents is rarely reduced more than 10 percent by conventional primary and secondary treatment and may be an aesthetic problem where receiving water flows are low.

Effluent Guidelines

The pulp and paper industry was foremost in the list of special industry categories designated in the Federal Water Pollution Control Act Amendments of 1972 to receive early attention in the setting of effluent guidelines. This action is currently in its final stages of promulgation and will require as a minimum the application of highly efficient primary and secondary treatment for the removal of suspended solids and biological oxygen demand. This requirement will, therefore, be the definition of "best practicable treatment currently available (BPCTCA)" for the pulp and paper industry for the purpose of complying with 1977 objectives of the Federal Water Pollution Control Act Amendments of 1972.

Individual mills are in the process of negotiating 5-year permits under the National Pollutant Discharge Elimination System (NPDES) with the federal Environmental Protection Agency (EPA). It is anticipated all these permits will be issued before

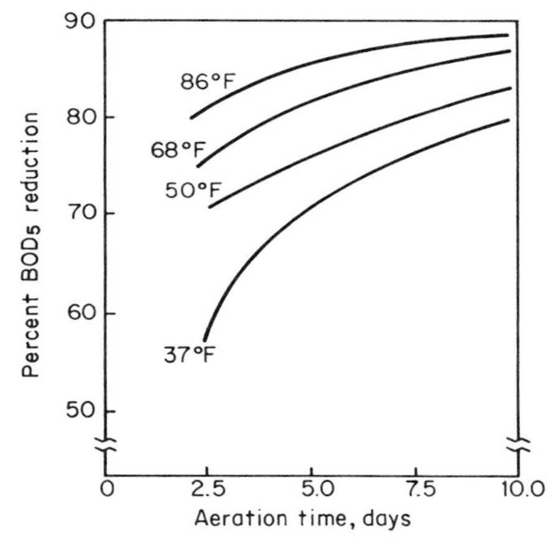

Fig. 6 Effect of temperature on BOD reduction in aerated stabilization basins.[3]

the end of 1975. As EPA has yet to delegate NPDES issuing authority to most states, mills are required to negotiate concurrently separate state discharge permits. The pulp and paper industry's early start in pollution control efforts should rank them among the forerunners in meeting 1977 goals. Beyond 1977, the picture appears hazy. Indications are that future agency requirements will center on "in-house" reduction of effluent raw load, by a combination of techniques, rather than any single application of tertiary treatment other than, perhaps, color removal.

Guideline Problems

A number of significant treatment problem areas remain to be resolved. A sharp reduction in biological removal efficiency due to decreased microbiological activity is a characteristic of aerated lagoons in the colder months of the year, particularly in northern climates. This phenomenon is not yet adequately recognized or quantified in proposed EPA guidelines (Fig. 6). This increase in effluent BOD from biological systems in the winter months does not, however, have any harmful effect on receiving water quality. The high dissolved oxygen values, increased flows, and diminished biological activity in the cold receiving water more than compensate for the incremental increase in effluent BOD.

An even more critical problem exists with respect to the generation of biological, suspended solids during secondary treatment. The amount of suspended solids in the effluent increases steadily as temperatures drop below 68°F. Unfortunately, conventional secondary clarifiers, or even mechanical filters, do not effectively remove these biological suspended solids. Much of the historical data on this subject is worthless because of past methods of measuring suspended solids. Most of the biological solids, for example, pass through the No. 40 Whatman filter paper used in the Technical Association of the Pulp and Paper Industry (TAPPI) standard method for fibrous solids analysis but would be retained in the APHA standard method for suspended solids analysis.

The discharge of secondary biological solids has not been shown to have any detrimental environmental impact on receiving water quality. They are, apparently, readily assimilated into the biosystem and disappear without trace shortly after discharge. Although substantial operational data has been submitted to EPA[6] as of this time, no provision has been made to allow for this temperature aberration in proposed suspended solids guidelines.

In summary, as the industry's current pollution control program is implemented, it can be anticipated that the discharge of pulp and paper mill effluents into receiving waters will have little or no effect on their beneficial uses by 1977.

WASTEWATER MANAGEMENT STUDIES

Water Use Survey

Before a treatment plant can be designed for an existing mill, a *water use balance sheet* must be prepared (Fig. 8). This is made up of a flowsheet showing **all** water supplies to **all** major production units, commencing with freshwater supply, **all** recycled water loops, and finally, **all** effluent discharges from each of the major process units. The flowsheet must include **all** sanitary waste sewers and those surface water sewers that can be contaminated by mill upsets and spills or are combined with wastewater before discharge. For each waterline or sewer, a maximum and a normal flow value is required.

Data should include flows, intermittency, temperature, and chief chemical and physical characteristics, collected over at least 1 week, but monthly or yearly figures are more desirable. Flow is best measured by continuous chart recorders (portable ones can be used) installed on weirs, orifice plates, or flume sections. A 24-hr composite automatic sampler located at the same site will provide representative samples of wastewater for laboratory analysis. In an older mill, quite often this information is not routinely available and it is necessary to go through a sewer survey to gather the data. The time and expense involved are well warranted and will pay handsome dividends before the design project is complete.

Maximizing Recycling

The balance sheet described should give a fairly good correlation between water supply, water lost in production, and wastewater discharge flow. Major discrepancies, after allowing for water introduced with raw materials and leaving with manufactured product, should be tracked down. Unrecognized outfall lines and overlooked supplementary municipal and well supplies are commonly found in these cases. Before determining the size of a waste treatment plant, additional opportunities for recycling waste streams should be checked out. An economic analysis of each of these recycling possibilities should be investigated to determine whether or not the ultimate design flowsheet for the waste treatment plant should be modified to anticipate them. In a large mill, the conduct of the sewer survey and planning of a water conservation program can be performed by existing technical or engineering personnel; however, in the smaller plants, it is usually necessary to hire outside specialists to carry out this work for the mill. Possible process changes that would reduce freshwater use, and thus the overall waste load, should now be considered; for example, the replacement of wet debarking of logs with a dry process (incidentally providing a Btu bonus in sending dryer bark to the hog fuel boiler). Countercurrent brown-stock washing and bleach plant recycle are key areas for additional savings in both heat energy and freshwater use. Furthermore, there is little need for freshwater makeup to a pulp mill and the entire system can be converted to recycled water, including washdown hoses.

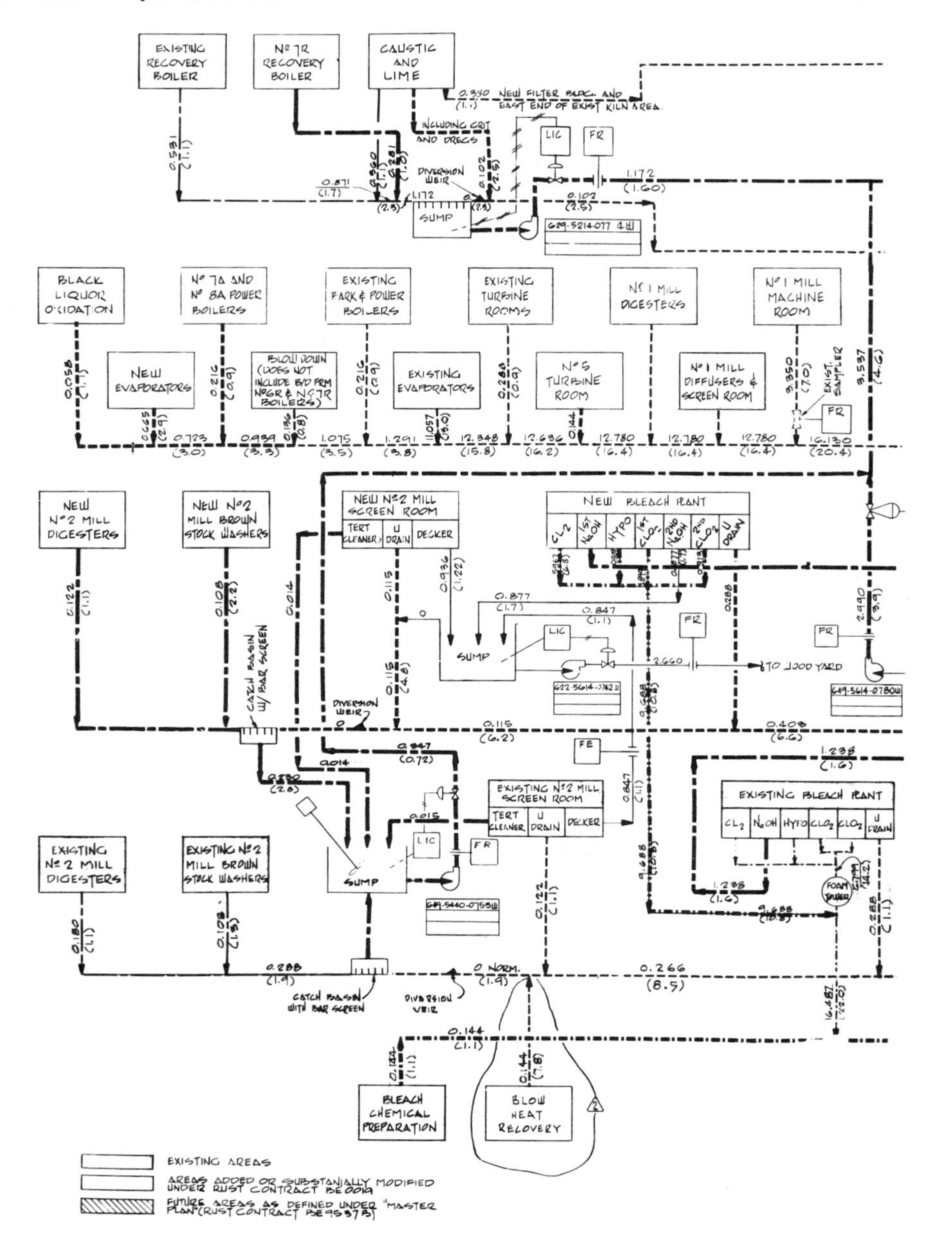

Fig. 7 Millwater distribution flowsheet.

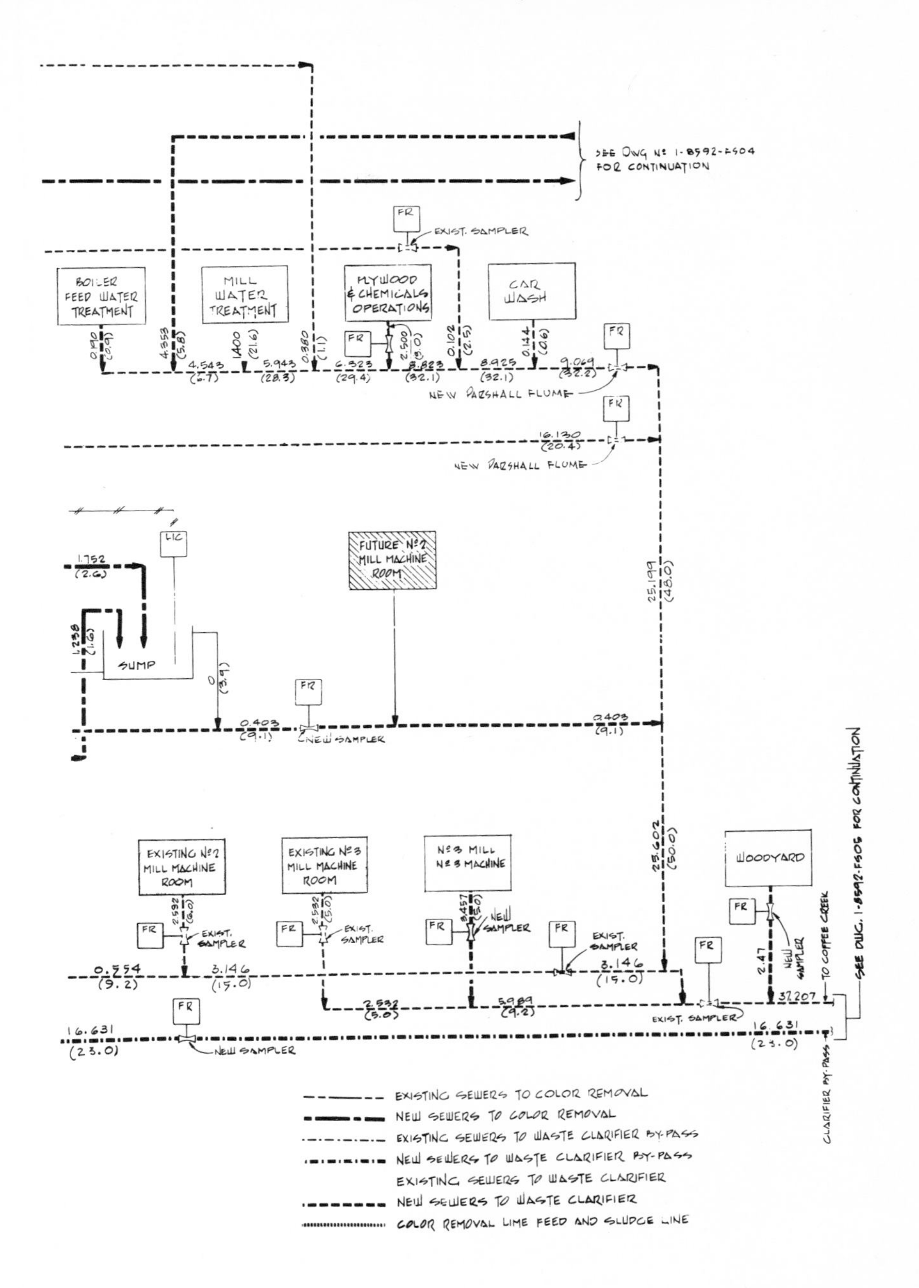
SEE DWG Nº 1-8592-F504 FOR CONTINUATION
EXIST. SAMPLER
BOILER FEED WATER TREATMENT
MILL WATER TREATMENT
PLYWOOD & CHEMICALS OPERATIONS
CAR WASH
NEW PARSHALL FLUME
FUTURE Nº 2 MILL MACHINE ROOM
SUMP
NEW SAMPLER
EXISTING Nº 2 MILL MACHINE ROOM
EXISTING Nº 3 MILL MACHINE ROOM
Nº 3 MILL Nº 3 MACHINE
WOODYARD
TO COFFEE CREEK
SEE DWG. 1-8592-F505 FOR CONTINUATION
CLARIFIER BY-PASS
EXISTING SEWERS TO COLOR REMOVAL
NEW SEWERS TO COLOR REMOVAL
EXISTING SEWERS TO WASTE CLARIFIER BY-PASS
NEW SEWERS TO WASTE CLARIFIER BY-PASS
EXISTING SEWERS TO WASTE CLARIFIER
NEW SEWERS TO WASTE CLARIFIER
COLOR REMOVAL LIME FEED AND SLUDGE LINE

In the face of energy shortages and increased fuel costs, a special effort should be made to reutilize hot and warm waste streams to maximize Btu conservation. Whereas the cost of recycling some streams may not be worthwhile strictly on a water conservation basis, by the time Btu savings are taken into consideration, ample justification for recycling may often be found. Care should be exercised, however, in selecting individual recycle streams to avoid introducing scaling or plugging problems due to increased dissolved or suspended solids content. Dependability of supply, distance from source, volume, temperature, pH, dissolved solids, corrosiveness, and malodorous nature are the more important components to be assessed in each case. Maximum use should be made of the sewer survey data in choosing the optimum recycle source. Prior screening or filtration before use may be necessary in some cases.

Determination of Design Raw Waste Load

Having prepared the water balance and flowsheet for all waters in the plant, the next consideration is a determination of raw waste load and its origin. In the sewer survey, wastewater from each of the major process units should be analyzed for BOD and suspended solids. These values, obtained during an extended period of representative mill operation and expressed both in milligrams per liter (mg/l) pounds per *air-dried ton* (lb/ADT) of production, should be entered on the flowsheet. One can now get a picture of the origin of the principal waste loads in the plant. Before proceeding further, each of these waste loads should be compared with published figures for comparable process units in the industry. This pinpoints immediately those units which have abnormally high loads that warrant further investigation before the determination of a final raw waste load for design purposes.

Reduction of Raw Waste Load

Minor process changes Minor process changes may be indicated at this point to avoid, for example, evaporator carryover; pulp-storage *chest* spills and black-liquor storage tank overflows due to absent or defective liquid-level controls and alarms; leakage from pump seals, control valves and pipe couplings. Effort should be made to get such problems corrected before proceeding in order to permit resampling of the waste streams to allow raw waste loads to be adjusted downward to reflect the process improvements.

Liquor spill control Provision should also be made to trap liquid spills caused by human error or mechanical failure by providing sumps, pumps, and tankage in strategic places. These spills, high in color and BOD, can then be intercepted before contamination from other mill wastes, and a means provided to eventually return them to the evaporators for reprocessing. The provision of a continuous conductivity or sodium-ion monitor on a sewer can be made to automatically trigger such spill collector systems.

Major process changes The next step is to consider how much further raw waste loads can be reduced by applicable in-plant techniques in a particular mill. Age of the mill and availability of space are the principal limiting factors that govern the economic feasibility in the case of an existing mill. In-plant changes could include:

The installation of additional screening and save-alls for fiber removal and possible upgrading of existing fiber-removal devices

Air or stream stripping of contaminated condensates if these are not reused in the brown-stock washers

Changes in sequence of bleaching plant stages to reduce color, or oxygen bleaching can be introduced into the sequence

Installation of a cooling tower might be necessary if effluent temperature is a problem

The probability is that, apart from fiber removal, few major changes will be feasible for existing mills.

Miscellaneous Wastewaters

Sanitary Sewage It is considered best practice to completely isolate sanitary sewage from all other paper mill wastes. This can be very expensive because of the cost of locating and gathering sanitary sewage in an old mill, but it would be preferable to the possible alternative of having to chlorinate the entire final effluent when sanitary sewage is included. After segregation the sanitary sewage is either piped to a municipal system or treated in a *packaged* primary and secondary plant and chlorinated before discharge. Dye tests should be run at all restrooms to ensure that **every** source is included in the sanitary sewer collection system.

Reclamation of Pulping Chemical After the molten smelt from the Kraft mill recovery furnace is dissolved in water, insolubles are removed in a *green-liquor* clarifier. The sludge is primarily a mixture of silicates and carbon and is best settled out, after washing, and disposed of as landfill.

The clarified green liquor is treated with a slurry of slaked lime in a second or *white-liquor* clarifier. The precipitated, impure calcium carbonate or *lime mud* is dewatered on a filter and calcined in a kiln to regenerate quicklime. When the filter or kiln is out of service, some backup provision is needed to handle the lime mud. Usually a large concrete holding basin is used from which the lime mud is eventually returned to the kiln. Lime mud or green-liquor dregs should be kept out of the mill's main primary clarifier. The volume of the lime mud can easily overwhelm the solids handling capacity of the clarifier and its desludging system. Keeping these nonvolatile solids out of the primary system is particularly important when the clarifier sludge is to be burnt as fuel in a power boiler.

Powerplant wastewaters Boiler and cooling tower blowdown, softener and demineralizer regenerants, and turbine cooling waters are usually discharged into the main effluent sewer. Their volume and content are of little significance in proportion to the total mill waste flow. However, once-through turbine cooling water may be high-volume, screened freshwater and should be dischargeable back to source if the temperature rise is small. In temperate climates it may be used as, or blended with, the mill raw water supply.

Boiler ash and particulate from stack-gas mechanical cleaners should be disposed of by use as landfill and kept out of the main mill sewer system.

Effluent Discharge Permit Requirements

The next step is to determine the final effluent discharge parameters that will be required by the appropriate state and federal (and occasionally inter- or intrastate) agencies for the mill in question. The current federal Environmental Protection Agency *effluent guidelines* can be used as the basis for arriving at the degree of treatment necessary. It can be considered that a minimum of primary and secondary treatment is needed to meet federal guidelines by 1977, except in isolated cases, e.g., discharges through specially designed saltwater outfall diffusers or an exceptionally *tight* unbleached Kraft mill with extensive in-house controls.

Normally, the implementation schedule and treatment plant design must be approved by the appropriate agencies before final construction can proceed. Such requirements will be spelled out in the federal National Pollutant Discharge Elimination System (NPDES) permit to be issued to the mill. Additional state permits presently are required in most instances and will have to be negotiated separately. They may include supplementary discharge restrictions.

If the mill, however, is situated on a stream or other small body of water, additional *receiving water quality standards* may be imposed by the agencies. Under these circumstances, the need for the temperature reduction, pH correction, or color removal should be ascertained before finalizing the design of the wastewater treatment plant.

WASTEWATER TREATMENT PLANT DESIGN

External Effluent Treatment

Once maximum and normal raw waste loads and flows have been determined, the design criteria for the treatment plant can be established. Allowance should be made for anticipated reductions in load due to in-plant conservation and recycling programs. Sewers and pumps must be designed for peak flows to avoid flooding the mill or bypassing the treatment plant. This author's preference is for pumping stations with three identical pumps, each designed for handling 60 percent of normal flow. One unit operates continuously, a second unit is on sump-level control, and a third standby unit is on a high-level controller with audio/visual alarm. The pumps should be maintained and rotated on a regular schedule. Poor engineering of pumps and sewers will lead to expensive mill shutdowns. Naturally, maximum use of gravity flow in sewers is an objective, but this will be controlled by the topography of a particular mill.

Primary Treatment

Gravity clarifier External treatment usually starts with a stage of solids removal. A design objective of 90 percent suspended solids and virtually complete settleable solids removal is normal. Ahead of the clarifier a traveling screen or some other form of self-cleaning trash screen, with approximately ⅝-in. slots, is necessary if mechanical operational problems are to be avoided. In most instances, a conventional gravity settling-type clarifier is employed with a conservative overflow rate of 0.4 gal/(sq ft)(min) or 600 gpd/sq ft of effective surface area. Units are generally circular with central intake and drive mechanism and circumferential weir. A rotating surface mechanism is essential to skim off foam, chips, knots, and other floating debris. The skimming discharge line should be no less than 6 in. in diameter, free of any sharp bends, and coupled to a skimmer pump which is able to handle large particles.

Sufficient torque must be developed to drive the clarifier mechanism under heavy load conditions and a reliable torque cutout and alarm are needed to protect the drive mechanism. In cold climates, the drive mechanism should be housed to protect it from adverse weather conditions such as ice buildup and water freezing in the lubrication system. Sound foundations are essential for the clarifier to prevent subsistence; use heavy piling when in doubt! Care is also essential where the water table is high since the unit can be uprooted when emptied.

The rotating scraper mechanism must just clear bottom if sludge fermentation problems are to be avoided. The bottom of the unit is sloped (usually 1:12) in order to facilitate sludge removal. Care must also be taken in choosing sludge removal pumps to avoid high maintenance and sludge-line plugging problems. Most clarifiers these days are located as close as possible to the mill so that clarifier sludge can be dewatered and disposed of in a hog fuel power boiler.

The preferred method of sludge dewatering for long-fibered sludges comprises a coil-spring filter followed by a V press. Solids content of the sludge increases to around 25 percent after filtration and 45 percent after use of the press. Pressed sludge can be fluffed and pneumatically conveyed to a boiler. For short-fibered sludges or sludges high in clay, centrifuging is the preferred means of dewatering. Disposal of these latter sludges is usually by use as landfill. Although much effort has been put into attempts to reclaim clay and titanium dioxide, no satisfactory method has been found. In designing the clarifier, provision should be made to bypass acid-bleach-plant flows and other suspended solid effluents around the unit. This keeps the pH in the clarifier above neutrality in most instances, reducing corrosion and, at the same time, decreasing hydraulic load permitting economies in physical size. As the bypass acid-bleach plant stream has a low pH, good quality *fiber reinforced plastic* (FRP) is the preferred construction material to convey this effluent to a point downstream where it can be combined with the clarified primary effluent and sent to a secondary treatment process.

Clarifier performance Good clarified effluents will average 90 percent suspended solids removal but will vary in a range from 75 to 95 percent depending on many factors. The nature of the solids is the major variable. Mills that have highly effective fiber recovery systems have greater difficulty in getting maximum efficiency due to preponderance of short fibers and bark particles. Secondary fiber and coated paper mills have high-ash suspended solids due to the presence of clays. In these cases, the percentage of removal of solids is usually satisfactory, but a turbid "clarified" effluent may result. The turbidity is enhanced where dispersives and wetting agents are used in making printing grade papers.

Clarifiers work best under steady-state conditions. Surges in flow and raw solids loadings cause boiling or localized solids carryover. Temperature differentials causing convection currents inside the unit are always troublesome, particularly as mill effluents run above ambient temperatures—sometimes as high as 130°F. Another clarifier operating problem, *entrained* air, is avoidable. Two common sources are faulty transfer-pump packing and eductor effects caused by badly designed piping runs. A more subtle cause is the aerating character of the newer curved trapezoid-section screens for fiber or bark. These high-efficiency units need a stilling chamber ahead of the clarifier to prevent air bubbles from causing troublesome floating floc in the clarifier.

A typical mill will have 3 to 5 lb/1,000 gal (350 to 600 ppm) of suspended solids going to the primary clarifier after screening. Efficient clarification will yield effluent containing 0.3 to 0.5 lb/1,000 gal (35 to 60 ppm).

New developments in clarifiers There are two important new clarifier modifications. Both involve the introduction of internals to create restricted, multipath flow inside the unit. The *tube clarifier* is a matrix of parallel plastic tubes of 2-in. square cross section, inclined at 60° to the vertical. As the particles have a longer hydraulic path to negotiate and convection currents are largely eliminated, more efficient settling takes place. Overflow rates can be increased by a factor of 1.5 to 4 depending on the type of suspended solid. The tube clarifier is considerably more expensive than a conventional unit and application has largely been limited to cases where an acute space problem exists or it is desired to increase the hydraulic capacity of existing clarifiers. The tubes, in honeycomb-like sections, can readily be installed in conventional units with only minimal structural changes.

A similar approach is the Swedish *lamella* clarifier where inclined plates replace the tubes. The distinction here is that the unit is a *downflow* design. Liquid and solids pass down between the plates. The clarified effluent returns to the surface and overflows through vertical takeoff pipes. The sludge slides down the inclined plates to the bottom of the unit.

Both of these modified primary clarifiers have their application in pulp and paper wastewater treatment; but careful on-site pilot-unit testing is recommended before deciding if they offer tangible advantage over conventional units.

Air flotation An alternative to the conventional clarifier which is finding increased favor is the *air flotation unit.* Air is introduced under pressure into the effluent entering the bottom of an upflow unit. Supersaturated air is released in the form of very fine air bubbles which become attached to suspended solids, carrying them to the surface. A mechanical scraper skims off the floating floc, separating it from the clarified effluent spilling over from the unit. Although this basic type of device has been around many years and has been used widely in mills as a flotation *save-all* for removing fiber from paper machine *white water,* recent interest in its use in effluent treatment came with the development of a more compact unit suitable for in-mill installation. The German-developed *Favair* device has internal *lamels* which permit higher flow rates and take up less space.

The air flotation unit gets away from clarifier drive and submersed sludge scraper mechanisms, but usually needs a flocculent aid (alum with or without a polyelectrolyte) to achieve performance equivalent to a conventional clarifier. It is most effective in-mill where the recovered solids can be recycled in the product; for example, secondary fiber mills. It is also particularly useful after high-efficiency, curved trapezoid-section screens. The natural aeration properties of the latter reduce the air supply needed to operate the flotation unit.

Although the air flotation unit is not sensitive to temperature, it dislikes large fluctuations in flow and solids loading as does the gravity clarifier. Flow sensitivity is eliminated by oversizing the unit and operating at fixed flow. Part of the treated water is bypassed back to the inlet to automatically maintain the optimum throughput. It is felt that increased interest will be shown in floation units, especially where the solids to be removed have a density close to 1.0. A rough separation from heavier solids is possible by purging the latter from the bottom of the unit.

Solids removal techniques have been discussed in some detail here because the finer points are often insufficiently understood by both designers and operators alike. The remarks made are of broad application to Kraft mills and to neutral sulfite, semichemical (NSSC) pulp mills with the following proviso. Acid sulfite pulp mills and some papermaking facilities using heavy doses of alum have corrosive, low pH effluents. Either neutralization with lime or soda ash or careful choice of construction materials is necessary if clarifying equipment is to give a reasonable length of service.

Many small paper mills and most secondary fiber mills will discharge directly to municipal systems after primary or *pretreatment*. The trend of larger plants to enter into joint municipal treatment systems has declined since the passage of the Federal Water Pollution Control Act Amendments of 1972. The new requirement that an industry reimburse the federal grant monies traceable to it has now removed the financial incentive to participate in such expensive systems. The move toward revenue or pollution bond financing is encouraging the building of more industry-operated secondary treatment plants.

Secondary Treatment

Aerated lagoon Where adequate space is available, the preferred means for secondary treatment for pulp and paper waste is a 5- to 10-day *aerated stabilization basin*. This type of treatment offers the greatest buffer to absorb plant upset conditions, a very significant advantage over the short retention of the *activated sludge* process. The extended holding time also allows a lagoon to serve as a cooling pond enabling the effluent to approach ambient temperature conditions before discharge. The aerated lagoon is usually designed with an initial quiescent zone or separate settling pond for removal of any postclarifier suspended solids and is terminated in a second quiescent zone for settling out biologically generated suspended solids.

The majority of today's installations use floating mechanical aerators with either high-speed (direct) or low-speed (geared) drives to introduce oxygen into a lagoon. There are, however, one or two installations using *molecular oxygen* for aeration where its cost is competitive.

Systems using plastic pipes that deliver air to a large number of submerged helical spargers have been installed and are giving satisfactory results. They are powered by on-shore, air-blower systems and give performance similar to that of floating aerators with somewhat less foam generation. Such systems require a slightly higher operating horsepower and are most suited for lagoons having irregular depth patterns and contours, as they function well in deep waters.

In determining lagoon configurations and flow patterns, the maximum use is made of natural contours using either *fully mixed* or *plug-flow* design criteria according to individual preference. The author admits to a personal bias in favor of the fully mixed basin configuration.

Aerated lagoon systems function with 85 to 90+ percent BOD removal efficiency under *ideal* conditions. The addition of nutrients, however, is usually necessary to achieve the higher BOD removal percentages. One of the poorest documented properties of extended aeration basins is their sensitivity to ambient temperature. A dramatic decline in biological efficiency occurs as lagoon temperature falls: below 65°F, performance drops very sharply and BOD removals as low as 70 to 75 percent are common during the winter months. Fortunately, the impact of the lower BOD removal efficiency in winter months is counterbalanced by diminished biological activity and the increased solubility of oxygen in cold water. Thus, in spite of the greater BOD discharges, dissolved oxygen levels in the receiving water remain high during the winter months. Mother Nature's excellent planning has provided that aerated lagoons are operating at their highest BOD removal efficiency when river flows and natural dissolved oxygen levels are low during the dry summer months.

A subject that has become a major issue is biological solids generation in aerated lagoon systems. At operating temperatures between 70 and 110°F, biological solids generation does not seem to create much of a problem as dead microorganisms are digested by an autolysis process. However, as the temperature falls, an increasing amount of biological detritus is generated which does not settle satisfactorily in conventional clarification devices. Furthermore, these solids are not adequately removed by conventional mechanical filtration devices. No doubt it would be theoretically possible, by a combination of chemical coagulents and mechanical filtration, to remove most of these biological solids. There would, however, be a real question as to the cost benefit of the capital and operating costs entailed plus the energy consumed, as weighed against the trivial environmental gain. Not one case has been reported where biological solids from an aerated stabilization system have caused a problem in the receiving water. These solids, in fact, are rarely detectable beyond the mixing zone at the outfall and appear to be readily assimilated into the natural ecosystem of the receiving water. Until more research is carried out on the mechanism of temperature effects, drawing conclusions can be hazardous; however, there is evidence of somewhat lower residual biological solids in effluents from fully mixed aeration systems than those from comparable plug-flow designs.

Mechanical aerators It is a consensus that there have been fewer maintenance problems with the high-speed, direct-drive mechanical aerators than with the gear-reducer-type units. There is also a trend toward the installation of fewer large horsepower units rather than a larger number of small ones; 75- and 100-hp units are popular sizes. A well-designed aerator will dissolve 40 to 50 lb of oxygen per horsepower day. The principal operating problems have been due to leaky seals, poor electrical wiring arrangements, and improper anchoring of the units in the lagoon.

Aerated lagoons should be kept clear of floating debris and trash screens should be installed where necessary. In cases where the lagoons are shallow, riprap should be installed immediately below the aerator to prevent erosion of the bottom. Care is also necessary in designing long electrical feeder lines to individual units. In some installations, the voltage drop across the line has been sufficient to overload the motor leading to severe maintenance problems. In cold climates there is a preference for aerators, permanently anchored on platforms, designed to minimize the ice buildup which can lead to premature destruction of the unit.[7]

Activated sludge treatment Where space limitations are a consideration, activated sludge processes have been used in the industry. Since the technology has been borrowed from sanitary waste treatment with little innovation, comments will be brief. Much shorter retention times are used, in the range of 3 to 8 hr. The effluent is discharged at a higher temperature and may require cooling in some instances. The short detention of activated sludge systems renders them much more susceptible to process upset due to spills and may take 2 to 3 weeks to return to optimum operating efficiency. Nutrient additions are essential, and secondary clarifiers are needed to recover the high biological solids loading associated with the process and return it as mixed liquor. Many potential users have avoided activated sludge units because of historic difficulties in dewatering the excess sludge produced.

Various combinations of both Kraft and sulfite pulp and paper mill effluents have been treated successfully by the activated sludge process, and BOD reductions of the order of 80 percent are normally achieved. Sludge *bulking* associated with growth of filamentous organisms is the most frequent and disconcerting operational problem. The presence of bleach plant wastes can also lead to unpredictable upsets in treatment effectiveness.

The main deterrent to greater application of activated sludge processes continues to be its high capital and operation costs; higher by a factor of 2 in most instances as compared with aerated lagoons. Activated sludge is, however, likely to remain the dominant system for joint municipal-industrial treatment plants.

Other biological treatment processes Trickling filters have found little application in pulp and paper wastewater treatment. BOD removal efficiency is low, usually less than 50 percent, far short of that needed to meet regulatory requirements. Large installations are bulky and expensive. Application is limited to unusual cases where some pretreatment or cooling is desired, perhaps on selected waste streams.

Rotating biological disks have been used in Europe, but the few installations now in North America are largely experimental. They combine some of the features of an efficient trickling filter with the sludge recycle of the activated sludge process. Difficulties in fabricating large, lightweight, vertical disks of sufficient structural strength have slowed down development. Initial reports indicate that 85 percent BOD removal is achievable if a sufficient number of disks are used. Rotation speed, submerged depth, and separation between disks are critical factors in determining operating performance. Initial capital costs are high but comparable with activated sludge. Rotating biological disks offer an alternative to the latter where space considerations dictate a compact treatment plant.

Contact stabilization and extended aeration The processes are hybrids of the activated sludge process and features of the aerated stabilization lagoon. Data from the few operating plants do not reveal at this time any substantive advantage over the component systems.

Natural stabilization basins These are included for historic purposes. They originated several decades ago in the southern states where large acreages were readily and cheaply available. The initial concept was to store a billion gallons or more of mill effluent for up to 6 months, usually after passage through a crude earthen settling basin, before controlled discharge to receiving water. The object was to discharge during periods of high flow in the winter and spring where impact on receiving water quality would be minimal. Not unexpectedly, it was found that substantial BOD reductions occurred during prolonged storage due to atmospheric oxidation. Reductions of 50 to 90 percent occurred at BOD loading of 50 to 60 lb/acre of surface, over periods of 1 to 6 months detention.

Due to the premium on land values in the northern and western states, no large tracts (100 to 1,000 acres) were available for this type of lagooning, thus confining this practice to the southern states. With the growth in size of the southern mills in recent years, conventional primary and secondary treatment became necessary. In most cases, however, the large lagoons were retained for polishing treatment as well as their original function of controlling discharge using an adjustable weir or penstock.

Special considerations for sulfite and semichemical pulp mills (NSSC) Sulfite and semichemical pulping mills generally have elected to install a variant of one of many chemical recovery processes before applying external primary and secondary treatment. In view of their declining economic importance and the extraordinary variety of sulfite mill subtypes, ranging from high yield to dissolving pulps, the reader is referred to the general references provided for details as to particular in-plant flowsheets and chemical recovery processes.

EFFLUENT STANDARDS AND ECONOMIC IMPACT

Federal Water Pollution Control Act of 1972

Prior to the passage of this new act, individual mills had *state permits* issued under existing implementation programs, filed with the federal government in conformance with the provisions of the *1965 Water Pollution Control Act.* Those permits regulated waste discharges consistent with the maintenance of *receiving water quality* standards. Each of the state permits was issued after a thorough investigation of the circumstances at each mill site and the control agency's assessment of the impact of any particular discharge on receiving water quality.

In response to political pressures, the *Army Corps of Engineers* dusted off the *1899 Rivers and Harbors Act* (Refuse Act), which had provisions for a federal permit program that had never been implemented. By *executive decree* in December 1970, the President directed that a *federal permit program* be set up under *Section 13 of the Refuse Act.* Under its terms, all industrial dischargers into navigable waters or their tributaries were required to apply for a permit from the Corps of Engineers prior to July 1, 1971. All pulp and paper operations complied with this deadline by filing forms that incidentally requested a great deal of unavailable and extraneous information.

Although only a handful of federal permits were issued under this program, it did signify for the first time a change in approach from receiving water quality standards to "end-of-the-pipe" *effluent limitations.* With the passage of the *Water Pollution Control Act of 1972,* this permit program was absorbed into the new *national water permit program* under which 22 basic industries were to have effluent guidelines established initially and these industries were to be issued with federal (NPDES) discharge permits by December 1974.

The pulp and paper industry headed this list of select industries and in accordance with the requirements of the 1972 act, the federal Environmental Protection Agency (EPA) retained contractors to study the industry and come up with a basis for setting *effluent limitation guidelines* as well as an assessment of the economic impact of the application of such guidelines. The time frame set by Congress for the conduct of these studies was unrealistic and the quality of the contractors' reports prepared reflect this.

After the contractors submitted their results for review and revision by EPA, proposed guidelines and standards were published in the *Federal Register* on January 14/15, 1974 for certain segments of the pulp and paper industry. Included were unbleached Kraft; sodium- and ammonium-base neutral sulfite (NSSC); unbleached Kraft/NSSC, cross-recovery, and paperboard from wastepaper. The technical support documents[5] for these proposed guidelines, however, were not made available until several weeks later, resulting in the industry having to apply for an extension of time to respond.

The proposed effluent guidelines for the remaining segments of the pulp and paper industry, including bleached Kraft and sulfite mills, will not be available until late in 1975.

Best Practicable Control Technology (BPCTCA) for Implementation by 1977

Apart from a standard requirement that effluent pH lie in 6 to 9 range, the specific guidelines proposed for the first segment of the pulp and paper industry are confined

TABLE 6 Best Practicable Control Technology Currently Available (BPCTCA)

PROPOSED EFFLUENT GUIDELINES (Environmental Protection Agency)

	Unbleached Kraft	NSSC, Na base	Kraft/NSSC combination	Waste paperboard
BOD:				
Annual average*				
30-day maximum	4.4	6.5	6.1	2.5
Daily maximum	8.0	9.0	12.7	4.4
TSS:				
Annual average*				
30-day maximum	9.2	10	10.6	3.0
Daily maximum	22.2	17	25	5.6

* EPA did not specify

RECOMMENDED EFFLUENT GUIDELINES (American Paper Institute)

	Unbleached Kraft	NSSC, Na base	Kraft/NSSC combination	Waste paperboard
BOD:				
Annual average	3.9–6.2	4.2–9.1	3.9–6.2	2.1–5.1
30-day maximum	6.8–10.8	7.4–15.9	7.2–12.4	3.7–8.9
Daily maximum	13.6–21.8	14.8–31.8	14.4–24.8	7.4–7.8
TSS:				
Annual average	10–14	9–30	9–12	2.0–4.5
30-day maximum	18–28	16–42	16–22	5.2–11.7
Daily maximum	36–56	32–84	32–44	14.4–23.4

Units: lb/ADT.

to limiting the discharge of 5-day biological oxygen demand (BOD_5) and total suspended solids (TSS). A comparison of the effluent guidelines proposed by EPA, with recommendations developed by an American Paper Institute (API) technical task force that analyzed the *same* raw data, is shown in Table 6. Substantial discrepancies are apparent between the two sets of proposals and API accordingly has retained legal counsel with the object of challenging the basis of the proposed EPA guidelines as arbitrary and defective in derivation.

Some examples of the deficiencies cited are as follows:

1. EPA departed from congressional direction by requiring best available control technology in place of best practicable by 1977. As a result, some control technology is inferred which more properly forms part of BATEA, 1983 requirements.
2. Proposed fixed numbers rather than *ranges* as was *congressional intent*.

3. Faulty identification of *exemplary* mills on which BPCTCA was to be derived; for example, inclusion of mills which operate under *supplementary, receiving water constraints* due to their location on small bodies of water.
4. Defective statistical analysis of data examined.
5. Missing data for several exemplary mills were arbitrarily assigned values.
6. Presupposed tighter control over biological system operation than is actually possible.
7. Did not provide for temperature dependency of biological systems in setting guidelines for 5-day BOD.
8. Did not recognize the temperature dependency of biological solids generation.
9. Failed to draw distinction between significance of mineral and fibrous solids

TABLE 7 Best Available Technology Economically Achievable (BATEA)

PROPOSED EFFLUENT GUIDELINES
(Environmental Protection Agency)

	Unbleached Kraft	NSSC, Na base	Kraft/NSSC combination	Waste paperboard
BOD:				
Annual average*				
30-day maximum	2.75	3.0	3.0	5.0
Daily maximum	5.0	4.2	5.9	7.5
TSS:				
Annual average*				
30-day maximum	3.7	4.0	4.2	5.0
Daily maximum	7.9	9.0	10.0	7.8

* EPA did not specify

RECOMMENDED EFFLUENT GUIDELINES
(American Paper Institute)

	Unbleached Kraft	NSSC, Na base	Kraft/NSSC combination	Waste paperboard
BOD:				
Annual average	2.0–3.1	2.1–4.6	2.0–3.1	1.0–2.6
30-day maximum	3.4–5.5	3.7–8.0	3.6–6.2	1.9–4.5
Daily maximum	6.8–10.9	7.4–15.9	7.2–12.4	3.7–8.9
TSS:				
Annual average	5–7	4.5–15	4.5–6.0	1.0–2.3
30-day maximum	9–14	8.0–21	8.0–11	2.6–5.9
Daily maximum	18–28	16.0–42	16.0–22	5.2–11.7

Units: lb/ADT.

removed in primary treatment, and *biological* suspended solids generated in secondary treatment.
10. Established a guideline for total suspended solids based on the assumed use of a technology not currently practiced at any mill in the United States.

Best Available Demonstrated Control Technology for Implementation by 1983

Guidelines have been proposed for the same industry segments as for BPCTCA with lower allowances for 5-day BOD and TSS discharge, together with a restriction on effluent color.

In Table 7, a comparison is again shown of proposed EPA guidelines with the API recommendations. Principal causes for the discrepancies are:

1. Proposed fixed numbers rather than ranges as was congressional intent.
2. Assumed that new, carefully controlled, laboratory scale technology can be extrapolated successfully and quantitatively to full-scale plant operation.

3. Assumed that inherent weaknesses in some of the proposed new technology can be resolved in time for 1983 implementation and still meet the test of economic feasibility.

4. Failed to establish an adequate foundation for the assertion that in-plant process changes necessary to meet proposed BATEA guidelines are economically feasible in an existing mill.

5. Did not properly take into consideration criticisms 6, 7, 8, and 9, described under BPCTCA, in establishing a base from which BATEA guidelines are to be developed.

6. Set a guideline for an aesthetic quality, *color,* whose perception is wholly dependent on receiving water characteristics. Color can be handled effectively, where necessary, as an individual permit requirement appropriate to the receiving water quality specification at each location.

TABLE 8 Recommended New Source Performance Standards

PROPOSED EFFLUENT GUIDELINES (Environmental Protection Agency)

	Unbleached Kraft	NSSC, Na base	Kraft/NSSC combination	Waste paperboard
BOD:				
Annual average*				
30-day maximum	2.75	3.0	3.0	1.3
Daily maximum	5.0	4.2	5.9	2.5
TSS:				
Annual average*				
30-day maximum	3.7	4.0	4.2	1.5
Daily maximum	7.9	9.0	10.0	2.2

* EPA did not specify

RECOMMENDED EFFLUENT GUIDELINES (American Paper Institute)

	Unbleached Kraft	NSSC, Na base	Kraft/NSSC combination	Waste paperboard
BOD:				
Annual average	2.7	3.3	3.0	1.5
30-day maximum	5.4	6.6	6.0	3.0
Daily maximum	10.8	13.2	12.0	6.0
TSS:				
Annual average	5.4	6.6	6.0	3.0
30-day maximum	10.8	13.2	12.0	6.0
Daily maximum	21.6	26.4	24.0	12.0

Units: lb/ADT.

7. The rationale for proposed guidelines does not adequately take into consideration their impact in creating increased air pollution and solid waste generation, or fully reflect the enormously increased energy consumption required with its own attendant pollution problems.

Proposed Guidelines for New Sources

These are shown in Table 8. They are essentially the same as BATEA 1983 requirements and similar comments would apply except that there is merit to a single number in place of a range in this instance.

These new source guidelines will surely make construction of new production facilities unattractive to many United States companies. Furthermore, equipment suppliers will be reluctant to guarantee performance to meet these restrictive permit conditions and thereby risk contingent liabilities.

The color limitations of 20 lb/ADT for *30-day average* and 30 lb/ADT for *1-day maximum* are the same proposed for unbleached Kraft mills by 1983. Only lime treatment or the use of polymeric resins could achieve this level.[8] As previously indicated, such guidelines are appropriate only in specific cases where receiving water quality criteria mandate color removal.

The arbitrary way EPA has developed proposed guidelines for the first segment of the pulp and paper industry makes it pointless at this time to indulge in speculation as to guideline numbers that may be proposed for the remaining sectors of the industry.

Economic Impact

Pollution control expenditures by the industry during the past 7 years are shown in Fig. 8. A leveling off is indicated now that most of the industry has installed primary and secondary treatment in compliance with existing state and federal permits. With the proviso that more rational thinking eventually leads to a workable

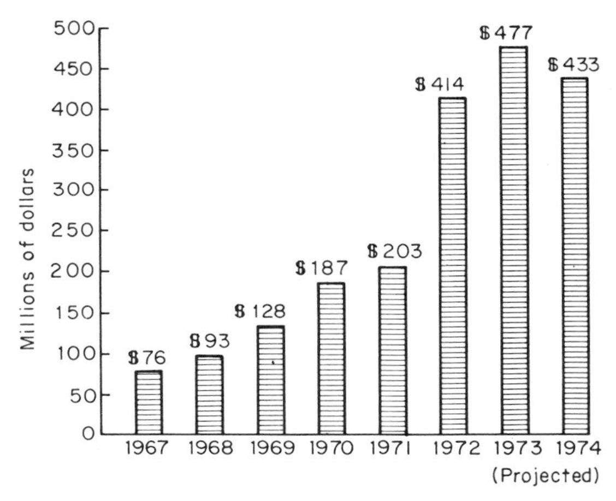

Fig. 8 Pollution control expenditures. *(United States Paper Industry)*

TABLE 9 Summary of Estimated Paper Industry Effluent Control Costs
(Millions of 1972 Dollars)

	Best practical control method (BPCM)*	Added costs for zero discharge	
		Half-median water usage	Median water usage
Capital costs:			
Reported expenditures prior to 1972	700		
Additional capital required	1,200	2,500	4,300
Cumulative totals	1,900	4,400	6,200
Operating costs, 1972 dollars/ton:†			
Average additional costs over 1971 expenditures	4.50	19.50	32.00
Ranges of cost averages for individual process categories	2.40–8.80	5–50	6–75

* Reflects cost for water discharges reported in 1971.

† Includes capital amortization and interest and also takes into account the annual costs of mills using municipal treatment facilities.

TABLE 10 Summary of Total Effluent Control Operating Cost Variability by Product Sector*

(In 1972 dollars per ton)

Product sectors	Best practical control method (BPCM)†	Zero discharge: Half median water usage	Zero discharge: Median water usage
Bleached market pulp:			
Sulfite	7.40–19.20	41–65	67–95
Kraft	4.40–11.60	33–44	57–68
Tissue	2.80–23.90	40–68	66–98
Bleached uncoated paper	5.00–17.30	21–58	33–89
Bleached Kraft board	4.40–9.60	30–40	54–65
Newsprint and uncoated groundwood	3.00–15.80	16–42	26–56
Coated groundwood paper	3.60–9.80	16–25	28–40
Semichemical corrugating medium	1.70–16.30	7–30	13–40
Unbleached Kraft paper and board	2.00–7.30	10–18	18–28
Paper mills not integrated to pulp	1.10–13.40‡	10–36	18–43
Recycled paperboard	0.50–10.70	3–22	4–31

* Reflects cumulative cost range including capital amortization and interest over the full-size range of reporting mills, including those using municipal treatment facilities.

† Reflects costs for water discharges reported in 1971.

‡ Excludes a number of small mills that reported extremely high water discharges per ton of production.

TABLE 11 Summary of Estimated Inflationary Impacts

(In 1972 dollars as a percent of 1972 prices)

Cause of price increases	Best practical control method (BPCM)	BPCM plus zero discharge: Half median water usage	BPCM plus zero discharge: Median water usage
Higher operating costs*	3–6.5	9–30	15–48
Return on capital employed†	2.0	4.5	6
Loss of productivity due to diversion of capital†	2.5	5.5	8
Total	7.5–11	19–40	29–62

* Reflects midpoints of cost ranges for high-cost mills in each product sector on the basis that they will be able to cover their full costs under tight supply and demand conditions.

† Aggregate for industry based on weighted average selling price of $200 per ton.

TABLE 12 Summary of Potential Mill Closure and Unemployment Impacts

	Best practical control method (BPCM)	Zero discharge
Probable number of mill closures	30–34	90–110
Loss of annual production capacity, thousands of tons	770–1,080	5,000–7,300
Loss of percentage of 1972 capacity,	1.3–1.8	8–12
Paper industry jobs lost*	3,700–5,200	19,000–27,000
Job losses in service and supply industries	5,600–7,800	28,500–41,000

* Includes wood harvesting.

compromise on biological TSS requirements, the industry will meet 1977 objectives well ahead of the schedule called for under the 1972 act.

For a detailed analysis of economic impact of the zero-discharge goal, the reader is referred to the Arthur D. Little study of December, 1973, carried out for the American Paper Institute.[9,10] Needless to say, the impact on a water-intensive industry like pulp and paper would be traumatic as can be seen from Tables 9 through 12 reproduced from the report. *Median water use* implies a 26 percent reduction of average 1971 consumption in the pulp and paper industry. Median water use is then assumed as a basis for cost calculations. A second set of costs is shown if water consumption is further reduced to 50 percent of 1971 median values.

REFERENCES

General

A basic guide to pulp manufacture is Sven A. Rydholm's "Pulping Processes," Interscience, 1965.

For more recent developments, the reader is referred to the monthly issues of *TAPPI,* The Journal of the Technical Association of the Pulp and Paper Industry. They also publish an excellent series of technical monographs on specific subjects.

The National Council for Air and Stream Improvement of the Pulp and Paper Industry (NCASI) is the 30-year-old research arm of the pulp and paper industry. It conducts research and development programs at four regional university research centers and has administrative headquarters in New York City. NCASI has published over 350 monographs on pulp and paper pollution control, most of which are still in print. In addition, literature surveys for air and water publications are published in the spring of each year and are, perhaps, the best single source of information available as to the progress of current technology and practice in the industry.

Finally, the Institute for Paper Chemistry (IPC) in Appleton, Wis., has an abstract service and provides another valuable information source.

Specific

1. American Paper Institute: "Statistics of Paper and Paperboard, 1973," 1973.
2. Schaumburg, F. D.: "The Influence of Log Handling on Water Quality," Dept. of Civil Engrg., Oregon State University, Corvallis, Ore. 1970.
3. Gehm, Harry: "State-of-the-Art Review of Pulp and Paper Waste Treatment," U.S. Environmental Protection Agency, 1973.
4. Graham, J., and F. D. Schaumburg: Pollutants Leached from Selected Species of Wood in Log Storage Waters, *Proc. Purdue University Industrial Waste Conf. XXIII,* Purdue Univ., Lafayette, Ind., 1968.
5. U.S. Environmental Protection Agency: "Development Document for Proposed Effluent Limitations Guidelines and New Source Performance Standards for the Unbleached Kraft and Semichemical Pulp Segment of the Pulp, Paper and Paperboard Mills Point Source Category," January 1974.
6. Deem, R. R., "Testimony before Effluent Standards and Water Quality Information Advisory Committee, Purdue University," Mead Corporation, Escanaba, Mich., 1974.
7. Timpany, P. L., L. E. Harris, and K. L. Murphy: "Cold Weather Operation in Aerated Lagoons Treating Pulp and Paper Mill Wastes," T. W. Beak Consultants, Ltd., Montreal, Canada, 1973.
8. Tyler, M. A., and A. D. Fitzgerald: A Review of Colour Reduction Technology in Pulp and Paper Mill Effluents, paper presented at the 58th Annual Meeting, Technical Section, Canadian Pulp & Paper Assn., Montreal, Canada, T. W. Beak Consultants, Ltd., 1971.
9. Arthur D. Little, Inc.: "Potential National Economic Impact of Federal Water Effluent Standards and Goals for the U.S. Paper Industry," American Paper Institute, New York, N.Y., December 1973.
10. Arthur D. Little, Inc.: Economic Impact of FWPCA Water Effluent Standards and Goals, *Paper Trade Journal,* pp. 35–38, April 1, 1974.

Chapter 7

Water Pollution Control in the Chemical Industry

WILLIAM A. PARSONS

Director, Corporate Environmental Control,
Arthur G. McKee & Company, Cleveland, Ohio

CHEMICAL INDUSTRY PROFILE

The chemical industry is highly diversified and supplies products for virtually every other industry. The number of synthetic compounds manufactured is estimated to range between 500,000 and 600,000, and a host of new products is introduced every year. Chemical production may be manifested as primary, intermediate, or finished products such as plastics or dyes. Basic chemicals may undergo many transformations prior to reaching the consumer. For example, the per capita consumption of products such as cleaning aids, carpets, textiles, automobiles, etc., is equivalent to 190 lb of sulfuric acid, 55 lb of caustic soda, and 51 lb of chlorine.[1] The chemical industry ranks fifth in assets and sixth in sales among the manufacturing industries and is second in company-financed research. It employs more than 1 million persons, more than 10,000 of whom are engaged in environmental research and the operation of pollution control facilities. New plant and equipment investments amounted to $3.4 billion in 1973 including an estimated $350 million for pollution abatement facilities.

Chemical industries are generally capital-intensive operations. Most plants operate continuously and must operate at 75 to 85 percent of capacity to maintain adequate levels of efficiency and profitability. Smaller plants often operate batch processes and, hence, tend to produce low-volume, high-cost, specialty chemicals. The principal products of the inorganic chemicals industry are mineral acids, alkalies, and salts. The principal products of the organic chemicals industry are miscellaneous cyclic and acyclic organic chemicals and chemical products, flavor and perfume materials, rubber-processing chemicals, plasticizers, and pesticides. The organic chemicals industry ordinarily includes production of monomers, but by classification excludes production of polymers such as synthetic fibers and plastics.

The diversification of chemical manufacturing operations renders classification difficult in terms of Standard Industrial Classification (SIC) codes. The following classifications were selected on the basis of significance of wastewater contributions in order to define the scope of this chapter.

SIC	*Industry*
2812	Alkalies and chlorine
2816	Inorganic pigments
2818	Organic chemicals not elsewhere covered
2819	Industrial inorganic chemicals not elsewhere covered
2871	Fertilizers
2879	Inorganic insecticides and herbicides
2892	Explosives

The chemical industry presently ranks second in industrial water consumption; however, projections have indicated that it will be the major consumer of industrial water by the year 2000. About 60 percent of present water use is for cooling and about 45 percent of the total is used in the production of organic chemicals. The most significant wastewater contributors from the group are SIC codes 2812, 2818, and 2819.

In comparison to other industries, the chemical processing industry has tremendous variety of special pollution problems because of the large number of products manufactured, the many different processes used, and the character of the wastes produced. In many cases, technology developed in other industries may not be applicable, and individual companies must work out solutions to their own specific problems. In addition, standardized methods of analysis are not applicable to some chemical wastes because of interferences, phase separations, etc. Thus, modified analyses or new analyses may have to be developed to obtain meaningful results.

MANUFACTURING PROCESSES AND WASTEWATER ORIGINS

Manufacturing processes in the chemical industry frequently involve a sequence of unit operations in which reactants are combined to yield products which are subsequently separated and purified. The completeness of the conversion of reactants to products is governed by thermodynamic laws and practicality of equipment size. Many commercial chemical reactions are complicated by the presence of impurities in the reactants, the presence of catalyst materials, and by the formation of side-products and by-products. Thus, separation and refining operations generally are necessary to obtain purified commercial products from complex reactor mixtures.

Separation and refining may include unit operations such as distillation, crystallization, filtration, centrifugation, sedimentation, adsorption, extraction, etc. The generation of waste at each step in chemical processing is inherent because of the incompleteness of the equilibrium condition governing the process and because of losses during transfer operations. Wastes containing process components (e.g., raw materials, reactants, products, or by-products) are classified as *process wastes*. Wastewater derived from indirect temperature control operations or utilities are classified as *clean wastes*. Storm water is generally a distinct third classification of waste.

Process Wastes

Most of the highly pollutional waste flows from a chemical plant originate from process areas. This category includes water formed or eliminated during reactions, wash waters from cleaning operations, steam condensate from stripping operations, water contacted with reactor contents as in direct cooling, mechanical losses from valves and seals, and accidental losses due to spills and careless operation. Process wastewaters may contain a variety of constituents including a portion of the feedstock chemicals, products, by-products, side-products, and spent catalysts. The wastes may also contain constituents from refining operations such as solvents from solvent extraction, acidic washes to extract/absorb alkaline contaminants, or caustic washes (sweetening) to extract/absorb acidic contaminants. Acidic and caustic washes are often followed by clear water rinses to remove the extraction medium to trace levels. Some typical process wastewaters associated with general processing are given in Table 7 of chapter 8 (page 8–16).

Brackish Wastes

Brackish wastes are derived from utility systems that concentrate water by evaporation. Typically, the systems may provide indirect evaporative cooling water service or steam generation. Waters from such sources have minimal contact with raw materials or products, hence, they have low potential for pollution except for thermal effects, dissolved solids, and conditioning chemicals added for control of corrosion, fouling, or frothing. In some cases additional contamination may be present from leakage of lubricant or reactor contents at bearings or seals. Chemical characteristics of some brackish wastes are illustrated in Tables 8–10 (p. 8–21) and 8–12 (p. 8–22).

Clean Wastes

Clean wastewaters may be characterized by once-through indirect cooling flows that are unexposed to process or other contamination except for heat. The flows are often large in magnitude; hence, it is important that they be segregated so as not to require treatment for removal of process contamination prior to discharge. Clean water flows are generally not included in wastewater tabulations.

Contaminated Storm Runoff

Storm runoff derived from shipping or tank farm areas is generally subject to contamination by spillage or leakage of raw materials or product. Such wastes must be collected by the process waste sewer in order to be treated prior to discharge. The necessity of processing storm runoff poses particular problems to designers of collection and treatment systems inasmuch as the wastes are subject to widespread variation in flow and concentration. The nature of the variation is illustrated by the hypothetical relation presented as Figure 8-8. Designers cope with the problem by resorting to the provision of equalization facilities or by the application of unsteady-state process designs. Since the principal contamination is often collected by the first element of runoff, designers frequently employ a treatment concept that will accommodate the first inch or so of runoff and bypass subsequent excessive storm water flows that are essentially uncontaminated.

Thermal Pollutants

Many chemical process operations generate excess amounts of thermal energy which is removed by transfer to cooling water flows or to air. Additional heat may be discharged with hot waste products (such as still bottoms or boiler blowdown). The thermal content of wastewater discharges can be controlled in many cases by utilization of cooling towers, spray ponds, or air-fin coolers. The utilization of evaporative cooling systems may introduce effluent problems from the presence of water-conditioning additives in the blowdown.

WATER CONSERVATION AND PRODUCT RECOVERY

Efficient water conservation and product recovery entail analysis of production process design, plant water system design, and plant operational procedures. Minimization of effluent is a major objective in the engineering of new chemical plant facilities or in the implementation of effluent control at existing plants. A broad and complete approach to effluent minimization entails thorough familiarity with production processes as well as with water management technologies.

Design Concept

Ideally, water conservation commences with the selection of production processes that are compatible with closed-circuit objectives. The second step is the development of a design concept that features a full measure of conversion of raw materials to products and minimum losses of products and by-products during transfer and handling operations. The design concept may utilize extended reaction times to more closely approach equilibrium product yields and full draining vessels and conduits to minimize losses during wash cycles. Significant reduction in water consumption and product loss can sometimes be achieved by utilization of the concept of countercurrent product washing. The design concept should also identify water usage and water quality requirements for specific unit operations in the process flowsheet. This information will enable the reduction of freshwater input, the maximization of water reuse, and the reduction of wastewater flow and pollutional constituents from the process. As a practical matter, all three objectives are closely related.

The production process design should include control of water usage in accordance with actual requirements and consideration of segregation of contaminated and clean effluents. For example, in the case of pump jacket water, the water used on the gland or mechanical seal is the only water which will normally come into contact with the pumped product. The input flow to such seals should be controlled in accordance with design requirement (e.g., 0.25 gpm), and the discharge should be routed to the appropriate wastewater collection system. Water used on the bearing jacket, gland jacket, and pedestal jacket is not directly exposed to contamination and is therefore suitable for discharge to the collection system of a recycle cooling tower circuit. An illustration of the concept is shown in Fig. 1.

Process Cooling

Process cooling is an area of vast potential for minimization of water consumption and pollution loading. The installation of air-fin coolers operating in conjunction with indirect heat exchangers offers the potential of zero-discharge cooling circuits. However, the practicality of implementation may be limited because of environmental considerations, excessive cost, or other process factors. Cooling towers or cooling ponds are alternatives that are generally less expensive than air-fin coolers but usually do not offer the potential of a completely closed circuit. That is, a blowdown from evaporative cooling systems is generally necessary to limit dissolved solids accumulation to acceptable levels. Evaporative cooling may be employed in conjunction with indirect heat exchange or direct heat exchange in which the cooling medium may acquire contamination through direct contact with process constituents. Evaporative cooling systems can be designed to provide for separation of settleables and floatables, or oxidation of BOD. In difficult situations, standby evaporative units or hybrid indirect-evaporative units can be provided to enable the removal of cooling components from service for specialized cleaning procedures. The concept features the potential of approaching zero discharge inasmuch as deposited fouling materials can be removed from the system in dry form. Dry collection of waste materials is invariably a prime objective in engineered design to minimize wastewater contributions.

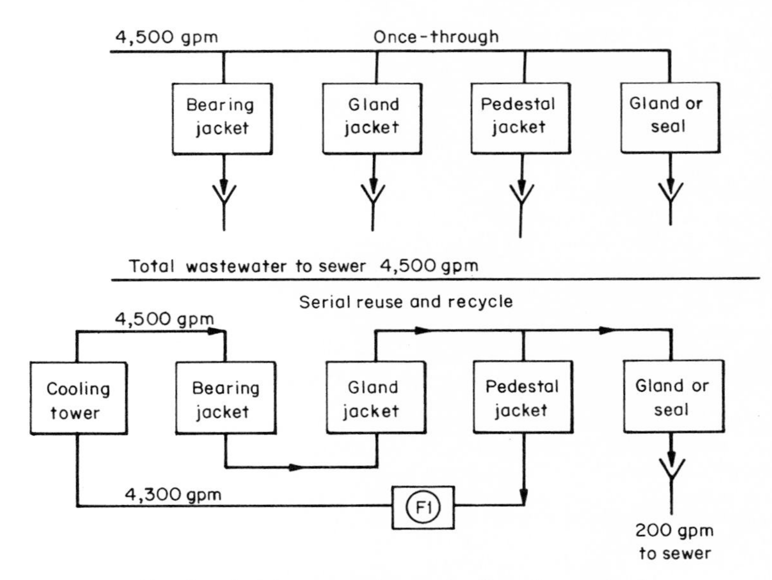

Fig. 1 Serial reuse and recycle of cooling water.[2]

Water Reuse

The plant water management system also offers the designer extensive opportunity to minimize water consumption and effluent contributions. The recycle of process water between absorber and stripper is often feasible. A basic approach is the incorporation of recycle in conjunction with serial reuse of component discharges. The objective is to effect a cascading of water from component to component in accordance with water quality requirements for the specific usage. The full implementation of the approach entails classification of input quality requirement and effluent characteristics for each wet unit operation in the plant. The classification can enable the connection of unit operations to independent water supply and effluent collection systems segregated on the basis of water quality characteristics. For example, modern water management practice at chemical plants may provide independent systems for potable water, for sanitary sewage, for clean industrial water, and for strong process wastes, plus independent closed-loop supply and collection systems for waters containing oils and high dissolved solids. Provision for separation of oils and suspended solids is incorporated in closed-loop water systems as required to improve performance. The concepts of closed circuits and serial reuse offer many virtues, but they also entail increased risk of operational problems of product contamination, corrosion, and fouling.

The provision of a functional system does not in itself ensure efficient water conservation; competent operation and management are essential for successful performance. Careful control of water usage is necessary to obtain the capability designed into a system. Excessive input to recycle systems results in a commensurate increase in discharge. Insufficient input can produce problems of corrosion, scale formation, or biological fouling. Management leadership is required to provide the incentive, the education, and the enforcement necessary to operate systems of increased complexity.

WASTEWATER MANAGEMENT PRACTICES

Process wastewaters from the chemical industry are characterized by the possible presence of acids, alkalies, salts, organic compounds (possibly nonaqueous), and dissolved gases. The complexity of the wastes depends on the products being manufactured and the degree of segregation afforded by the wastewater collection system. Effluent control can be achieved by upgrading production process yield; by implementing supplementary processes for recovery of product, by-product, or raw material; by serial reuse of effluent in subsequent manufacturing operations, or by terminal wastewater treatment.

Containment of Pollution

The most efficient means of effluent control is waste prevention; the antithesis is terminal treatment in a consolidated waste treatment plant. Consolidated waste treatment plants are nonproductive costs. However, improved product capture or recovery of by-product/raw material can offset a portion of the cost of pollution arrest. In some instances a return on investment has been realized from implementation of an improved harvest of products and by-products generated from a production process.

Containment of pollution to the production area also forces production managers and superintendents to assume responsibility for effluent generation and purification from facilities under their jurisdiction. Deficiencies in effluent quality must be rectified in the same manner as deficiencies in product quality. The concept encourages the utilization of process development specialists to optimize the overall production/effluent control operation as a package. In most instances, such a package can be lifted from the parent plant and applied directly at another, which is rarely the case with consolidated terminal treatment systems.

Implementation of Containment

Process considerations A process material balance combined with definitive information regarding time rates of discharge is the first step in implementation of a concept featuring containment of pollution at the process. The material balance should include documentation of all forms of impurities in the raw materials and products. The formulation of the material balance may require a program of step-by-step process observation and sampling to determine composition, concentration, and flow of effluents throughout the process cycle. Objectives of the effluent characterization program are to establish the magnitude of fluctuations resulting from process upset or operational lapse, as well as to discover whether the sources of the waste are related to process chemistry or to the equipment employed to carry out the chemistry. Effective waste containment depends on a thorough understanding of the process combined with insight into alternatives.

The availability of waste characterization information enables the engineering of collection systems designed to contain amenable discharges into treatment/reuse systems. The most common criteria for segregation of collection systems are: contaminated versus uncontaminated (e.g., process waste versus cooling water), aqueous versus nonaqueous (e.g., nonoily versus oily), concentrated versus dilute (e.g., process liquors versus wash waters), and amenability to treatment (e.g., biodegradable versus biorefractory). Other criteria may be amenability to recovery, hot versus cold, acidic versus basic, etc. Resourceful segregation of collection systems is essential for engineered effluent control from complex chemical production operations.

Effluent control by process revisions can be manifested as revised chemical routes to the product (e.g., titanium dioxide by the chloride process versus titanium dioxide by the sulfate process) or can be manifested as revised unit operations to improve product yield or to obtain more compatible collection of effluents. The potential of process revision can be established by optimization studies of alternate processes with effluent control included as an integral unit process. Such studies are performed most effectively on a joint basis by production process and environment control specialists. Revision of production process unit operations to effect effluent control can consist of upgrading phase separations which are notorious as sources of preventable pollution.

Equipment considerations When organic phases are separated from water, improved completeness of separation can drastically reduce effluent loadings. Inadequately designed decantation equipment is a prominent source of product loss that becomes sewered as waste. If simple decantation is insufficient to accomplish complete separation of phases, a secondary device (such as a coalescer) may upgrade performance substantially. In some situations the installation of a coalescer to back

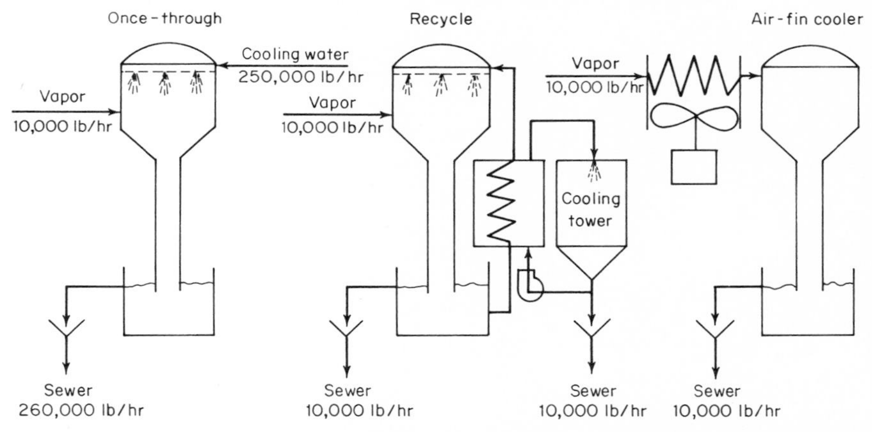

Fig. 2 Process cooling concepts involving once-through cooling water, evaporative cooling, and air-fin cooling.[3]

up a decanter can realize the recovery of as much as 90 percent of passed product. Thus, a minor investment can at times yield a substantial dividend. Secondary filtration is another additive unit operation that is often applicable for improvement of phase separations. The addition of coagulating agents (such as polymers) or collecting agents (such as light oil) are alternative approaches to improved separations.

The combination of direct (barometric) condensers with vacuum-jet ejectors constitutes a system that is rugged and reliable but possesses a high potential for pollutional emissions. If the jets are not connected to condensers or scrubbers, vaporized reactor contents are emitted to ambient surroundings. If direct-contact condensers are employed, the vaporized reactor contents are collected in a large volume of water. The substitution of air-fin condensers or indirect condensers, as in Fig. 2, will provide a concentrate that would generally be more amenable to recovery or treatment. An alternative approach is the substitution of vacuum pumps for vacuum-jet ejectors.

Substitution of unit operations in a production process holds potential for effluent control. The conceptually simple revision of the institution of dry collection of waste materials can be an excellent means of limiting hydraulic and loading surges on collection and treatment systems during cleanup periods. Dry collection or the utilization of an organic solvent to collect a concentrate may also enable direct disposal by dumping or may bring incineration into practicality. Contracted costs of incineration of organic concentrates typically range from 2 to 8 cents/lb depending on the halogen content and the nature of inorganic components. Waste with high halogen content poses technical problems for incineration equipment. Revisions to equipment in distillation/evaporation vacuum systems also can facilitate product recovery, as can conversion of scrubbers to closed-circuit systems so as to obtain a concentrated blowdown flow.

Collection and Recovery

Resourceful collection of effluent discharges, preferably as relatively pure concentrates, can facilitate the application of unit processes to effect recovery of products or by-products. The installation of a condensate stripper in conjunction with a direct-contact water quench can provide a concentrated, low-volume flow. Or the substitution of a nonaqueous medium (such as furnace oil) for water in direct-contact quench may eliminate a waterborne effluent. If collection of a concentrate is impractical,

TABLE 1 Relative Amenability to Adsorption of Various Chemical Constituents[4]

Compound at 1,000 mg/l initial concentration	Percentage removal of compound at a 5 mg/l powdered carbon dosage
Ethanol	10
Isopropanol	13
Acetaldehyde	12
Butyraldehyde	53
Di-*N*-propylamine	80
Monoethanolamine	7
Pyridine	47
2-Methyl-5-ethyl pyridine	89
Benzene*	95
Phenol	81
Nitrobenzene	96
Ethyl acetate	50
Vinyl acetate	64
Ethyl acrylate	78
Ethylene glycol	7
Propylene glycol	12
Propylene oxide	26
Acetone	22
Methyl ethyl ketone	47
Methyl isobutyl ketone	85
Acetic acid	24
Propionic acid	33
Benzoic acid	91

* Benzene test at near saturation level, 420 mg/l.

soluble organic compounds may be amenable to separation by adsorption from relatively dilute solutions. Activated carbon is the most popular adsorbent in wastewater technology. It has a remarkable capacity for adsorption of organic solutes, often ranging from 0.1 to 0.6 lb organic per lb carbon, and systems can be designed to pass only minute residuals in the effluent. Table 1 is a listing of the relative effectiveness of activated carbon for adsorption of specific compounds.

Many activated carbon systems are not operated as recovery devices inasmuch as the spent carbon is discarded or regenerated by controlled thermal oxidation which combusts the adsorbed materials. However, operation as a recovery process can be achieved if the carbon is regenerated by steam stripping, solvent extraction, or pH-induced ionization. The desorption operation yields a concentrate that can have potential for recovery of adsorbates.

Recovery using activated carbon and pH-induced ionization has been employed on a 100-gpm scale by Dow Chemical Company on the by-product sodium chloride brine from the manufacture of phenol by the chlorobenzene process.[5,6] Phenol and acetic acid were adsorbed separately in a two-stage adsorption process and desorbed using dilute sodium hydroxide regenerant solutions as illustrated in Fig. 3. The process commenced with the addition of an anionic polymer to the hot steam stripped brine (18 percent NaCl, 150 to 200 ppm phenol, 1,400 to 2,000 ppm sodium acetate, 105°C and pH=8) to coagulate suspended iron hydroxide. Following sedimentation and cooling, the clarified flow was passed through carbon columns for adsorption of phenol. The next steps were the adjustment of the pH to 3 to transform the acetate ion to adsorbable un-ionized acetic acid, prior to passage through the second-stage carbon columns. The effluent brine from the process was neutralized with sodium hydroxide and transmitted to caustic-chlorine production facilities.

The phenol-saturated adsorption columns were concurrently regenerated with 4 percent sodium hydroxide. The desorbed sodium phenate, amounting to 6 percent of the throughput volume, was recycled to the phenol production plant. The capital investment (1970) of $592,000 recovered phenol and brine valued at $60,000 per year. The unit costs of phenol recovery were 9 cents/lb per year for capital costs

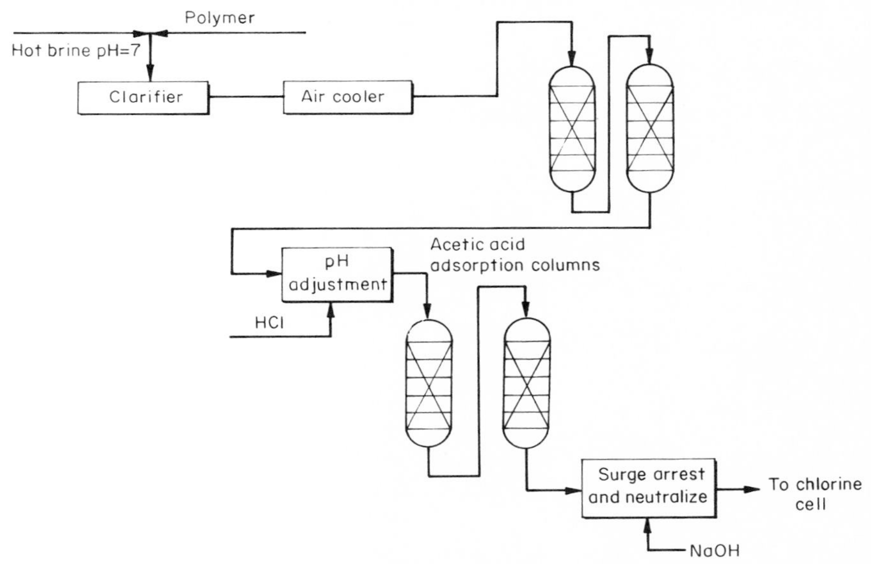

Fig. 3 Recovery of phenol and acetic acid by carbon adsorption with pH adjustment.[5,6]

and 6 cents/lb for noncapital costs. The service loading on the carbon ranged from 0.09 to 0.16 lb phenol/lb carbon with some deterioration of performance over 85 cycles of regeneration. A representative service loading with thermal regeneration would be 0.25 lb phenol/lb carbon.

The acetic acid adsorption was operated over 105 cycles of regeneration of loadings of 0.04 to 0.06 lb acetic acid per lb carbon. The effluent from the columns contained less than 200 ppm of acetic acid. The desorbed sodium acetate was discarded to waste inasmuch as recovery of acetic acid on the 100-gpm scale was not practical. A 10 percent solution of sodium hydroxide was employed for regeneration, and the volume of regenerant was 4 to 4.5 percent of the brine treated. The unit costs of acetic acid recovery were 6 cents/lb per year for capital costs and 16 cents/lb per year for noncapital costs.

Carbon regeneration by pH adjustment is applicable to a number of organic compounds that possess acidic or basic properties. Another reported example is carbon adsorption and caustic desorption of 2,4-dichlorophenoxyacetic acid (2,4-D) from spent brine. Such an operation is reported to have been successfully carried out for 220 cycles of regeneration over a period of 13 months.[6]

Solvent extraction is another approach to separation of organic compounds from wastewater flows. Liquid-liquid systems (such as have been employed to recover phenolics) have substantial application, but they possess limitations since separation of the recovered material from the solvent may be complicated and some residual of solvent becomes entrained in the wastewater flow. Extraction can also be utilized in conjunction with solid phase adsorbents as the regenerating medium.

TREATMENT PROCESSES

Terminal treatment has been practiced widely by the chemical industry for pH adjustment, suspended solids separation, oil separation, and removal of organic substrates. More attention to the removal of dissolved solids is expected in the future. Presentation of technologies available for removing suspended solids, oil, and organic substrates from chemical-type wastes has been given in Chap. 8. A generalized schematic illustrating alternatives for treatment of a hypothetical chemical plant waste for pH adjustment, suspended solids removal, and dissolved solids removal is given in Fig. 4. It is noted that present practical technology generally resorts to disposal

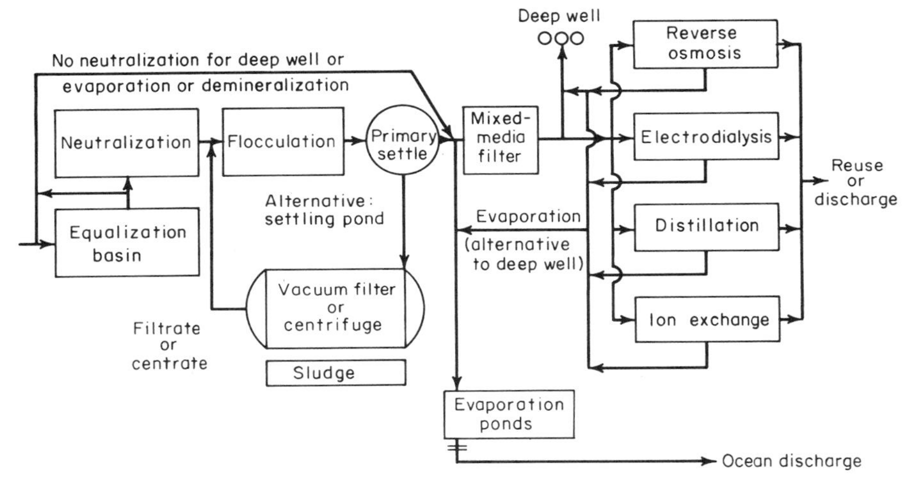

Fig. 4 Generalized flow schematic for inorganic chemical plant wastewater treatment and disposal.[7]

of a concentrate to solar evaporation, deep-well, or controlled discharge rather than production of a mechanically dried product.

In the conception of terminal treatment facilities, one of the initial decisions is whether to employ batch or continuous-flow reactors. Batch reactors are often preferred for flows of less than 0.1 mgd, especially if production is subject to change from week to week as in many fine chemical plants. The batch treatment concept can provide maximum flexibility, premium reliability, ease of design, and ease of automation. Unit operations of neutralization, flocculation, and sedimentation can be performed in the same vessel. Effluent quality can be certified as meeting standards prior to discharge. Automation may be accomplished by application of level controls, cycle timers, sensors, and turbidimeters. Process development is relatively simple as is scale-up. However, problems of scale-up are solved most reliably by verification of laboratory studies in a single prototype reactor. Space requirement is a principal limitation of batch systems.

Neutralization

Acidic and alkaline discharges are characteristic of most chemical plants as well as of many other manufacturing and processing operations. Neutralization is accomplished by the addition of alkali to acids or by the addition of acid to alkalies as required to effect the required pH adjustment. In practical situations, neutralization often involves more than pH adjustment since complications (such as the formation of sludge or scale) are common. The presence of auxiliary precipitation during neutralization usually results in decreased reaction rates.

The selection of the neutralization agent entails considerations of waste properties, reactivity, sludge characteristics, and delivered price. In the case of alkali reagents, waste alkalies and limestones are lowest in delivered cost per unit of basicity. However, their application is often restricted to the neutralization of acid systems with soluble end products or because of reactivity considerations or availability.

Ammonia, sodium carbonate, and dolomitic lime contain weak alkalinity components that may restrict application if neutralization to an alkaline range of pH is required. Parenthetically, they may possess assets of low cost or soluble reaction products, depending on the specific situation.

Sodium hydroxide and high calcium lime are the principal strong alkalies employed for acid neutralization. High calcium lime is lower in cost but is somewhat less reactive and more inclined to yield insoluble reaction products. Both alkalies are unrestricted with regard to pH range of application. Procedures for the handling and feeding of neutralization agents are available from other publications.[8, 9]

A schematic of a neutralization plant is given as Fig. 5. This illustrates some common mechanical components and processing units, but it does not depict the instrumentation and control systems necessary to produce a stabilized effluent.

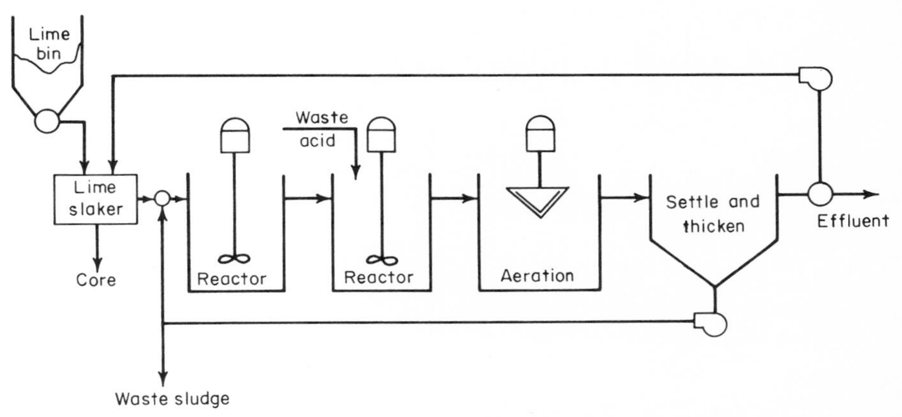

Fig. 5 Schematic of lime neutralization of waste acid using sludge recycle and aeration to improve precipitate compaction properties.[11]

Adjustment of pH can be engineered as batch or continuous systems depending on applicability to the specific situations. Since tanks are used for wastewater neutralization, the size of the treatment facility depends on flow and surge characteristics plus the kinetics of the neutralization reaction. Usually 2 to 3 ft of freeboard are provided in neutralization tanks but more may be required if frothing occurs. The reaction tanks may be circular, square, or rectangular. Baffling is often provided to control short-circuiting. Engineered agitation and corrosion control are required.

The simplest operating procedure in a batch operation is one in which the operator titrates an aliquot sample to the desired pH to determine the dosage of alkali or acid required to achieve the objective pH value. Following addition of reagent and a suitable reaction period, a sample would be checked for pH to verify that the reactor contents met discharge specifications. This method requires a minimum investment in equipment at the expense of increased operating labor. A more automated system would utilize a recording-controlling-type pH instrument with field-adjustable control capabilities that would sense the pH of the tank contents and feed neutralizing reagent until a preset pH level was obtained.

Flow and concentration surge characteristics are critical factors in determining the system design and control methods in continuous-flow units. If wastewater flow rate and composition are relatively uniform, the feed of the neutralizing agent can be regulated in response to signals from a feedback pH controller. When flow rate and composition are variable, a dynamic process design may employ a rationally derived combination of equalization, feed of the neutralization agent in response to continuous-flow rate and pH measurements, and sequential reactors to meet effluent objectives for specified input disturbances. Conventional feedback control systems have a rangeability of about 20 to 1 per stage. Feedforward control systems (Fig. 8) may have a rangeability of 1,500 to 1 by virtue of improved control concept and more sophisticated instrumentation.

Fouling of electrodes due to coating with oils or precipitated reaction products may present a difficult problem. The use of electrodes coated with nonwetting compounds may ease the problem. Electrode assemblies designed to maintain a controlled level of turbulence resist fouling in many situations; ultrasonic cleaning has also been employed. In any event, the sampling point should be selected from a zone of minimum contamination (i.e., avoid settleable tars and floating oils), and a maintenance program should be tailored to suit the fouling frequency.

The engineering of neutralization processes involves more than pH adjustment if precipitates are reaction products because the cost of sludge disposal may exceed the cost of reagent consumption. The settling and dewatering properties of many precipitates may be improved by executing the reaction in the presence of previously precipitated materials. Sludge properties are influenced by reaction temperature, return sludge dosage, rate of addition of reagents, agitator configuration, agitation intensity, and seed sludge properties.[9,10] In the case of iron oxide sludges, temperature and the degree of oxidation are important variables inasmuch as partial conversion of the precipitate to magnetic iron oxide can favorably modify sludge properties. Hot process conditions of about 70°C also favor the conversion of iron precipitates to magnetic iron oxide. A remarkable improvement in sludge properties was obtained by Kostenbader et al.[11] by a combination of controlled oxidation of mine drainage with high-dosage sludge recycle to the lime feed. The process (shown in Fig. 5), has been effective at other industrial neutralization operations involving metallic precipitates.[12] Similar concepts have been developed using limestone as the alkaline agent.

Considerable research has been devoted recently to the improvement of neutralization technology with respect to sludge properties. Crystallization procedures utilizing return sludge nuclei in conjunction with deliberate feed and temperature control have been notably successful in improving the properties of crystalline sludges. The principle involves the control of supersaturation levels during neutralization so that deposition occurs on the nuclei rather than by spontaneous precipitation of microcrystals.

Less theoretical, but highly effective, procedures have been applied to gelatinous precipitates such as metallic hydroxides. The procedures have employed, independently or collectively, temperature effects on hydration states, oxidation state, prereactive chemical environments, and reaction product nuclei to effect improvement in sludge properties. Reaction of return sludge with lime prior to contacting with acid is an example of control of the prereactive chemical environment that has frequently been effective.

Scale formation can be a problem when calcium sulfate or calcium sulfite are reaction products. Scale deposition may inactivate limestone or otherwise cause operating problems by coating instrumentation, controls, pipes, and equipment. Neutralization in the presence of previously precipitated nuclei assists in the control of scale formation. Procedures for scale control by use of seed nuclei have been published.[9]

If sludge properties are a controlling factor in the design of a neutralization system, the agitation scale-up from laboratory or pilot-plant studies may be challenging. Scale-up may be attempted by extrapolating parameters developed from multisize pilot-plant studies or studies can be performed on an element of the prototype system. Few studies have been made regarding the effect of agitator types on sludge properties. Logic would suggest low-shear agitation; inconclusive study results have suggested that pitched turbines produce better precipitate settling properties than straight-blade turbine agitators.[13] Agitator power consumption commonly ranges from 1 to 4 hp/1,000 gal of reactor volume.

Demineralization

Control of discharge of mineral salts is a key challenge in the chemical industry. Mineral salt discharges from production processes can be minimized by application of design concepts to collect such effluents as a low-flow—high-purity concentrate. The practicality of demineralization is improved when the feed concentration is high and organic contaminants are minimal. Demineralization processes differ in regard to applicability to feed concentrations and in regard to performance in terms of degree of separation. It is convenient to consider all demineralization processes as involving a semipermeable barrier, which is selectively permeable to either the water or the salt.[14] The barrier may be a real one such as a membrane or a phase boundary. Distillation utilizes a phase boundary since mineral salts are restricted in regard to migration into the vapor phase which is subsequently condensed as purified product.

Osmosis and electrodialysis Two of the methods employing true membranes and operating in an essentially isothermal manner are reverse osmosis and electrodialysis. In reverse osmosis the mineralized water is separated from the freshwater by a membrane supported by a structure. The application to the mineralized water of a pressure greater than the osmotic pressure causes demineralized water to pass through the membrane, which is more permeable to the water than to the minerals retained.

Electrodialysis exploits the fact that minerals exist in water in ionic form. Mineralized water is passed through closely spaced channels which are alternately constructed of positive- and negative-ion permeable membranes, many of which constitute a stack. Passage of a direct current through the stack effects a depletion and accumulation of minerals in alternating channels as a result of the migration of the ions toward the electrode of opposite charge.

Ion exchange Another demineralization process is ion exchange which also utilizes a "membrane-like" barrier. The method is analogous to electrodialysis because it depends on minerals being in the ionic form and because the composition of the ion-exchange resin beads in contact with the solution is chemically similar to that from which electrodialysis membranes are made. The ion-exchange resins contain a fixed matrix of a bound ion plus a mobile ion of opposite charge which is free to migrate from the resin and thereby exchange with another ion in solution of the same charge. The exchange occurs because of relative bond strength and species concentration gradient, that is, the difference between the concentration in solution and the concentration in the resin.

Practical applicability The practical applicability of demineralization processes depends to a large extent on whether the driving potential operates to transport the mineral fraction or the water fraction across the semipermeable barrier. In distillation or reverse osmosis, it is the water fraction that is transported through the phase or membrane boundary; therefore, the energy expended is nearly proportional to the water recovered and relatively independent of the feed concentration of minerals. Thus, the unit product cost with electrodialysis and ion exchange may be expected to be less for dilute than for concentrated wastewater feeds.

Desalination Substantial progress has been achieved in the desalination of seawater and of brackish waters over the past decade as a result of crash programs of research and development. However, a notable lack of progress has been evident in regard to the development of generalized methods of disposal of coproduct brines, ranging in concentration from 0.5 to 10 percent solids, that are generated by desalination processes. The control of corrosion and scale formation in evaporation equipment has been a challenging proposition. Present practical desalination technology stops at the point where excessive coproduct brine concentrations strangle the efficiency of the semipermeable barrier by scale formation, polarization, poisoning, or fouling. That is, practical desalination presently depends on disposal of brine to watercourses, to disposal wells, or to solar evaporation ponds.

Guidelines Some guideline ranges of applicability of demineralization methodology are illustrated in Fig. 6 for distillation, reverse osmosis, ion exchange, and electrodialysis. In general, distillation and reverse osmosis are most applicable to effecting a high degree of separation from concentrated solutions whereas ion exchange and electrodialysis are more applicable to partial separations from dilute solutions.

It is reasonable to expect that demineralization of industrial wastes will generally require case-by-case process development because of the increased complexity of the feed with respect to composition and concentration as compared to seawater or brackish waters. The practicality of brine disposal will differ immensely from case to case and will be strongly favored by sites that offer the prospect of solar evaporation ponds. Because of differences in pretreatment requirements, corrosion control, and process applicability, the costs of industrial waste demineralization may be abstractly related to those for conventional desalination technology.

EXAMPLES OF APPLICATIONS

Applications of pollution control technology demonstrate actual performance of prototype systems and operational anecdotes. Because of the vast scope of the chemical industry, all-inclusive coverage is not feasible but pollution control concepts properly should be drawn from process principles and overall experience rather than from provincial segments of an industry. The principles and methodology exhibited by

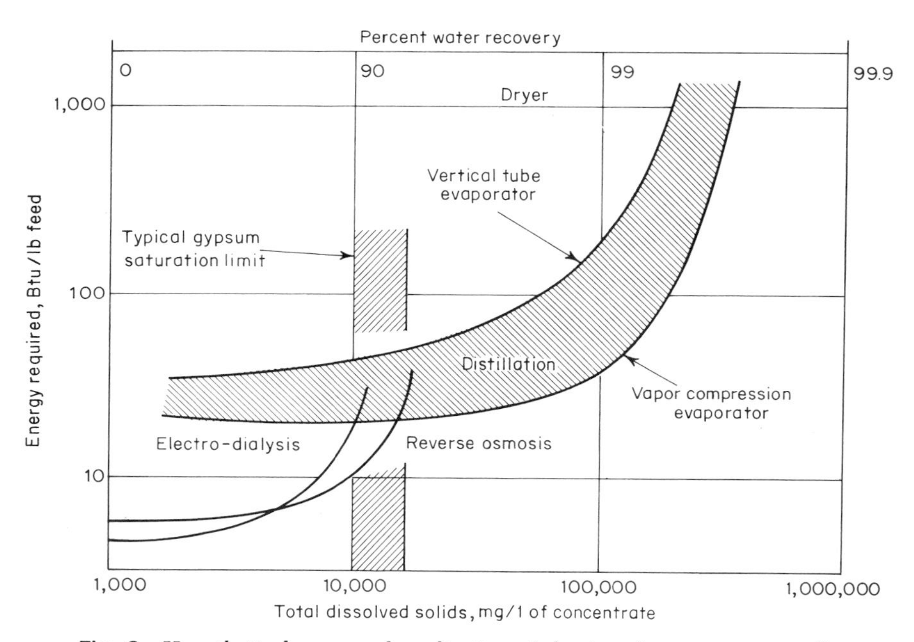

Fig. 6 Hypothetical ranges of application of demineralization processes.[15]

the following case histories are presented as examples of resourceful application of industrial waste technology to actual plant problems.

Mercury Emission Control

The manufacture of chlorine and caustic soda by electrolysis of brine in a mercury cell requires control of mercury emissions. In the process, brine is fed into a cell fitted with graphite-plate anodes and a pool of mercury flowing in a bottom trough is the cathode. A sodium amalgam formed with the mercury is decomposed external to the cell by the addition of water. Hydrogen is a product of the reaction.

Wastewater discharges from the process consist of a brine slipstream, brine purification sludges, and sulfuric acid employed for drying the chlorine product. The acid discharge, amounting to about 20 lb of sulfuric acid per ton of chlorine, is substantially recoverable.

The primary source of mercury emission is waste brine and sludge from the cells with the hydrogen gas being a minor contribution. The FMC Corporation developed and patented an emission control process for installation at their 175 tons/day chlorine plant at Squamish, British Columbia.[16] The system receives all mercury-bearing liquid wastes which are treated with sodium sulfide as shown in Fig. 7. Soluble mercury precipitates as mercury sulfide. The dilute slurry is filtered to remove mercury sulfide and other solids. The filter cake is held for further processing. The filtrate containing less than 0.1 lb/day of mercury is discharged.

The filter cake, containing mercury sulfide, is combined with muds from brine treating and is reacted with caustic and chlorine in an agitated vessel to solubilize mercury compounds. The slurry is filtered and the mercury-bearing filtrate is returned to the electrochemical cells where it is reduced to elemental metallic mercury which settles to combine with the mercury pool cathode.

The wet solids, amounting to about 40,000 lb/week, are used as landfill. The mercury emission contributed by the solids amounts to slightly over 1 lb/week.

Since installation of the effluent control process, the combined mercury emission from the solids and liquid discharges has averaged less than 1.5 lb/week. The system is reported to be simple to operate and positive in performance.

The capital investment for a 300 ton/day chlorine plant was estimated to be in the $300,000 to $400,000 range. The amortized cost of capital recovery and operation was estimated as $1.25 per ton of chlorine. Molecular sieves and organic-media filters are alternate concepts for consideration.

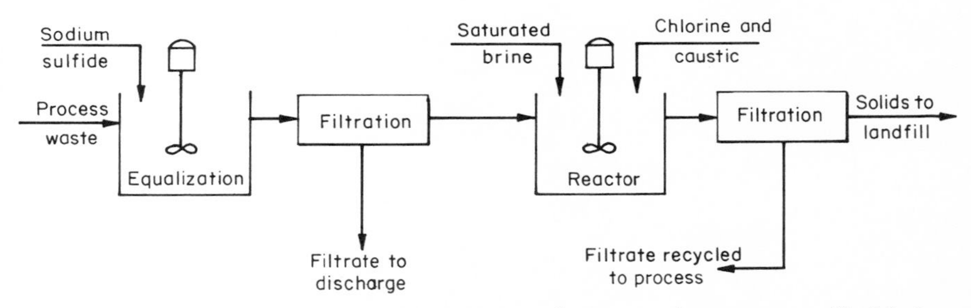

Fig. 7 Schematic of mercury emissions control concept for mercury-cell chlorine-caustic plant.[16]

Neutralization

An example of chemical plant neutralization has been provided by the Warners Plant of the American Cyanamid Company which has employed sophisticated instrumentation and sound neutralization technology to solve a challenging effluent pH control situation in a manner which minimizes the space requirement.[17] The waste flow averages about 200,000 gpd and is normally acidic, but intermittent process variations cause gross flow fluctuations and occasional slugs of alkaline waste. Space limitations precluded the use of an equalization facility to dampen transients. Effluent guidelines require the maintenance of the pH of the discharge within the range of 6.5 to 8.5.

Because of the extreme variation in the requirement for the neutralization agent, three tanks in series were employed to enable sequential pH adjustment as illustrated in Fig. 8. In the first tank, the neutralization agent (sodium hydroxide or hydrochloric acid) is intermixed with waste in the influent pipe so as to limit short-circuiting through the reactor. The dosage of neutralization agent is determined by a summing amplifier that receives signals from a feedforward controller and a nonlinear feedback controller. The feedforward controller operates from a pH sensor in the influent pipe, and the feedback controller operates from a pH sensor monitoring the flow leaving the reactor. Agitation is provided by a 1-hp, 13-in. propeller with a rated pumping capacity of 1,900 gpm at 420 rpm.

In the second tank, acid or caustic addition is governed by a nonlinear feedback trim controller that operates from a pH sensor monitoring the flow leaving the reactor. Agitation is provided by a 3-hp, dual-propeller agitator with a rated pumping capacity of 5,100 gpm at 420 rpm. The third tank is unagitated but houses a pH sensor and recorder. All tanks are baffled to minimize short-circuiting of inflow to outflow.

The control system is designed to operate in the following manner. When the influent pH is less than 5 or greater than 9, the active controllers are the feedforward and feedback controllers in the first tank and the trim controller in the second tank. When the pH is between 5 and 9, only the trim controllers in the second tank operate. Equal percentage parabolic needle valves were used to compensate for the nonlinearity of the pH curve. The large- and medium-sized acid and caustic valves are sequenced and split-ranged.

The very wide range feedforward pH control system has successfully maintained effluent pH within specified limits. It is reported that only routine maintenance has been required to sustain the operation since its start-up in October 1971. The neutralization agent combination of sodium hydroxide and hydrochloric acid minimizes insoluble reaction products.

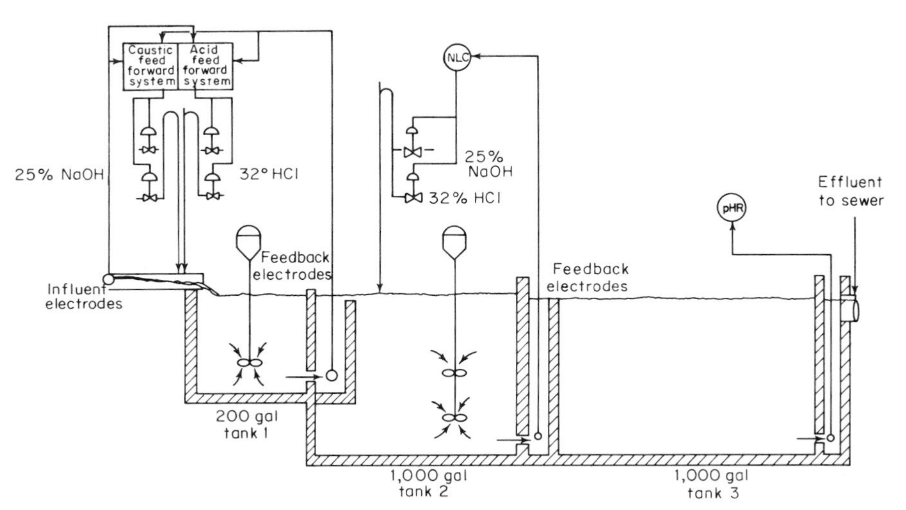

Fig. 8 Schematic of neutralization concept employing coordinated feedforward and feedback control systems.[17]

Chromate Precipitation

Problems of corrosion, biological fouling, and scale formation commonly are experienced with recycle water systems. Various inhibitor formulations are available for application to recycle water systems, but formulations containing a chromate base are preferred by many industrial plants. Chromate inhibitors have a record of providing reliable corrosion protection over a range of conditions with many mono- or multimetal systems and can simultaneously contribute to inhibition of biological fouling. A principal limitation to chromate inhibitor formulations is the potential toxicity of the blowdown from the recycle systems to receiving waters or biological wastewater treatment plants.

Fiber Industries, Incorporated, Shelby, N.C., observed chromium accumulations at their activated sludge wastewater treatment plant and elected independent removal of chromium from cooling tower blowdown rather than conversion to nonchromate inhibitor formulations.[18] The plant manufactures polyesters and employs a series of 7,000-gpm cooling towers which discharge chromate-containing blowdown to the process sewer.

After investigation of various processes for removal of chromium from the blowdown, the popular sulfur dioxide reduction–alkaline precipitation process illustrated in Fig. 9 was selected. In operation, the blowdown flows at a controlled rate to an agitated PVC-lined 1,200-gal tank where sufficient sulfur dioxide is added from a sulfonator to reduce hexavalent chromium to the trivalent state. The pH in the reactor is maintained at 3.5 by addition of sulfuric acid. Reagent feed is automated with feed of sulfur dioxide regulated by an oxidation-reduction potential controller and sulfuric acid addition regulated by an electrometric pH controller.

Following the reduction process, the blowdown flows to a 2,400-gal neutralization tank where sufficient sodium hydroxide is added to raise the pH to 8.5 where essentially complete precipitation of trivalent chromium occurs. Addition of sodium hydroxide is regulated by an electrometric pH controller. A 20-min agitation-flocculation period is provided to effect formation of a rapid settling floc. The effluent from neutralization is discharged to a settling lagoon where the chromium-bearing floc is captured and the overflow is delivered to the process sewer.

The blowdown treatment plant has a design capacity of 90,000 gpd and the total installed cost was slightly over $46,000. Operating experience over 2½ years has demonstrated that the system is virtually 100 percent effective for the removal of chromium from the blowdown. Maintenance and operating costs were reported to be less than $3,500 per year with chemical costs averaging about 47 cents/lb of chromium removed. Removal of chromate in this situation was adjudged by the company to be more practical than conversion to nonchromate inhibitors. Continuous countercurrent ion exchange is a promising concept for chromate recovery.

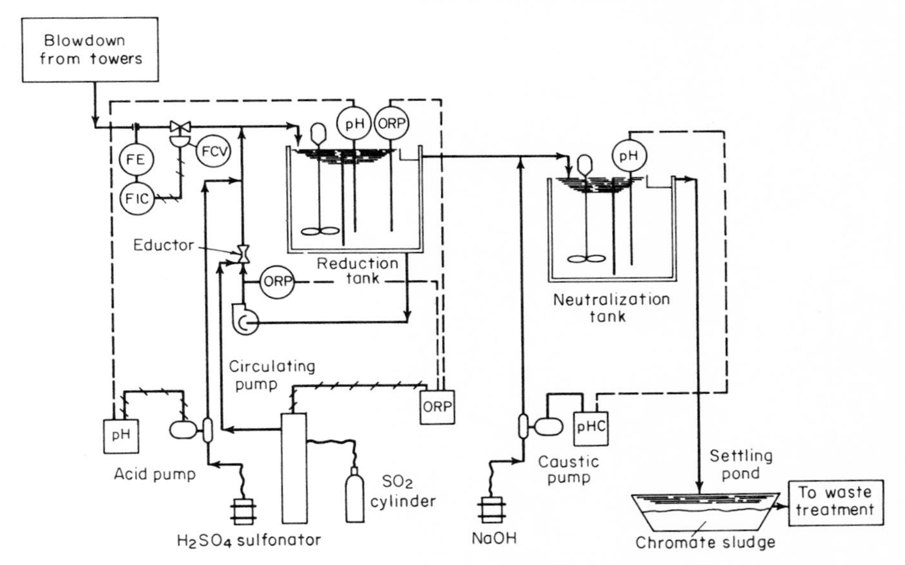

Fig. 9 Schematic of chromate removal system.[18]

Demineralization

Evaporation has been instituted to reclaim wastewater at the Odessa, Texas plant of the General Tire and Rubber Company.[19] The plant manufactures styrene-butadiene rubber. The condensate from evaporation is reused as makeup for boilers and cooling towers as well as for rubber-processing operations.

The evaporator system includes a 14-effect vertical-tube evaporator that yields 10.6 lb of water per 1,000 Btu input on an inflow of 440,000 gpd. Feedwater treatment consists of degasification and pH control. The condensate contains less than 10 ppm total dissolved solids from an input value of 3,600 ppm. The concentrate is discharged to 90 acres of solar evaporation ponds. Evaporation was selected as the reclamation process on the basis of comparative cost and the ability to cope with 200 ppm of influent oil.

The cost of evaporator hardware was $489,000. The project cost was reported as $940,000 exclusive of evaporation ponds. The operating requirement is limited to twice-a-shift readings plus indicated adjustments.[20]

Pollution Containment and Control

The establishment of a domestic water supply reservoir immediately downstream from an operating chemical plant may necessitate the implementation of drastic pollution control procedures. Such a situation was reported by Gloyna et al.[21] concerning the Conroe Plant of the Jefferson Chemical Company, Houston, Texas. The plant manufactured specialty organic chemicals including amines, polypropylene glycols, alkaline carbonates, and acid salts of organic amines. The wastewater characteristics were exceptionally variable because of the diversity of the product line. The achievements obtained by the pollution control program are testimony to results attainable through exemplary engineering and management practices.

The effluent control program commenced with in-plant surveys to quantitatively identify sources of pollution. Material balances were made to verify survey results with the objective of accounting for 95 percent of pollution sources. Water conservation and in-plant pollution containment practices were implemented. These included installation of recycle systems, segregation of storm water and dilute wastes, and ammonia recovery. All pollution sources were evaluated for possible elimination, reduction or concentration. Concentrated wastes were segregated for independent disposal. Training programs were conducted for employees to inspire water conservation practice.

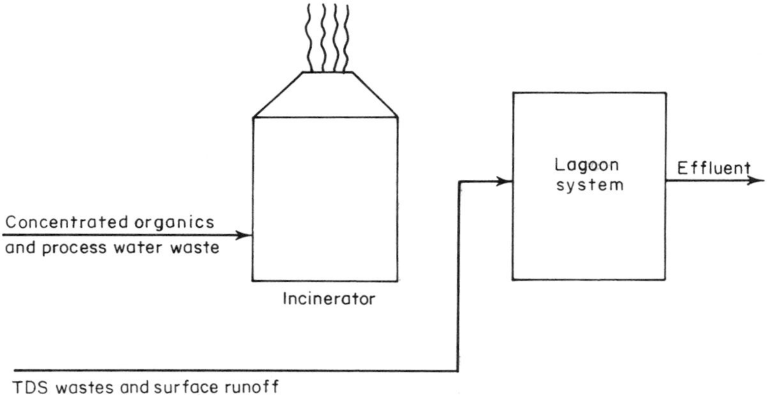

Lagoon system
Effluent
Concentrated organics and process water waste
Incinerator
TDS wastes and surface runoff

Fig. 10 Schematic of incineration concept for chemical plant wastes.[21]

Treatment and disposal studies were initiated to evaluate approaches to terminal treatment and/or disposal of residual effluents. The studies included coagulation, carbon adsorption, distillation, foam separation, biological oxidation, deep-well disposal, and thermal oxidation. Extended aeration activated sludge followed by stabilization ponds seemed to be potentially practical for application. Subsequent developmental studies demonstrated that certain waste combinations, under less than optimum process conditions, required unreasonably long aeration periods (9 to 14 days) to obtain the desired 90 to 95 percent removal of BOD. Therefore, a thermal oxidation-stabilization pond system was selected for implementation. The thermal oxidation system was sized to incinerate 100 gpm of process waste containing from 600 to 100,000 mg/l of organic materials.

A flow schematic for the selected terminal treatment/disposal system is presented in Fig. 10. Process wastewater is collected and stored in a 1.2-million-gal holding pond prior to incineration. Process area storm water plus nonprocess wastewaters (such as boiler and cooling tower blowdown), demineralizer recharge rinses, etc., are delivered to a collection sump that discharges to a series of stabilization ponds. The collection sump is monitored by a total organic carbon (TOC) analyzer/controller that automatically diverts flow to the process sewer system if a spill or other cause produces a TOC appreciably more than 300 mg/1. The principal assets of the thermal oxidation system were its applicability to biodegradable and biorefractory organic wastes under all environmental conditions and the reduction of the period of start-up from possible months to hours. In addition, the system could be automated to minimize operator attention.

The dramatic success of the effluent containment program in arresting discharges of chemical oxygen demand (COD) and flow is illustrated in Fig. 11 for the period 1963 to 1969. The containment of COD exceeded 99 percent whereas the reduction in flow amounted to 82 percent on a unit production basis. The attendant investment and operating costs associated with the program are illustrated in Fig. 12. The cumulative investment cost over the period has totaled $842,000 and the cost of operation has risen to about $200,000 per year. The success of the endeavor can be attributed to the development and implementation of a soundly conceived, engineered, and managed effluent control program.

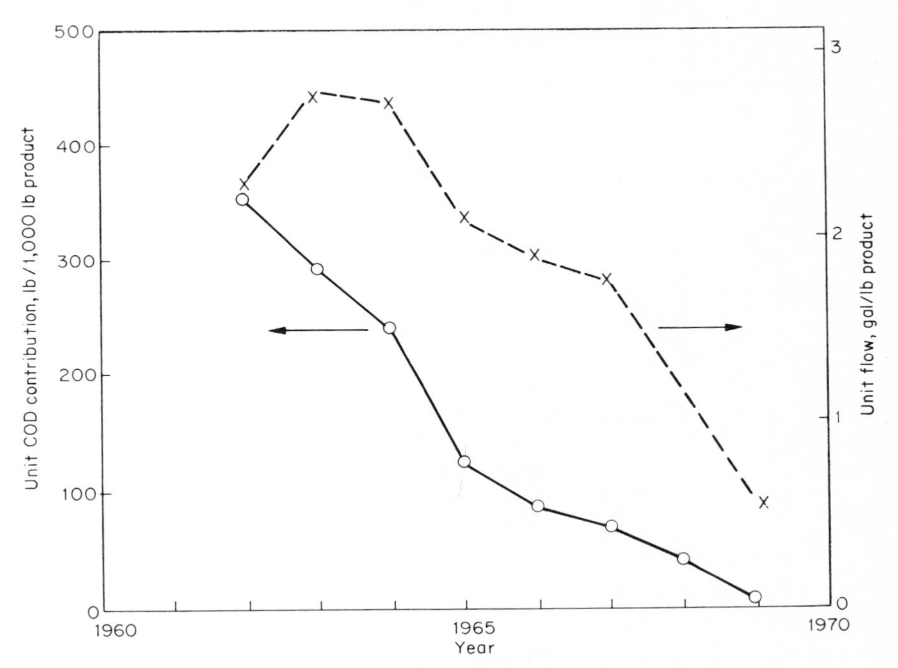

Fig. 11 Effect of pollution control implementation on COD and wastewater contributions.[21]

Organic Chemicals Plant Waste Treatment

The effluent control program for a multiproduct organic chemical plant which is maintained by the Rohm and Haas Company at Deer Park, Texas, has been described by Parrot and Smith.[22] The plant produces intermediates and products, including ammonia, methanol, acetylene, alkyl amines, acrylic monomers, and nonionic surfactants. Wastewater from production operations is discharged to the Houston Ship Canal after treatment. The wastewater treatment facilities have undergone a series of revisions to accommodate changes in production and revised water quality regulations.

The wastewater flow delivered to the treatment plant is a complex mixture of salts and organic compounds that averages about 1,400 gpm. The composition of the wastewater after separation of the oil phase may be characterized by the analytical values presented in Table 2. A study of component flows indicated that 75 percent of the total COD is contained in 500 gpm of flow and that 50 percent of the COD is contained in 150 gpm. The flowsheet of the treatment plant includes gravity separation of oil and sludge, equalization, neutralization, bioaeration, and biological filtration.

The 6-acre aerated lagoon employed for bioaeration provides a detention time of 15 days. Aeration is supplied by twenty-five 60-hp floating aerators. Spacial uniformity is improved by engineered distribution of inflow to eight feed points within the lagoon. The on-stream factor for the aerators has been about 90 percent, and the oxygen transfer rate has been about 1.8 lb/(hp) (hr) based on COD removal performance as compared to 2.1 predicted from laboratory measurements. The values of the oxygen transfer coefficient α and the oxygen saturation coefficient β were experimentally determined as 0.83 and 0.95, respectively. The bioaeration process

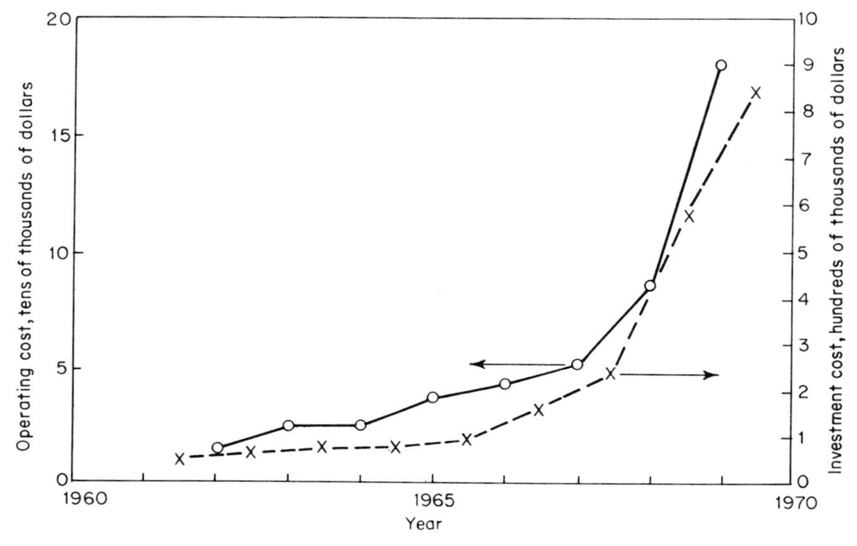

Fig. 12 Investment and operating costs associated with implementation of pollution control.[21]

TABLE 2 Characteristics of Untreated Wastewater[22]

Chemical oxygen demand	5,700 mg/l
Biochemical oxygen demand	2,700 mg/l
Total organic carbon	1,800 mg/l
Suspended solids	200 mg/l
Dissolved solids	10,000 mg/l
pH	4–6

with no recycle of culture was selected inasmuch as dispersed culture growth was obtained in process development pilot-plant studies. It has subsequently been demonstrated that culture flocculation is improved if the aeration tank pH is maintained at 6.5 to 7.0 instead of the uncontrolled pH level of 8.5. The bioaeration process operates at a culture concentration of 400 mg/l which provides a total of 100,000 lb of culture which consume 60,000 lb COD/day.

The treatment plant is staffed with two operators on the day shift only; the plant runs unattended on the other shifts. Operating personnel have responsibility for waste-oil incineration as well as for the wastewater treating operations. Vigil on in-plant pollution control is maintained by monitoring discharges from production units via gas chromatography and wet analysis for raw materials and products. The gas chromatogram registers 18 significant compounds that relate to specific production processes. Daily results are transmitted to production unit managers in terms of monetary values of lost constituents. Total treatment costs including depreciation, were 2.2 cents/lb COD removed or 77 cents/1,000 gal of flow. Waste oil was separated and incinerated at a total cost of 3.5 cents/gal, including depreciation.

Water Reuse

A closed-loop process water system has been installed at the Dalton, Georgia plant of the Dow Chemical Company.[23] The plant manufactures styrene-butadiene latex for utilization in carpet manufacture. The latex is produced as a water suspension of very minute synthetic rubber particles formed by emulsion polymerization of styrene and butadiene. The latex particles produced are finely divided with a particle size in the neighborhood of from 1500 to 2500 Å. Due to the large surface area of the particles, a cloudy appearance is imparted to water at very low concentrations. The process wastewater contains bits of latex plus trace quantities of unreacted monomers and ammonia. The wastewater also has a high chemical oxygen demand (COD).

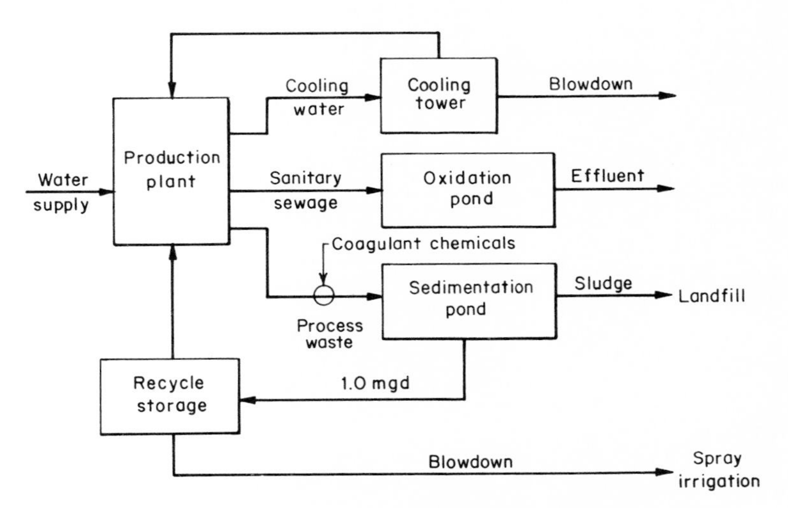

Fig. 13 Closed-circuit concept for styrene-butadiene latex plant.[23]

The company elected the provision of a closed-circuit process water system to conserve water usage and minimize effluent loadings. The water management concept selected (Fig. 13) employs independent systems for cooling water, sanitary wastes, and process water. The cooling water system employs a cooling tower to enable the recirculation of 2.0 mgd. Sanitary sewage is treated in an oxidation pond prior to discharge. The process wastewater is treated and recycled.

All drips, spills, wash water, and process waste are collected for treatment by coagulation. The coagulation process consists of addition of metered dosages of alum plus adjustment of pH to about 7.0. The coagulated wastewater is transmitted to one of four settling ponds operated on a fill and draw basis. Each pond provides 1.5 million gal of storage capacity. After settling for a day or so, the clarified water is discharged to a 10.5 million-gal storage pond which serves as process and firewater reservoir to the plant, thus completing the recycle loop.

Sludge from the settling ponds is occasionally excavated for disposal to a landfill. Excess storm water collected in the settling ponds and storage reservoir necessitates provision for periodic blowdown to a spray irrigation field.

Biological Treatment

The operation of a major organic wastewater treatment operation adjacent to a suburban residential community was a challenge accepted by Lederle Laboratories of the American Cyanamid Company.[24] The plant manufactures pharmaceutical and biological products primarily by fermentation. Characteristic odor problems had been experienced with an earlier treatment plant and also at the municipal treatment plant that further processes the treated industrial waste effluent.

Following comprehensive pilot-plant studies, the decision was reached to adopt a pure oxygen activated sludge process to treat the waste to 250 ppm BOD prior to discharge to municipal sewers. The revised system is designed to accommodate an average flow of 1.5 mgd containing 40,000 lb BOD. The system is illustrated by the flow schematic presented in Fig. 14. The overall treatment process consists of chemical coagulation and sedimentation, pure oxygen activated sludge, final settling, and chlorination. The oxygenation system consists of a 15 ton/day oxygen generator plus a 15 ton/day liquid oxygen storage and delivery unit. The oxygenation tank is an 820,000-gal closed reactor in six bays. Eight mechanical surface aerators are employed to effect transfer of oxygen to the activated sludge culture. Oxygenation capacity is 27,000 lb/day at 90 percent transfer efficiency with 5 ppm residual in the reactor effluent. Ozone generators were provided for "as needed" treatment of reactor and sludge handling off-gases.

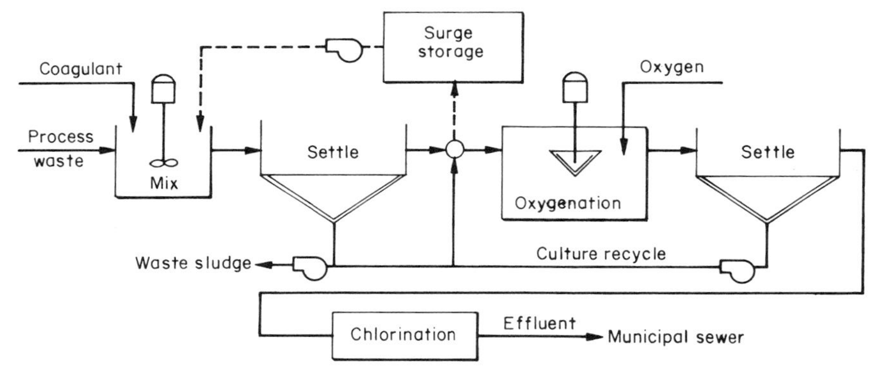

Fig. 14 Process schematic for treatment of pharmaceutical plant waste by pure oxygen activated sludge.[24]

The use of pure oxygen in the activated sludge reactor necessitated special precautions to protect against possible surges of solvents from manufacturing operation lapses. Sensor devices were installed in production areas to activate alarms upon detection of high concentrations of solvents. In addition, the oxygen atmosphere of the reactor is monitored continually to interrupt automatically the treatment operation if solvent levels exceed 25 percent of the lower explosive limit. The remedial action consists of stopping the oxygen flow, purging the reactor with compressed air, and diverting the influent waste to storage.

On the basis of early operating results, the system has exceeded design BOD removals and has been odor-free. The cost of the facility was reported as $4 million.

Biological Denitrification

Removal of low concentrations of ammonia, nitrites, and nitrates from wastewater has been a challenging problem for waste treatment plant designers. Biological denitrification has been identified as a theoretically promising process but has not demonstrated, to date, the reliable performance necessary to qualify as a practical process suitable for generalized application. According to Climenhage,[25] sufficient developmental studies have been completed to justify the prototype system recently installed at the Maitland, Ontario, works of Du Pont of Canada.

The wastewater from the Maitland plant contains a variety of nitrogen and carbon compounds derived from the manufacture of the nylon intermediates adipic acid and hexamethylene diamine. Adipic acid is manufactured by air oxidation of cyclohexane followed by nitric acid oxidation and purification by crystallization. The wastewater from these operations contains nitrite, nitrate, and organic compounds. The organics are principally short-chain monobasic acids. Hexamethylene diamine is manufactured by ammoniation of adipic acid to nitrite, followed by reduction with hydrogen to diamine and refining by distillation. The wastewater contains ammonia, organic nitrogen compounds, and organic carbon. Representative wastewater characteristics are given in Table 3.

Prior to commencement of treatability studies, production process revisions were implemented to recover and recycle ammonia and nitric acid to effect a 40 to 50 percent reduction in nitrogen discharge. Extensive developmental studies followed which included evaluation of high-temperature wet oxidation, incineration, and various biological schemes. Repeated studies confirmed that biological treatment would provide the highest performance in terms of nitrogen and carbon removal at minimum cost.

TABLE 3 Wastewater Characteristics of Du Pont of Canada Maitland Works[25]

TOC	4,000 mg/l
BOD	8,000 mg/l
NO_3–N	300 mg/l
NO_2–N	240 mg/l
NH_3–N	320 mg/l
Organic nitrogen	100 mg/l

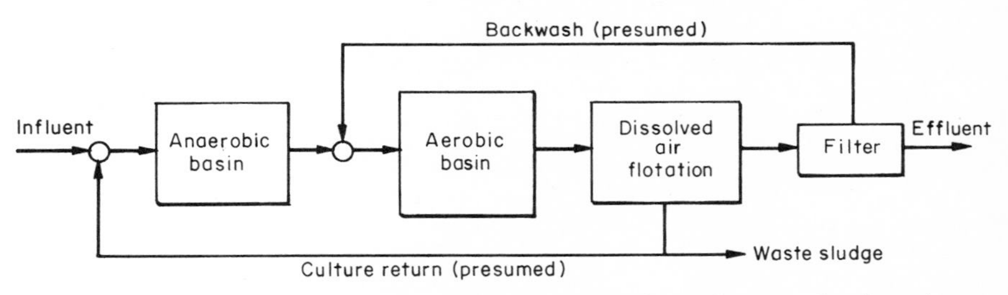

Fig. 15 Presumed process schematic for biological denitrification of nylon chemicals wastes.[25]

The treatment system, for which patent application has been filed, consists of an anaerobic reactor followed in series by an aerobic reactor and culture separation as depicted in Fig. 15. The anaerobic reactor provides 36-hr detention at an oxygen concentration of less than 0.2 mg/l to promote intermolecular respiration in accordance with the reaction:

$$NO_3^- \text{ or } NO_2^- + \text{organic carbon} \xrightarrow{\text{Bacteria}} CO_2 + N_2 + \text{bacteria cells}$$

The reactor is agitated by two 30-hp mixers to maintain uniformity of contents. Oxidation of carbonaceous matter ensures depletion of dissolved oxygen. Removal of nitrite and nitrate in excess of 95 percent was normally achieved.

The aerobic reactor is aerated to maintain dissolved oxygen for decomposition of carbonaceous matter and nitrification of ammonia. Oxygenation and mixing are provided by six 150-hp, slow-speed mechanical aerators. The detention time in the basin is 5 days.

The flow from the aerobic reactor is delivered to a dissolved air flotation unit for separation of activated sludge culture. The system was selected to overcome the potential problem of rising sludge (due to denitrification) in a clarifier and to cope with sludge-bulking problems sometimes associated with extended aeration activated sludge systems. The effluent from air flotation is passed through a dual-media filter to assure complete removal of suspended solids.

Removals of as high as 98 percent BOD, 90 percent TOC, and 85 percent total nitrogen have been obtained in developmental studies. Although some deterioration in performance is expected in cold winter months, removals of 90 to 95 percent BOD, 80 to 90 percent TOC, and 60 to 80 percent total nitrogen are expected.

The estimated cost of the 2.5-mgd treatment system is $2 million. The system has the design capacity to remove 45,000 lb BOD/day and 8,000 lb nitrogen/day. The total operating cost for labor, electrical power, maintenance, and chemicals was estimated as $175,000 per year.

EFFLUENT LIMITATIONS GUIDELINES

The Federal Water Pollution Control Act Amendments of 1972 directed that the Environmental Protection Agency develop effluent limitations guidelines and standards of performance and pretreatment for point source discharges other than publicly owned treatment works. The objectives of the amended act are for existing industry to comply with effluent limitations guidelines specifying the best practical control technology currently available (BPCTCA) by July 1, 1977. In addition, existing industry is to comply with effluent limitations guidelines specifying the best available technology economically achievable (BATEA) by July 1, 1983. New industries constructed after formulation of effluent limitations guidelines will comply with a guideline specifying the best available demonstrated control technology (BADCT). New industries discharging to a publicly owned treatment works shall comply with the BADCT guideline as well as with such other restrictions as may be imposed to ensure the effluent quality of the publicly owned treatment facility. A detailed analysis of the Federal Water Pollution Control Act, as amended, is given in Chap. 2.

Guidelines for Organic Chemicals Manufacturing

The formulation of effluent limitations guidelines for the chemical industry is complicated by the tremendous diversity of production processes. Categorization of production processes was necessary in order to provide meaningful applicability to the guidelines. The organic chemicals industry was divided into four subcategories representing an estimated 75 percent of production capacity.[26] The guidelines specify effluent limitations in terms of maximum unit contribution for any single day and for maximum mean contribution for any 30 consecutive days.

The best practical control technology currently available (BPCTCA) for the four subcategories was defined as biological treatment. An illustrative treatment system would include equalization, pH control, oil separation, activated sludge with chemical coagulation to aid in clarification of suspended solids. Other treatment schemes providing equivalent performance whether biological or chemical-physical are not precluded.

The best available demonstrated control technology (BADCT) for the four subcategories involved application of best in-process control measures in conjunction with terminal treatment. Examples of in-process controls would include substitution of indirect heat exchangers for direct-contact water cooling (barometric condensers) and the recycling of process water, for instance, between absorber and stripper. Illustrative terminal waste treatment would consist of biological waste treatment as per BPCTCA with additional suspended solids removal by processes such as coagulation, flotation, or filtration. In addition, it may be necessary to remove certain waste constituents that interfere with or pass terminal treatment processes. Equivalent chemical-physical or other processes are not precluded.

The best available technology economically achievable (BATEA) for the four subcategories was considered to be a combination of the best in-process control and the best treatment technologies. A goal was minimizing the chemical oxygen demand (COD) of the effluent. Applicable in-process pollution containment such as that specified under BADCT would be employed. The illustrative terminal treatment would involve addition of activated carbon to the biological waste system proposed for BADCT. The application of equivalent systems (e.g., zero discharge) was not precluded.

SUBPART A pertained to nonaqueous processes having minimal contact between water and reactants or products within the process. The proposed effluent limitations guidelines for Subpart A are presented in Table 4.

SUBPART B pertained to production processes with water usage in the form of dilution steam, direct-contact quench, or as an absorbent for reactor effluent gases. Subpart B was divided into groups B1 and B2 to improve applicability to chemical manufacturing processes. The proposed effluent limitations guidelines for Subpart B are given in Table 5.

TABLE 4 Effluent Limitations Guidelines for Organic Chemicals Manufacturing Industry Subpart A[26]

		BPCTCA		BATEA		BADCT	
Subpart	Effluent characteristic	Maximum 24-hr average	Maximum 30-day average	Maximum 24-hr average	Maximum 30-day average	Maximum 24-hr average	Maximum 30-day average
A	COD, kg/1,000 kg product			0.062	0.045		
A	BOD_5, kg/1,000 kg product	0.045	0.02	0.015	0.0085	0.037	0.017
A	TSS, kg/1,000 kg product	0.067	0.03	0.022	0.013	0.034	0.015
A	pH	6–9	6–9	6–9	6–9	6–9	6–9

Subpart A: Nonaqueous processes having minimal contact between water and reactants or products, e.g., BTX aromatics by hydrotreatment of pyrolysis gasoline or by solvent extraction from reformate, cyclohexane by hydrogenation of benzene, and vinyl chloride by addition of hydrochloric acid to acetylene.

TABLE 5 Effluent Limitations Guidelines for Organic Chemicals Manufacturing Industry Subpart B[26]

		BPCTCA		BATEA		BADCT	
Subpart	Effluent characteristic	Maximum 24-hr average	Maximum 30-day average	Maximum 24-hr average	Maximum 30-day average	Maximum 24-hr average	Maximum 30-day average
B1	COD, kg/1,000 kg product			0.80	0.58		
B1	BOD_5, kg/1,000 kg product	0.13	0.058	0.044	0.025	0.11	0.048
B1	TSS, kg/1,000 kg product	0.2	0.088	0.017	0.010	0.10	0.044
B1, B2	pH	6–9	6–9	6–9	6–9	6–9	6–9
B2	COD, kg/1,000 kg product			1.32	0.95		
B2	BOD_5, kg/1,000 kg product	0.95	0.42	0.32	0.18	0.76	0.34
B2	TSS, kg/1,000 kg product	1.42	0.64	0.048	0.029	0.72	0.32

Subpart B1: Processes with direct contact with water as steam diluent or absorbent, e.g., acetone, butadiene (coproduct of ethylene), ethyl benzene, ethylene and propylene, ethylene dichloride, ethylene oxide, formaldehyde, methanol, methyl amines, or vinyl chloride (cracking of ethylene dichloride).

Subpart B2: Processes with direct contact with water as steam diluent or absorbent, e.g., acetaldehyde (dehydrogenation of ethanol), acetylene (partial oxidation of methane), butadiene (dehydrogenation of *n*-butane), butadiene (oxidative dehydrogenation of *n*-butane), styrene.

Note: These effluent guidelines have a record of instability. They are cited for general perspective only. The reader should verify them by reference to current regulations.

SUBPART C pertained to aqueous liquid–phase reaction systems. In these reactions the catalyst is generally in aqueous media, such as dissolved mineral salt or acid and caustic solutions. Regeneration of the catalyst system often involves water input, and discharge of spent inorganic salt by-products may also be required. Additional process water may be employed in final purification or neutralization of products. Subpart C was divided into groups C1, C2, C3, and C4 to improve applicability to chemical manufacturing processes. The proposed effluent limitations guidelines for Subpart C are given in Tables 6 and 7. An effluent limitations guideline for phenol discharge is stipulated for the manufacture of phenol and acetone, bisphenol A, or *p*-cresol. The 30-day mean values are 0.020, 0.017, and 0.02 kg/1,000 kg of product for BPCTCA, BATEA, and BADCT respectively.

Guidelines for Inorganic Chemicals Manufacturing

The inorganic chemicals manufacturing industry is very large and diverse. For purposes of formulation of effluent limitations guidelines, the industry was divided into 22 discrete subcategories consistent with chemicals produced since raw materials and production processes are specific for each chemical product. Effluent limitations guidelines were proposed for the production of the following chemicals: aluminum chloride, aluminum sulfate, calcium carbide, calcium chloride, calcium oxide and hydroxide, chlorine and sodium or potassium hydroxide, hydrochloric acid, hydrofluoric acid, hydrogen peroxide, nitric acid, potassium metal, potassium dichromate, potassium sulfate, sodium bicarbonate, sodium carbonate, sodium chloride, sodium dichromate and sulfate, sodium metal, sodium silicate, sodium sulfite, sulfuric acid, and titanium dioxide.[27]

TABLE 6 Effluent Limitations Guidelines for Organic Chemicals Manufacturing Industry Subpart C, Groups C1 and C2[26]

		BPCTCA		BATEA		BADCT	
Subpart	Effluent characteristic	Maximum 24-hr average	Maximum 30-day average	Maximum 24-hr average	Maximum 30-day average	Maximum 24-hr average	Maximum 30-day average
C1	COD, kg/1,000 kg product			0.52	0.37		
C1	BOD_5, kg/1,000 kg product	0.28	0.12	0.093	0.053	0.23	0.10
C1	TSS, kg/1,000 kg product	0.42	0.19	0.14	0.085	0.21	0.94
C1, C2	pH	6–9	6–9	6–9	6–9	6–9	6–9
C2	COD, kg/1,000 kg product			1.75	0.98		
C2	BOD_5, kg/1,000 kg product	0.55	0.25	0.12	0.068	0.45	0.20
C2	TSS, kg/1,000 kg product	0.56	0.25	0.19	0.11	0.28	0.12

Subpart C1: Aqueous phase reaction systems, e.g., acetic acid, acrylic acid, coal tar (distillation), ethylene glycol, terephthalic acid (oxidation of *p*-xylene), or polymer grade terephthalic acid (purification of terephthalic acid).

Subpart C2: Aqueous phase reaction systems, e.g., acetaldehyde (oxidation of ethylene with oxygen), caprolactam, coal tar (pitch forming), oxo chemicals or phenol and acetone (cumene process).

TABLE 7 Effluent Limitations Guidelines for Organic Chemicals Manufacturing Industry Subpart C, Groups C3 and C4

		BPCTCA		BATEA		BADCT	
Subpart	Effluent characteristic	Maximum 24-hr average	Maximum 30-day average	Maximum 24-hr average	Maximum 30-day average	Maximum 24-hr average	Maximum 30-day average
C3	COD, kg/1,000 kg product			6.07	4.37		
C3	BOD_5, kg/1,000 kg product	1.15	0.51	0.067	0.043	0.94	0.42
C3	TSS, kg/1,000 kg product	0.15	0.068	0.05	0.03	0.076	0.034
C3, C4	pH	6–9	6–9	6–9	6–9	6–9	6–9
C4	COD, kg/1,000 kg product			39.25	28.26		
C4	BOD_5, kg/1,000 kg product	3.08	1.37	0.62	0.35	2.56	1.14
C4	TSS, kg/1,000 kg product	2.80	1.25	0.94	0.57	1.40	0.63

Subpart C3: Aqueous liquid-phase reaction systems, e.g., acetaldehyde (oxidation of ethylene with air), aniline, bisphenol A, or dimethyl terephthalate.

Subpart C4: Aqueous phase reaction systems, e.g., acrylates, *p*-cresol, methyl methacrylate, terephthalic acid (nitric acid process) or tetraethyl lead.

The effluent limitations guidelines for best practical control technology currently available (BPCTCA) was "no discharge of pollutants" for a substantial number of subcategories as listed in Table 8. Table 8 also lists some of the control concepts advocated by the contractor for the EPA guideline document.[15] Parameters limited under the effluent guidelines included pH, total suspended solids, cyanides, and heavy metals.

Effluent limitations guidelines specifying no discharge of process waste were proposed for 19 of the 22 subcategories with respect to best available technology economically achievable (BATEA) and best available demonstrated control technology (BADCT). Sodium carbonate and titanium dioxide were the subcategories that did not receive an effluent limitations guideline of no discharge of process waste under the BATEA criterion. Titanium dioxide production was the only subcategory whose effluent limitations guideline did not specify no discharge of process waste under the BADCT criterion.

TABLE 8 Suggested Inorganic Chemicals Manufacturing Industry Effluent Control Technology

	Control technology	BPCTCA	BATEA
Aluminum chloride	*a, b, c*	NPD	NPD
Aluminum sulfate	*d*	R	NPD
Calcium carbide	*a*	NPD	NPD
Calcium chloride	*d*	R	NPD
Calcium oxide and calcium hydroxide	*a, d*	R	NPD
Chlorine and sodium or potassium hydroxide	*d, g, o, p*	R	NPD
Hydrochloric acid	*c, e, g*	NPD	NPD
Hydrofluoric acid	*c, e*	R	NPD
Hydrogen peroxide	*d, e, k*	R	NPD
Hydrogen peroxide (electrolytic)	*d, e, m*		
Nitric acid	*c, e*	NPD	NPD
Potassium metal	*a*	NPD	NPD
Potassium dichromate	*j*	NPD	NPD
Potassium sulfate	*d, f, g*	NPD	NPD
Sodium bicarbonate	*d, f, g*	NPD	NPD
Sodium carbonate	*d*	R	R
Sodium chloride (solar process)	*f, h*	R	R
Sodium chloride (brine-mining process)	*e, g*	R	NPD
Sodium dichromate and sodium sulfate	*e, m*	R	NPD
Sodium metal	*d, g*	R	NPD
Sodium silicate	*d, h*	R	NPD
Sodium sulfite	*d, e*	R	NPD
Sulfuric acid	*a, b, c, e, g*	NPD	NPD
Titanium dioxide (chloride process)	*c, d, q*	R	R
Titanium dioxide (sulfate process)	*c, d, q*	R	R

NPD = no pollutant discharge.
R =
[a] Dry control of gaseous emissions.
[b] Marketing of recovered waste product.
[c] Neutralization.
[d] Clarification.
[e] Isolation and containment.
[f] Evaporation to recover product.
[g] Recycle to process.
[h] Pond evaporation
[i] Dryprocess technology.
[j] Conversion to indirect cooling.
[k] Oil separation.
[l] Oxidation.
[m] Ion exchange.
[n] Reduction.
[o] Incineration.
[p] Subsurface disposal.
[q] Recovery of by-products.

TOXIC POLLUTANT EFFLUENT STANDARDS

The Environmental Protection Agency was charged with the responsibility for the development of standards for toxic pollutants under the 1972 Water Pollution Control Act Amendments. A list was published in December, 1973, which identified the following substances as toxic pollutants: aldrin-dieldren (combined), benzidine (4-4′—diaminobiphenyl), cadmium, cyanide, DDT-DDD-DDE (combined), endrin, mercury, polychlorinated biphenyls and toxaphene.[28] The regulations accompanying the list were subsequently withdrawn for revision. The formulation of rational regulations for toxic pollutants is complicated by many factors including polymorphism, the influence of conditions in the ambient environment and the limited correlation of biological responses to chemical concentrations.

REFERENCES

1. The Chemical Industry and Pollution Control, *National Industrial Pollution Control Council Sub-Council Report,* June 1971.
2. Gowdy, F. W.: Process Wastewater Reduction and Reuse in a Petroleum Refinery, preprint for Environmental Water Technology—Reuse and Treatment of Wastewater Symp., ASME, March 1972.
3. Weston, Roy F., Inc.: "Development Document for Proposed Effluent Limitations Guidelines and New Source Performance Standards for the Major Organic Chemicals Manufacturing Point Source Category," U.S. Environmental Protection Agency, December 1973.
4. Conway, R. A., et al.: "Treatability of Wastewater from Organic Chemical and Plastics Manufacturing—Experience and Concepts," Res. and Dev. Dept., Union Carbide Corp., South Charleston, West Va., February 1973 as cited in Ref. 3.
5. Fox, R. D., R. T. Keller, C. J. Pinamount, and J. L. Severson: Purification of a Waste Brine by Carbon Adsorption with Emphasis on Wastewater Reuse, *Proc. 25th Industrial Waste Conf.*, Purdue Univ., Lafayette, Ind., pp. 322–330, May 1970.
6. Fox, R. D.: Pollution Control at the Source, *Chem. Engrg.*, vol. 80, no. 18, pp. 72–82, 1973.
7. Datagraphics, Incorporated: "Inorganic Chemicals Industry Profile (Updated)," U.S. Environmental Protection Agency, July 1971.
8. Lime Handling, Application and Storage, *Bull.* 213, National Lime Assn., Washington, D.C., May 1971.
9. Parsons, W. A.: "Chemical Treatment of Sewage and Industrial Wastes," National Lime Assn., Washington, D.C., 1965.
10. Judkins, J. F., Jr., and W. A. Parsons: Optimization of Acid Waste Sludge Characteristics, *J. Water Pollution Control Fed.*, vol. 41, no. 9, pp. 1625–1634, 1969.
11. Kostenbader, P. D., and G. F. Haines, Jr.: High Density Sludge Treats Acid Mine Drainage, *Coal Age,* vol. 75, no. 9, pp. 90–95, September 1970.
12. Smith, J. H., III: The Advantage of a Crowd for Acid Waste Liquors, *Mining Engrg.*, vol. 24, no. 12, pp. 57–59, December 1972.
13. Morgan, J. M.: "Optimization of Acid Waste Sludge Characteristics," M.S. thesis, Virginia Polytechnic Institute, Blacksburg, Va., September 1967.
14. Probstein, R. F.: Desalination, *American Scientist,* vol. 61, no. 3, pp. 280–293, May–June 1973.
15. General Technologies Corp.: "Development Document for Proposed Effluent Limitations Guidelines and New Source Performance Standards for the Major Inorganic Products Segment of the Inorganic Chemicals Manufacturing Point Source Category," U.S. Environmental Protection Agency, August 1973.
16. Manufacturing Chemists Assn.: Extraction Cuts Mercury from Wastewater, Solids, *Before . . . After Eco Action,* 1973.
17. Influent with Broad pH Narrowed to 6.5–8.5, *Chem. Processing,* vol. 36, no. 1, p. 14, January 1973.
18. Steinmetz, C. E., et al.: Blowdown Toxicity Banished in 90,000-gpd System, *Chem. Processing,* vol. 34, no. 9, p. 17, September 1971.
19. Evaporator Tackles Wastewater Treatment, *Chem. Engrg.*, vol. 79, no. 6, p. 68, Mar. 20, 1972.
20. "Projects of the Industrial Pollution Control Branch," U.S. Environmental Protection Agency, July 1971.
21. Gloyna, E. F., M. C. Herring, and D. L. Ford: Treatment of Complex Petrochemicals by Incineration and Waste Stabilization Ponds, *Proc. 25th Industrial Waste Conf.*, Purdue Univ., Lafayette, Ind., pp. 389–397, 1970.
22. Parrot, J. W., and W. M. Smith: Water Pollution Control at the Rohm and Haas Houston Plant, *Proc. 25th Industrial Water Conf.*, Purdue Univ., Lafayette, Ind., pp. 617–625, 1970.
23. American Chemical Society: Putting the Closed Loop into Practice, *Environmental Science and Technology,* vol. 6, no. 13, p. 1072, December 1972.
24. Manufacturing Chemists Assn.: Oxygenation Controls Odors, BOD from Fermentation, *Before . . . After Eco Action,* 1973.
25. Climenhage, D. Ch.: Biological Denitrification System, *Engrg. Digest,* vol. 19, no. 3, pp. 26–27, March 1973.
26. U.S. Environmental Protection Agency: Effluent Guidelines and Standards, Organic Chemicals Manufacturing Point Source Category, *Federal Register,* vol. 39, no. 81, pp. 14676–14685, Apr. 25, 1974.
27. U.S. Environmental Protection Agency: Effluent Guidelines and Standards, Inorganic Chemicals Manufacturing Point Source Category, *Federal Register,* vol. 39, no. 49, pp. 9612–9639, Mar. 12, 1974.
28. U.S. Environmental Protection Agency: Proposed Toxic Pollutant Effluent Standards, *Federal Register,* vol. 38, no. 247, pp. 35388–35395, December 27, 1973.

Chapter 8

Water Pollution Control in the Petroleum Industry

DAVIS L. FORD

Senior Vice President, Engineering-Science, Inc.,
Austin, Texas

INTRODUCTION

The increasing energy demand over the last four decades has resulted in a corresponding growth and expansion in the refining and processing of crude petroleum. The proliferation of refineries and petrochemical plants around the country, combined with the increasingly stringent quality requirements for effluents discharged from these facilities, has underscored the need for perfecting existing pollution control technology and developing improved approaches for minimizing the pollution potential in this sector of our production economy.

The purpose here is to consider the spectrum of topics which are pertinent in the control of refinery and petrochemical wastewaters. Although it is difficult to categorize the production facilities which discharge these effluents, applicable Standard Industrial Classification (SIC) numbers include the following:[1,6]

SIC Code	*Industry*
2911	Petroleum refining
2815	Cyclic intermediates, dyes, organic pigments, and crudes
2818	Organic chemicals
2819	Inorganic chemicals derived from petroleum
2821	Plastic material and resins

A petroleum refinery is comprised of many interrelated processes which generally separate, alter, and rebuild the crude molecular configuration into the desired products. These products include kerosene, gasoline, distillate fuel, residual fuel oil, and other miscellaneous products. The 12 processes as defined under SIC 2911, for example, include the following:

1. Storage and transportation
2. Crude desalting
3. Fractionation
4. Cracking
5. Hydrocarbon rebuilding
6. Hydrocarbon rearrangement
7. Solvent extraction or refining
8. Hydrotreating
9. Grease manufacturing
10. Asphalt production
11. Product finishing
12. Auxiliary activities

As of January 1, 1973, there were 247 operating petroleum refineries in the United States with a capacity of almost 14 million barrels of crude daily. A tabulation of these plants by states is shown in Table 1.[2]

A significant refinery expansion program is currently taking place in the United States. This is in response to increased demand. A change in this trend might occur, however, as crude supply limitations obviously influence refinery expansion decisions. This is underscored by the recent manifestation of the "energy crisis" and the impact of future Middle East embargoes and restrictions. As indicated in Fig. 1, however, an accelerated growth of refining has been predicted by some sources for the next 10 years.[3,4] The precision of this extrapolation is, of course, a function of many economic, political, and social factors and should be interpreted in this context. Within this constraint, a growth of 10 percent per year is indicated. The present best estimate of annual capital investment for this expansion is slightly in excess of $1 billion.

Although the ideal method in controlling petroleum refining and petrochemical wastewater discharges is to eliminate them at the source, process modifications and in-plant control practices are often rendered impractical from a technological and economic point of view. Therefore, physical, chemical, and biological treatment processes must be perfected and properly utilized to effectively remove the critical pollutants contained within these effluents.

The American Petroleum Institute (API) has classified petroleum refineries as follows:

Classification	*Refinery Type*
A	Topping plants
B	Topping and cracking plants
C	Topping, cracking, and petrochemical plants
D	Integrated plants (topping, cracking, catalytic cracking, plus lube processing)
E	Integrated and petrochemical plants

A reclassification of refineries proposed for the purpose of establishing effluent guidelines has recently been presented.[5] This categorization was proposed pursuant to effluent limitation guidelines, federal standards of performance, and pretreatment standards for the industry, to implement Sections 304, 306, and 307 of the Federal Water Pollution Control Act (P.L. 92–500). They are:

CATEGORY A. Refineries with topping or crude distillation processes only.

CATEGORY B-1. Refineries with topping and cracking operations. These refineries have a degree of cracking less than or equal to 50 percent of total crude charge

TABLE 1 Crude Capacity of Petroleum Refineries by State as of Jan. 1, 1973[2]

State	Number of plants	Rated crude capacity
Alabama	5	40,650
Alaska	4	56,300
Arkansas	4	47,800
California	34	1,796,700
Colorado	3	53,950
Delaware	1	150,000
Florida	1	5,500
Georgia	2	12,900
Hawaii	2	71,000
Illinois	11	1,088,500
Indiana	7	555,000
Kansas	11	405,500
Kentucky	3	165,400
Louisiana	18	1,606,200
Maryland	2	25,400
Michigan	6	134,190
Minnesota	3	178,500
Mississippi	5	328,700
Missouri	1	106,200
Montana	8	149,575
Nebraska	1	5,500
New Jersey	5	620,800
New Mexico	6	48,700
New York	2	106,000
North Dakota	2	55,000
Ohio	8	584,000
Oklahoma	12	474,000
Oregon	1	18,000
Pennsylvania	11	684,715
Rhode Island	1	10,000
Tennessee	1	30,000
Texas	40	3,645,550
Utah	5	125,000
Virginia	1	50,000
Washington	7	349,200
West Virginia	3	20,500
Wisconsin	1	36,500
Wyoming	9	149,750
Totals	247	13,991,580

capacity. The degree of cracking includes the capacity of the following operations: catalytic cracking, hydrocracking, thermal cracking, coking, and hydroprocessing. Also included in categories B-1 and B-2 are all conventional first-generation refinery associated products or intermediates, such as BTX, alkanes, alkenes, alkynes, and other miscellaneous items such as sulfur, hydrogen, coke, and ammonia.

CATEGORY B-2. Refineries with cracking capacities greater than 50 percent of the crude capacity.

CATEGORY C. Refineries with topping, cracking, and petrochemical operations. Petrochemicals excludes all first-generation conventional production, as described under category B. To qualify as a category C refinery, intermediate chemical produc-

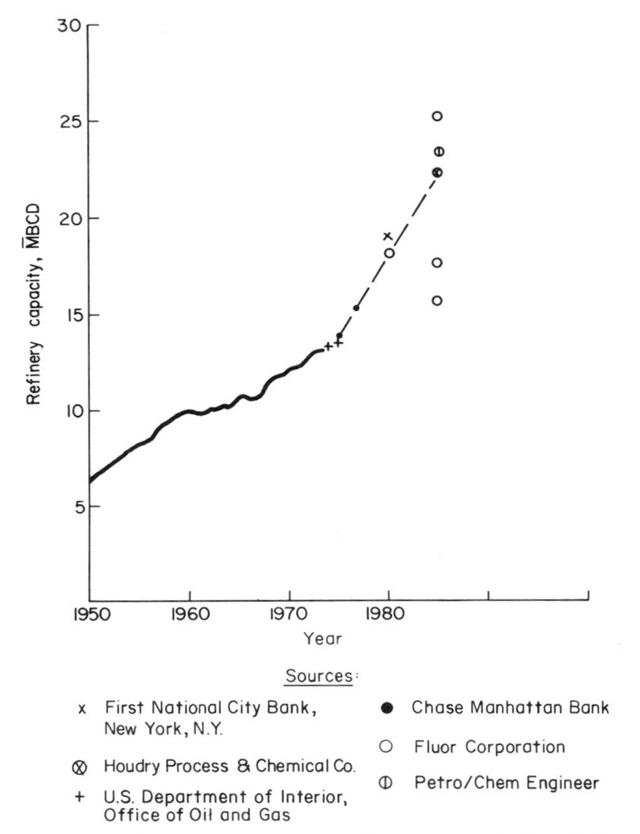

Fig. 1 Projected refining capacity in the continental United States.

tion must be shown, including such typical products as cumene, phthalic anhydride, alcohols, ketones, and styrene.

CATEGORY D. The operations under categories B-1, B-2, and C are expanded to include lubricating operations, which require the production of lubricating oil blending stocks via operations such as dewaxing or hydrotreating.

The first topic discussed is the characterization of wastewaters discharged from these production facilities. Effluent characterization information is used not only as a basis for conceiving and designing treatment systems, but also as the "yardstick" for monitoring and regulating discharge of pollutants and receiving bodies of water.

The second topic considered in this chapter is defining the sources of pollutional output within a refinery or petrochemical complex. As treatment systems must be designed to control all sources of wastewater pollutants which have either an immediate or potential deleterious effect on the receiving environment, a comprehensive understanding of source and magnitude is required. This includes process wastewaters, utility blowdowns, contaminated storm water runoff, ballast handling, and inordinate spills, and miscellaneous discharges.

Treatment processes are then discussed within the context of their effectiveness in handling refinery and petrochemical wastewaters. These unit processes are categorized in the general format used by API.[6] These are:

- Primary treatment
  - Gravity separation
- Intermediate treatment
  - Neutralization
  - Chemical coagulation-sedimentation
  - Dissolved air flotation
  - Filtration
- Final treatment (biological/physical/chemical)
  - Activated sludge
  - Aerated lagoons
  - Trickling filters
  - Cooling tower oxidation
  - Filtration
  - Carbon adsorption

Although the theoretical aspects of these processes and a detailed approach for their design are covered in the references, a description of their concepts, applicability, capacity, and process limitations in treating refinery and petrochemical wastewaters is included in this chapter.

The last segment of this treatise on control of refinery and petrochemical wastewaters is dedicated to water reuse. Although this always has been emphasized in the industrial decision-making process, recently passed federal pollution control legislation has underscored the importance of pollution control through recycling and reuse.[7]

CHARACTERIZATION AND SOURCE DEFINITION OF REFINERY AND PETROCHEMICAL WASTEWATERS

The characterization of refinery and petrochemical wastewaters in terms of flow, organic constituents, and inorganic constituents is the real basis for in-plant segregation and control, treatment process sizings, system operational control, and effluent regulation. The representativeness of the sampling, the techniques of sample preservation, and the methods of analysis all dictate the overall accuracy of the characterization program. It also should be recognized that the volume of wastewater discharged as well as the analyses indicating the organic and inorganic components require statistical validity before making major process decisions which are predicated on characterization information.

Development of Wastewater Flow Information

The volume and loading of wastewater discharged from industrial production or processing units are of paramount importance in identifying pollution sources, while the flow from the total complex dictates the hydraulic design features of a treatment system and indicates the potential for water conservation.

The most fundamental approach in expressing wastewater flow from a refinery or petrochemical complex is in terms of crude throughput. This flow from a refinery-petrochemical complex or from an individual process unit can be measured using the commonly accepted methods such as weirs, flumes, flowmeters, or some less-sophisticated approach to flow calculations. This flow can then be expressed in terms of crude throughput or some applicable measurement of production capacity. The effect of shift change, weekend operation, and process variation should be considered in the flow measurement program to reflect a true picture. It also should be recognized that other flows not involved with process or cooling but which require treatment are common to many refineries. This includes ballast blowdown, storm water runoff, and inordinate dumps, spills, or washdowns. Proper allowance for these wastewaters in terms of treatment capacity should be made. This subject is more thoroughly discussed in subsequent portions of this chapter.

Definition of Wastewater Constituents

Parameters used to characterize refinery and petrochemical wastewaters can be categorized as organic and inorganic analyses. The organic content of wastewater is estimated in terms of oxygen demand using biochemical oxygen demand (BOD), chemical oxygen demand (COD), or total oxygen demand (TOD). Additionally, the organic fraction can be expressed in terms of carbon using total organic carbon (TOC). It should be recognized that these parameters do not necessarily measure the same constituents. Specifically, they reflect the following:

BOD—Biodegradable organics in terms of oxygen demand
COD—Organics amenable to chemical oxidation as well as certain inorganics (such as sulfides, sulfites, ferrous iron, chlorides, and nitrites)
TOD—All organics and some inorganics in terms of oxygen demand
TOC—All organic carbon expressed as carbon

The inorganic characterization schedule for these wastewaters should include those tests which provide information concerning:

1. Potential toxicity, such as heavy metals, ammonia, etc.
2. Potential inhibitors, such as total dissolved solids (TDS), chlorides, sulfates, etc.
3. Contaminants requiring specific pretreatment such as pH, alkalinity, acidity, suspended solids, etc.

A brief discussion of some of the more pertinent aspects of these parameters is included.

Organic parameters

Biochemical Oxygen Demand (BOD). The BOD is an estimate of the amount of oxygen required to stabilize biodegradable organic materials in a refinery or petrochemical wastewater by an acclimated microbial population. The general procedures for performing the BOD tests are described in "Standard Methods for the Examination of Water and Sewage."[8] The BOD, however, is subject to many variables and constraints, particularly when considering complex petrochemical wastes. These are discussed as follows:

1. *Time of incubation.* The importance of the incubation time variable is indicated in the basic BOD equation. The usual time is taken as 5 days, although the time for complete stabilization to occur (the ultimate BOD) will depend on the nature of the substrate and the viability of the seed microorganisms. Many hydrocarbons can be substantially degraded in 20 days and the 20-day BOD is considered the ultimate BOD in various applications. For example, the ultimate oxygen demand in many receiving bodies of water is predicated on 20-day values, and the effluent quality criteria are therefore expressed in terms of 20-day BOD. It should be recognized, however, that many organic compounds require longer periods of time before the ultimate oxygen demand is satisfied biologically. For example, recently published BOD curves for tertiary butyl alcohol (TBA) using acclimated seed indicated that 2 percent of the theoretical yield occurred in 5 days, approximately 65 percent occurred in 20 days, and the ultimate demand was satisfied in excess of 30 days.[9] Based on these data, the oxygen requirement for a long-term biological detention basin receiving substantial quantities of TBA could be underestimated if based on 5- or 20-day BOD values. This underscores the importance of properly assessing the BOD time variable with respect to the ultimate oxygen demand.

2. *Nitrification.* The oxygen demand is generally exerted by carbonaceous materials during the first 5 to 10 days with a second-stage demand being exerted by nitrogenous materials. The nitrification rate constants are much lower than those for carbonaceous destruction; and, although the two reactions may occur simultaneously, the nitrification demand is not normally conspicuous until the carbonaceous demand has been satisfied substantially. The measurement of oxygen demand exerted by the carbonaceous fraction of the waste can be isolated in one of two ways; namely, by retarding nitrification in the test bottle by the addition of nitrifying inhibitors, or by allowing nitrification to occur and subtracting its demand from the overall result. It should be noted that the nitrogenous oxygen demand is usually a significant portion of the ultimate BOD when considering refinery and petrochemical wastewaters due to the presence of oxidizable nitrogen in the form of ammonia, nitrites, and nitrogen functional groups.

3. *Seed acclimation.* The use of a biological seed which is not properly acclimated to the test sample is probably the factor most commonly responsible for erroneous results reported for refinery and petrochemical wastewaters. For example, the 5-day BOD value of an acrylamide monomer was determined using a properly acclimated seed and a sewage seed. The 5-day BOD value obtained using the sewage seed was only 17 percent of the value reported using the acclimated seed.[10] Even a microbial seed which is acclimated to a compound closely related in structure to the test compound may not give the highest possible BOD value. The 5-day BOD yield from the acrylamide monomer using a microbial seed acclimated to acrylonitrile was only 22 percent of the value obtained with the monomer acclimated seed. A biological seed should be developed in a continuous or batch laboratory reactor (preferably the former) by feeding the diluted wastewater in question to the initial microbial seed. The waste composition is increased to full strength over a period of time and, once the organic removal or oxygen uptake in the reactor reaches the maximum level, the seed can be considered acclimated. The time required to obtain this acclimation depends on the nature of the seed and wastewater. For most refinery wastewaters, this period is less than 1 week. However, for wastes containing high concentrations of complex organic compounds (such as those discharged from petrochemical operations), a period of several weeks may be required.

4. *Toxicity.* The presence of toxic materials in the wastewater sample may have a biotoxic or biostatic effect on the seed microorganisms. This effect is usually evidenced by "sliding" BOD values where the BOD yield increases with increasing sample dilution. Once there is the indication of the presence of toxic materials, steps should be taken to identify and remove the toxicants or use dilution values above which the BOD yields are consistent. Constituents in refinery and petrochemical wastewaters which interfere with the BOD test include such substances as chlorinated hydrocarbons and heavy metals.

Chemical Oxygen Demand (COD). The COD is a measure of the oxygen equivalent of those constituents in a sample which are susceptible to permanganate or dichromate oxidation in an acid solution. Although it is independent of many of the variables which affect the BOD test, there are still factors which influence the COD value of the sample in question. Although many soluble hydrocarbons are completely oxidized by dichromate in the COD test, some of the more stable compounds are not measured. Benzene, for example, is a significant petrochemical pollutant which is resistant to dichromate oxidation. It should be emphasized that the silver sulfate catalyst is necessary for dichromate oxidation of most straight-chain hydrocarbons.

Total Organic Carbon (TOC). Although TOC is a parameter that has been applied in the field for many years, the advent of the carbon analyzer has provided a rapid and simple method for determining organic carbon levels in aqueous samples, enhancing the popularity of TOC as a fundamental measure of pollution. The organic carbon determination is free of the many variables inherent in COD or BOD analyses, with more reliable and reproducible data being the net result.[11] As the analysis time using the carbon analyzer is only several minutes, the efficacy of using this parameter is apparent particularly when a TOC/COD or TOC/BOD correlation can be established.

Total Oxygen Demand (TOD). Another analyzer has been developed to measure the amount of oxygen required to combust the impurities in an aqueous sample. This measurement is achieved by providing a continuous analysis of the oxygen concentration present in a nitrogen carrier gas. The oxidizable constituents in the liquid are converted to their stable oxides in a platinum-catalyzed combustion chamber. This disturbs the oxygen equilibrium at the platinum surface which is restored by the oxygen in the carrier gas stream. This depletion is detected by a silver-lead fuel cell and is recorded as a negative peak related to the oxygen demand of the sample. The TOD method measures the amount of oxygen consumed in the chemical reactions shown in Table 2.[12] The TOD and TOC analyzers have similar applications, the output data being correlated to COD and BOD values when possible.

Other Organic Parameters

1. *Oil and grease.* One of the more important parameters applied in characterizing refinery and petrochemical wastewaters is the oil and grease measurement. This

is particularly true since oils have both a recovery value and a deleterious effect on treatment systems and receiving bodies of water.

The definition of oil and grease is based on the analytical procedure employed and depends on the source, the test solvent used, the sample-to-solvent ratio, the pH of the sample, and the analytical inclusion of nonoily material.[13] The most widely accepted methods for measurement of oil and grease are tabulated in Table 3. While these methods are recognized within their respective society or institute, the method applied must also conform to the regulatory agency which controls effluent quality in a specific area.

A second definition relating to oil commonly discharged from refinery and petrochemical facilities can be made in terms of its phase. Oil may be free, emulsified, or soluble. A phase separation must take place prior to analyzing the oil using one of the methods cited in Table 3. The methods used to separate these oil phases are discussed as follows:

TOTAL OIL. Determine the oil content of the raw wastewater sample.

FREE OIL. Place a measured amount of wastewater in a separatory funnel and shake vigorously; then let the sample stand quiescently for 2 hr. Draw off the subnatant (aqueous layer) and determine its oil content. The oil measured is the emulsified and soluble oil fraction. The difference between the total oil content and that measured is the free oil content of the wastewater sample.

SOLUBLE OIL. Place a measured amount of wastewater in a separatory funnel and acidify with 10 ml concentrated hydrochloric acid. Next add 200 g/l sodium chloride and 5 g/l diatomaceous earth. Shake the mixture vigorously and let stand 8 hr or more. Filter the mixture through a wet filter paper and measure the oil content of the filtrate. The oil content measured is the soluble oil fraction of the wastewater oil content.

TABLE 2 Total Oxygen Demand Reactions[12]

Reaction	Highest stable oxidation state	Percent reaction efficiency
$C + O_2$	CO_2	95–100
$H_2 + \frac{1}{2}O_2$	H_2O	95–100
$N^{+3} + \frac{1}{2}O_2$	NO	95
$S^{-2} + 2O_2$	SO_4^{-2}	78
$SO_3^{-2} + \frac{1}{2}O_2$	SO_4^{-2}	72

EMULSIFIED OIL. The difference between the oil content measured as emulsified and soluble oil, and the soluble oil content is the emulsified oil content.

According to information recently cited, a typical refinery effluent oil concentration would be approximately 70 percent free, 25 percent emulsified, and 5 percent soluble oil.[14]

2. *Phenolic compounds*. Phenols and related compounds are generally prevalent in refinery and petrochemical wastewaters and are of particular significance since they are potentially toxic to marine life, create an oxygen demand in receiving waters, and impart a taste to drinking water with even minute concentrations of their chlorinated derivatives. Primary sources of phenolics in wastewaters are from benzene refining plants, oil refineries, coke plants, chemical operations, and plants which are processing phenols to plastics.

Phenols, or the hydroxy derivatives of benzene, are measured using the distillation approach as per "Standard Methods"[8] or by other miscellaneous colorimetric, spectroscopic, or chromatographic techniques. A rapid, precise, and selective method using ultraviolet differential adsorption has also been reported recently.[15]

Inorganic parameters There are many inorganic parameters which are pertinent when determining potential toxicity, general characterization, or process response. Although the evaluation of any number of inorganic analyses may be required for a particular situation, some of the more prevalent analyses are considered herein.

TABLE 3 Methods for Determination of Oil in Water and Wastewater

Society or Institute	Method name and designation	Solvent used	Solvent boiling point, °C	Method description	Interference material
American Public Health Assn., American Water Works Assn., and Water Pollution Control Federation (2)	Oil and Grease	Petroleum ether	35–60	Direct extraction	
	Grease	*n*-hexane	69	Soxhlet extraction method	Elemental sulfur and organic dyes
American Society for Testing and Materials (ASTM) (1)	Oily Matter in Industrial Wastewater	Benzene, carbon tetrachloride, or chloroform	60–80	Distillation of volatile oils followed by direct extraction	Phenolic-type material and colloidal sulfur
American Petroleum Institute (API)	Volatile and Nonvolatile Oily Material, Method 731-53	Benzene	80	Distillation of volatile oils followed by direct extraction	Alcohols, cresols, and organic acids
(3)	Nonvolatile Oily Material, Method 732-53	Ethyl ether	35	Ferric hydroxide flocculation followed by direct extraction of oil from floc by solvent	Elemental sulfur and chlorophyll
(4)	A Safe Solvent for Oil and Grease Analysis	Freon ($CCl_2F-CClF_2$)	48	Direct or soxhlet extraction	

Acidity. The acidity of a wastewater, or its capacity to donate protons, is important because a neutral or near-neutral water is required before biological treatment can be deemed effective, and many regulatory authorities have criteria which establish strict pH limits for final discharges. Acidity in a refinery or petrochemical wastewater can be contributed by both organic and inorganic compound dissociation. Most mineral acids found in petrochemical wastes are typically strong acids, such as sulfuric, nitric, or phosphoric. Weaker acids common to these wastewaters include carboxylic acid and carbonic acid.

Alkalinity. Alkalinity of a wastewater is often defined as its acid-consuming ability and is measured by titrating a given volume of waste with a standardized acid until all of the alkaline material has reacted to form salts.

Both organic and inorganic compounds can contribute alkalinity, but the most important alkaline wastes in the petrochemical industry are the spent caustics containing sodium, calcium, and potassium salts. Other process wastes, such as nitrogen in the ammonia form, can contribute to the alkalinity of a solution.

Inorganic Ions. In many cases it is important to measure the inorganic dissolved anions in solution such as chlorides, sulfates, nitrates, and phosphates. This is particularly important in quality control of cooling tower and boiler blowdown waters. Moreover, regulatory agencies are controlling dissolved salt concentrations in effluents, particularly when discharged to fresh receiving waters.

Ammonia Nitrogen and Sulfides. Ammonia nitrogen and sulfides are normally present in refinery effluents resulting from the use of steam in the refining process. The condensation of steam in the presence of a hydrocarbon vapor phase containing NH_3 and H_2S is the primary source of these contaminants depending on the process, feedstock origin, and pressure level at which the steam is condensed.[16]

Ammonia nitrogen is usually measured by controlled distillation with titration of the distillate which is held in an acid solution.[10] It should be recognized that other constituents common to these wastewaters (such as amines, alcohols, and sulfides) can interfere with the results.

Sulfide-laden waters, or "sour water," are common in refinery effluents and, if no in-plant control through sulfide stripping is practiced, impart a significant immediate oxygen demand (IOD) to the total discharge. Hydrogen sulfide is also corrosive and causes an objectionable taste and odor in the water.

Sulfides usually are measured colorimetrically although alternative analytical techniques are available.[8]

Miscellaneous parameters

Surface Active Substances. Surface active compounds are those which tend to concentrate at the gas/liquid interface, the molecular arrangement being such that a film is formed. Surface active agents contain two important functional groups: one water soluble and the other oil soluble. The water soluble or hydrophilic group may be composed of one of four general types of polar groups:

1. Anionic groups consisting of sulfonates, sulfates, and carboxylic acid groups
2. Cationic groups, such as amine salts and ammonium compounds
3. Amphoteric groups in which the molecule contains both anionic and cationic groups
4. Nonionic groups which do not ionize but are water soluble, such as alcohols and glycols which are commonly found in refinery and petrochemical effluents

Various laboratory procedures are available for the determination of synthetic detergents in water.[8] Other surface active chemicals (sulfonic acids, carboxylic acids, etc.) must be determined by laboratory analyses which are not commonly used as pollutional parameters.

Taste and Odor. Methods used to classify and measure taste and odor in wastewaters are strictly arbitrary and most involve the use of human testers who determine the dilution required to make the taste and odor of a particular wastewater satisfactory. Since taste and odor are human senses, this is probably the most suitable method for their determination. Another possibility is the isolation, identification, and measurement of substances which cause taste and odor, but this procedure is currently impractical.

Temperature. Thermal pollution is a serious problem within refinery and petrochemical installations, primarily attributable to blowdown of various condensates and boiler and cooling waters. As maximum water temperatures are established by regulatory agencies because of deleterious effects on receiving waters, cooling is often an integral part of the treatment system requirements.

Heavy Metals. Heavy metallic ions are generally common to refinery and petrochemical wastewaters resulting from corrosion-inhibitor additives, catalyst usage, product additives, and laboratory and instrument wastage. As the potential or real impact of these constituents on the receiving environment is significant, there is a continuing emphasis on their detection and control.

Several techniques for heavy-metal analysis are given in "Standard Methods."[8] Atomic absorption flame photometry can also be used quantitatively to detect small quantities of metals. This method is based on the measurement of light adsorbed at a given wavelength.[17]

Color and Turbidity. Color and turbidity are physical properties related to the concentration of certain solutes and suspended particles in wastewaters. Many of the wastes produced by the petrochemical industry contain color-producing compounds.

Color in wastewater, true and apparent, can be attributed to two types of physical phenomena. Certain materials in solution or suspension in water will absorb incident light and the wavelengths of visible light absorbed will determine the color of the liquid. The other color effect is caused by the scattering of incident light by colloidal or suspended materials. Liquids which exhibit this light-scattering effect are termed *turbid.* Both of these effects are highly undesirable in waters receiving waste effluents. Color and turbidity diminish light penetration in natural waters, and also affect the domestic use of water in that they must be removed prior to public acceptance. This removal process often adds great expense to water treatment costs.

Color in water is measured by comparing the sample with a standard cobalt-platinum solution. Turbidity is measured by using several different types of proprietary instruments which measure either scattered or transmitted light. Color which is caused by dissolved contaminants is often termed *true color* and color caused by petrochemical wastes is predominantly of this type. Color caused by suspended or colloidal material is referred to as *apparent color.*

REFINERY AND PETROCHEMICAL SOURCE AND QUALITY ANALYSIS

The first consideration in the evaluation of a plant effluent which leads to conceptualization and engineering of the treatment system is locating source flows and estimating their characteristics. This evaluation must be made not only for current effluent levels but also for future wastewater flows. A logical approach in formulating these estimates is to categorize contributive pollutional inputs into logical source components. These components as defined by the author are:

NORMAL PROCESS OPERATIONS. Discharged directly from production units.

UTILITY OPERATIONS. Blowdown from boiler and cooling systems.

SANITARY SEWAGE. Sewage from administrative areas, control houses, and locker and shower facilities.

CONTAMINATED STORM RUNOFF. Runoff from process areas requiring treatment.

BALLAST WATER BLOWDOWN. Dirty ballast discharged from tankers receiving product.

MISCELLANEOUS DISCHARGES. Resulting from inordinate discharges, spills, turnarounds, etc.

Each of these components as graphically depicted in Fig. 2 will be discussed individually.

Process Operations

The many combinations of process operation, type of crude charge, and age of plant make it difficult to classify a refinery-petrochemical wastewater as "typical." Intraplant differences in effluent segregation systems, in-plant treatment systems, and process design, operation, and maintenance also contribute to these variations.

The most commonly used method for predicting the quality of these wastewaters is to relate the quantity and quality of pollutant produced by a unit process to production units. The inherent nature of production and processing, however, mitigates this approach. Nevertheless, this information combined with general effluent characterization data offers an overall knowledge of pollutants which are present and their concentration range.

The American Petroleum Institute Refinery Effluent Profile has tabulated process flow in terms of production units for the five refinery classifications based on questionnaire responses as shown in Table 4. The wide range is primarily attributable to water use for cooling purposes as this accounts for approximately 70 percent of refinery water demand.[18] Once-through cooling, for example, as practiced in many refineries would keep the effluent volume based on crude throughput on the high side, while water conservation through recycle and reuse would reduce this value to the low side of the scale. A similar representation in terms of quality for eight process operations is shown in Table 5.[19]

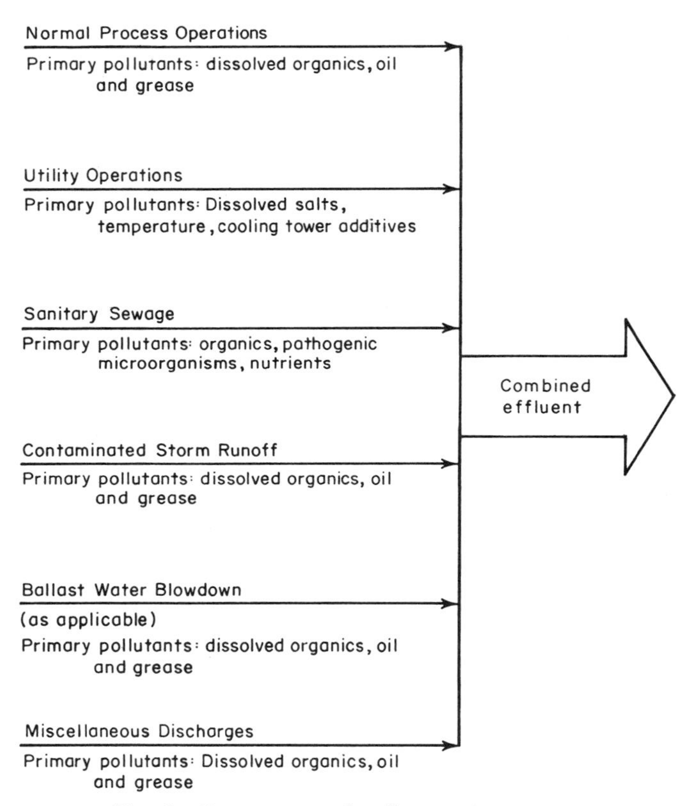

Fig. 2 Components of pollutants by source.

TABLE 4 Wastewater Discharge as a Function of Crude Throughput

Refinery classification	Number of refineries reporting	Gallons of effluent per barrel of crude throughput		
		Maximum	Minimum	Average
A	15	499.8	0.4	57.5
B	70	1,658.6	2.1	116.3
C	20	1,399.9	17.6	181.0
D	18	759.4	14.8	143.4
E	4	1,700.2	32.8	410.1

TABLE 5 Waste Loadings and Volumes per Unit of Fundamental Process Throughput in Older, Typical, and Newer Technologies[19]

Fundamental process	Older technology				Typical technology				Newer technology			
	Flow, gal/bbl	BOD, lb/bbl	Phenol, lb/bbl	Sulfides, lb/bbl	Flow, gal/bbl	BOD, lb/bbl	Phenol, lb/bbl	Sulfides, lb/bbl	Flow, gal/bbl	BOD, lb/bbl	Phenol, lb/bbl	Sulfides, lb/bbl
Crude oil and product storage	4	0.001	*	*	4	0.001	*	*	4	0.001	*	*
Crude desalting	2	0.002	0.20	0.002	2	0.002	0.10	0.002	2	0.002	0.05	0.002
Crude fractionation	100	0.020	3.0	0.001	50	0.0002	1.0	0.001	10	0.0002	1.0	0.001
Thermal cracking	66	0.001	7.0	0.002	2	0.001	0.2	0.001	1.5	0.001	0.2	0.001
Catalytic cracking	85	0.062	50.0	0.03	30	0.010	20	0.003	5	0.010	5	0.003
Hydrocracking	Not in this technology				Not in this technology				5	*	*	*
Reforming	9	t	0.7	t	6	t	0.7	0.001	6	t	0.7	0.001
Polymerization	300	0.003	1.4	0.22	140	0.003	0.4	0.010	Not in this technology			
Alkylation	173	0.001	0.1	0.005	60	0.001	0.1	0.010	20	0.001	0.1	0.020
Isomerization	Not in this technology				Not in this technology				*	*	*	*
Solvent refining	8	*	3	t	8	*	3	t	8	*	3	t
Dewaxing	247	0.52	2	t	23	0.50	1.5	t	20	0.25	1.5	t
Hydrotreating	1	0.002	0.6	0.007	1	0.002	0.01	0.002	8	0.002	0.01	0.002
Deasphalting	*	*	*	*	*	*	*	*	*	*	*	*
Drying and sweetening	100	0.10	10	*	40	0.05	10	*	40	0.05	10	*
Wax finishing	*	*	*	*	*	*	*	*	*	*	*	*
Grease manufacturing	*	*	*	*	*	*	*	*	*	*	*	*
Lube oil finishing	*	*	*	*	*	*	*	*	*	*	*	*
Hydrogen manufacture	Not in this technology				Not in this technology				*	*	*	*
Blending and packaging	*	*	*	*	*	*	*	*	*	*	*	*

t = trace.
* Data not available for reasonable estimate.

A general list of pollutants associated with petrochemical processes is tabulated in Table 6.[1] Concentration ranges reported for petrochemical and chemical production are included in Table 7.[1] The wastewater characteristics in terms of the parameters previously cited for selected process operations are given in Table 8.[1] Information such as this is indicative of wastewater characteristics which might be expected

TABLE 6 Petrochemical Process as Waste Sources[1]

Process	Source	Pollutants
Alkylation ethylbenzene		Tar, hydrochloric acid, caustic soda, fuel oil
Ammonia production	Demineralization	Acids, bases
	Regeneration process condensates	Ammonia
	Furnace effluents	Carbon dioxide, carbon monoxide
Aromatics recovery	Extract water	Aromatic hydrocarbons
	Solvent purification	Solvents—sulfur dioxide, diethylene glycol
Catalytic cracking	Catalyst regeneration	Spent catalyst, catalyst fines (silica alumina hydrocarbons, carbon monoxide, nitrogen oxides)
	Reactor effluents and condensates	Acids, phenolic compounds, hydrogen sulfide soluble hydrocarbons, sulfur oxides
Catalytic reforming	Condensates	Catalyst (particularly Pt, Mo), aromatic hydrocarbons, hydrogen sulfide, ammonia
Crude processing	Crude washing	Inorganic salts, oils, water soluble hydrocarbons
	Primary distillation	Hydrocarbons, tars, ammonia, acids, hydrogen sulfide
Cyanide production	Water slops	Hydrogen cyanide, unreacted soluble hydrocarbons
Dehydrogenation:		
Butadiene products from *n*-butane and butylene	Quench waters	Residue gas, tars, oils, soluble hydrocarbons
Ketone production	Distillation slops	Hydrogen polymers, chlorinated hydrocarbons, glycerol, sodium chloride
Styrene from ethylbenzene	Catalyst	Spent catalyst (Fe, Mg, K, Cu, Cr, Zn)
	Condensates from spray tower	Aromatic hydrocarbons, including styrene, ethyl benzene, and toluene, tars
Desulfurization		Hydrogen sulfide, mercaptans
Extraction and purification:		
Isobutylene	Acid and caustic wastes	Sulfuric acid, C_4 hydrocarbon, caustic soda
Butylene	Solvent and caustic wash	Acetone, oils, C_4 hydrocarbon, caustic soda, sulfuric acid
Styrene	Still bottoms	Heavy tars
Butadiene absorption	Solvent	Cuprous ammonium acetate, C_4 hydrocarbons, oils
Extractive distillation	Solvent	Furfural, C_4 hydrocarbons
Halogenation (principally chlorination):		
Addition to olefins	Separator	Spent caustic
Substitution	HCl absorber, scrubber	Chlorine, hydrogen chloride, spent caustic hydrocarbon isomers and chlorinated products, oils

TABLE 6 Petrochemical Process as Waste Sources[1] (Continued)

Process	Source	Pollutants
	Dehydrohalogenation	Dilute salt pollution
Hypochlorination	Hydrolysis	Calcium chloride, soluble organics, tars
Hydrochlorination	Surge tank	Tars, spent catalyst, alkyl halides
Hydrocarboxylation (OXO process)	Still slops	Soluble hydrocarbons, aldehydes
Hydrocyanation (for acrylonitrile, adipic acid, etc.)	Process effluents	Cyanides, organic and inorganic
Isomerization in general	Process wastes	Hydrocarbons; aliphatic, aromatic, and derivative tars
Nitration:		
Parafins		By-product aldehydes, ketones, acids, alcohols, olefins, carbon dioxide
Aromatics		Sulfuric acid, nitric acid, aromatics
Oxidation:		
Ethylene oxide and glycol manufacture	Process slops	Calcium chloride, spent lime, hydrocarbon polymers, ethylene oxide, glycols, dichloride
Aldehydes, alcohols, and acids from hydrocarbons	Process slops	Acetone, formaldehyde, acetaldehyde, methanol, higher alcohols, organic acids
Acids and anhydrides from aromatic oxidation	Condensates, still slops	Anhydrides, aromatics, acids, pitch
Phenol and acetone from aromatic oxidation	Decanter	Formic acid, hydrocarbons
Carbon black manufacture	Cooling, quenching	Carbon black, particulates, dissolved solids
Polymerization, alkylation	Catalysts	Spent acid catalysts (phosphoric acid, aluminum chloride)
Polymerization (polyethylene:	Catalysts	Chromium, nickel, cobalt, molybdenum
Butyl rubber	Process wastes	Scrap butyl, oil, light hydrocarbons
Copolymer rubber	Process wastes	Butadiene, styrene serum, softener sludge
Nylon 66	Process wastes	Cyclohexane oxidation products, succinic acid, adipic acid, glutaric acid, hexamethylene, diamine, adiponitrile, acetone, methyl ethyl ketone
Sulfation of olefins		Alcohols, polymerized hydrocarbons, sodium sulfate, ethers
Sulfonation of aromatics	Caustic wash	Spent caustic
Thermal cracking for olefin production (including fractionation and purification)	Furnace effluent and caustic treating	Acids, hydrogen sulfide, mercaptans, soluble hydrocarbons, polymerization products, spent caustic, phenolic compounds, residue gases, tars and heavy oils
Utilities	Boiler blowdown	Phosphates, lignins, heat, total dissolved solids, tannins
	Cooling system blowdown	Chromates, phosphates, algicides, heat
	Water treatment	Calcium and magnesium chlorides, sulfates, carbonates

TABLE 7 Wastewater Characteristics Associated with Some Chemical Products[1]

Material	Flow, gal/ton	BOD, mg/l	COD, mg/l	Other characteristics
Primary petrochemicals:				
Ethylene	50–1,500	100–1,000	500–3,000	Phenol, pH, oil
Propylene	100–2,000	100–1,000	500–3,000	Phenol, pH
Primary intermediates:				
Toluene	300–3,000	300–2,500	1,000–5,000	
Xylene	200–3,000	500–4,000	1,000–8,000	
Ammonia	300–3,000	25–100	50–250	Oil, nitrogen
Methanol	300–3,000	300–1,000	300–2,000	Oil
Ethanol	300–4,000	300–3,000	1,000–4,000	Oil, solids
Butanol	200–2,000	500–4,000	1,000–8,000	Heavy metals
Ethyl benzene	300–3,000	500–3,000	1,000–7,000	Heavy metals
Chlorinate hydrocarbons	50–1,000	50–150	100–500	pH, oil, solids
Secondary intermediates:				
Phenol, cumene	500–2,500	1,200–10,000	2,000–15,000	Phenol, solids
Acetone	500–1,500	1,000–5,000	2,000–10,000	
Glycerin, glycols	1,000–5,000	500–3,500	1,000–7,000	
Urea	100–2,000	50–300	100–500	
Acetic anhydride	1,000–8,000	300–5,000	500–8,000	pH
Terephthalic acid	1,000–3,000	1,000–3,000	2,000–4,000	Heavy metals
Acrylates	1,000–3,000	500–5,000	2,000–15,000	Solids, color, cyanide
Acrilonitrile	1,000–10,000	200–700	500–1,500	Color, cyanide, pH
Butadiene	100–2,000	25–200	100–400	Oil, solids
Styrene	1,000–10,000	300–3,000	1,000–6,000	
Vinyl chloride	10–200	200–2,000	500–5,000	
Primary polymers:				
Polyethylene	400–1,600		200–4,000	Solids
Polypropylene	400–1,600		200–4,000	
Polystyrene	500–1,000		1,000–3,000	Solids
Polyvinylchloride	1,500–3,000	50–500	1,000–2,000	
Cellulose acetate	10–200	500–2,000	1,000–5,000	
Butyl rubber	2,000–6,000	800–2,000	2,500–5,000	
Dyes and pigments:	50,000–250,000	200–400	500–2,000	Heavy metals, color, solids, pH
Miscellaneous organics:				
Isocyanate	5,000–10,000	1,000–2,500	4,000–8,000	Nitrogen
Phenyl glycine	5,000–10,000	1,000–2,500	4,000–8,000	Phenol
Parathion	3,000–8,000	1,500–3,500	3,000–6,000	Solids, pH
Tributyl phosphate	1,000–4,000	500–2,000	1,000–3,000	Phosphorus

TABLE 8 Typical Waste Characteristics[1]

	Spent Caustic Stream			
Characteristics	Benzene sulfonation scrubbing	Orthophenyl-phenol washing	Alkylate washing	Polymer-ization
Alkalinity, mg/l	33,800	18,400	46,250	209,330
BOD, mg/l	53,600	18,400	256	8,440
COD, mg/l	112,000	67,600	3,230	50,350
H_2S, mg/l				
pH	13.2	9–12	12.8	12.7
Phenols, mg/l	8.3	5,500	50	22.2
NaOH, wt %	1	0.2–0.5		
Na_2SO_4, wt %	1.5–2.5			
Sulfates, mg/l	3,760	2,440		
Sulfides, mg/l			2	3,060
Sulfites, mg/l	7,100	4,720		
Total solids, mg/l	90,300	40,800		

TABLE 8 Typical Waste Characteristics[1] (Continued)

PROCESS WASTE

Characteristic	Crude desalting	Catalytic cracking	Naphtha cracking	Sour condensates from distillation, cracking, etc.
Ammonia, mg/l	80			135–6,550
BOD, mg/l	60–610	230–440		500–1,000
COD, mg/l	124–470	500–2,800	53–180	500–2,000
Oil, mg/l	20–516	200–2,600	160	100–1,000
pH, mg/l	7.2–9.1			4.5–9.5
Phenols, mg/l	10–25	20–26	6–10	100–1,000
Salt (as NaCl), wt %	0.4–25			
Sulfides, mg/l	0–13			390–8,250 (H_2S)

ACID WASTE

Characteristic	Acid wash-alkylation	Acid wash-phenol still bottoms	Acid wash-orthophenyl-phenol	Sulfite wash liquid OP-phenol distillation
Acidity, mg/l	1,105–12,325		24,120	675
BOD, mg/l	31	20,800	13,600	105,000
COD, mg/l	1,251	248,000	23,400	689,000
Dissolved solids, mg/l		340,500	81,300	176,800
Oil, mg/l	131.5			
pH	0.6–1.9	1.0	1.1	3.8
Phenols, mg/l		3,800	1,500	16,400
Sulfate, mg/l			54,700	
Sulfite, mg/l		34,800	2,920	74,000
Total solids, mg/l		403,200	81,600	176,900

from specified operations and can be applied as a basis for programming wastewater surveys and preliminary engineering designs. Information recently obtained in a unit-by-unit production survey in three refinery-petrochemical installations has indicated the main source of organic output. The BOD from eight sampling points within a refinery complex representing over 90 percent of the total process BOD contribution is shown in Fig. 3.[20] A similar representation of organic output from production units in terms of COD is shown in Fig. 4.[20] The relative contribution of COD and oil reported in a comprehensive wastewater survey is shown in Fig. 5.[20]

Utility Operations

Utility operations which are an integral part of any refinery-petrochemical complex contribute to the wastewater flow in the form of blowdown. The primary sources of this blowdown are from boilers, process steam generators, and cooling towers.

It is necessary to control excessive scaling and fouling of tubes in boilers and process steam generators. This is accomplished by limiting the solids and alkalinity concentrations within the boiler or steam generator drums. When treated makeup water is fed to the system, a portion of the water is blown down. Although the volume of blowdown will vary, approximately 5 percent of the water used to produce the steam can be expected as blowdown flow. Although this generally represents a small part of the utility flow when compared to cooling tower blowdown, their constituents may be significant if the combined flow is marginal in terms of meeting certain quality requirements. The American Boiler Manufacturers' Association recommends that water within steam drums be maintained at the quality limits shown in

Table 9.[21] Providing these limits are maintained, they represent the quality of the boiler blowdown. Typical quality data of boiler blowdown from a refinery recently surveyed are shown in Table 10.

Blowdown water from cooling towers represents a sizable portion of the combined flow, and certainly the preponderance of the utility blowdown. If a once-through system is used, the cooling tower effluent quality will be the same as the supply water plus treating chemicals that may have been added. When a recirculating system is used, the salts are concentrated as pure water is evaporated from the system cooling tower. Thus TDS, cooling tower additives, and contaminants entering the water via exchanger leaks constitute the contaminants of cooling tower blowdown. With heavy

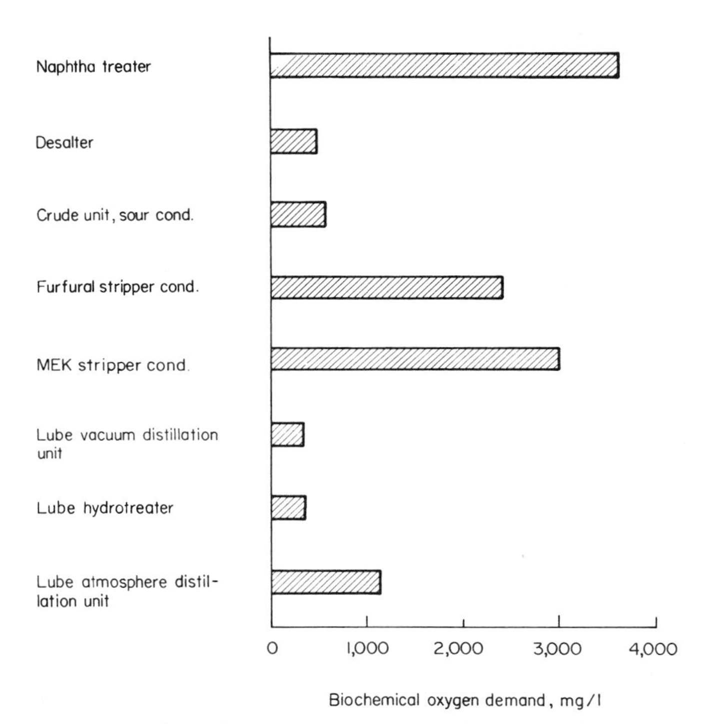

Fig. 3 Sources of Biochemical Oxygen Demand in a Petroleum Refinery.

metals and phosphorus considered by most regulatory agencies as critical pollutants, emphasis on cooling tower additives is of particular significance. Specifically, attention is focused on chromates and phosphates. The most commonly used additives for corrosion and algae control are listed in Table 11.[21] As these chemicals are present in the effluent, their use must be evaluated not only in terms of corrosion and algacide effectiveness but also their impact on effluent quality as related to permissible levels. Quality data from a recirculating cooling tower in a refinery recently surveyed is listed in Table 12.

Blowdown from boilers and cooling towers, if kept segregated from process effluents, is sometimes referred to as *clean streams*. This nomenclature is predicated on relative organic content and is valid if the segregation of streams rigidly follows process-utility blowdown lines. It should be recognized, however, that utility blowdown streams *still* contain organic pollutants, even though they exist at low concentrations. The composition of typical "clean" streams is listed in Table 13.[1] It should again be emphasized that clean stream quality concern is centered around TDS, temperature, chromates, and phosphates while process or "dirty" streams contain concentrated organic materials as well as a myriad of inorganic constituents. The decision of segregating or combining these streams is a complex one and is based on their individual or combined impact in the areas of treatment and water reuse. This will be more fully discussed in subsequent sections of this chapter.

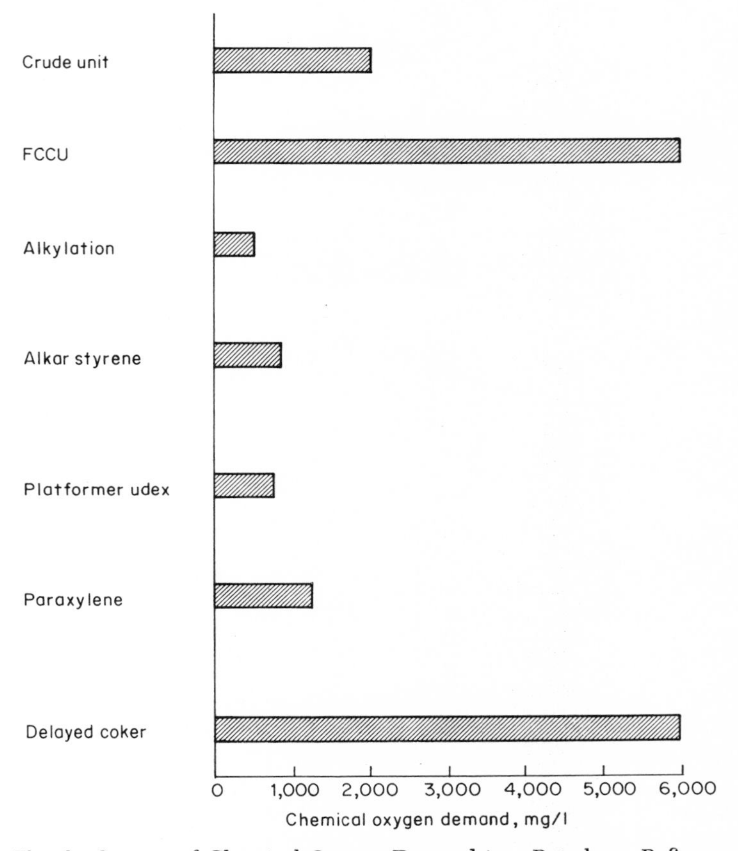

Fig. 4 Sources of Chemical Oxygen Demand in a Petroleum Refinery.

Sanitary Sewage

Sanitary sewage from process control houses, administrative areas, and locker and shower facilities should be considered a separate category. Some installations service these areas either by using septic tanks and drain fields or by connecting sewage lines to the process sewers. In other cases, sanitary sewage is collected and treated separately or sent to nearby municipal sewage systems. Although combining sanitary sewage discharged from within the refinery complex with process wastewaters has many advantages, consideration must be given to pathogenic microorganisms commonly found in sewage. Most regulatory agencies require chlorination of industrial effluents which contain sewage. As chlorinating the combined flow is uneconomical, segregating sanitary sewage for separate treatment or prechlorination of this flow before commingling with process waste is usually practiced.

The volume of sanitary sewage can easily be predicted based on the number of personnel employed for each shift. The quality of sewage is well documented but must reflect conditional factors which might affect relative strength (such as special shower and cleaning installations, lavatory facilities, etc.).

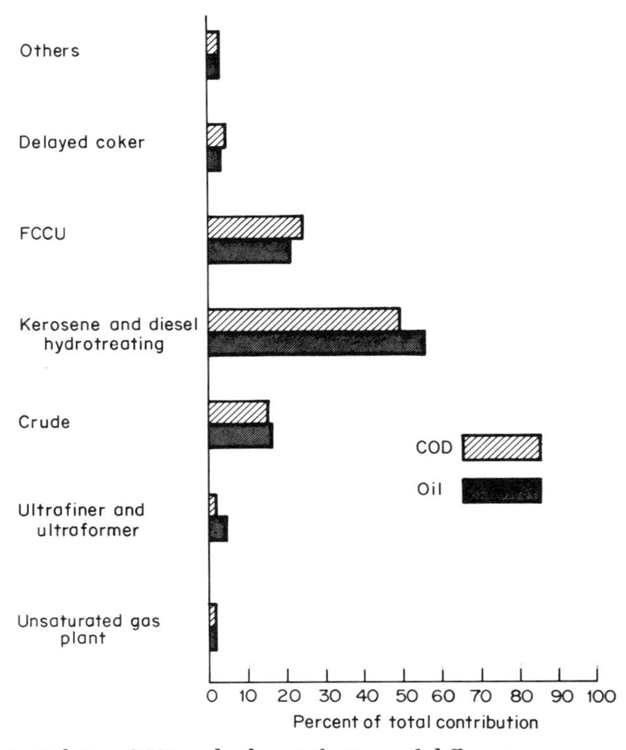

Fig. 5 Relative COD and oil contributions of different process sources.

TABLE 9 Boiler Quality Limits[21]

Steam pressure, psig	Dissolved solids, ppm max.	Suspended solids, ppm max.	Alkalinity,* ppm max.
0–300	3,500	300	700
301–450	3,000	250	600
451–600	2,500	150	500
601–750	2,000	100	400

* Total alkalinity as $CaCO_3$.

Contaminated Storm Runoff

Contaminated storm runoff from industrial production areas has become an area of increasing concern in the development of pollution abatement programs, particularly with respect to regulatory agency policy of definition and control. Storm runoff is intermittent and unpredictable in nature from a quantitative and qualitative point of view. The flow rate and degree of contamination not only vary with time during the course of a storm, but also with each individual area within a refinery-petro-

TABLE 10 Statistical Analysis of Boiler Blowdown

Parameter	Number of analyses reported	Mean	Standard deviation
pH	22	11.6	0.34
Total suspended solids, mg/l	22	40	24.03
Volatile suspended, mg/l	22	24.9	16
Settleable matter, mg/l	22	18.8	23.4
Immediate oxygen demand, mg/l	13	12.4	8.3
Biochemical oxygen demand (5-day), mg/l	7	60.9	26.9
Chemical oxygen demand, mg/l	22	201	70
Oil and grease, mg/l	22	14	5.3
Temperature, °C	22	174	8.2
Chromium, mg/l	3	0.8	0.3
Phenols, mg/l	19	−0.1	0.2
Fluorides, mg/l	15	6.8	9.4
Total residue, mg/l	8	4,947	300
Ammonia, mg/l	10	3.3	2.2
Oxygen demand index, mg/l	9	69.3	45.9

chemical complex since each has its own geometric characteristics which influence patterns of surface runoff. This is best illustrated in Fig. 6 showing the variable pattern of storm runoff organics (COD) from different process areas within a petrochemical complex.[22]

The direct treatment of contaminated storm runoff (being a high-volume, intermittent wastewater stream) is not economically practical. Therefore, handling techniques such as storage and/or segregation followed by controlled feeding to treatment must be investigated. An investigation of storm flows must be oriented toward obtaining data to evaluate three salient aspects:

1. Probable volume collected
2. Quality characteristics
3. Peak flow rates

TABLE 11 Cooling Tower Additives[21]

Additive	Description
Sulfuric acid	Used to prevent scaling by converting insoluble carbonates to the more soluble sulfate salts
Inorganic chromate salts	Used for corrosion control. Concentrations in the circulating water range from 300 to 2,000 mg/l
Inorganic and organic phosphates and polyphosphates	Used for corrosion control. Concentration ranges from 2 to 30 mg/l
Combined chromate and phosphate	Used for corrosion control. Concentration for chromate ranges from 10 to 60 mg/l; concentration for phosphate from 20 to 50 mg/l
Organic chromates	Used for corrosion control. Concentration may be 5 to 20 ppm CrO_4 and 5 to 20 ppm organics
Chlorinated phenols	Used for control of algae and bacterial slime. Intermittent dosage may be as high as 300 to 400 ppm
Chlorine or bromine	Used for control of algae and bacterial slime. Usually, a chlorine level of 1 ppm is maintained in the system for at least 4 hr a day
Quaternary ammonium copper complexes	Used for algae and bacteria control. Intermittent dosage may be as high as 200 ppm

TABLE 12 Statistical Analysis of Cooling Tower Blowdown (24-hr composites)

Parameter	Mean	Standard deviation
pH	7.3	0.3
Total suspended solids, mg/l	34	
Volatile suspended solids, mg/l	26	
Biochemical oxygen demand (5-day), mg/l	33	35
Chemical oxygen demand, mg/l	141	98
Oil and grease, mg/l	7	3
Temperature (grab samples), °C	27	3
Sulfides (grab samples), mg/l	0	0
Chromium, mg/l	12.2	
TKN, mg/l	12	18
Total phosphate, mg/l	4.9	0.9
Total dissolved solids, mg/l	7,650	2,428
Dissolved organic carbon, mg/l	60	59

TABLE 13 Composition of Typical Clean Water Effluent[1]

Water sources	Total wastewater, %	Flow range	Potential pollutants		COD range, mg/l
			Sources	Type	
Cooling water (excluding seawater)	40–80	100–200,000 gal water/ton product	Process leaks: Bearings, exchangers, etc.	Extractables	1–1,000
				Mercaptans	
				Sulfides	
				Phenols	0–1,000, but usually less than 1 mg/l
				Cyanide	
				Misc. nitrogen compounds	
				Acids	
			Water treatment	Chromate	0–60
				Phosphate	0–60
				Heavy metals	0–30
				Fluoride	0–30
				Sulfate	100–10,000
				Biocides, algacides	0–50
				Misc. organics	0–100
			Scrubbed from air through tower	Hydrogen sulfide	
				Sulfur dioxide	0–1,000
				Oxides of nitrogen	
				Ammonia	
				Particulates	0–300
			Makeup water	Total dissolved solids	100–5,000
				Particulates	0–100
				Phosphates	0–5
				Fluoride	0–2
Steam equipment	10	50–1,000 gpm	Boiler blowdown	Total dissolved solids	500–10,000
				Particulates	5–300
				Extractables	0–10
				Phosphate	1–50
				Sulfite	0–50
				Sulfide	0–5
				Misc. organic compounds	0–200
				Misc. nitrogen compounds	1–100
				Heavy metals	0–10
				Alkalinity	50–400
			Waste condensate	Extractables	0–100
				Ammonia	0–10

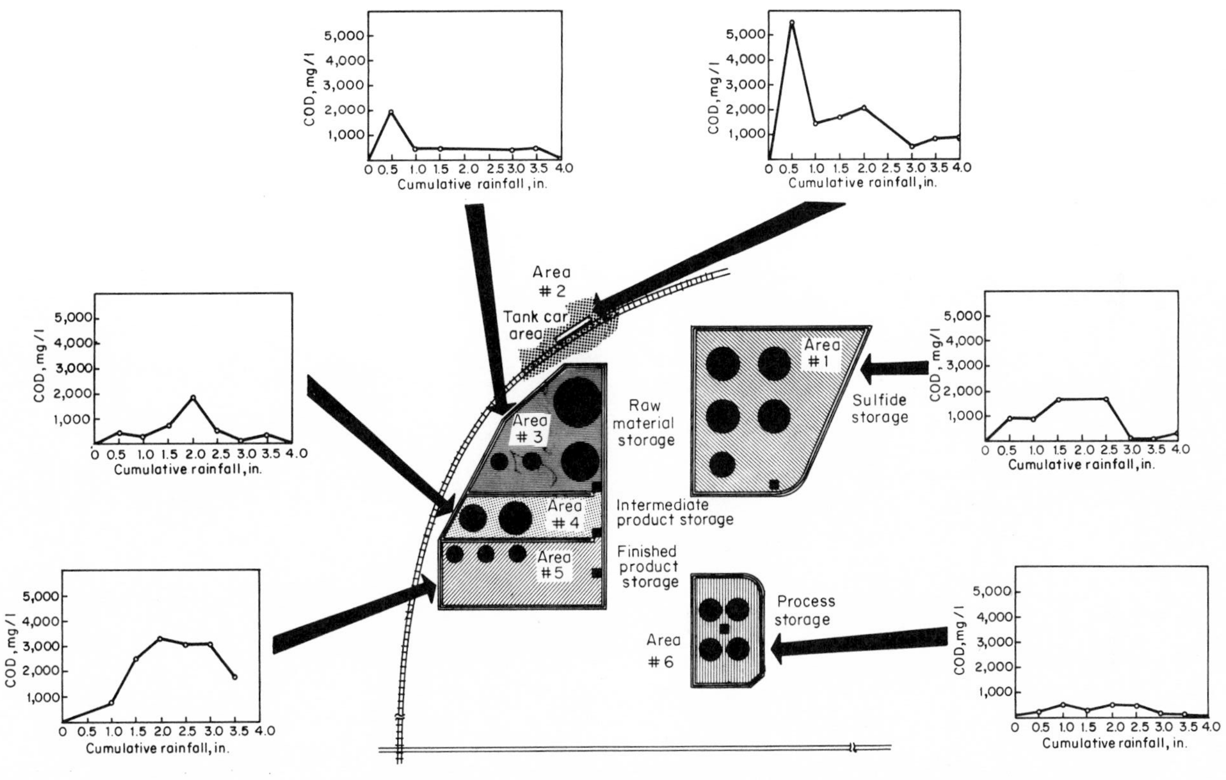

Fig. 6 Variable patterns of COD in storm runoff from different areas of a petrochemical complex.

If runoff is to be stored or surged prior to eventual treatment, anticipated rainfall volumes must be estimated. Such estimates should be developed statistically from long-term precipitation records, for a specific year's precipitation pattern will never occur again in the same fashion. Fortunately, the National Weather Service has developed such estimates of probable rainfall for periods up to 10 days in length for many areas. In order to develop estimates for periods of a longer duration, a more sophisticated approach is required. The mathematical properties of the laws of probability are well known and can be used with sufficient accuracy to allow computation of meaningful probability statements concerning future events. An approach using the gamma probability function has been used to approximate the distribution of total rainfall at a given location for a fixed time interval.[23] Using this technique, rainfalls for various recurrence intervals can be computed for various periods of time. For example, the inches of rainfall from a specified recurrence interval curve for a stated time period can be interpreted to mean the area in question will receive x inches of total rainfall during the specified period of days at least once during the recurrence interval. Based on the projected runoff volume for a design storm, appropriately corrected for precipitation losses not reflected in runoff, volumes of runoff and peak flows can be predicted.

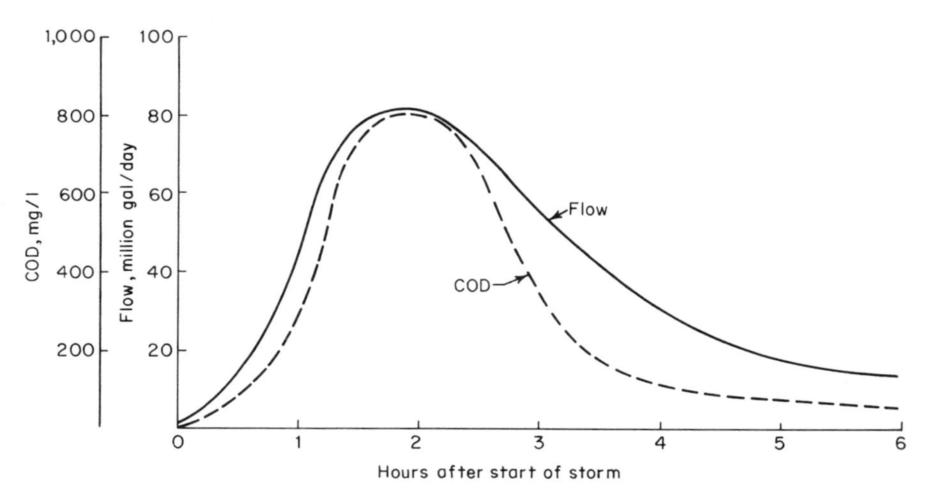

Fig. 7 Representative COD and rain flow run-off curves for a refinery.

The relationship of organic contaminant concentration to flow for one refinery is shown in Fig. 7. As noted, the contaminant mass peaks at the approximate time of maximum flow, but declines more rapidly than flow. The analysis of numerous storm flow COD concentration relationships has indicated between 60 and 80 percent of the COD mass is washed out during a 1-hr period centered about the peak flow axis.

Once the volume and quality of contaminated storm runoff for the design storm are established, a definitive program for handling and treatment can be formulated.

Ballast Water Blowdown

Tankers and barges which transport crude or products to and from refinery and petrochemical facilities in coastal areas seldom carry payload on both legs of a journey. This is particularly true of refineries in crude-producing areas which means that tankers are used primarily for exporting finished products, the excess ballast from incoming tankers having to be discharged at the debarkation port. The quantity and quality of ballast water in cases such as this can have a significant impact on the total effluent from an installation requiring treatment.

Ballast is normally taken aboard an empty tanker during its departure from port. The quantity of ballast required during calm weather is usually 1.5 bbl (63 gal) per ton of tanker deadweight displacement but is affected to some extent by the judgment of the ship's captain and the individual characteristics of the tanker. Additional ballast is taken aboard at sea as weather conditions warrant. Initially, the ballast has characteristics similar to the body of water from which it was taken. When loaded, however, it is contaminated with the remnants of the previous cargo which remain clinging to the product holds. As only the most modern tankers have separate ballast holds, there is little, if any, truly clean ballast. The degree of ballast contamination primarily depends on the nature of the previous cargo and the condition of the tanker's holds. Ballast-handling procedures at sea vary considerably. Foreign tankers apparently have minimal pollution control discipline. This includes flushing dirty ballast at sea through the seacocks and replacing it with fresh seawater as required. In contrast to the practices of the foreign tankers, domestic tankers follow a more disciplined ballast-handling procedure. Ballast tanks are washed at sea; however, an attempt is made to decant the oil-free water underflow by discharging it through the seacocks, consolidating the emulsion and slop oil upper layers in specific dirty ballast tanks. A Butterworth washing head which resembles a high-powered rotary lawn sprinkler is used for the hold cleaning operations. Fresh seawater is then used to flood the emptied ballast tanks and is generally considered clean ballast. Though these procedures are highly efficient, it is difficult to assess the reliability of this practice. However, this procedure does serve a dual purpose; first, by the con-

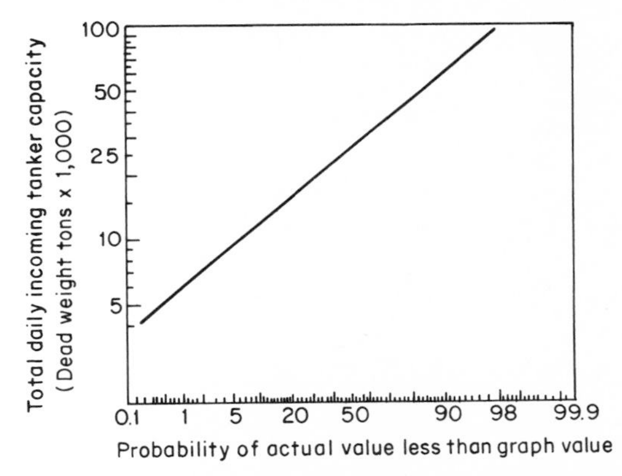

Fig. 8 Typical tanker arrival analysis for calculating ballast storage.

solidation of the dirty ballast in one or more special tanks, the volume of ballast to be discharged is reduced, and secondly, sea washings prepare the tanker holds for future product loading.

Ballast unloading operations are also extremely varied. Domestic ships, as a rule, release clean ballast through their seacocks as they proceed toward port. Foreign ships follow a similar procedure, though apparently their discrimination between clean and dirty ballast is generally less discerning. The deballasting operation is by necessity a hurried one, for demurrage charges on even a medium-size tanker are expensive.

In order to ascertain a ballast volume requiring treatment, it is first necessary to estimate the tanker arrival pattern and corresponding ballast volume to be discharged. A typical tanker arrival analysis for one refinery is shown in Fig. 8. Using the anticipated volume based on tanker capacity, a surge period can be established to determine ballast storage capacity by constructing a mass curve for the storage time selected. An example of a typical graphical solution using this approach is shown in Fig. 9.

The characteristics of ballast water are best described by their organic content in terms of BOD or COD and the concentration of oil. As ballast is first pumped to a storage tank and then sent either to treatment or to the receiving environment, the characteristics of the underflow from a ballast holding tank are of most interest. The results of ballast water characterization studies conducted at two refineries are tabulated in Table 14.

Although ballast water quality can be expected to vary significantly based on the point of ballast pickup and handling practices, the data in Table 14 indicate that treatment would be required by most regulatory agencies before this water could be released.

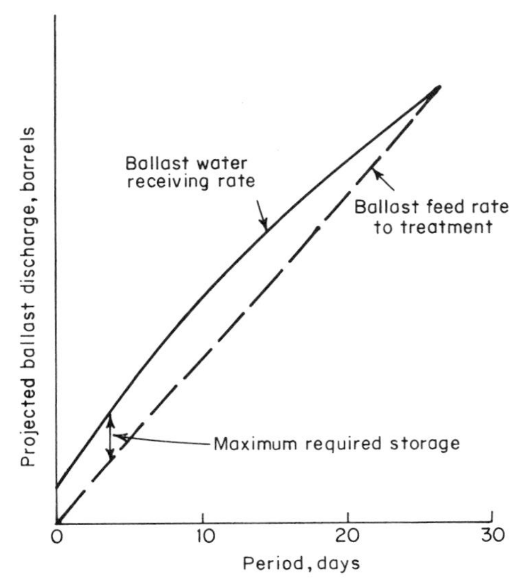

Fig. 9 A graphical solution for estimating ballast storage capacity.

TABLE 14 Ballast Water Characteristics for Two Refineries*

	High value	Low value	Mean
Refinery 1:			
COD, mg/l	472	207	342
BOD_5, mg/l	389	23	168
Oil, mg/l	148	9	44
Chlorides, mg/l	18,500	14,200	16,900
Refinery 2:			
COD, mg/l	1,600	1,173	1,456
Oil, mg/l	280	147	183

* Quality of underflow from ballast receiving and holding tank.

Miscellaneous Discharges

There are many discharges from refinery-petrochemical complexes which are difficult to categorize. These sources result from events such as tank draining or cleaning, product spills, off-spec product dumps, line breaks, and cleaning operations. Wastewaters discharged during turnarounds also can be included in this category.

The pollutional output from a complex which is attributable to most of these sources generally can be reduced through tight management control. The problem areas must first be identified by monitoring specified quality parameters at selected points within the refinery. The best indication of dumps and spills is the geometry of the statistical distribution curve. Significant departures from either an arithmetical or log normal distribution at the higher intervals as illustrated in Fig. 10 infer infrequent but unusually severe levels of pollution in terms of effluent COD and oil. Methods of control must be incorporated into a pollution control system by use of alarms, temporary bypass and storage facilities, equalization basins, and treatment capacity for such occurrences.

Summary

Five categories of refinery-petrochemical wastewater pollution based on source have been cited herein. Process and utility operations are common to all refineries and petrochemical installations, but the nature of the wastewater will vary according to process idiosyncrasies, crude charge, and age of the plant. Contaminated storm runoff from process areas is a very real source of water pollution and the level of this contribution depends on the cleanliness of the installation, the degree of dikes, curve, and other physical features separating clean or contaminated runoff, and the climatological features of the area. Ballast water, if applicable, needs to be considered in the pollution control system, as case histories indicate the level of organic contamination is high and allowances for handling and treating miscellaneous spills, dumps, and washdowns should be made in a pollution control program. To put these categories of pollutional output in perspective, an example of the respective hydraulic and organic contributions from two refineries is presented in Table 15.

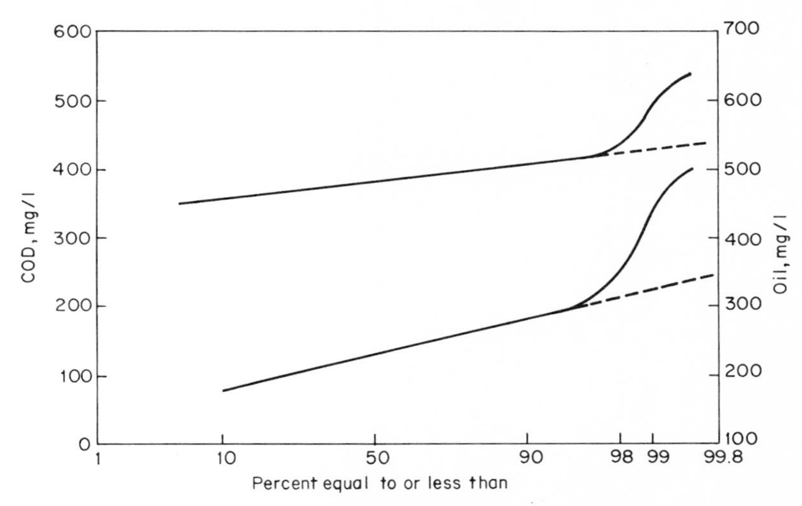

Fig. 10 A statistical distribution curve for determining significant dumps and spills.

TREATMENT PROCESSES

The treatment of wastewaters discharged from refinery-petrochemical installations encompasses the removal of diverse pollutants, some rather obvious and standard in nature and some not so obvious. Most of the attention in refinery pollution control is focused on organic removal. Oil and grease are of immediate concern and are usually removed by physical separation processes. Biological treatment, carbon adsorption, and filtration are currently used in the removal of suspended and dissolved organic constituents, and chemical treatment processes are often required for neutralization, emulsion breaking, and chemical precipitation. Although it is difficult to categorize the treatment processes which constitute a pollution control system in a true generic sense, the processes which are discussed in this chapter are classified as follows:

PRIMARY

- API separators
- Tilted-plate separators

Filtration for oil removal
pH control
Stripping processes

INTERMEDIATE

Dissolved air flotation
Coagulation-precipitation
Equalization

SECONDARY-TERTIARY

Activated sludge
Aerated lagoons
Trickling filters
Waste stabilization ponds
Cooling tower oxidation
Chemical oxidation
Filtration
Carbon adsorption

In this discussion, general comments about the process and its applicability will be considered as well as process information developed from case histories.

TABLE 15 Basis for Treatment Facility Design

	Flow, % of total	BOD, % of total	COD, % of total
Refinery 1:			
Normal process operations	21	70	71
Utilities operations	26	13	14
Contaminated storm runoff	20	7	5
Ballast water blowdown	23	8	8
Sanitary sewage	5	1	1
Allowances for misc. discharges	5	1	1
	100%	100%	100%
Refinery 2:			
Normal process operations	25	42	
Utility operations	33	15	
Contaminated storm runoff	16	12	
Ballast water blowdown	10	15	
Sanitary sewage	1	<1	
Allowance for misc. discharges	15	15	
	100%	100%	

Primary Treatment

API separators Gravity separation using API separators involves the removal of materials less dense than water (such as free oils and air-entrained particulates), and the removal of suspended materials which are more dense than water by sedimentation. The current design principles of the API separator are based on extensive studies and testing programs and include inlet and outlet arrangements, shape factors, and the effect of appurtenances on hydraulic characteristics in separation chambers. The principal factors which affect the design of oil separators are:

The specific gravity of the oil
The specific gravity of the wastewater
The temperature of the wastewater stream
The presence or absence of emulsions
The suspended solids concentration

The specific gravities of the oil and water determine the separation rate while they are in turn related to the temperature. These factors determine the allowable overflow rate from the oil separator. Graphical solutions of oil water separation rates which can be used for separator design have been prepared.[24]

Since segregation of wastewater streams is a basic principle of refinery waste disposal practice, special-purpose separators frequently are used for streams containing readily separable oil and low suspended solids concentrations. These units are usually sized on an arbitrary basis. A schematic showing application of API and special-purpose separators within a refinery is shown in Fig. 11.[24]

Reported efficiencies of oil separators from refineries around the country are listed in Table 16. The efficiency, of course, is a function of many design and operating

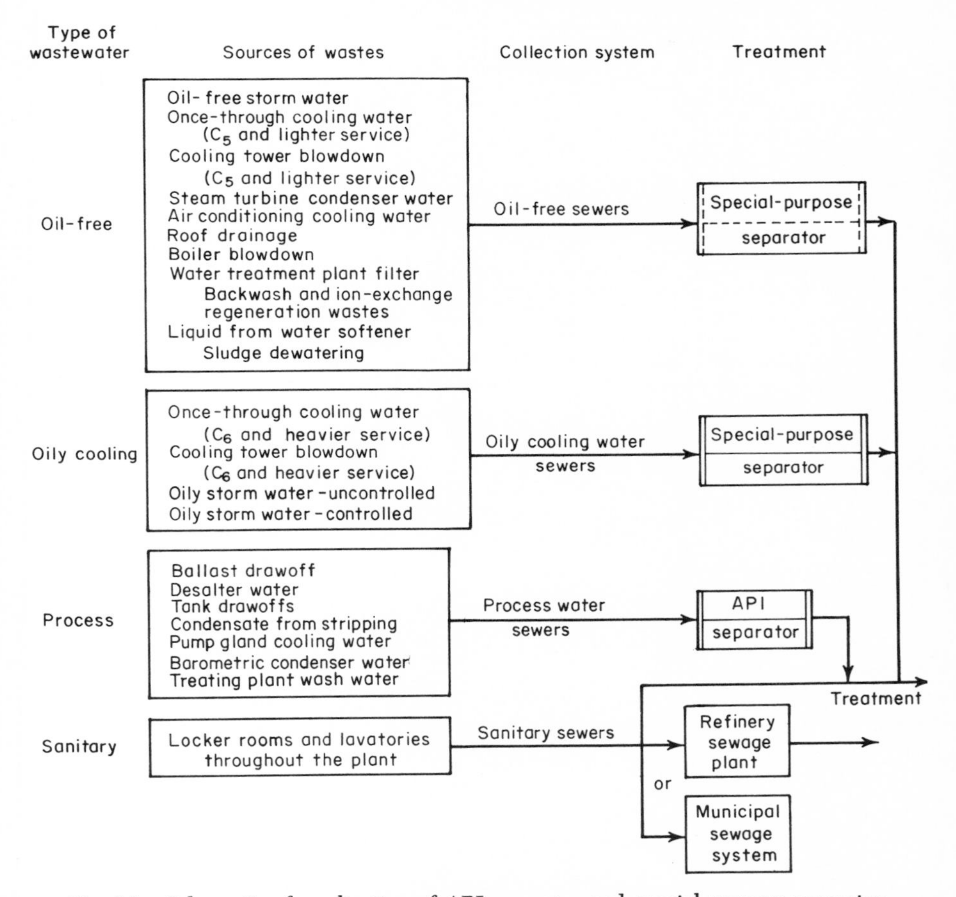

Fig. 11 Schematic of application of API separator and special-purpose separator.

variables. Perhaps the two most significant factors are flow rate and influent oil concentration. Separators must be hydraulically protected to prevent "flushing" during periods of high flow. Bypass or overflow lines generally are used to provide this protection. The effect of flow on separator effluent oil concentration is best illustrated in Fig. 12. The oil concentration is significant as higher oil concentrations are removed with greater efficiency than low oil concentrations since the lower limit of oil in the separator effluent is usually around 50 mg/l. The influence of initial oil concentration on separator efficiency is illustrated in Fig. 13.

Removal of other contaminants in a separator is highly variable. As indicated in Table 16, COD removal efficiencies vary from 15 to 80 percent and suspended solids removal ranges from 30 to 65 percent. This, of course, depends to a large extent on sampling techniques and analytical procedures.

Tilted-plate separators The tilted- or parallel-plate separator is a recent development for removal of free oils and consists of corrugated-plate modules. These modules are installed at an angle of 45°, reducing the separator distance of the lighter-than-water materials and thus the required detention time. The light components coalesce in the trough of the corrugated plate, rise to the top of the module, and are skimmed. Similarly, the settleable particles in the wastewater fall to the bottom of the corrugations and slide to the low end of the module for removal. A schematic diagram of the tilted-plate separator is shown in Fig. 14.[26]

TABLE 16 Typical Efficiencies of Oil Separation Units

Oil content					
Influent, mg/l	Effluent, mg/l	Oil, % removed	Type of separator	COD, % removed	SS, % removed
300	40	87	Parallel plate	—	—
220	49	78	API	45	—
108	20	82	Circular	—	—
108	50	54	Circular	16	—
98	44	55	API	—	—
100	40	60	API	—	—
42	20	52	API	—	—
2,000	746	63	API	22	33
1,250	170	87	API	—	68
1,400	270	81	API	—	35

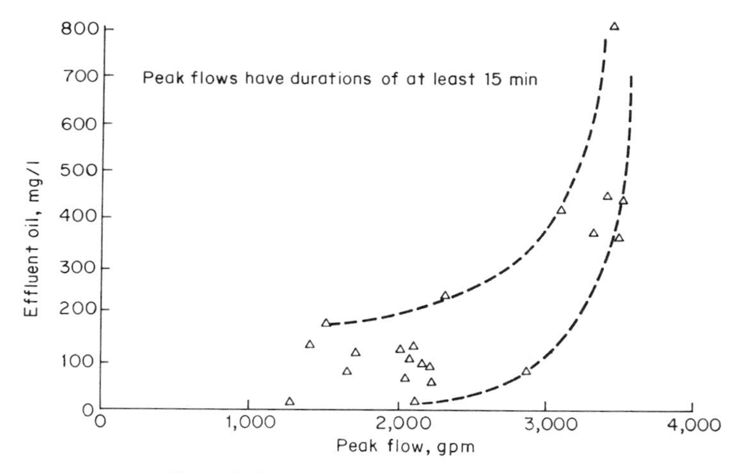

Fig. 12 Effect of flow on separator effluent oil concentration.

As tilted-plate separators have only recently been applied to the removal of free oil from refinery effluents, little operating data are available. One test program conducted by a manufacturer indicated oil removal as a function of oily water throughput. These data are shown in Table 17.[26] Another refinery survey evaluated a pilot-scale tilted-plate separator used both in parallel and in series with an existing API separator. The effluent oil concentration as a function of influent levels for three flow rates is shown in Fig. 15. A comparison of oil removal efficiency achieved by the pilot-scale tilted-plate separator compared to that achieved in a full-scale API separator receiving the same oily wastewater is shown in Fig. 16.

There is a broad application for tilted-plate separators for the removal of free oil from refinery-petrochemical wastewaters. As little space is required, they can be installed adjacent to an existing API separator which is either overloaded or improperly designed, thereby reducing the effluent oil levels obtained by gravity separation. They also can be installed in parallel with existing separators, reducing the hydraulic load and enhancing the oil removal capacity of the system.

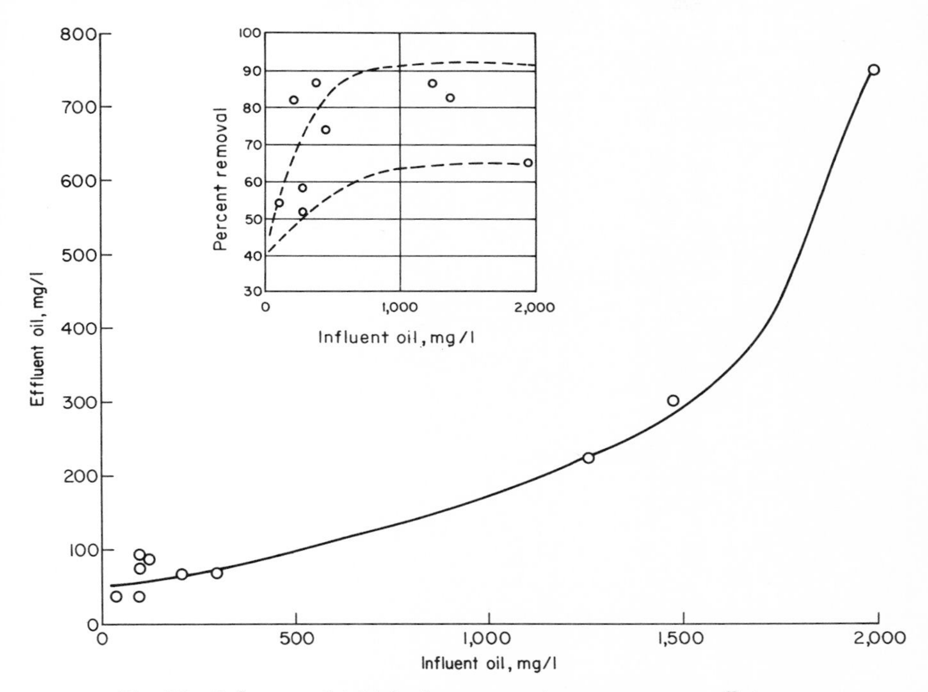

Fig. 13 Influence of initial oil concentration on separator efficiency.

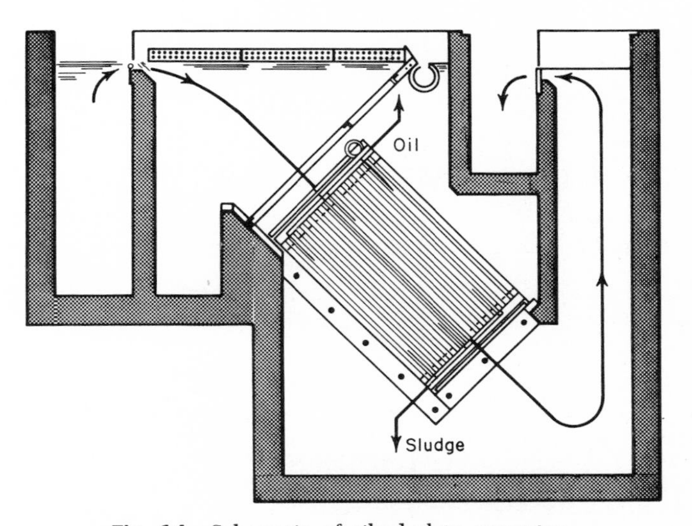

Fig. 14 Schematic of tilted-plate separator.

TABLE 17 Oil Removal, Tilted-plate Separator[26]

Oily water throughput, gph	Influent oil, mg/l	Effluent oil, mg/l	Percent removal
8,000	150	50	67
8,000	375	66	82
8,000	500	86	83
16,000	500	178	65
18,600	500	190	62
18,600	570	185	67
18,600	700	330	53

Filtration for oil removal Filtration as a pretreatment step for oil and solids removal is a candidate system which can be used singularly or in conjunction with gravity separators or air flotation systems. Several types of filtration devices have proven effective in removing free and emulsified oils from refinery-petrochemical wastewaters. These vary from filters with sand media to those containing special media which exhibit a specific affinity for oil. One type is upflow using a graded silica media as the filtering and coalescing section. Here, even small particles and globules are separated and retained on the media. The oil particles which flow upward by gravity differential and fluid flow to rise through the coalescent media

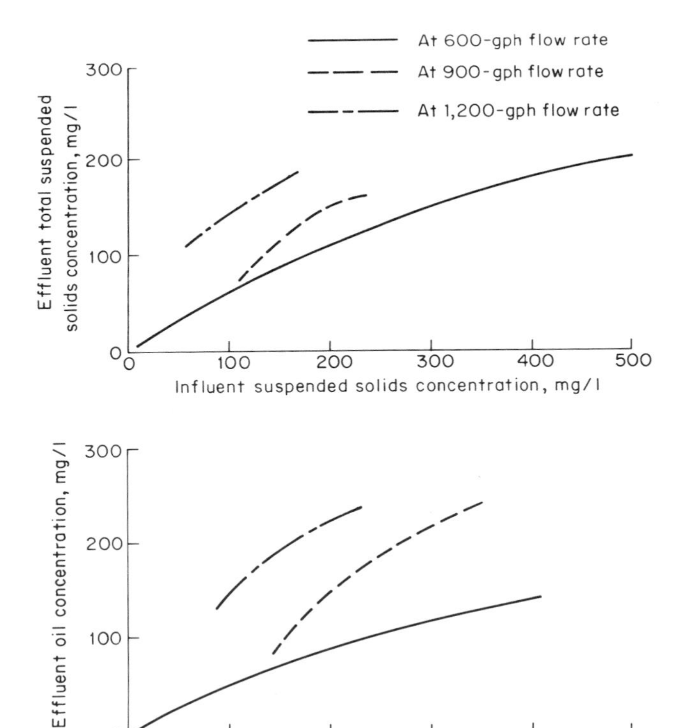

Fig. 15 Effluent oil concentration as a function of influent levels for three different flow rates.

and through the water phase from which it is separated are collected near the top of the separator. In a solids-free stream, the cycle duration is long since the media serves as a coalescer and not as a collector of oil. Regeneration of the bed is accomplished by introducing a rapid rate of wash water and evacuating the solids and remaining oil. This filtration and coalescing process is often enhanced by the use of polymer resin media.

The advantages of going to filtration as a pretreatment step in oil removal are the compactness of the units, favorable economics in some cases, and flexible operation through control of water and oil draws, flow rate, and backwash regeneration. Some of the disadvantages include reported problems with solids, stabilized oil emulsions, dirt and grit collecting rapidly (resulting in higher operational and maintenance costs), and efficiencies which in some cases may be no better than gravity separation units. Manufacturers, however, have reported 90 to 95 percent removal of oils at design flow rates. The application of these units based on most observations is for selected in-plant streams which are dirt-free. Another application would be ballast water treatment following phase separation in a receiving tank.

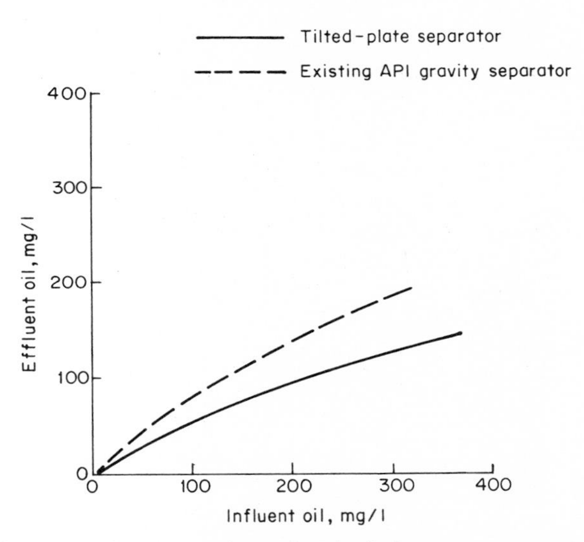

Fig. 16 Removal efficiency of pilot-scale tilted-plate separator compared to full-scale API separator.

pH control Neutralization is commonly required in the treatment of petrochemical and refinery wastewaters because many process streams are highly acidic or alkaline. Typical neutralization steps are included in the following applications:

1. Emulsion breaking through acidification, and reneutralization following gravity separation
2. Neutralization prior to biological treatment
3. Neutralization on specified streams to prevent corrosion
4. pH adjustment to prevent unwanted precipitation of certain constituents
5. pH adjustment to enhance coagulation and sedimentation

Although refineries and petrochemical installations have many individual streams in the highly acid or alkaline range, the combined effluent is generally on the slightly basic side of the pH 7 to 10 range. There are many installations with primary and secondary steps which do not require any neutralization steps within the treatment complex. Separate discharge of certain streams, however, requires neutralization steps. Such applications include dilute acid or alkaline wash waters, spent caustics from caustic treating operations, acid sludges from alkylation, sulfonation, and acid treating processes, and spent acid catalysts.

Acid streams are neutralized by one of several candidate modes. These include fluidized mixing of the waste with lime slurries, dolomitic lime slurries, caustic, or soda ash. Limestone beds operated either as an upflow or downflow system occasionally are used. Alkaline streams can be neutralized with acid (sulfuric or hydrochloric) or with boiler flue gas (carbon dioxide). Neutralization often can be accomplished by combining internal refinery wastewater streams. For example, spent caustic can often be neutralized with spent acid. Spent caustic neutralization with an acid can be designed as a batch or a continuous system. A typical process flow schematic is shown in Fig. 17.[1]

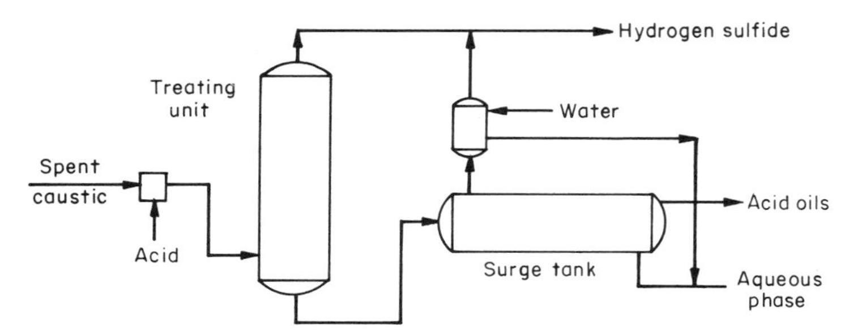

Fig. 17 Typical process flow schematic for a spent caustic neutralization system.

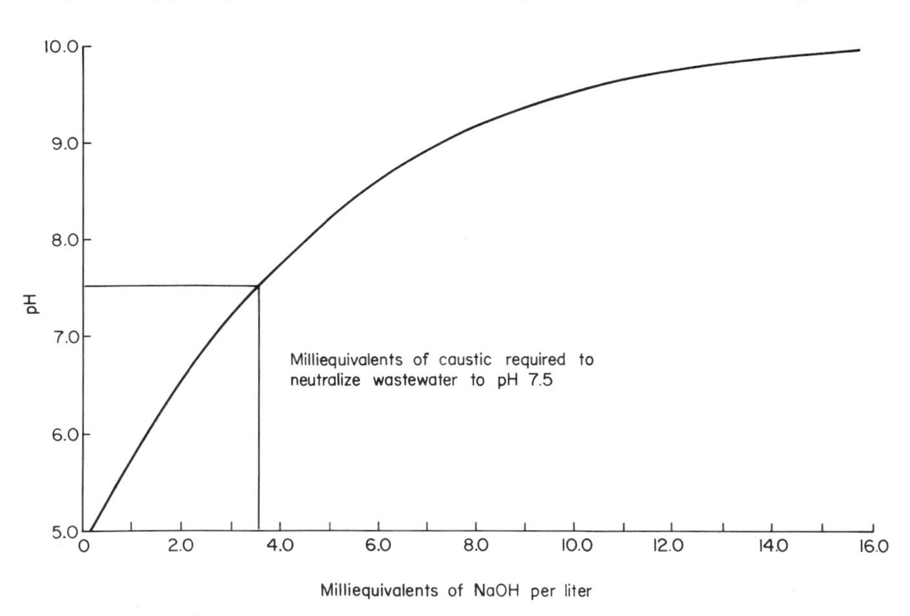

Fig. 18 Typical titration curve for determining the total acidity or basicity of a solution.

Design of a neutralization system is predicated on titration curves which determine the total basicity or acidity of a solution. This curve graphically depicts the pH change per unit addition of reagent. A typical curve for one petrochemical waste is shown in Fig. 18, indicating the caustic requirement to obtain a desired effluent of pH 7.5. There are many intricacies in the design and control of a neutralization process, including consideration for mixing, reagent feed systems, and control systems.[27] The most economical method of neutralization depends on the characteristics and quantity of the wastewater being neutralized and the source and supply of the neutralizing agent.

Typical applications of neutralization and pH adjustment requirements for treating refinery and petrochemical wastewaters are cited in Table 18.[1]

Stripping processes Stripping processes are used to remove selected constituents from liquid streams. The two most prevalent pollutants found in refinery waste waters which are susceptible to stripping are hydrogen sulfide and ammonia resulting from the destruction of essentially all the organic nitrogen and sulfur compounds during desulfurization, denitrification, and hydrotreating. The use of steam within the processes is the primary source of conveyance, as the condensation occurs simultaneously with the condensation of hydrocarbon liquids and in the presence of a

TABLE 18 Typical Applications of Neutralization or pH Adjustment to Petrochemical Wastes[1]

Process or products manufactured	Waste components	Agent
Acid treating processes	Spent sulfuric acid	Spent caustic
Adipic acid	Organic acid	Ammonium hydroxide
Alkylation, sulfonation for detergents, etc.	Sulfonic acids, sulfonates	Lime
Amines, amides		
Butadiene	Cuprous ammonium acetate	Spent caustic
Butadiene, olefins		
Catalytic processes	Aluminum chloride phosphoric acid	Lime
Chemicals for lubricating oils		
Freon	Inorganics	
Herbicides	Chlorinated hydrocarbons	Lime
Many petrochemical operations	Emulsified oils	Lime
Mixed petrochemicals	Aliphatic acids, esters, alcohols, aromatics, amines	Soda ash
Mixed petrochemicals—olefins, aromatics, nitriles, resins, detergents, etc.	Oily wastes	Lime
Orlon	Mixed organics and inorganics	
Phenol, salycylic acid, rubber chemicals, aspirin	Mixed organics	Lime
Polyethylene	Hexane, catalyst alcohols	
Polyvinylchloride plastics		Lime
Spent caustics from caustic treating operations	Spent caustic	
Styrene	Acid wastes	Waste alkaline sodium aluminate
Tetraethyl lead	Lead; sodium chlorides, sulfates; ethyl chloride	

hydrocarbon vapor phase which contains H_2S and NH_3.[1] Phenols also may be present in these sour water condensates and can be stripped from solutions although the efficiency of removal is less than for sulfide and ammonia. Other aromatics also can be stripped from solution at various levels of efficiency. Since the regulatory agencies are imposing increasingly stringent quality standards for refinery wastewater in terms of immediate oxygen demand (sulfide causative) and ammonia, the necessity of in-plant control through stripping towers may be required whether it can be justified in terms of product recovery or not.

The design criteria for sour water strippers are well documented and are outlined in detail elsewhere.[1,6] There are various types of strippers but most involve a single tower equipped with trays or some type of packing. The feedwater enters at the top of the tower and steam or stripping gas is introduced at the bottom. As H_2S is less soluble in water than NH_3, it is more readily stripped from solution. High temperatures (230°F +) are required to remove NH_3 where H_2S could be stripped at 100°F if NH_3 were fixed or not present. Therefore, acidification with a mineral acid or flue gas is often used to fix the NH_3 and allow more efficient H_2S removal. Average operating characteristics of some sour water strippers are cited in Table 19.[6] Although acidification enhances sulfide removal, it fixes the ammonia and prevents its removal. This has led to a two-stage stripping and recovery process developed by the Chevron Research Company.[7] The process flowsheet, as shown in Fig. 19, includes a degasser-surge tank combination which allows operational flexibility. Following skimming of any floating hydrocarbon, it is routed to the first column where

TABLE 19 Average Operating Characteristics of Sour Water Strippers[6]

Type of stripper	Flow rate of stripping medium, scf/gal	Removal		Temperature	
		H_2S, %	NH_3, %	Tower Feed, °F	Tower bottom, °F
Steam:					
Without acidifying*	8–32	96–100	69–95	150–240	230–270
With acidifying†	4–6	97–100	0	200	230–250
Flue gas:					
With steam‡	12.7	88–98	77–90	235	235
Without steam‡	11.9	99	8	135	140
Natural gas with acidifying	7.5	98	0	70–100	70–100

† Data from only one tower.
‡ Data from two towers.
* Data from eight towers.

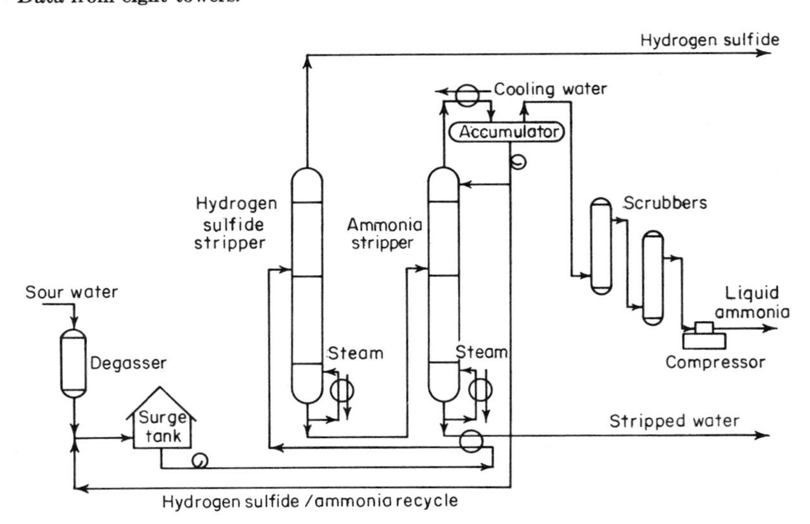

Fig. 19 Flowsheet for a two-stage Sour Water stripping and recovery process.

the H_2S is stripped and sent to a sulfur recovery plant. The water-ammonia mixture then goes to a second fractionator for ammonia stripping. The overhead ammonia, approximately 98 percent pure as it leaves the condenser, is further purified by passing it through a scrubber system, and it is then liquified as high purity ammonia. The cooled water bottoms from the system are then sufficiently free of H_2S and NH_3 to satisfy most quality criteria since they contain less than 5 mg/l H_2S and 50 mg/l NH_3.

Volatile organic compounds can be stripped from aqueous wastes by using air or intense mixing as the stripping agent. The stripping of wastewater containing high concentrations of volatile organics results in a substantial removal of wastewater COD. The amount of BOD removed, however, is questionable. Laboratory tests involving stripping of some biodegradable volatile organic compounds indicated that most of the BOD removal in an aeration tank was due to biological action rather than to physical stripping. This investigation indicated that the stripping of biodegradable wastes is not usually significant, even if the organics are quite volatile. If an organic compound is nonbiodegradable and volatile, however, air stripping may be a significant mechanism for removing this pollutant from a liquid system. For example, benzene and nitrobenzene, both of which are relatively nonbiodegradable, can be effectively air stripped from wastewater. Air-stripping systems are often not followed by condensation units because of economic considerations, and the practice of releasing volatile compounds to the atmosphere often creates air pollution problems which limit the applicability of this treatment technique.

Intermediate Treatment

Dissolved air flotation Dissolved air flotation (DAF) is a process commonly used in refinery and petrochemical installations to enhance oil and suspended solids re-

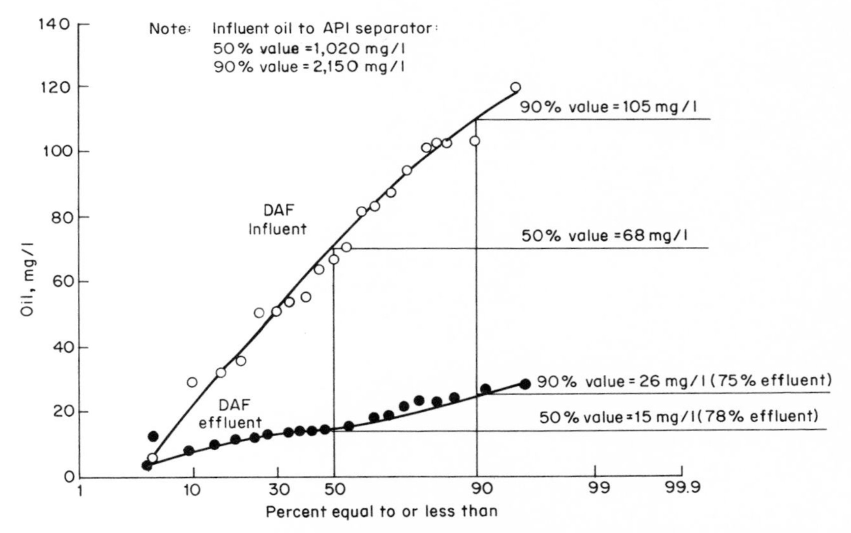

Fig. 20 Case 1: Graphical representation of operation of DAF unit and API separator.

moval. It is generally preceded by a gravity oil separator to remove gross quantities of free oil and suspended matter. The process basically involves the pressurization of the influent or recycled wastewater the release of which, in either a circular or rectangular tank, creates minute bubbles that float the suspended and oily particulates to the surface. The float solids are removed to disposal or recovery by a mechanical surface collector, while the underflow represents the clarified effluent. While DAF units are not as economical as gravity separators, they have the capacity for producing a better quality of effluent and are therefore commonly required to meet the effluent oil levels prior to subsequent treatment or discharge. If a significant portion of the oil is emulsified, chemical addition with rapid-mix and flocculation chambers are a part of the flotation unit, breaking the emulsion and enhancing the phase separation. Chemicals normally employed include aluminum, iron, and calcium salts. Polyelectrolytes frequently are added either individually or in combination with these salts.

In order to predict the oil levels in the DAF effluent, it is first necessary to refer to case histories where DAF units are being used to treat refinery oily wastewaters.[30] The first case history is graphically represented in Fig. 20 where a rectangular DAF unit has been in operation in series with an API separator for several years. As noted, the DAF unit reduces the total oil from 68 to 15 mg/l at a 50 percent probability and from 105 to 26 mg/l at a 90 percent probability. The separator influent oil concentration is 1,020 mg/l (50 percent) and 2,150 mg/l (90 percent). The second case history where sufficient data were collected to perform a statistical analysis is shown in Fig. 21. This refinery has two circular DAF units preceded by an API gravity separator. Because of in-plant segregation, the oil content in the feedwater is higher than would normally be expected. The DAF units reduce the oil from 580 to 68 mg/l (50 percent) and from 1,930 to 128 mg/l (90 percent). The third case history indicates the variation of oil from a circular DAF unit over 2 years of analyses as shown in Fig. 22. No influent oil concentrations were available, but this plot does indicate 50 and 90 percent effluent levels. It should be noted that high oil concentrations which occur 10 percent of the time or less reflect occasional oily dumps or spills which can be expected in most refinery operations.

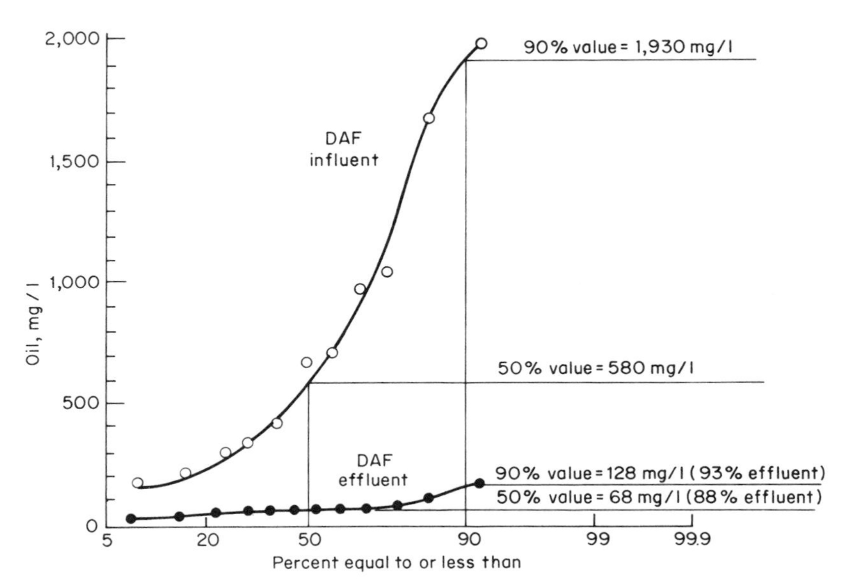

Fig. 21 Case 2: Two circular DAF units preceded by API gravity separator.

Although reported data in the literature is usually insufficient to make a statistical analysis, cited average values are indicative of DAF oil removal capacities over a wide range of influent oil concentrations. A tabulation of this reported data is given in Table 20. DAF efficiency in terms of oil removal is a function of many factors; namely, design overflow rate, retention time, recycle volume, pressurization level, air/solids ratio, type and volume of chemical addition, and the concentration and form of the influent oil. The data tabulated in Table 20 accounts for these variables to the maximum extent possible. For example, all cases cited (with one exception) use chemicals, design overflow rates fall within the accepted design spectrum of 1.5 to 3.0 gpm/sq ft, and all use pressurized recycle. Assuming the systems are properly operated, a most significant factor with respect to process capacity and efficiency is the influent oil concentration. This effect is underscored when the data from Table 20 is plotted so that effluent oil concentration and oil removal efficiency are shown as a function of influent oil concentration. As shown in Fig. 23, the efficiencies of DAF systems range from 60 to 94 percent, depending on the influent oil form and concentration and assuming proper design and operation.

Coagulation-precipitation The use of reactor-clarifiers for the coagulation-precipitation removal of suspended and colloidal pollutants in refinery-petrochemical wastewaters is effective for selected streams. The applicability of this process in the removal of these pollutants can be determined through the use of a bench-scale jar test noting the change in organics or the critical pollutant in the upper layers of the liquid following chemical addition, rapid mix, flocculation, and sedimentation. An assessment of the effect of pH, flocculation time, and chemical selection on pollutant removal can be used to optimize the process. A typical example of the flocculation time influence on the effluent suspended solids concentration is shown in Fig. 24.

The conventional coagulation system utilizes a rapid-mix tank followed first by slow agitation of the mixture in a flocculation tank to promote the growth of floc particles,

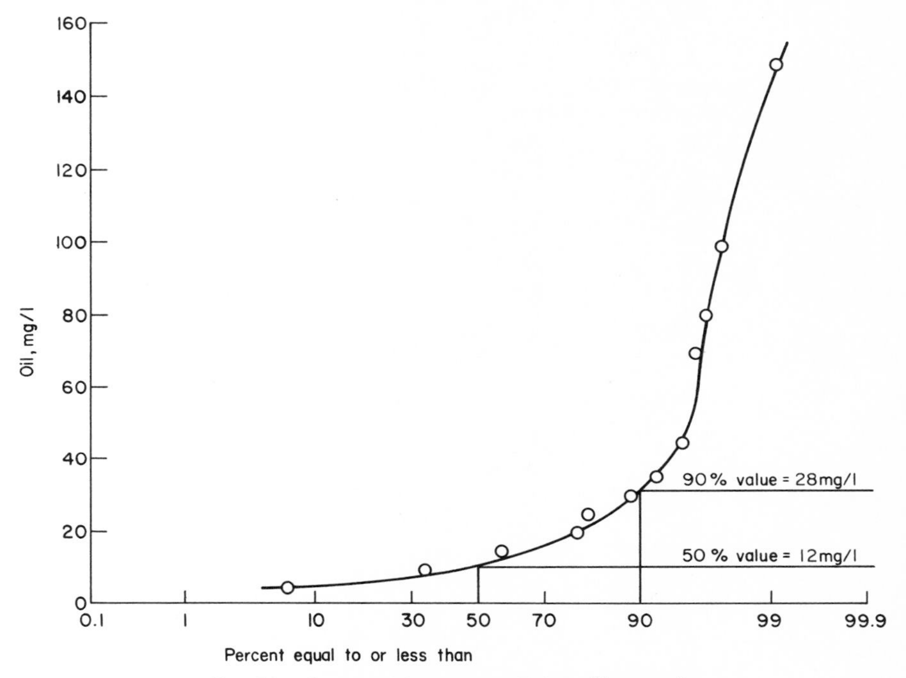

Fig. 22 Case 3: Variation in DAF effluent oil.

TABLE 20 DAF Performance Data

Influent oil, mg/l	Effluent oil, mg/l	% removal	Chemicals*	Configuration
1,930 (90%)	128 (90%)	93	Yes	Circular
580 (50%)*	68 (50%)	88	Yes	Circular
105 (90%)*	26 (90%)	78	Yes	Rectangular
68 (50%)	15 (50%)	75	Yes	Rectangular
170	52	70	No	Circular
125	30	71	Yes	Circular
100	10	90	Yes	Circular
133	15	89	Yes	Circular
94	13	86	Yes	Circular
638	60	91	Yes	Rectangular
153	25	83	Yes	Rectangular
75	13	82	Yes	Rectangular
61	15	75	Yes	Rectangular
360	45	87	Yes	Rectangular
315	54	83	Yes	Rectangular

* Alum most common, 100–130 mg/l. Polyelectrolyte, 1–5 mg/l occasionally added.

then by sedimentation. The sludge blanket clarifier which provides mixing, flocculation, and settling in the same unit has had many industrial applications because of its compact dimensions. This type of unit recycles preformed floc which aids in the development of new floc particles and enhances the entrapment of colloids. Occasionally, some form of coagulant aid is required to help form a good settling floc by promoting bridging between floc particles and rendering the floc more settleable. The most common coagulant aids are activated silica and the organic polyelectrolytes. There are three types of these polyelectrolytes: a cationic, which adsorbs on a negative colloid or floc particle; an anionic which replaces the anionic groups on a colloidal particle and permits hydrogen bonding between the colloid and the polymer; and the nonionic which adsorbs and flocculates by hydrogen bonding between the solid surfaces and the polar groups in the polymer. The most effective coagulant can only be determined through a series of laboratory tests. The chemical compounds most often used in the coagulation-precipitation process are listed in Table 21.[24]

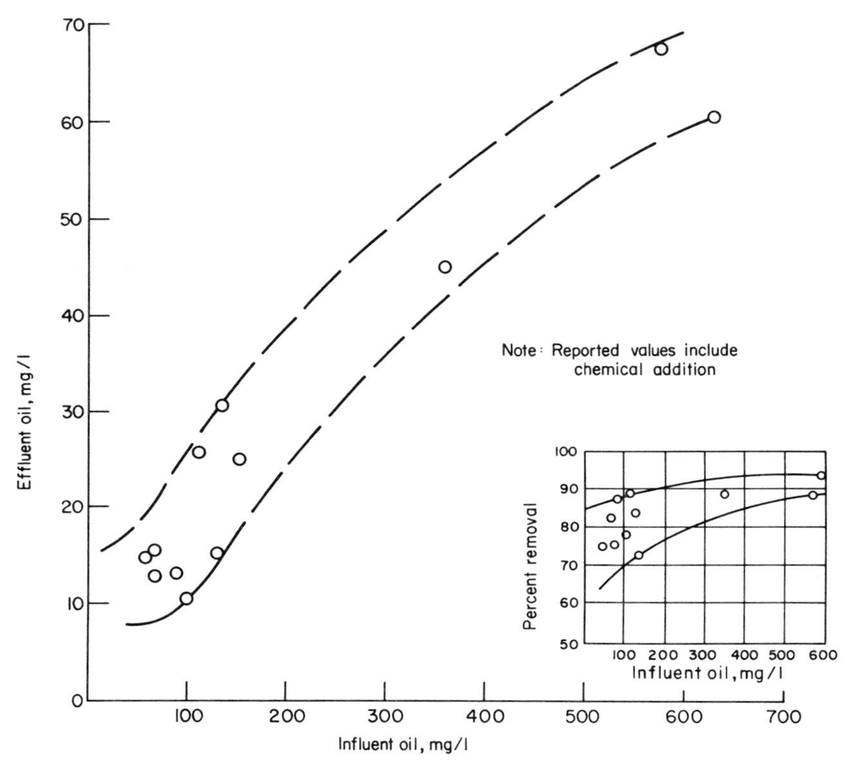

Fig. 23 Range of efficiencies of DAF systems.

The most common use of reactor-clarifiers in the treatment of refinery and petrochemical wastewaters is the removal of suspended and colloidal material from solution which is pollutional in nature. This process also is effective in reducing nutrients (for example, through the precipitation of phosphates) and in reducing heavy metals since most drop out as insoluble metallic hydroxides in the higher pH range. Water-soluble alkyl-aryl sulfonates can be removed by coagulation with lime which forms an insoluble precipitate.

It should be recognized that sludge handling and disposal may be the most important component of the reactor-clarifier treatment unit. Landfills are the most common form of inorganic sludge disposal, while organic sludges generally are dewatered and buried or incinerated.

Equalization The need for equalizing and/or surging wastewaters discharged from refinery and petrochemical processing units as an intermediate step in a treatment system is well established. Biological processes as well as physical-chemical systems operate more effectively if the composition and volume of the wastewater feed is relatively constant. Many waste-water discharges within refinery complexes are from washdowns, tank cleanings, batch operations, and inadvertant spills, necessitating a basin capable of receiving these waters and sequestering their fluctuant nature. Moreover, such basins often permit the neutralization of wastewaters by mixing

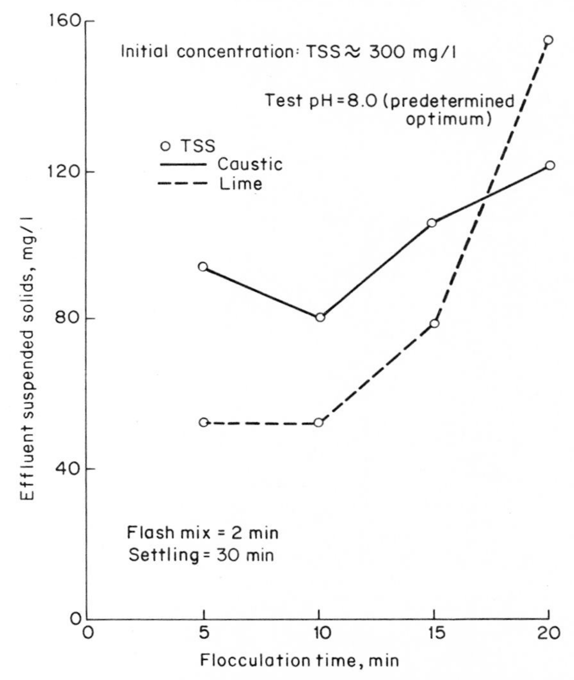

Fig. 24 Influence of flocculation time on effluent suspended solids concentration for reactor-clarifiers.

acidic and alkaline streams which would normally be discharged from the plant at different times. The required size and mixing features of the basin depend on the waste characteristics, the plant operating schedule, and consequent cyclic fluctuations. If sufficient flow and quality information can be obtained from a wastewater survey, a rational basis for designing the equalization facility can be developed. One approach[31] is the use of the following equation:

$$x_{(t+\Delta t)} = C_t\left[1 - \exp\left(-\frac{Qt}{v}\right)\right] + x_t\left[\exp\left(-\frac{Qt}{v}\right)\right]$$

where t = time increment chosen for the numerical step-by-step calculation
C_t = input concentration averaged over Δt
x_t = basin concentration before addition of the increment of flow at concentration of C_t
$x_{(t+\Delta t)}$ = basin concentration after addition of increment of flow
Q = volumetric flow rate
v = basin volume
t = time, varies between zero and Δt in the equation, the expression need only be evaluated at $t = \Delta t$

TABLE 21 Chemical Compounds Used in Coagulation Processes

Compounds	Formula	Commercial strength	Grades available	Weight, lb/cu ft	Remarks
		COAGULANTS			
Aluminum sulfate	$Al_2(SO_4)_3 \cdot 18H_2O$	17 percent Al_2O_3	Lump, powder, granules	Powder: 38–45 Other: 57–67	Coagulation and sedimentation systems; prior to pressure, filters for removal of suspended matter and oil
Sodium aluminate	$Na_2Al_2O_4$	55 percent Al_2O_3	Crystals	50–60	Usually added with soda ash to softeners
Ammonium alum	$Al_2(SO_4)_3(NH_4)_2SO_4 \cdot 24H_2O$	11 percent Al_2O_3	Lump, powder	60–68	Coagulation systems—not widely used
Potash alum	$Al_2(SO_4)_3 \cdot K_2SO_4 \cdot 24H_2O$	11 percent Al_2O_3	Lump, powder	64–68	Coagulation systems—not widely used
Copperas	$FeSO_4 \cdot 7H_2O$	55 percent $FeSO_4$	Crystals, granules	63–66	Suitable coagulant only in pH range of 8.5–11.0
Chlorinated copperas	$FeSO_4 \cdot 7H_2O + \frac{1}{2}Cl_2$	48 percent $FeSO_4$	. . .		Ferrous sulfate and chlorine are fed separately
Ferric sulfate	$Fe_2(SO_4)_3$	90 percent $Fe_2(SO)_3$	Powder granules	60–70	Coagulation—effective over wide range of pH, 4.0–11.0
Ferric chloride hydrate	$FeCl_3 \cdot 6H_2O$	60 percent $FeCl_3$	Crystals		Coagulation—effective over wide range of pH, 4.0–11.0
Magnesium oxide	MgO	95 percent MgO	Powder	25–35	Essentially insoluble—fed in slurry form
		COAGULANT AIDS			
Bentonite	. . .	. . .	Powder	60	Essentially insoluble—fed in slurry form
Sodium silicate	$Na_2O(SiO_2)_{3-25}$	40 Bé solution	Solution	86	. . .
		pH ADJUSTERS			
Lime, hydrated	$Ca(OH)_2$	93 percent $Ca(OH)_2$	Powder	25–50	pH adjustment and softening
Soda ash	Na_2CO_3	99 percent Na_2CO_3	Powder	34–52	pH adjustment and softening
Caustic soda	NaOH	98 percent NaOH	Flake, solid, ground, solution		pH adjustment, softening, oil removal systems
Sulfuric acid	H_2SO_4	100 percent H_2SO_4	Liquid		pH adjustment

Using this model, the equalization basin concentration of a critical pollutant or that discharged to the treatment process can be calculated at selected time intervals for various equalization volumes. This assumes that the critical pollutant in the industrial discharge was measured at time intervals of sufficient frequency to accurately define the variation. The standard deviation of the equalized concentration will decrease with increasing basin retention time. The relationship then can be used for selecting the retention time which corresponds to the maximum fluctuation that can be tolerated in the biological system. For example, it is recognized that the standard deviation of effluent discharge is a valid statistical parameter for defining the relative degree of the equalization achieved. As shown in Fig. 25, the standard deviation for COD loading without equalization for a petrochemical wastewater discharge is approximately 8,000 lb/day. Using 2-day time increments, the reduction of the standard deviation by virtue of equalization is graphically depicted in Fig. 25. If the transient effect on the treatment system is understood, then the cost effectiveness of an equalization basin can be determined and the optimum size selected.

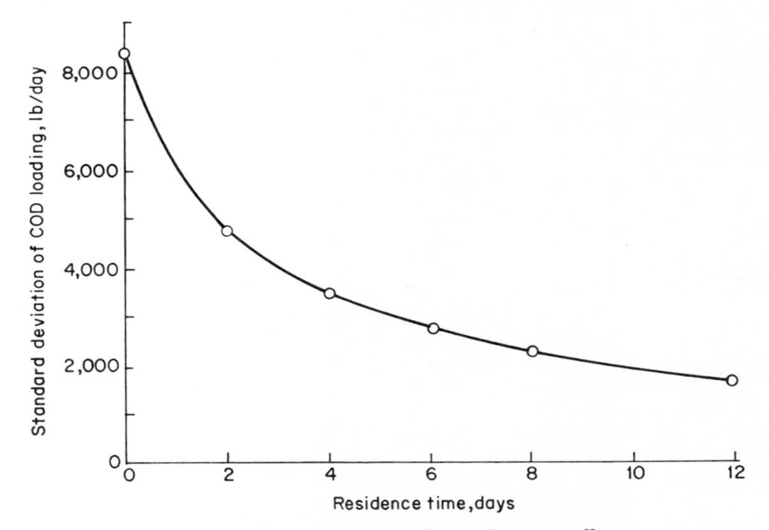

Fig. 25 Statistical evaluation of equalization efficiency.

Various types of construction have been used for equalization basins, including steel tanks, concrete or "shotcrete" basins, earthen lagoons, and vinyl or butyl rubber–lined lagoons. The type of tank selected will depend on the wastewater characteristics, the relative cost of materials and labor, and the land area availability. Mixing equipment such as mechanical mixers or baffling devices is required to ensure adequate basin equalization.

Secondary-Tertiary Treatment

Activatd sludge The activated sludge process, a continuous system where a biological population is mixed with wastewater and then separated by gravity from the treated liquor, is effective in the treatment of refinery-petrochemical effluents. Although the basic theory and kinetic development are adequately described elsewhere, their special applicability to the treatment of refinery and petrochemical wastewaters is described herein.[32,33]

The basis for the design of an activated sludge system is predicated on producing and maintaining an environment of microorganisms so that their growth and activity are as near optimal as possible. The activated sludge system, by virtue of its high mixed liquor suspended solids (MLSS) concentration accomplished through recycle, is classified as a high-rate biological process and therefore can tolerate higher contaminant concentration in the influent wastewater. Major design considerations for the successful activated sludge treatment of refinery-petrochemical wastewaters include:

1. The organic loading in terms of BOD applied per day per unit weight of mixed liquor biological solids
2. The BOD removal kinetics of a specific refinery-petrochemical wastewater
3. The organic and inorganic fluctuations of the feedwater to the activated sludge system
4. The free oil loading to the system
5. The temperature effects of the biological removal capacity of the system
6. The potential biotoxic or biostatic effects of the refinery-petrochemical effluents on the biological system
7. The oxygen requirements and biological sludge production rates of the given activated sludge system treating a wastewater of specified quality
8. The ability of the biological sludge in the system to separate from the treated liquor by gravity in the secondary clarifier, and to concentrate to the point of obtaining the desired MLSS level in the aeration basin through recycle
9. Operational flexibility to maximize process stability and continuity through the inclusion of parallel aeration basins, equalization facilities, off-spec holding basins, complete mixing, etc.

In general, refinery wastewaters are highly amenable to high-rate biological treatment using the activated sludge process; thus these systems are widely applied throughout the United States. The exact treatability of a refinery-petrochemical installation is, of course, a function of the effluent quality which depends on the classification of the refinery, the type of crude charge, the age of the facility and nature of its collection system, the relative effluent volume attributed to utility water blowdown, and the degree of in-plant control. For these reasons, design practices of the basic activated sludge process may vary from one installation to another. Treatability studies using bench- or pilot-scale process simulation techniques therefore are used to formulate the basic design criteria and predict treated effluent quality. It should be recognized, however, that the accuracy of information developed from these treatability studies depends on the accuracy of several assumptions. These include

1. The characteristics of the wastewater used in the activated sludge tests are representative of those anticipated in field tests.
2. The physical nature of the bench- or pilot-scale process is similar to the proposed full-scale unit.
3. Independent and dependent operational variables are considered.
4. Environmental parameters affecting process efficiency are defined.

It is apparent from these constraints that process simulation techniques can provide predictor relationships and mathematical expressions for the activated sludge treatment process receiving the refinery effluent in question, but they do not necessarily define a specific model with general applications. However, a treatability study which is properly programmed and judiciously implemented does afford the basis for the logical development of unit process selection, design, and predictive performance.

The design organic load for most activated sludge systems ranges from 0.10 lb BOD_5/(day) (lb MLSS) (extended aeration) to as high as 0.8 to 1.0 lb BOD_5/(day) (lb MLSS). Higher loadings can be imposed, but generally at the expense of poorer efficiency and higher organic levels in the treated effluent.

Oil and grease are of paramount importance when designing activated sludge systems for wastewaters such as those discharged from petroleum refinery and petrochemical installations. Hexane extractables adversely affect a biological system as the concentration in the mixed liquor approaches 50 to 75 mg/l. A recent study conducted for the Environmental Protection Agency indicated that an activated sludge system will perform satisfactorily with a continuous loading of hexane extractables of 0.1 lb/lb MLSS. It was recommended that the influent to the biological system should contain less than 75 mg/l hexane extractables and preferably less than 50 mg/l. The most significant problem related to oils in biological systems was attributed to lowering floc density to a level where the sludge-settling properties were destroyed.[34] The removal of free and, to some extent, emulsified oils through gravity separation, air flotation, or possibly filtration, as described in the previous sections of this chapter is therefore required in most instances.

Temperature is a particularly important variable in the biological treatment of refinery petrochemical wastewaters. If the combined effluent flow contains a proportionately high volume of cooling tower blowdown, cooling might be required during summer months to satisfy effluent temperature criteria. Conversely, excessive temperature losses through a biological system during winter months in the northern climate might lower biological activity to the point of failing to meet effluent BOD quality standards. As most of the new activated sludge systems are using mechanical aerators to oxygenate and mix the contents of the aeration basin, an approach was developed recently to predict the temperature in activated sludge basins.[35] The approach assumes the usual "water warmer than air" case, predicts the basin temperature by calculating the heat balance around the system and plots the calculated aeration basin temperature as a function of the wastewater temperature at the inlet to the aeration basin. An example of this relationship, developed for a refinery in the Midwest using a 10 percent probability basis for the coldest month, is shown in Fig. 26. The influence of temperature on biochemical reactions is well docu-

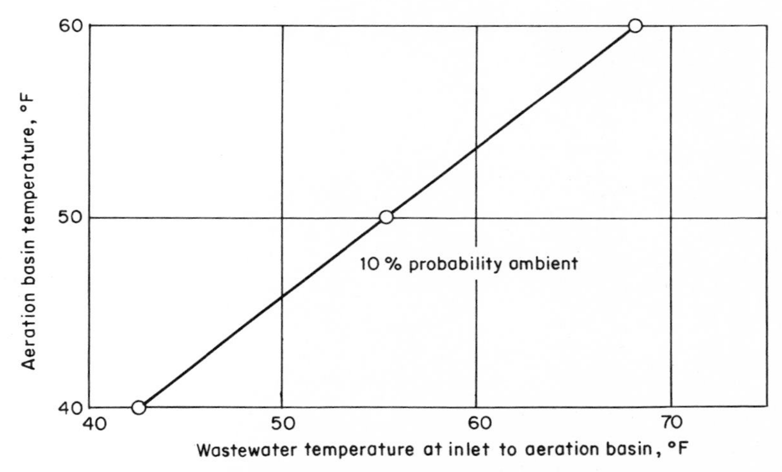

Fig. 26 Aeration basin temperature as a function of wastewater temperature at the aeration basin inlet.

mented.[36,37] The most traditional expression for relating the organic removal rate via biochemical oxidation with temperature is the Phelps equation

$$K_T = K_{20°C}\theta^{(T-20)}$$

where K_T = organic (BOD) removal rate at temperature T
$K_{20°C}$ = organic (BOD) removal rate coefficient at 20°C
T = liquid temperature, °C
θ = temperature coefficient

The coefficient θ is a function of many variables; namely, the nature of the wastewater and type of biological process. Few investigations recognize the significance of the type of wastewater on the temperature effect. For example, an activated sludge process treating an easily degradable potato processing waste as well as a domestic sewage activated sludge plant were not severely affected by basin temperature changes as shown in Fig. 27. This is attributed to the fact that both wastes were easily degradable by many biological genera and some removal was undoubtedly the result of *biosorption* which is not as temperature-dependent as straight biochemical oxidation. However, activated sludge treatment of a complex chemical petrochemical waste, mostly soluble, was significantly affected by basin temperature. From these plots and other available data, it can generally be stated that the temperature effect is more pronounced with increasing solubility and complexity.

Biotoxicity in an activated sludge process treating refinery and petrochemical wastewaters can be minimized or circumvented by in-plant control, proper equalization, and complete mixing of aeration basins. Most plant upsets, based on experience, result from inadvertent dumps or spills which discharge to the process sewer, shocking the biological system, or from the discharging of streams to the treatment system containing excessive levels of known biotoxicants (such as chromates, sulfides, ammonia, free oil, and other constituents common to refinery-petrochemical effluents).

In order to assess the treatment effectiveness of activated sludge systems in the treatment of refinery-petrochemical wastewaters, a list of performance data has been compiled and is presented in Table 22.

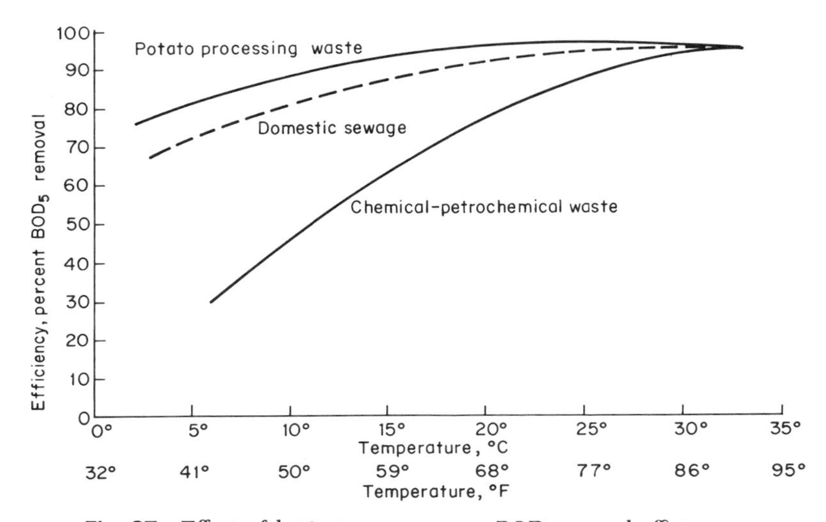

Fig. 27 Effect of basin temperature on BOD removal efficiency.

Biological treatment methods, specifically high-rate activated sludge systems, are considered to be compatible with the tenets of the Federal Water Pollution Control Act of 1972 (5.B. 2770 as amended). Proven performance of these systems as cited in Table 22 constitute what most interpret as "best practical treatment," particularly when considering the state-of-the-art of alternative nonbiological systems. More importantly, activated sludge systems are adaptable to system upgrading by the addition of effluent polishing processes.

Aerated lagoons Aerated lagoons are low-rate biological systems which provide a *flow-through basin* allowing microorganisms in contact with the wastewater to reduce organic constituents biochemically. Oxygenation and mixing are normally provided by mechanical aeration devices, although power levels are normally too low to maintain dissolved oxygen in all portions of the basin or to completely mix the system. Unlike the activated sludge system, there are no clarification and recycle steps and, therefore, a lower degree of system control. As the operating MLSS level is normally only 2 to 10 percent of an activated sludge basin, aerated lagoons are more sensitive to transient organic loading, toxic substances, and temperature effects. Aerated lagoons are being used in the treatment of refinery-petrochemical wastewaters in many instances, either as a process preceding waste stabilization ponds or as an interim treatment process which can be converted to an activated sludge system by increasing aeration and mixing and adding secondary clarification and recycle facilities. Recent federal legislation combined with increasingly stringent effluent quality requirements have mitigated the attractiveness of aerated lagoons as a "total system." Their application in the treatment of refinery wastewaters is, therefore, limited to *first-stage* or *interim treatment.*

TABLE 22 Activated Sludge Treatment of Refinery-Petrochemical Wastewaters[1]

Product and/or Process	Flow, mgd	BOD In, mg/l	BOD Out, mg/l	BOD Rem, %	COD In, mg/l	COD Out, mg/l	COD Rem, %	Organic loading, lb BOD_5/(day)(lb MLSS)	Nutrients required	Remarks
Refinery, natural gas liquids, chemical specialties, sanitary sewage	4.87	90	20	78	200	90	55	0.1	None	Effluent phenol 0.05, effluent oil 0.5 mg/l
Phthalic anhydride, phenol, salicylic acid, rubber chemicals, aspirin, phenacetin	2.54	45.7	6.1	86.7				0.031	None	Brush aeration, treats trickling filter effluent, 55% sludge return
Refinery, detergent alkylate	2.45	345	50–100	71–85.5	855	150–200	76.6–82.5	0.08	PO_4	Phenols in = 160 mg/l, sulfide in = 150 mg/l, laboratory scale
Butadiene, maleic acid	2.0	2,000	25	98.8	2,990	480	84	0.24	NH_3	
Butadiene, alkylate	1.5	1,960	24	98.8	2,980	477	98.3			
Butadiene, maleic anhydride fumaric acid, tetrahydrophthalic, anhydride, butylene isomers, alkylate	1.5	1,960	24	98.8	2,980	51	84	0.24 (MLVSS)	NH_3	Surface aerators, wastes contain: alcohols, maleic acid, fumaric acid, cetic acid, C_1–C_4 aldehydes, furfural, water-soluble addition products
Ethylene, propylene, benzene	1.44	600	90	85	700	105	85		None	Oily waters: C_4–C_{10} oils 90% phenol removal
Naphthalene, butadiene, phenol, acrylonitrile, soft detergent bases, resins, other aromatics	0.43	500	60	85–90	600	90	80–85	1.5	NH_3 PO_4	Sour waters: oil in = 500 mg/l, phenol in = 65 mg/l, pH adjustment, preceded by trickling filter, phenol removal = 99.9%
Phenol, 2,4-D, aniline, nitrobenzene, rubber, chemicals, polyester resins, misc. chemicals	0.97	370	76	76.2				0.4	NH_3 PO_4	Accelator pilot-plant sewage added in ratio 1:600 once a week
Ethylene, propylene, butadiene, benzene, polyethylene, fuel oils	0.63	85	10	99	200	200	62.5			Quench waters, polyethylene and benzene wastes: preceded by trickling filter, effluent phenol 0.01 ppm

TABLE 22 Activated Sludge Treatment of Refinery-Petrochemical Wastewaters[1] (Continued)

Product and/or process	Flow, mgd	BOD In, mg/l	BOD Out, mg/l	BOD Rem, %	COD In, mg/l	COD Out, mg/l	COD Rem, %	Organic loading, lb BOD_5/(day)(lb MLSS)	Nutrients required	Remarks
Refining processes	0.51–0.63	125	15–25	80–88			65–80	0.28–0.4	PO_4	Phenol removal 85–94%; oil removal 75–85%; effluent phenol 0.5 mg/l; effluent oil 1–2 mg/l; temperature −30°C
Nylon	0.4	1,540	250	83.8						
Petroleum products	0.27	440	5	98.8	500	60	88			Phenol in = 25 ppm, phenol out = 1 ppm
Acrylic fibers	0.252	2,260	118–226	90–95				0.4		Wastes contain acrylonitrile, dimethylamine, dimethylformamide, formic acid; temperature 35–37°C, return sludge 10–50% mechanical aeration
Acetone, phenol *p*-cresol, ditert.-butyl-*p*-cresol	0.216	3,560–4,400	1,030–750	71–83				0.89–1.1		Waste phenol 600 ppm, waste BOD 7,500–8,000, waste diluted with effluent or water; pilot plant
Resins-formalin, aminoplasts, phenol-formaldehyde, epoxy resins, textile auxiliaries	0.2	890	444–266		50–70			0.8–1.2		Diffused air; domestic waste added; trickling filter follows 100% recycle sludge
Ethylene and propylene oxides, glycols, morpholines, ethylene-diamines, ethers, piperazine	0.15	1,950	20	99	7,970–8,540	5,120–5,950	25–40	0.51	None	Laboratory scale; extended aeration; high nonbiodegradable fraction followed by stabilization ponds

2,4-D, 2,4,5-T (acid wash wastes)	0.1	1,670	125	92.5	2,500	500	80	0.78 (MLVSS)	NH_3 PO_4	1:1 mixture of acid wash streams diluted 9:1 prior to treatment to reduced chlorides, toxicity laboratory scale 90–95% phenol removed; laboratory scale
Cracking, isomerization of butane and naphthene, alkylation, benzene, toluene, alcohols, ketones, cresylic acids		1,100	55–110	90–95				0.5		
Ethylene, acetylene			20					0.23–0.33	PO_4	Effluent phenol 0.1 mg/l, effluent oil 1 ppm
Nylon manufacture				95			85	1.0–3.0	PO_4 NH_3	NH_4OH used as nutrient and neutralizing agent, waste diluted 2:1
Petrochemical plant	2.4	2,850	65	97				0.5	None	Pilot-plant study
Large integrated refinery—Class D incl. once-through cooling water	32.4	270	20	92				0.5	None	Pilot-plant study
Class E refinery	4.6	340	40	88	850	250	71	0.4	None	Pilot-plant study
Class E refinery	2.0	575	50	91	980	200	71	0.4	None	Operating plant
Class C refinery	1.2	205	30	85	544	150	80	0.4	None	Operating plant preceded by API, DAF
Class D refinery	1.8				270	115	58	0.1	None	Operating plant
Class E refinery	25.0	270	25	91	490	150	70	0.4	None	Bench-scale treatability study
Petrochemical complex	7.8				1,500	350	78	0.4	None	Bench-scale treatability study
Petrochemical complex	18.3	600	50	92	1,500	600	60	0.4	None	Bench-scale treatability study

The approach for designing aerated lagoons is outlined elsewhere,[32] but basically entails consideration of influent organic levels, the predetermined organic removal rate, the estimated temperature of the lagoon during the critical month, and the anticipated amount of *organic feedback* resulting from any anaerobic decomposition which may occur on the bottom of an incompletely mixed aerated lagoon basin.

Aerated lagoons are operated at high organic loading levels because of the low concentration of microorganisms suspended in the basin. These loadings usually exceed 1.0 to 2.0 lb BOD_5/(day) (lb MLSS). As in activated sludge basins, the organic removal rate is high for most hydrocarbons (such as those discharged from topping plants) but is reduced for wastewaters of increasing complexity such as those discharged from completely integrated facilities. Since the solids level maintained in an aerated lagoon is low, temperature variation will exert a profound effect on the rate of organic (BOD) removal. In order to predict the basin temperature at an extreme summer or winter month, the following aerated lagoon temperature relationship is normally used:[32]

$$T_i - T_w = \frac{(T_w - T_a)fA}{Q}$$

where T_i = influent wastewater temperature, °F
T_w = basin temperature, °F
T_a = air temperature, °F
Q = wastewater flow, mgd
S = surface area
f = proportionality factor (a function of geographical location)

Another factor which influences aerated lagoon performance is wind, particularly when the basin geometry exhibits a long fetch in the direction of the prevailing wind. Such winds stir up bottom sediments, causing a deterioration of effluent quality in terms of suspended solids, solids-stabilized oily material, and settleable solids. Organic feedback is another factor to be considered in design. As large volumes of oily solids tend to settle in the bottom of the basins because of the low mixing levels, subsequent decomposition anaerobically releases by-products from the bottom sediments back to the overlying water. These by-products are then utilized in the upper layers by aerobic or facultative microorganisms resulting in an additional BOD load to the system. This feedback has been estimated to be as high as 20 percent of the influent organic load in the summer months at one refinery located in the Southwest.

A compilation of aerated lagoons treating refinery-petrochemical wastewater operations at various locations in the United States and the reported operation efficiencies is shown as Table 23.

Trickling filters Trickling filters have been used in treatment for industrial wastes for many years although the trend is away from filters as high-rate secondary treatment facilities in the refinery-petrochemical industry. They do, however, have some application as *roughing* devices preceding other biological or physical-chemical units.

The trickling filter is a packed-media bed covered with biological slime through which the wastewater is passed. As the organic-laden waste flows over the slime, organics and oxygen diffuse into the biological mass where they undergo biochemical oxidation to carbon dioxide, water, and metabolic by-products. Granular media is generally used to support the biological mass although the introduction in recent years of synthetic filter media has caused a variety of changes in the design and construction of trickling filters. These media, with low bulk density, have resulted in the use of deeper filters operated at greatly increased organic and hydraulic loading rates.

Most design to date is formulated on empirical standards which must be modified to accommodate the nature of the industrial wastewater. The number of variables which influence trickling filter performance have complicated the development of a dependable model which can be applied or modified to existing conditions. An attempt to quantify some of these variables and verify predictive equations for the trickling filter process performance has recently been published.[38]

Some of the variables of design and operation include organic loading, hydraulic loading, nature of organic constituent, temperature, media type and distribution, and

TABLE 23 Aerated Lagoon Treatment of Petrochemical Wastes

Product and/or process	Flow, mgd	BOD			COD			Nutrients required	Remarks
		In, mg/l	Out, mg/l	Rem, %	In, mg/l	Out, mg/l	Rem, %		
Refinery butadiene, butyl rubber	19.1	225	100	55	610	350	43	PO_4	Followed by stabilization pond, temperature = 32°C 30% COD is nonbiodegradable, laboratory scale
Refinery	2.45	345	50–100	71–85	855	150–200	77–83	PO_4	Influent phenols 160 mg/l, influent sulfides 150 mg/l, laboratory scale
Petrochemical facility	0.51	100	25	75					Surface aeration, waste is extensively pretreated. Followed by pond
Chemicals for lubricating oils production unit	0.2	465	180	61	1,050	600	43		
Class A refinery	24.0	275	80	71	560	270	52	None	Followed by stabilization pond, power level = 0.08 hp/1,000 gal, detention time = 1 day
Class C refinery	2.0	330	50	84	730	220	70	None	
Class D refinery	30	200	100	50	700	400	45	None	Followed by small stabilization pond, detention time = 2.5 days

TABLE 24 Trickling Filter Data

Chemical plant	Filter depth, ft	Size of medium, in.	BOD_5 loading, 1,000 cu ft/day	BOD_5, % reduction	Hydraulic loading, gal/gd³/D
A	9.75	3	25.0	60.0*	590
B	5† 5‡		42.0	91.0§	743
C	6† 6‡	4	35.0	97.5§	257
D	6† 8‡		36.8 18.3	71.0§	1,720 1,290
E	14	3–5	94.5	80.0	1,000
F	10	3	44.0	58.3 91.0	492 537

* On gross phenol basis.
† First stage treatment.
‡ Second stage treatment.
§ Overall basis.

filter geometry and construction. Control of ventilation and plugging is necessary because anaerobic action (which is always present to some extent in a filter) becomes excessive when plugging occurs and ventilation is inadequate.

The recorded performance of trickling filters in the treatment of refinery and petrochemical effluents ranges from 10 to 20 percent removal when used as a roughing device to 50 to 90 percent when applied as a total process for secondary treatment. Performance data for filters using rock media and treating chemical wastes are listed in Table 24. Performance data across a filter using synthetic media for one chemical waste are shown in Table 25. The removal of BOD through a roughing filter using synthetic media is tabulated in Table 26. Additional data for BOD and COD reduction across a trickling filter receiving various petrochemical wastewaters are reported elsewhere.[1]

Waste stabilization ponds Waste stabilization ponds depend on the natural aquatic processes of bacterial and algal symbiosis, requiring sunlight as a primary energy source, and have been used successfully in the treatment of refinery and petrochemical wastewaters. Although ponds are often used to provide long-term polishing for effluents discharged from upstream biological units, they have been used in some instances as a total treatment system.

Empirical equations which take into consideration organic loading, temperature, and toxic substance effect have been developed and successfully used to design facultative waste stabilization ponds.[39] Application of such empirical relationships

TABLE 25 Typical Performance Data for Filter Using Synthetic Media

BOD, mg/l		BOD, lb/(1,000 cu ft)(day)		Percent removal
Inf.	Eff.	Loading	Removal	
558	205	586	369	63
567	232	596	348	59
489	233	513	267	52
389	155	408	245	60
428	187	450	252	56
374	157	393	228	58
340	150	357	207	58
450	190	470	275	58

TABLE 26 Roughing Treatment—General Chemical Waste

(Synthetic biological oxidation media)

Flow rate, gpm/cu ft	COD, mg/l		COD, lb/(1,000 cu ft)(day)		COD, % reduction
	Influent	Effluent	Loading	Removal	
1.0	2,115	1,800	1,176	178	16
1.5	2,150	1,870	1,810	237	14
2.0	2,010	1,780	2,258	257	11

System outline: Standard pilot tower (7 cu ft packed to 21.6 ft depth).
Waste description: Clarified general chemical waste. No recycle. No clarification of tower effluent practiced.

makes certain assumptions, however, and may not apply to the waste stabilization pond treatment of refinery and petrochemical wastewaters. For example, ponds are susceptible to wind action and short-circuiting which would prevent conformance to predictive efficacy and performance. Moreover, the accumulation of emulsions in waste stabilization ponds prevents sunlight penetration, resulting in excessive anaerobic action.

The tendency is to construct single ponds although series ponds may be more efficient since short-circuiting is reduced and overall organic removal may possibly be increased. The first pond is usually anaerobic because of the imposed surface loading and will be odoriferous. It does trap floating organic material, however, and provides for easier removal of these floating materials. The retention time in waste stabilization ponds ranges from 1 to 90 days. The exact retention time depends on the land available as well as the design requirement. As land is generally quite expensive in area contiguous to refinery and petrochemical operations, the use of waste stabilization ponds is limited. Additionally, new effluent guidelines are in most cases too stringent for pond capability. The proliferation of algal and bacterial material in ponds, for example, adds to the effluent suspended solids level even though the soluble organic fraction may be reduced to acceptable levels.

As previously mentioned, waste stabilization ponds are not widely used in the United States to treat refinery and petrochemical effluents. Typical waste stabilization pond operation data from five refineries as reported by API are given in Table 27.[24] Additional operating data from petrochemical plants are found in Table 28.[1]

TABLE 27 Typical Oxidation Pond Operating Data

Parameter	Refinery A		Refinery B		Refinery C		Refinery D	
	Retention time, days							
	5		7		20		10	
	Influent	Effluent	Influent	Effluent	Influent	Effluent	Influent	Effluent
Oil content, mg/l	30	12	37	8	105	8		
Phenolics, mg/l	29	22	29	0.2	3.1	0.5	26	0.5
BOD, mg/l	250	175	107	32			100–300	82–150
Suspended solids, mg/l					52	9		
Ammonia, mg/l							58	58
Turbidity, mg/l					196	22		
Nitrogen bases, mg/l								
Sulfides, mg/l			1.2	0.1			1	0
pH			10.8	9.5	8.7	8.3	7–8	7.1–8.6
Temperature, °F					115	38		

TABLE 28 Waste Stabilization Pond Treatment of Petrochemical Wastes

Product and/or Process	Flow, mgd	BOD			COD			Organic loading, lb BOD_5/(acre)(day)	Nutrients required	Remarks
		In, mg/l	Out, mg/l	Rem, %	In, mg/l	Out, mg/l	Rem, %			
Refinery butadiene, butyl rubber	19.1	100	50	50	350	200	43	Primary pond 91; total ponds 46	None	Ponds in series after aerated lagoon, laboratory scale
Resins, alcohols,	5	500–1,000	400–700	20–60				96	None	Anaerobic
amines, esters,	5	400–700	25–50	88–96				164	None	Anaerobic
styrene, ethylene	5	25–50	5–30	40–90				5	None	Aerobic
Butane, propane natural gas, ethanol, ethyl chloride, polyethylene, ammonia, H_2SO_4	3.25	150	7–15	90–95	260			75	None	Facultative pond, 18 days detention, influent SO_4 = 650 mg/l
Refinery, detergent alkylate	2.45	50–100	20–50	50–80	150–200	120	20–40	95	None	After aerated lagoon or activated sludge, laboratory scale
Plastics	1.69	686	186		1,681	590	65			Facultative ponds
Ethylene and propylene oxides, glycols, morpholines, ethylenediamines, ethers, piperazine	0.15	20			5,120–5,950	4,610–4,450	10–25	25	None	Laboratory scale Faculative ponds to remove some residual COD. High nonbiodegradable fraction. After activated sludge
Mixed petrochemicals				95–99			75–96	100		Facultative ponds

Cooling tower oxidation The use of cooling towers as biological oxidation systems has been applied successfully in the treatment of refinery wastewaters although there are certain inherent disadvantages in such practices. If the primary drawback of fouling heat exchangers can be resolved, cooling tower organic reduction has been shown to be successful.[24,40] These studies indicated that the use of wooden cooling towers as a combined biological wastewater treatment and cooling system was workable considering biological efficiency, heat-transfer efficiency, tower packing disintegration, and solid buildup and sloughing.

The bacterial growth resulting from the organic removal through a tower has been reported as finely dispersed and nonfilamentous.[24] Even though the predominant microorganisms did not result in a type of sludge mass which caused a fouling or slime problem, daily backwash of the condensers and coolers was required.

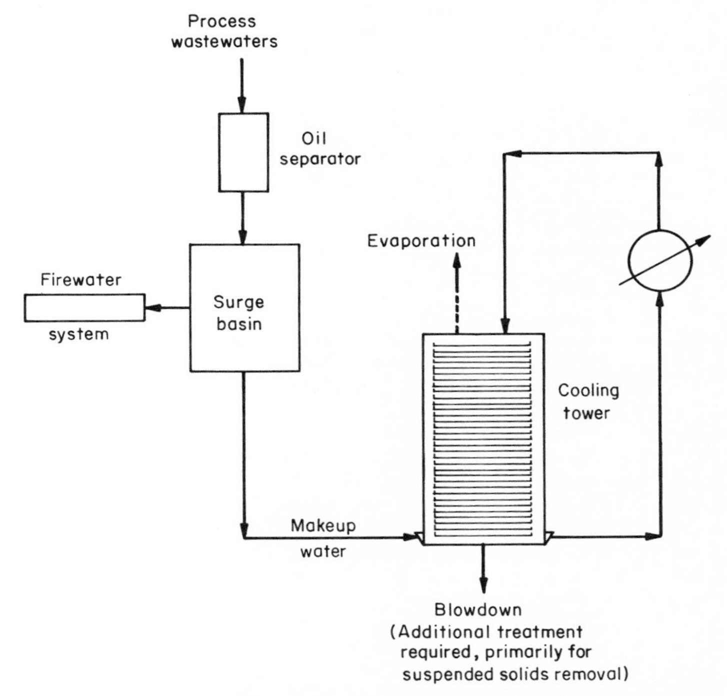

Fig. 28 Schematic of a cooling tower biological oxidation system.

Periodic blowdowns are necessary to keep the dissolved and suspended solids in the cooling water at required levels. The BOD of this blowdown will still be high because of the presence of suspended biological sloughing so that subsequent treatment of blowdown is required. Generally, only a few problems associated with additional equipment corrosion have been observed while using this type of system. Although cooling water treatment has been used exclusively in refinery complexes, such systems undoubtedly have application for reuse of specific petrochemical wastewaters.

A simplified schematic of a cooling tower biological oxidation system is shown in Fig. 28. Reported operation data from two cooling tower waste treatment systems are shown in Table 29.[24]

Chemical oxidation Chemical oxidation of selected waste streams within a refinery or petrochemical complex may be an appropriate method of treatment, depending on the oxidation reaction time, the characteristics of the oxidation products, and

TABLE 29 Average Operating Data from Two Cooling Tower Waste Treatment Systems

Parameter	Refinery A		Refinery B	
	Influent	Effluent	Influent	Effluent
Flow, gpm	2,500	700		
Temperature, °F	70	75	77	80
Suspended solids, mg/l	28	100		
Sulfides, mg/l	0	0		
Phenolics, mg/l	12	0.09	3	0.06
BOD, mg/l	158	111	30	15
COD, mg/l	327	231		
pH	7.5	7	9.2	7.3
Alkalinity, mg/l as $CaCO_3$	150	75		
Oil, mg/l	30	30	30	20
Chlorides, mg/l			1,300	3,200

overall process economics. Chemical oxidation, raising the oxidation level of a substance or reducing its BOD and COD, can be accomplished using the primary oxidizers of oxygen, ozone, permanganate, chlorine, or chlorine dioxide. Catalytic oxidation offers a practical means of oxidizing small volumes of concentrated organic waste which are not susceptible to other forms of treatment. A brief discussion of each of these oxidation approaches follows.

Gaseous or dissolved oxygen is used both as a stripping agent for such gases as carbon dioxide, hydrogen sulfide, methane, and other low boiling organic compounds as well as for chemical oxidation.[41] Although the use of pure oxygen may be applicable from a process point of view, economics may render it impractical. Pure oxygen is, however, being used for biological systems with reported savings in cost over conventional systems. Air oxidation is used for sulfide oxidation as well as for removal of divalent forms of iron and manganese. The oxidation of iron, however, is strongly pH dependent.

The chemistry and theory behind the oxidation of sulfides is well documented.[21] Most sulfide oxidation units presently used are patented designs. The design criteria and operating conditions for several of these units are listed in Table 30. All of the units mentioned oxidize 100 percent of the influent sulfides, but if large quantities of mercaptans or mercaptides are present in the waste, a reoxidizer may be required to ensure complete oxidation. The reoxidizer should be operated at a temperature of 130 to 150°F with a pressure of 50 psi to prevent mercaptan stripping. The data in Table 30 indicate that sulfides can be oxidized to thiosulfates more easily than to sulfates. It is possible that some sulfate was produced in the towers but, to obtain maximum conversion, low sulfide loadings are required. The oxidation of sulfides in a liquid phase using a typical sulfide oxidation unit is shown in Fig. 29. Heavy oils should be eliminated from the waste prior to oxidation since pilot-plant studies indicated that 5 percent of such oil could decrease the oxidation rate by 50 percent.

TABLE 30 Design and Efficiency of Selected Sulfide Oxidation Units

Oxidation products	Tower temp. (top), °F	Feed, lb sulfide/min	Air flow, lb air/lb sulfide oxidized	Detention time, hr	Pressure (top), psia	Sulfur oxidized, lb/(hr)(cu ft tower)	Remarks
100% thiosulfite	185–250	1.4–11.7	7.3–12.2	1.1–7.9	50–79	0.29–0.39	
54% thiosulfite, 46% sulfate	230	0.68	6.8	3.87	75	0.03	Concurrent air/water flow, no catalyst
44% thiosulfite, 56% sulfate	239	0.17	27.0	3.31	57	0.01	
37% thiosulfite, 63% sulfate	239	0.08	57.5	6.62	57	0.05	
100% sulfate	265	0.73	28.4	3.52	72	0.035	

Ozone is an oxidizing agent used for phenols, cyanides, and unsaturated organics destruction since it is a considerably stronger oxidizing agent than chlorine. It is a powerful oxidant which reacts rapidly with a majority of organic compounds and microorganisms present in wastewaters. The primary disadvantage is the high capital cost associated with the ozone-generation equipment. It does, however, effectively oxidize many constituents and is used for color removal, disinfection, iron and manganese removal, phenol oxidation, and cyanide oxidation. The efficiency of ozone destruction of chlorinated hydrocarbons for various ozone dosage levels is indicated in Table 31.[1]

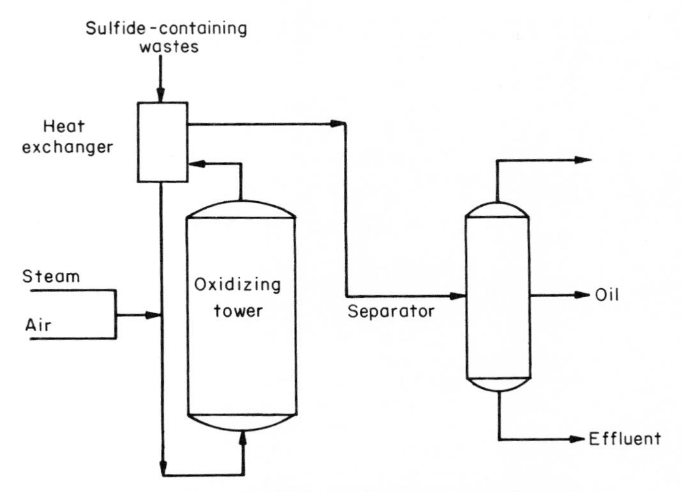

Fig. 29 A typical sulfide oxidation process flow sheet.

TABLE 31 Ozonation of Chlorinated Hydrocarbons

		COD		
Ozone dosage, mg/l	pH initial	Raw waste, mg/l	Treated waste, mg/l	Reduction, %
994	12.2	3,340	1,410	57.8
2,530	12.6	3,340	900	73
2,700	7.0	3,340	1,460	56.5
3,920	12.6	3,340	745	77.5
4,640	12.6	3,340	450	86.5
5,400	12.6	3,340	314	90.5

Permanganate oxidation has been and is being used in treating water to remove taste, odor, iron, and manganese but is not generally used for the specific removal of BOD.

Chlorine has been applied in oxidizing phenol and cyanides in petrochemical wastes. The oxidation of phenols, however, must be carried to completion to prevent the release of chlorophenols which can cause objectionable odors and tastes in drinking water, even at very low concentrations. An excess of chlorine usually is required because of the reaction with various other chemical compounds (such as ammonia, sulfides, and various organics which can interfere with the chlorination process). To prevent the formation of chlorophenols, the pH of the waste is kept at 7 or higher and the usual reaction time required is 1 to 2 hr. Chlorine can be applied either as free chlorine or as hypochlorite. Cyanides can be oxidized to carbon dioxide and nitrogen by chlorination. The wastewater must be kept at a pH value greater than 8.5 during treatment to prevent the release of toxic cyanogen. Ammonia, which is being singled out as an initial pollutant in refinery and petrochemical effluents, can be oxidized by chlorine to free nitrous oxide gas. However, the chlorine demand is high and the process economics should be evaluated. Nevertheless, chemical oxidation of ammonia may be more practical from an economic and process viewpoint than alternate ammonia removal processes.

Chlorine dioxide has gained wide acceptance in water treatment and can be considered in refinery wastewater treatment for certain applications since phenol oxida-

TABLE 32 Oxidation Processes Used in Petrochemical Waste Treatment

Product or process	Waste components (if known)	Type of oxidation process	Remarks
Acrylic fibers nitriles	Cyanides	Ozone	Optimum pH 11–12
Acrylic fibers	Dimethylamine, dimethylformamide	Catalytic oxidation	Pt catalyst, 310°C, combined with direct combustion
Acrylic fibers, nitriles	Cyanides	Chlorination	1–2-hr treatment time pH 8.5 required
Caustic treating operations	Sulfidic spent caustics	Air and steam	Oxidizes sulfides to thiosulfates and sulfates
Ethylene glycol	—	Catalytic oxidation	Copper-chromite catalysts 97% organic destruction
Mixed petrochemicals	Hydrocarbons	Catalytic oxidation	Metal oxide catalysts
Mixed petrochemicals	0.5–1.0% organic from column heads	Catalytic oxidation	575°C Pt. catalyst added to control oxidation
Mixed petrochemicals	3–5% organic acids	Thermal cracking	800°C, natural gas
Synthetic rubber	Probably unsaturated hydrocarbons (some chlorinated)	Ozonation	Optimum pH 12.6, 90.5% COD reduction
Nylon intermediates	16% NaCl, 0.5% metal salts, 1% misc. organics	Air	Converts metals to insoluble hydroxides
Phenol, resins, refining crude	Phenolics	Ferrous salts and hydrogen peroxide	Expensive
Phenol	Sulfite liquors	Chlorine	
Phenol	Sulfite liquors	Ozone	Optimum pH 12
Phenol	Sulfite liquors	Air-iron catalyst in liquid	Aerations in venturi units 99.9% SO_3 removed in 11 hr
p-Cresol	Sulfite liquors	Air	Mixco agitator with sparge ring
β-Naphthol	Sulfite liquors	Air	Mixco agitator with sparge ring
Refinery	Petroleum products	Ozonation	75–85% removal of petroleum products 16-hr detention

tion using chlorine dioxide avoids the formation of chlorophenols.[41] Like ozone, the instability of gaseous chlorine dioxide necessitates generation in situ, and initial capital costs for these systems are quite expensive.

A tabulation of oxidation processes used in petrochemical wastewater treatment is given in Table 32.[1]

Filtration Filtration, having been used for years as a polishing step in treating water for domestic use, is finding application as an effluent-treating polishing process. More filtration polishing can be anticipated in the future for industrial treatment facilities as effluent criteria are becoming more stringent and filter units can easily be adapted to existing biological systems. Moreover, a filtration step usually is required before carbon adsorption polishing units can be put on-line.

Filtration is particularly applicable for polishing an activated sludge or extended aeration plant receiving refinery or petrochemical wastewaters as much of the effluent organic material is in suspended or colloidal form. Filtration removes most of these constituents, and the backwash can be treated separately or rechanneled back through the biological treatment plant. The filtrate, or effluent, can then be discharged directly to the receiving environment, recycled for reuse, or possibly sent to carbon columns for removal of residual dissolved organic materials.

The design and operating factors for filters include the mode of throughput, the type of media and its distribution, the underdrain system, and the type of backwashing operation. Gravity filters using the downflow or upflow modes of operation generally are used for effluent polishing, although pressure filtration may offer some advantages as part of a tertiary treatment system. The principal advantages of pressure filtration include single pumping requirements, ease of automation, absence of negative pressure, and ability to adsorb higher pressure losses through the sand or anthracite media before backwashing is required.

The efficacy of filtration as an effluent polishing device to a biological plant can first be assessed by measuring the difference between the filtered and unfiltered COD or 5-day BOD. If this difference is significant and the filtrate samples meet organic concentration criteria, then filtration can be evaluated further using a pilot-plant approach for testing. A filtration polishing system was installed behind an extended aeration system at one Midwest refinery; the design criteria were based on pilot studies using the upflow filter unit shown in Fig. 30. A sand and gravel media was used, and water from the existing secondary clarifier was pumped to the pilot filter. Composite samples of the filter influent and effluent were collected throughout each filter run. The operational procedures used for each filter run were:

1. The filter was backwashed prior to each test run. The backwash cycle included bumping the filter with 30 cfm of air for 3 to 4 min. The 100-gpm backwash rate was then continued for an additional 6 to 10 min until a clear effluent was produced.
2. The filtration cycle was initiated, controlling the hydraulic flow rate manually with a valve.
3. Turbidity tests were performed on grab samples of the effluent throughout the filter run. The break point was established when the turbidity reached a predefined level.
4. Chemical addition to the discharge side of the feed pump was made with an air-operated positive displacement pump.

Pilot tests of the sand filter were performed at surface loadings of 4, 6, and 8 gpm/sq ft. Moreover, filter runs were made at 8 gpm/sq ft using polyelectrolytes as chemical additives.

The performance of the pilot filter unit, which was translated into the full-scale filter design criteria, is graphically depicted in Fig. 31. This figure shows turbidity, total organic carbon (TOC), and pressure differential as a function of throughput volume for one filter run. Based on these pilot-scale results, an acceptable effluent could be produced with a filtration system complementing the existing biological facility, and the filtration system was installed.

Carbon adsorption Although the carbon adsorption process has not been widely used in the field of refinery and petrochemical wastewater treatment to date, preliminary pilot work and limited experience indicate selected applicability.

The efficacy of utilizing carbon adsorption for the treatment of refinery and petrochemical wastewaters at any point in a process sequence can be determined only after a thorough investigation using continuous-flow pilot systems has been performed. There is a tendency for investigators and equipment developers to oversimplify the process adaptability for industrial wastewater applications. Specifically, the translation of data from carbon systems receiving domestic wastes into design criteria for industrial utilization has limited validity, and the use of batch isotherm information under any testing condition as a basis for process selection is imprecise. The technical and economic justification for including carbon adsorption as a treatment process in a refinery or petrochemical complex must be predicated on pilot-plant simulation, particularly in the absence of case histories and full-scale operational experience. A proper interpretation of the results is then necessary to consummate the process evaluation, determine the economics, and select the most appropriate treatment sequence.

The complexity of refinery and petrochemical wastewaters and the extremes in adsorbability of compound groups further mitigate the applicability of general rate equations. The influence of molecular structure and other factors on adsorbability, for example, is presented in Table 33.[42] This relative adsorbability, combined with unpredictable effects or process variables, forces an empirical approach for investigating carbon process applicability. Breakthrough curves defining contaminant

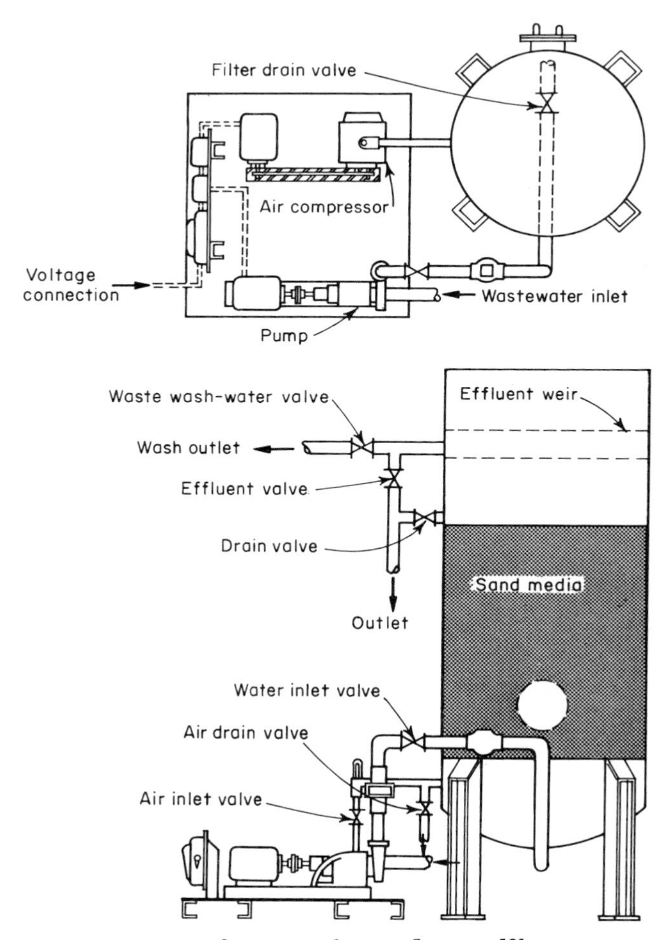

Fig. 30 Schematics of an upflow sandfilter.

removal rates and residuals (in terms of BOD, COD, TOC, color, etc.), carbon capacities and influence of process variables can, therefore, be developed using continuous-flow columns.

Consideration for placement of the carbon adsorption process includes biological-carbon series treatment, carbon-biological series treatment, and carbon adsorption as a total process. Each of these applications requires primary treatment for the removal of oily substances and suspended matter using gravity separators and, in some instances, dissolved air flotation. A conceptual flow diagram for each of these prospective systems is shown in Fig. 32.

Of the applications indicated, the series biological-carbon treatment scheme will probably be most prevalent in the immediate future. This is, by necessity, true for many refineries because they have already made the capital investment in secondary biological plants and require a tertiary process to meet the new quality criteria. In the case of a new facility, this approach lends itself to phase construction by installing biological facilities to meet interim effluent polishing when required.

The series carbon-biological system is being considered by some refineries and chemical plants. Its apparent advantages are a more effective use of carbon, less chance of biological upset because of carbon removal of biotoxic substances with dampening of organic surges, and a reduction of excess biological sludge inherent with the reduced organic loading. Although these stated advantages merit considera-

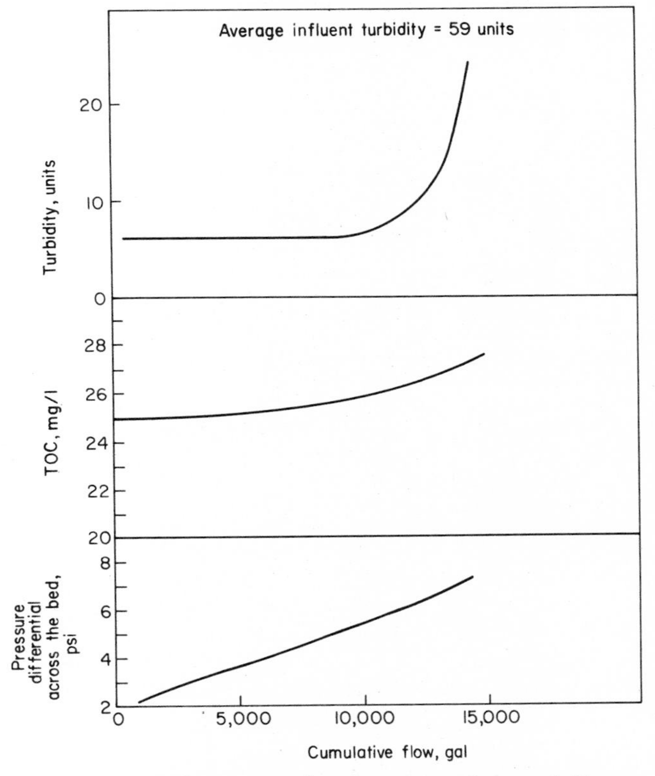

Fig. 31 Typical operating data for pilot upflow sand filters.

tion, one must also recognize the disadvantages; namely, a potential effluent suspended solids and color problem often associated with biological systems, a less efficient biological removal of organics, and the dependence on a sometimes sensitive biological population to consistently produce an effluent which will meet stringent quality requirements.

Columnar studies have demonstrated some interesting aspects when evaluating performance using primary effluent (from an API separator) for the column feed as compared to using biologically treated effluent as the feed. For example, the carbon appeared to be nonselective with respect to its affinity for adsorbing compounds responsible for BOD and COD, respectively. This is evidenced by the fact that the BOD/COD ratio (the fraction of dichromate oxidizable compounds which are biodegradable) remained relatively constant throughout the carbon test series, regardless

TABLE 33 Influence of Molecular Structure and Other Factors on Adsorbability

1. Aromatic compounds are generally more adsorbable than aliphatic compounds of similar molecular size.
2. Branched chains are usually more adsorbable than straight chains.
3. Substituent groups affect adsorbability:

Substituent Group	*Nature of Influence*
Hydroxyl	Generally reduces adsorbability; extent of decrease depends on structure of host molecule
Amino	Effect similar to that of hydroxyl but somewhat greater. Many amino acids are not adsorbed to any appreciable extent
Carbonyl	Effect varies according to host molecule; glyoxylic and more adsorbable than acetic but similar increase does not occur when introduced into higher fatty acids
Double bonds	Variable effect
Halogens	Variable effect
Sulfonic	Usually decreases adsorbability
Nitro	Often increases adsorbability

4. An increasing solubility of the solute in the liquid carrier decreases its adsorbability.
5. Generally, strongly ionized solutions are not as adsorbable as weakly ionized ones; i.e., undissociated molecules are in general preferentially adsorbed.
6. The amount of hydrolytic adsorption depends on the ability of the hydrolysis to form an adsorbable acid or base.
7. Unless the screening action of the carbon pores intervene, large molecules are more sorbable than small molecules of similar chemical nature. This is attributed to more solute carbon chemical bonds being formed, making desorption more difficult.

of the throughput volume. This was true when both the API separator effluent and the activated sludge effluent were applied to the columns. These results are plotted in Fig. 33 and illustrate the magnitude of this ratio for both sequences of the biological-carbon series treatment. The reduction of the BOD/COD ratio through an activated sludge system is well documented and has been reported previously. Unfortunately, this ratio stability is responsible for unacceptable effluent BOD levels in many instances when applying the carbon system as a total process. Therefore, the

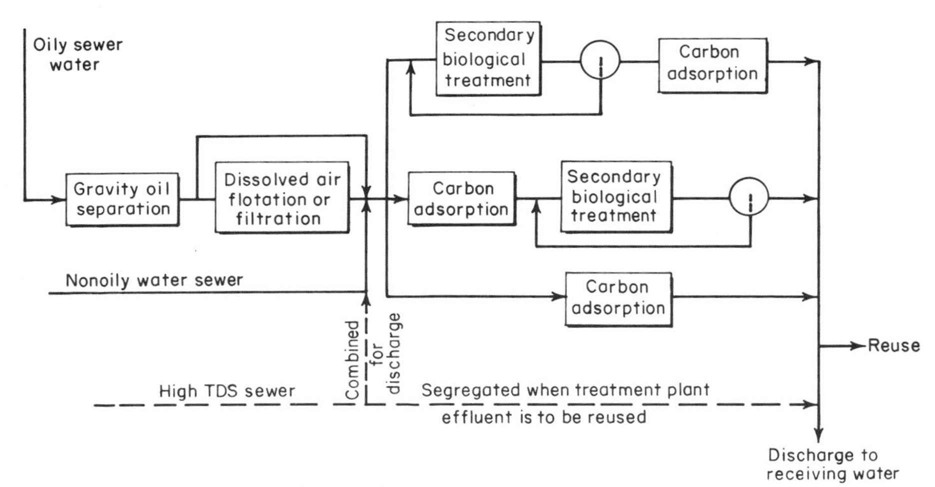

Fig. 32 Treatment schematics for Oily, Nonoily, and high TDS wastewaters.

advantage of using carbon as a tertiary process following biological treatment is apparent when considering stringent effluent BOD criteria.

Based on pilot studies, the anticipated removal of refinery wastewater constituents by activated sludge, total carbon, and combined treatment systems is tabulated in Table 34. These levels of removal may not apply in all cases since most of the data presented herein is from integrated refineries (crude distillation, lubricating oils, petrochemicals). However, they are indicative of general treatment effectiveness.

In-Plant Control

The genesis of pollution control programs is to minimize and control unavoidable losses at the source. Such practice reduces the cost of waste treatment and, in some cases, may provide an economic plus. Such measures include salvage of unreacted chemicals, recovery of by-products, good housekeeping techniques to reduce leaks and spills, and changes in processing methods. A discussion of some methods of reducing refinery pollution output follows.

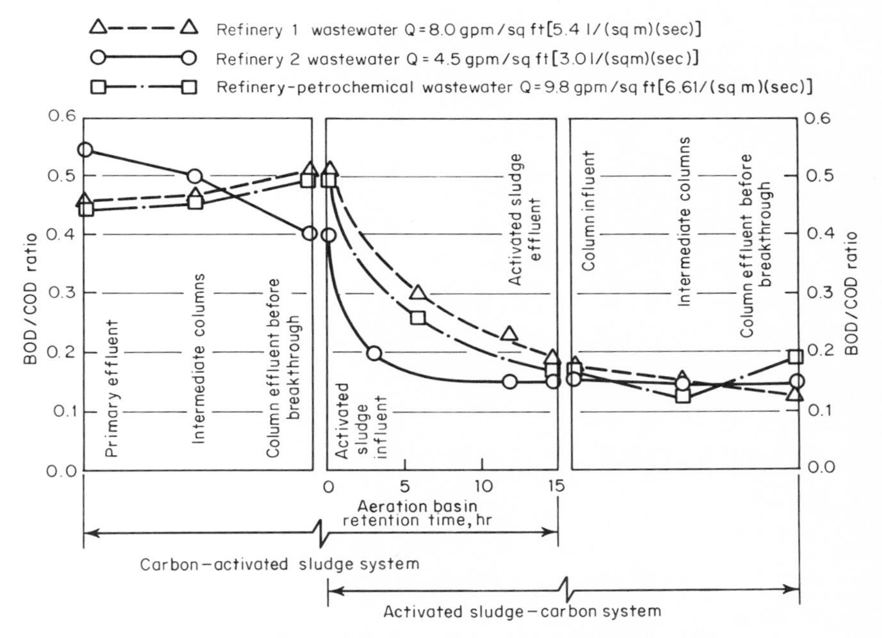

Fig. 33 BOD/COD ratios for various treatment levels.

Reduction of raw material losses The losses of raw materials from storage, transport, and processing facilities are an important source of water pollution in the petrochemical industry. Several improvements can be made by the industry to reduce the magnitude of these losses. The evaporation of light hydrocarbons from storage tanks can be controlled through the use of floating roof tanks. Additionally, vapor recovery lines in tank vents and purge lines used for process start-up and shutdown can be connected to vapor recovery systems. The hydrocarbon losses from vacuum jets can be reduced by installing refrigerated condensers ahead of the jets or by connecting the jet exhaust to vapor recovery systems.[1]

Pipeline systems should be used to transfer raw materials whenever feasible in order to minimize transfer losses. Many petrochemical industries minimize transport hydrocarbon losses either by having subsidiary companies which supply raw materials or by producing their own. Probably the most important source of hydrocarbon raw material loss is from malfunctioning equipment lines, leakages, pump gland leakage, etc. These losses can be corrected only by careful and persistent in-plant control.

TABLE 34 Estimated Effluent Quality for the Carbon and Combined Activated Sludge–Carbon Treatment of Refinery Wastewaters*

Constituent	Mean value range primary effluent, mg/l	Total carbon effluent, mg/l	Combined activated sludge–carbon effluent, mg/l	Remarks
COD	500–700	100–200	30–100	Exact COD residuals vary with complexity of refinery and design contact times in the activated sludge and carbon treatment plants
BOD_5	250–350	40–100	5–30	BOD residual depends on BOD/COD ratio which characterizes relative biodegradability of wastewater
Phenols	10–100	<1	<1	Phenols(ics) are generally amenable to biological and sorption removal
pH	8.5–9.5	7–8.5	7–8.5	pH drop in activated sludge systems attributed to biological production of CO_2 and intermediate acids. pH change in carbon columns depends on preferential adsorption of acidic and basic organics
SS	50–200	<20	<20	Primary effluent solids depend on design and operation of oil removal units. Activated sludge effluent solids depend on effectiveness of secondary clarifier. Low effluent solids characterize carbon column effluent
TDS	1,500–3,000	1,500–3,000	1,500–3,000	TDS is essentially unchanged through all three treatment systems
NH_3–N	15–150	10–140	2–100	Exact concentration depends on prestripping facilities, nitrogen content of crude charge, corrosion additive practice and biological nitrification
P	1–10	1–10	<1–7	Only removal attributed to biological synthesis

* Based on wastewater characterization data and treatability studies conducted by the author at eight refineries and petrochemical installations.

Recovery of usable reaction products By-products represent a significant pollutional fraction of petrochemical wastewaters and, in many cases, by-product recovery from the process wastes is justified not only in terms of producing a product but also in reducing the pollutional load. The recovery of sulfur from crude oils, for example, minimizes the sulfide and mercaptan pollution. Many petroleum feedstocks contain large amounts of these sulfur compounds which must be removed to prevent the poisoning of process catalysts and products. It is possible to recover sulfur from these hydrocarbon feedstocks by removing hydrogen sulfide in the form of acid gas using hydrodesulfurization. Hydrodesulfurization consists of removing the hydrogen sulfide from a process stream by stripping with steam or water. The hydrogen sulfide is then stripped from the water or condensate as acid gas.

Other sources of usable materials found in petrochemical wastes are the catalyst complex metals and the tars from catalytic processes. For example, one chemical company has sold a copper-containing tar to a smelter, who subsequently recovers the copper. Other metals (such as nickel) may also be present in evaluating quantities in tars and metal complexes. Chemical recovery companies also have reclaimed useful organic materials from tars. Usually the recovery of materials from these tars does not result in a direct profit to the petrochemical plant, but it may prove economically justified in terms of a reduced pollutional discharge.

Alkaline wastes from caustic washes are most significant, and there are several methods available utilizing these caustic wastes which may prove more feasible than attempting to treat and discharge them. Some spent caustic solutions containing sulfides, phenolates, cresolates, and carbonates are marketable. Spent caustics containing large amounts of phenols and cresols can be sold to processors who separate and purify the cresylic acid fractions for commercial use. The recovery and marketing of spent caustics are probably the most economical and desirable method for eliminating these wastes.

The recovery and recycle of process effluents containing unreacted raw materials may allow substantial savings in raw material purchases and are common to most petrochemical processes in which the process reaction is incomplete. Many of the secondary reaction by-products are also valuable for use within the petrochemical plant or as marketable products. An example of the in-plant use of a by-product is the use of hydrogen chloride for hydrochlorination processes as one of the reactants in the additional chlorination of olefins. Hydrogen chloride can also be recovered and marketed as a saleable product. The removal of phenols from effluents containing recoverable quantities of these compounds is often economical. For example, the Emscher River Association in Germany recovers large quantities of phenol from wastewater at a substantial profit.

The recovery and reuse of oils are extremely common in the petrochemical industry. Recoverable oils are reprocessed while those which are uneconomical to purify are used as a fuel source. Solvent recovery is also often practiced, especially when the high costs of solvents are considered.

Process modifications Process modifications incorporated into the design and operation of petrochemical processing units can often lead to reductions in the pollutional load from the plant. These modifications can be classified as follows:

1. Process selection
2. Prevention of product and chemical losses
3. Modification of operating conditions

Initially, the problems of waste control should be considered during the development and design of petrochemical processes since they can often be an important factor in the economics of operation. Pilot plants used in the design of petrochemical processes can be sampled to estimate the process losses and the type of pollutants which will be discharged from the prototype unit. Analyses of these samples will indicate possible process modifications which can be implemented to reduce the pollutional load.

The incorporation of spent caustic regeneration schemes in process and plant design is an example of process selection used to reduce the waste load. The substitution of continuous processes for batch processes also tends to eliminate peak discharges of wastes and to reduce the cost of treatment required for the waste. Treatment facilities designed to absorb the effects of shock discharges of wastes through equalization basins or overdesigned tanks are considerably more expensive than those which are designed to treat a waste of relatively constant discharge level.

The use of downgraded chemicals in processes which do not require high-quality reactants can facilitate both process and waste control. This type of design utilizes the waste effluents from one process as reactants in another. In the ideal scheme, a chemical could be carried through several processes, each using a slightly lower quality reactant. Caustic washes are often so used in refining operations. For example, caustic washes used to treat light hydrocarbons can later be used as makeup caustic for gasoline treating.

The hydrocarbon losses associated with the use of barometric condensers are an important source of pollution in petrochemical processes. The use of shell and tube heat exchangers rather than barometric condensers can significantly reduce this source of pollution. Process sampling taps connected directly to sewers are a source of pollution which can be avoided by returning drainage to the process unit rather than the sewer. Distillation of waste streams can also be used to eliminate the loss of volatile materials. Furfural, for example, is recovered by azeotropic distillation, eliminating this compound from wastewaters while producing a valuable solvent for use in extraction processes. One example of waste control by process modification has been the elimination of oil emulsion losses from barometric condensers on pipe stills. By rearranging the interior of the pipe still to reduce friction losses through the trays and by lowering the temperature in the still, losses were reduced to one-sixth of their original quantity.

Reduction of chemical cleaning materials The chemical cleaning of exchangers, process drums, or fractionating towers can add a significant pollutional load to the refinery effluent. If possible, the cleaning contractor should be required to collect and haul the cleaning chemicals outside of the plant for disposal at contract facilities. If this cannot be accomplished, the deleterious effects of the chemical cleaning agents on the treatment facility can be mitigated by dumping the chemicals as slowly as possible to the sewer system to reduce slug loading. In some instances, neutralization of the chemical cleaners may assist in their subsequent treatment. Additionally, the use of biodegradable detergents would obviously enhance the performance of a biological treatment system.

Handling of tank bottoms Sludges and liquids from tank cleaning operations vary greatly depending on the service of the tank and method of cleanout. The method of cleanout and the mode of disposal can significantly influence the resulting pollution load attributable to this source. For example, the practice of pumping water to the tank and agitating the liquid mixture before opening may free some of the oil from the bottom sludges and tank sides, the upper oil phase and some water then being pumped to the slop oil recovery system. Another practice is to dig a pit within the firewall, convey the sludge to the pit, decant the excess water, and concentrate the sludge. This sludge can then be plowed into the ground, biodegraded by soil bacteria, or hauled away by vacuum trucks to land farming or contract disposal. The primary considerations for the adoption of methods for tank cleaning or tank bottoms disposal are:

1. The cleaning method should keep as much oil and solids out of the sewer as possible.
2. Any solids disposal method should prevent recycling of solids to the sewer separator system.

General housekeeping Good housekeeping must be stressed continually. Experience has shown that it can be attained by instilling the proper attitude in *all* personnel. Experience has also shown that the proper attitude cannot be maintained without a continuing program of reemphasis and some system of enforcement. This means there must be an inspection system. An operator is less inclined to allow something to be discharged to the sewer if he knows that there is a good chance that the discharge will be detected and management will be informed of it. There must be an enforcement program and an enforcer.

The inspection and policing procedures can be greatly simplified by monitoring instruments that alert the inspector to unusual amounts of any unwanted material in the sewer. The more sophisticated monitoring systems can both identify and quantify material in the sewer. This allows management to inform the operator at a given unit that he lost so many pounds of the material found. This type of instrumental monitoring is very effective, although expensive.

Periodic analysis of composite wastewater samples by gas chromatography can identify many individual contaminants in the water and thus allow fixing responsibility for them. The frequency of sampling can be adjusted with need. A pH recorder will warn of caustic spills if it is monitored occasionally.

An alert operator at the oil/water separators can, with a little experience, identify many unusual conditions and can notify the proper supervisor immediately.

Whatever the degree of complexity of the policing system that is adopted, the responsibility for use of the data must be assigned to an individual. The data should not only be used for day-to-day policing but also used to establish long-range trends.

This allows predicting possible difficulties in advance, thus providing time to optimize solutions to the difficulties.

Educational program In order to have a successful pollution control program in a refinery, it is essential to get as many employees involved in the effort as possible. For best results, the involvement should include everyone from the plant manager down to the operator who actually turns the valve that discharges an unwanted substance to the sewer, or does not close the valve that causes a drum or tank to overflow to the sewer.

With the current publicity and concern about pollution, it is not as difficult to get people involved as it has been in the past when most people were indifferent to the problem. In most refineries, a large number of employees are fishermen or hunters, and these persons can easily be involved in a conservation program.

The most important step in the involvement process is for upper management to be dedicated to eliminating pollution as far as is possible. This dedication must be sincere. Token support of the idea will not fool many people and most employees are only going to be as dedicated as they think management is. Once management is sincerely interested in pollution control, that fact will be obvious and this philosophy will filter down through the organization.

The next step in involvement is to draw the entire plant personnel into the effort. An effort should be made to convince them that each of them has an important part to play in the control effort and that the effort cannot succeed without their help. In order to help develop the feeling of personal responsibility on the employees' part, they should be kept informed about what is taking place. The problems and solutions should be outlined and explained. If they are convinced that management is sincere and that they each have an important role to play, they will provide worthwhile suggestions on methods of achieving the desired goal. How these suggestions are received and acted on is an important part of the program.

The problem of communication between upper management and the lowest level of operators is a difficult one. One method that does not work is for the plant manager to give the message to the first line of supervisors and hope that they will pass it on down the chain.

If the refinery has a newsletter, a personal message from the manager can be inserted in that medium. Short personal messages at safety meetings or any other meetings that are attended by all operations employees can be fairly effective.

Although the manpower cost is rather high, the most effective means of getting people involved in an all-out pollution control program is to have a series of meetings encompassing all shift workers in operations. All technical and engineering personnel that could be involved in design of pollution control facilities or new operating units also should be included.

WATER REUSE

It has been estimated that the petroleum refining and petrochemical industry of the United States today would require more than 12 billion gpd of water if none of the water was used more than once. The actual water intake of United States refineries, however, is only slightly in excess of 20 percent of this amount. A graphical depiction of this water use delineation is shown in Fig. 34.

The bulk of the water in the refinery is composed of recirculated water. Recycle of cooling water over cooling towers and back through heat exchangers is one of the most widely applied reuse practices and accounts for approximately 90 percent of the reused water. It has a lower quality requirement than most process applications and, therefore, provides an excellent opportunity for water reuse and conservation.

Steam condensate provides a high quality of water and this source can be used for recycle. This condensate can be collected and returned to boiler feed systems, then thermal conservation and water saving result in substantial cost reductions. In some cases, steam which is used for heating or other uses can be reused in a lower pressure system.

The use of air fans can result in a twenty-five-fold decrease in the volume of contaminated cooling water used in barometric condensers. Boiler feedwater requirements may be reduced by reusing intermediate and high-pressure boiler blowdown in low-pressure boilers. Additionally, the approach of recycling boiler blowdowns and using them for stripping operations has been practiced at several petrochemical installations.

Many refineries are charging used water to electrical crude oil distillers, a process designed to remove salts, solids, and formation water from unrefined crude before the crude is given subsequent processing. Process condensate and sour water stripper bottoms are often used as desalter makeup. Phenolic-laden water is often recycled back to desalters as phenols tend to be taken up by the crude.

Water reuse is often practiced in cokers where large volumes of high-pressure water are required to cut coke from the coke drums. This water can be recycled through a gravity separator to remove floating oil and settleable coke fines, then back to the coking unit. As some water leaves with the bulk coke, makeup water is required. This makeup has a low quality tolerance and provides an excellent opportunity to bring in used water from another source within the refinery.

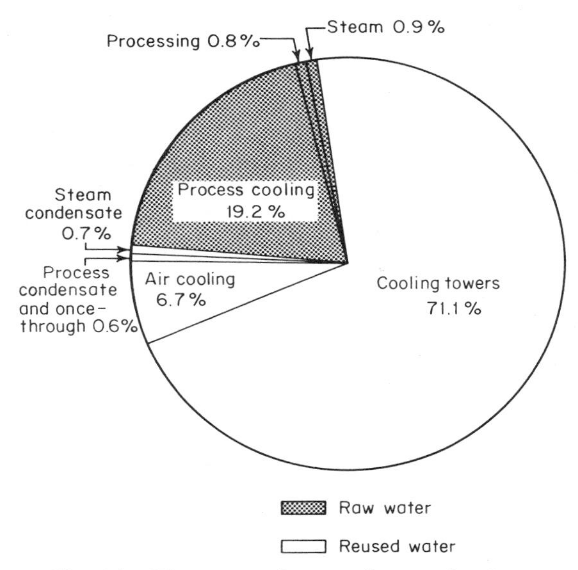

Fig. 34 Water reuse by petroleum refineries.

It has been estimated that there is an approximate loss of 4 percent volume as cooling water makes one pass through the tower. The primary water quality constraint for makeup water to offset this loss is total dissolved solids (TDS). If selected waste streams containing low dissolved solids can be treated for oil removal, they provide an excellent source for cooling tower makeup. This practice will not only reduce the plant water consumption, but also provide organic removal biochemically in the tower as previously discussed.

Another application of used water is storage as a firewater source. The quality requirements for this water are relatively lax and treated refinery effluent commonly is used for this purpose. Moreover, this water can be used for washdown operations and other similar applications.

Reuse can be better applied if a segregated wastewater collection system exists. Segregation systems used by the petrochemical industry vary widely depending on the reuse requirements, effluent quality requirements, and undesirable effects of commingling specific streams. The bases for the segregation of waste streams are outlined as follows.

1. *Uncontaminated sewers.* Sewers and drains carrying low- or nonorganic wastewaters, such as cooling tower and boiler blowdown, uncontaminated storm runoff, etc. This stream may be segregated further into low TDS and high TDS sewers.

2. *Contaminated sewers.* Sewers and drains receiving contaminated wastewater primarily discharged from process operations. The flow from dumps, spills, and cleaning operations normally is conveyed to this system. It should also have capacity for storm runoff from dirty process areas. Further segregation of contaminated waters may be on an oily and nonoily basis.

3. *Sanitary sewage system.* This system receives from sanitary facilities in the process areas, administrations facilities, and central shower and lockerroom buildings.

An example of a segregation system at one refinery and the treatment facilities is illustrated in Fig. 35.

Most water reuse schemes also require additional waste stream segregation, and the design of the segregation system will depend on the type of water reuse being employed at the individual plant. If biological treatment is used to stabilize petrochemical wastes, the sanitary sewage is usually added to it prior to treatment as a source of biological nutrients. However, many regulatory agencies require effluent chlorination when sewage is added, making such a combination unfeasible.

Treatment, reuse, and economics are, of course, all interrelated. The higher the quality demand for reuse, the more costly the treatment processes required to produce this quality. This is illustrated in Fig. 36. As noted in Fig. 36, there is a surcharge associated with reuse when the corresponding water quality requirements are more stringent than those for discharge to the receiving environment. This is not expected to occur frequently, however, since quality levels for final discharge (as imposed by the EPA and state regulatory agencies) are becoming increasingly stringent. Conversely, when the quality requirements for reuse are less stringent than for final discharge, there is a direct saving involved. Therefore, the incentive for reuse in light of increasingly stringent effluent quality requirements is apparent. However, this emphasis should be tempered by a recognition of the relative difficulty associated with treating reused waters. There is a treatment penalty caused by increased water losses through conveyance and evaporation coupled with increasing levels of TDS, residual organics, inert or benign inorganics, and heat. The application of control measures and/or treatment processes required for reuse or disposal of refinery effluents are summarized in Table 35. Contrary to the tenets of the Water Pollution Control Act of 1972,[7] blowdown at some point within a refinery-petrochemical water system will have to occur, and this stream will be highly contaminated. Moreover, the solids-generation rates will still prevail and are not reduced proportionately to water reduction through reuse.

An estimate of blowdown from a water use/reuse system within a refinery-petrochemical complex can only be accomplished by calculating a water and constituent mass balance. A simplified diagram for a refinery reuse scheme (such as the one shown in Fig. 37) can first be prepared to facilitate the mass balance circulation.

Economics of Refinery Wastewater Treatment

Implementation of the water pollution control objectives as set forth in the Federal Water Pollution Control Act Amendments of 1972 (P.L. 92–500) will have an express economic impact on the petroleum refining and petrochemical industry. A comprehensive economic analysis was recently conducted by the American Petroleum Institute to predict the cost of reaching the three incremental levels of effluent quality objectives as stated in the aforementioned legislation. The first level of treatment generally corresponds to "best practicable control technology currently available (BPCTCA)," the second level is the "best available demonstrated control technology (BADCT)," and the third level is the complete elimination of discharge of pollutants (EDOP).

The first level of treatment (BPCTCA) has been defined elsewhere[1,8] but is generally interpreted as including pretreatment, activated sludge, and effluent polishing using filtration. The second level of treatment (BADCT) includes the additional steps of elimination of once-through cooling water, reuse of treated effluent, and the addition of carbon adsorption. The third level (EDOP), has not yet been clearly defined but generally is construed to mean complete recycle of effluent and the elimination of pollutants discharged from the refinery complex.

Based on the work done by API, the estimated capital costs to achieve Levels I, II, and EDOP are presented in Tables 36 to 38, respectively.[44] It is noted from these

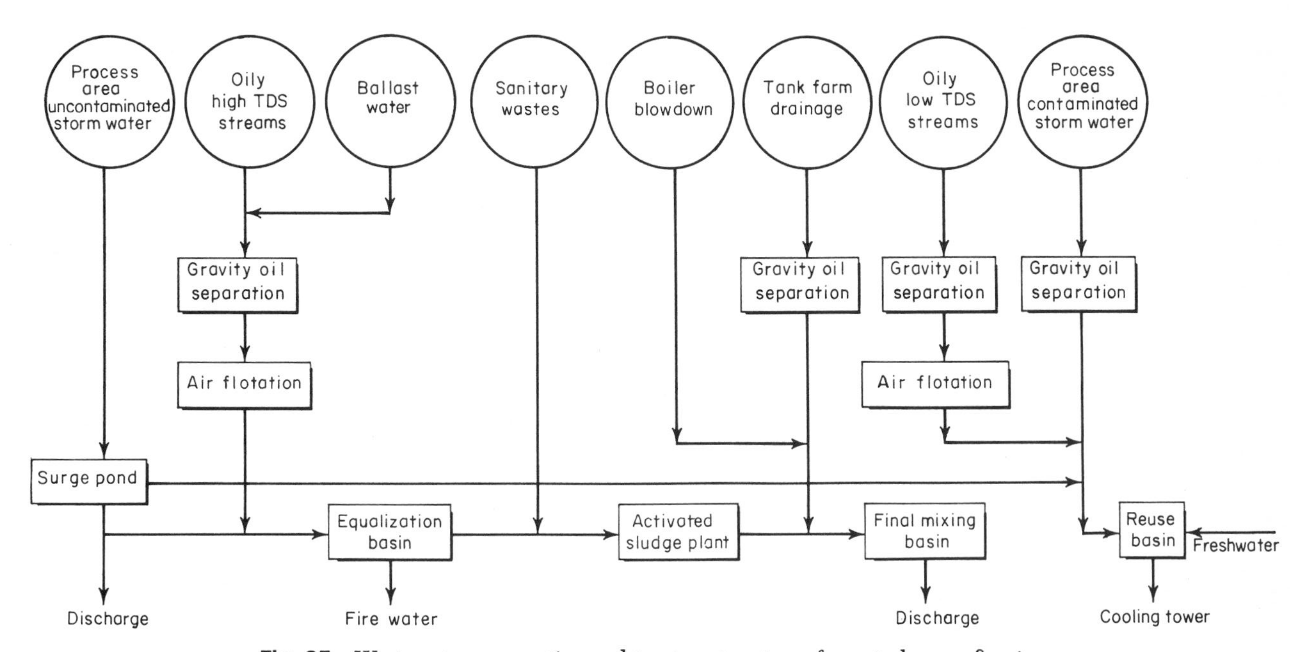

Fig. 35 Wastewater segregation and treatment systems for petroleum refineries.

TABLE 35 Treatment Required for Reuse and/or Discharge of Refinery Effluents

Contaminants	In-Plant	Primary	Intermediate	Secondary	Tertiary	Quaternary
Oil	Segregation, concentration, housekeeping	API separator, tilted-frame separator, filtration	Air flotation, mechanical flotation, media filtration			
Soluble COD	Housekeeping		Chemical precipitation, flotation or gravity separation, equalization	Activated sludge, aerated lagoon, chemical oxidation	Media filtration, carbon adsorption	Reverse osmosis
Hardness	Segregation				Chemical precipitation	Ion exchange
Other TDS	Segregation					Ion exchange, reverse osmosis, electrodialysis
Phosphorus	Segregation, substitution			Activated sludge, aerated lagoon	Chemical precipitation	
Heavy metals	Housekeeping, substitution, segregation	Ponding			Chemical precipitation, chemical oxidation, media filtration	Ion exchange
Sulfides	Segregation, steam stripping				Chemical oxidation	
Ammonia	Substitution, segregation, steam stripping		Trickling filter	Activated sludge	Denitrification	Ion exchange

tables that $907 million (all on 1971) is required to meet Level I, and an additional $819 million is required to meet Level II. A final increment of $725 million is required to satisfy the EDOP provisions of P.L. 92-500. The cost levels are those required for existing refineries which have a crude refining capacity of approximately 12.4 million barrels per stream day. Including grassroots refineries to be built be-

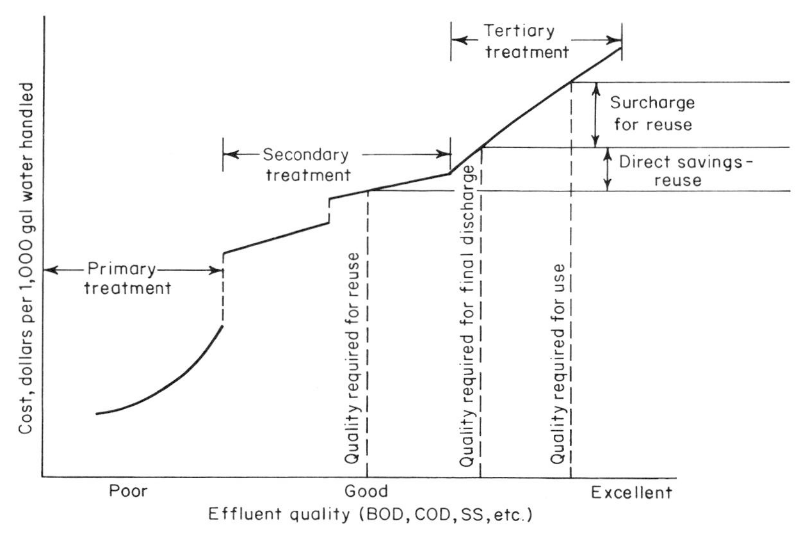

Fig. 36 Effluent quality versus costs of treatment.

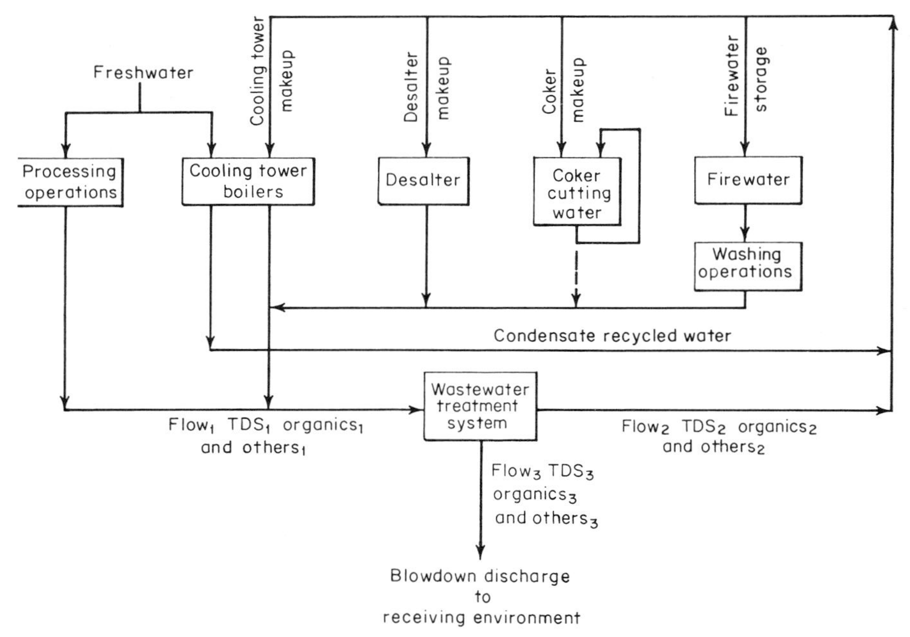

Fig. 37 A simplified diagram for a refinery water use/reuse system to calculate the water and pollutant mass balance.

tween 1972 and 1985 as well as refinery expansions, the capacity should increase to approximately 22 million barrels per stream day. At this capacity, the estimated capital cost to reach the first-level treatment is $1.8 billion; to obtain second-level treatment, the estimated cumulative total is $3.4 billion; and to reach EDOP is a cumulative total of $4.8 billion (all expressed as 1972 dollars).[44]

TABLE 36 Summary of Costs to Reach Level I

Refinery class	Number studied	Capacity, MBPD*	Cost, dollars per daily barrel	Cost, thousands of dollars per refinery	Total cost, thousands of dollars
A	8	173	96	2.1	16.6
B	64	3,407	97	5.2	331
C	25	3,201	64	8.2	204
D	11	1,030	104	9.8	107
E	13	3,358	74	19.1	248
	121	11,169	435	47.4	906.6

* 1,000 bbl/day

TABLE 37 Summary of Costs to Reach Level II

Refinery class	Number studied	Capacity, MBPD	Cost, dollars per daily barrel	Cost, thousands of dollars per refinery	Total cost, thousands of dollars
A	8	173	86	1.9	14.9
B	64	3,407	80	4.3	274
C	25	3,201	71	9.2	239
D	11	1,030	95	8.9	98
E	13	3,358	57	14.8	193
	121	11,169	389	39.1	818.9

TABLE 38 Additional Estimated Cost to Reach EDOP

Refinery class	Number studied	Capacity, MBPD	Cost, dollars per daily barrel	Cost, thousands of dollars per refinery	Total cost, thousands of dollars
A	9	187	34	0.7	6.4
B	65	3,458	61	3.2	212
C	26	3,361	56	7.2	188
D	11	1,030	64	8.6	66
E	13	3,358	76	19.6	255
	124	11,394	291	39.3	727.4

NOTES: All costs are in 1972 dollars. Above costs do not include any wastewater costs for refinery expansions or for new refineries. These costs will be developed in final report.

The estimated annualized cost, which includes operation, maintenance, and amortization of capital, is $321 million per year for existing United States refineries to meet Level I, $597 million per year to achieve Level II treatment, and $795 million per year to obtain EDOP assuming this can be accomplished technically. Assuming the United States refining capacity is increased to 22 million barrels per stream day by 1985, these annual costs climb to $620 million for first level, $1.09 billion for second level, and 1.48 billion for EDOP.[44]

Economic Impact and Cost Effectiveness

In order to put these capital and annualized costs in perspective, one can take the $1.7 billion to be spent on United States refineries having a crude capacity of 12.4 million barrels per stream day and by assuming current refinery capital investments at around $1 billion per year, approximately 17 percent of this capital investment would be directed toward water pollution control systems in refineries to meet the Level II requirements. Moreover, assuming the cost of processing crude is $1 per bbl and considering $600 million of annualized cost to obtain second-level treatment, 13 cents/bbl of crude processed, or 13 percent of the processing cost, will be required for water pollution control.

REFERENCES

1. Gloyna, E. F., and D. L. Ford: "The Characteristics and Pollutional Problems Associated with Petrochemical Wastes," prepared for Federal Water Pollution Control Administration, Ada, Okla., 1970.
2. Annual Refining Surveys: Survey of Operating Refineries in the U.S., *The Oil and Gas Journal*, April 1, 1973.
3. Martin, R.: The Refining Industry, The Future, 1985, *PetroChem. Engr.*, March, 1970.
4. Morrell, G. P.: "Trends in Capacity and Utilization," Office of Oil and Gas, U.S. Department of the Interior, December, 1972.
5. Roy F. Weston, Inc.: "Development Document for Effluent Guidelines and Standards of Performance—Petroleum Refining Industry," draft for U.S. Environmental Protection Agency, Contract No. 68-01-0598, June, 1973.
6. "1967 Domestic Refinery Effluent Profile," American Petroleum Institute Committee for Air and Water Conservation, September 1968.
7. "Federal Water Pollution Control Act Amendments for 1972," Report No. 92-1465, U.S. House of Representatives, September 1972.
8. "Standard Methods for the Examination of Water and Sewage," 12th ed., American Public Health Assoc., 1965.
9. Love, R. M.: "In-Plant Removal of Tertiary Butyl Alcohol," Texas Water Pollution Control Assoc., Houston, Tex., 1970.
10. Cherry, A. B., A. J. Gabaccia, and H. W. Senn: The Assimilation Behavior of Certain Toxic Organic Compounds in Natural Water, *Sewage and Industrial Wastes*, vol. 28, September 1956.
11. Eckenfelder, W. W., Jr., and D. L. Ford: Laboratory and Design Procedures for Wastewater Treatment Processes, The University of Texas Center for Research in Water Resources, Rept. EHE-10-6802, CRWR-31, 1968.
12. Clifford, D.: "Total Oxygen Demand, A New Instrumental Method," American Chemical Society, Midland, Mich., November 4, 1967.
13. "1968 Book of ASTM Standards," part 23, American Society for Testing and Materials, Philadelphia, Pa., 1968.
14. Boyd, J. L., G. L. Shell, and D. A. Dahlstrom: Treatment of Oily Wastewaters to Meet Regulatory Standards, *American Institute of Chemical Engineering Conf.*, Toledo, Ohio, March 1971.
15. Martin, J. M., et al.: Ultraviolet Determination of Total Phenols, *J. Water Pollution Control Federation*, January 1967.
16. Beychok, M. R.: "Manual on Disposal of Refinery Wastes, Volume on Liquids," chap. 10, American Petroleum Institute, Division of Refining, Washington, D.C., to be published.
17. Willard, N. H., L. L. Merritt, and J. A. Dean: "Instrumental Methods of Analysis," Van Nostrand, Princeton, N.J., 1965.
18. Jewell, W., and D. L. Ford: "Preliminary Investigational Requirements—Petrochemical and Refinery Waste Treatment Facilities," prepared for the U.S. Environmental Protection Agency, Ada, Okla., 1971.
19. U.S. Department of the Interior: The Cost of Clean Water, Vol. III, Industrial Waste Profile No. 5—Petroleum Refining, Federal Water Pollution Control Administration, 1967.
20. Ford, D. L.: Confidential report.

21. Beychok, M. R.: "Aqueous Wastes from Petroleum and Petrochemical Plants," Wiley, New York, 1967.
22. Gloyna, E. F., D. L. Ford, and J. M. Eller: Water Reuse in Industry, Water Pollution Control Federation Annual Meeting, Dallas, Tex., 1969.
23. Ford, D. L.: Confidential report.
24. Liquid Wastes, in "Manual on Disposal of Refinery Wastes," 1st ed., American Petroleum Institute, Washington, D.C., 1969.
25. Ford, D. L.: Confidential report.
26. Morrison, J.: Tilted Plate Separators for Refinery Wastewater, *Oil and Gas Journal,* December 14, 1970.
27. Hoffman, F.: How to Select a pH Control System for Neutralizing Waste Acids, *Chem. Engrg.,* October 30, 1972.
28. Annessen, R. J., and G. D. Gould: Some Water Processing Turns Problems into Payout, *Chem. Engrg.,* March 22, 1971.
29. Englebrecht, R. S., and B. B. Ewing: Treatment of Petrochemical Wastes by Activated Sludge Process, *Proc. 2nd Ind. Water and Waste Conf.,* Texas Water Pollution Control Assoc., Austin, Tex., 1962.
30. Unpublished report, Engineering-Science, Inc., Austin, Tex., September 1972.
31. Eller, J. M., and D. L. Ford: Confidential report, Engineering-Science, Inc., Austin, Tex., 1971.
32. Eckenfelder, W. W., and D. L. Ford: "Water Pollution Control; Experimental Procedures for Process Design," Pemberton Press, Austin, Tex., 1970.
33. Busch, A. W.: "Aerobic Biological Treatment of Waste Waters; Principles and Practice," Oligodynamics Press, Houston, Tex., 1971.
34. "The Impact of Oily Materials on Activated Sludge Systems," Hydroscience, Inc., EPA Project No. 12050 DSH, March 1971.
35. Ford, D. L., C. S. Shih, and E. C. Sebesta: Temperature Prediction in Activated Sludge Basins Using Mechanical Aerators, prepared for the 27th Annual Purdue University Industrial Waste Conf., May 1972.
36. Phelps, E. B.: "Stream Sanitation," Wiley, New York, 1944.
37. Eckenfelder, W. W.: "Industrial Pollution Control," McGraw-Hill, New York, 1966.
38. Gromiec, M. J., J. F. Malina, and W. W. Eckenfelder, Jr.: Performance of Plastic Medium in Trickling Filters, *J. Intern. Assoc. Water Pollution Res.,* vol. 6, November 1972.
39. Gloyna, E. F.: "Waste Stabilization Pond Design," design manual prepared for Poland Project 26, vol. 1, World Health Organization, 1967.
40. Elkin, H. F., E. F. Mohler and C. R. Kummik: Biological Oxidation of Oil Refinery Wastes in Cooling Tower Systems, *Sewage Industrial Wastes,* vol. 28, p. 12, 1956.
41. Weber, W. J.: "Physiochemical Processes for Water Quality Control," Wiley, New York, 1972.
42. Hassler, J. W.: "Activated Carbon," Chemical Publishing Co., New York, 1963.
43. Ford, D. L., and M. A. Buercklin: The Interrelationship of Biological-Carbon Adsorption Systems for the Treatment of Refinery and Petrochemical Wastewaters, presented in the 6th Intern. Assoc. of Water Pollution Res. Conf., Jerusalem, Israel, June 1972.
44. Brown and Root, Inc.: "Economics of Refinery Wastewater Treatment," draft for Committee on Environmental Affairs, American Petroleum Institute, August, 1973.

Chapter 9

Water Pollution Control in the Metals Industry

HENRY C. BRAMER
President, Datagraphics, Inc., Carnegie, Pennsylvania

INTRODUCTION

The primary metal industries (SIC 33) and fabricated metal products (SIC 34) together comprise the metals industries. These industries account for about 15 percent of the economic activity of the manufacturing industries; the 2.7 million employees in these industries represent about 13.5 percent of the total employment in all manufacturing industries. The data of Table 1 show the principal industry subgroups and relative economic importance as measured by values of shipments and values added by manufacturers in 1969.

TABLE 1 The Metals Industries, 1969
(In millions of dollars)

SIC code	Industry group	Value of shipments	Value added
331	Blast furnace and basic steel products	26,345	11,280
332	Iron and steel foundries	5,021	3,187
333	Primary nonferrous metals	5,665	1,926
334	Secondary nonferrous metals	1,895	360
335	Nonferrous rolling and drawing	11,609	3,470
336	Nonferrous foundries	2,195	1,232
339	Miscellaneous primary metal products	2,422	1,260
341	Metal cans	3,621	1,455
342	Cutlery, hand tools, and hardware	4,160	2,575
343	Plumbing and heating, except electric	2,165	1,126
344	Fabricated structural steel products	11,257	5,474
345	Screw machine products, bolts, etc.	2,997	1,822
346	Metal stampings	6,898	3,532
347	Metal services, not elsewhere classified	1,530	1,021
348	Miscellaneous fabricated wire products	1,419	825
349	Miscellaneous fabricated metal products	5,528	3,012
33	Primary metal industries	55,152	22,714
34	Fabricated metal products	39,574	20,841
	All manufacturing industries	643,490	305,908

The metals industries are basic to almost all other manufacturing industries. While it is difficult or impossible to categorize any particular industry group as "most important," the metals industries are often considered second to none. The most important end uses of the products of these industries are automobiles, machinery, appliances, electrical equipment, structures, furniture, and containers. These industries are critical, of course, to the economy; the steel industry in particular being a principal bellwether.

There are some 6,837 establishments in SIC 33 and 27,418 in SIC 34. Insofar as significant wastewater problems are concerned, the numbers of plants of concern are, respectively, 841 and 569 in SIC 33 and 34. These are the plants that consume more than 20 million gal/year of water for all purposes. A total of 7,949 billion gal/year of water are used by these plants. The remaining 32,845 plants use less than 657 billion gal annually. Thus, 4 percent of the plants use 92 percent of the water. The geographical distributions of those plants consuming more than 20 million gal/year of water are shown in Table 2 with total water uses and value added by manufacturer. Statistics on plants in some states are withheld by the U.S. Department of Commerce to avoid disclosing figures for individual companies.

TABLE 2 The Metals Industries by State, 1969

(In billions of gallons of water and millions of dollars)

	SIC 33			SIC 34		
State	Number of plants	Value added, dollars	Water use, gal/year	Number of plants	Value added, dollars	Water use, gal/year
Massachusetts	18	135	4.5	10	205	7.9
Rhode Island	13	123	7.4			
Connecticut	33	316	33.9	31	223	5.5
New York	52	799	331.1	22	261	8.8
New Jersey	40	305	36.7	16	176	2.3
Pennsylvania	116	3,002	1,508.2	50	504	10.4
Ohio	113	2,108	1,152.7	81	878	38.1
Indiana	55	1,577	1,118.8	34	228	8.8
Illinois	65	1,127	531.3	70	677	21.8
Michigan	69	1,034	626.4	65	872	31.4
Wisconsin	32	272	13.8	35	264	6.2
Minnesota	9	35	19.1	8	30	1.0
Iowa	7	83	25.7	4	47	0.6
Missouri	11	116	31.7	16	138	2.0
Maryland	8	481	372.6	7	69	1.4
Virginia	8	74	11.2	5	44	0.7
West Virginia	12	469	221.4	7	49	0.7
North Carolina	7	48	4.5	4	24	0.9
Georgia	6	47	28.2			
Florida				5	33	0.6
Kentucky	11	159	72.8	13	110	8.1
Tennessee	12	152	33.4	8	70	2.0
Alabama	25	545	335.5	6	80	0.9
Mississippi	...	...	...	6	22	1.3
Arkansas	...	...	...	4	11	0.2
Louisiana	...	...	...	5	42	0.4
Oklahoma	4	29	2.5	4	47	0.3
Texas	20	409	421.4	11	63	0.7
Arizona	9	41	69.6			
Washington	16	258	128.1			
Oregon	7	70	14.8			
California	27	416	166.6	20	118	1.4

The past and projected growth of the metals industries can be seen in the values of shipments in the principal primary metals industries from 1967 through 1980 as in Table 3. Projections through 1980 are as estimated by the Bureau of Domestic Commerce, U.S. Department of Commerce.

Industry growth as measured by values of shipments should be considered in the light of inflation, which is indicated by the Wholesale Price Indexes in Table 4.

The general tendency in these industries is toward reduced numbers of employees and, particularly in the steel industry, improved production facilities to reduce costs. The outlook in the metals industries through 1980 is generally good insofar as growth and profitability are concerned, but is not expected to match the performance of the economy as a whole. As the gross national product (GNP) increases to nearly

$2 trillion in 1980, i.e., 2.05 times the $977 billion level in 1970, the metals industries in total can expect to increase the value of shipments by a factor of 1.81. As indicated in Table 3, growth will by no means be uniform among the industry groups; brass mills are expected to exceed the rate of growth in GNP, while the steel industry will lag most of all.

The metals industries use nearly as much water as any other industry group, as shown in Table 5. The differences in the nature of water uses are illustrated in the data of Table 6, which shows the percentages of process water intakes.

TABLE 3 Primary Metals—Value of Shipments

(In millions of dollars)

Industry group	1967	1970	1972	1975	1980
Aluminum	4,300	5,200	6,050	7,300	10,400
Brass mills	2,196	2,775	3,000	4,200	6,050
Copper wire mills	2,975	3,750	4,055	5,200	7,100
Ferrous castings	4,367	4,607	5,309	6,323	8,112
Steel mill products	15,250	17,150	19,600	23,000	29,000
Totals	29,088	33,482	38,014	46,023	60,662

TABLE 4 Primary Metals—Wholesale Price Indexes

Industry group	1967	1969	1971	1967–1971 ratio
Aluminum	93.8	99.8	102.6	1.09
Brass mills	100.0	119.0	118.0	1.18
Copper wire mills	100.0	109.0	118.0	1.18
Ferrous casting	100.0	113.4	124.7	1.25
Steel mill products	100.0	107.4	122.5	1.23

TABLE 5 Industrial Water Uses, 1968

(In billions of gallons)

SIC code	Industry group	Intake	Use	Use rate
20	Food and kindred products	811	1,346	1.66
22	Textile mill products	154	328	2.13
24	Lumber and wood products	118	205	1.74
26	Paper and allied products	2,252	6,522	2.90
28	Chemical and allied products	4,476	9,416	2.10
29	Petroleum and coal products	1,435	7,290	5.08
33	Primary metal industries	5,005	7,780	1.55
34	Fabricated metal products	68	169	2.48
	All industries	15,467	35,701	2.31

The overall recirculation and reuse of water in the primary metals industries are thus much lower than the average in all industries, while the portion of intake water devoted to process uses is about equal to the overall average. In fabricated metal products, conversely, recirculation and reuse are similar to the average in all industries, while process uses are much higher than the overall average.

Most of the water used in the primary metals industries is taken from company-owned surface or groundwater systems; only 3.9 percent is purchased from public water systems. In the fabricated metal products industry, 69.7 percent of the water used is purchased from public water systems. Most of the water discharged by the primary metals industries is discharged to surface water bodies, with 3.1 percent discharged to municipal sewers. In contrast, 59.4 percent of the water discharged by the fabricated metal products industry is to municipal sewers.

From the standpoint of wastewater management, the metals industries are best considered in terms of water use. In Table 7, these industries are grouped and ordered in terms of water use.

These industries generate wastewaters which vary in quantity by orders of magnitude, but which have similarities insofar as the nature of pollutants is concerned. The principal exception to this generality is the by-product coke plant in an integrated steel mill. The production of alumina from bauxite and leaching of copper ores are mining-related operations and iron-ore-concentration operations and will not be considered here.

TABLE 6 Process Water Intakes, 1968

SIC code	Industry group	Process water intakes	
		Billions of gallons	Percent of total
20	Food and kindred products	291	35.8
22	Textile mill products	109	70.7
24	Lumber and wood products	37	31.3
26	Paper and allied products	1,478	65.6
28	Chemicals and allied products	733	16.3
29	Petroleum and coal products	95	6.6
33	Primary metal industries	1,207	24.1
34	Fabricated metal products	37	54.4
	All industries	4,295	27.8

TABLE 7 Water Use in the Metals Industries, 1968
(In billions of gallons)

SIC code	Industry group	Gross use
	Metals industries, total	7,948.7
3312	Blast furnaces and steel mills	6,154.0
333	Primary nonferrous metals	917.0
3313	Electrometallurgical products	320.3
	All other primary metals	263.0
34	Fabricated metal products	168.9
	All other primary ferrous metals	125.5

BLAST FURNACES AND STEEL MILLS

The principal departments in an integrated steel mill are coke production, blast furnace operation, steelmaking process, hot-rolling mills and finishing operations. Integrated mills incorporate all these operations; though some sizeable mills utilize only electric furnaces for making steel from scrap, followed by hot-rolling and finishing operations.

Coke Plant Operations

Coke plants are operated as parts of integrated steel mills to supply the coke necessary for the production of pig iron in blast furnaces. Nearly all coke plants today are by-product plants, i.e., products such as coke-oven gas, coal tar, crude and refined light oils, ammonium sulfate, anhydrous ammonia, ammonia liquor, and naphthalene are produced in addition to coke. Economic factors, particularly competition from the petrochemical industry, have changed the traditional coke plant operation. Tar and coke-oven gas remain valuable by-products, the former for sale and the latter for internal use. Light oil production, particularly refined products, and ammonium sulfate production are not usually profitable. The production of sodium phenolate is probably never profitable.

A by-product coke plant consists essentially of the ovens in which bituminous coal is heated, out of contact with air, to drive off the volatile components. The residue remaining in the ovens is coke; the volatile components are recovered and processed in the by-product plant to produce tar, light oils, and other materials of potential value, including coke-oven gas.

Each coke oven is a narrow chamber made of silica brick, typically 18 in. wide, 15 ft high, and 40 ft long, arranged side by side in groups of 30 or more, each group called a *battery*. The ovens are heated by burning coke-oven gas in flues between the sidewalls of the adjacent ovens. About 40 percent of the gas produced by the coking process is used to heat the coke ovens; the remaining gas is used as a fuel in other mill operations.

Coal is charged through holes into the tops of the ovens from hopper bottom cars which run on tracks over the top of the battery. During the 17- to 20-hr coking period, the gases and volatile materials distilled from the coal escape through the ascension pipes on the top of the ovens and pass into the collection main which runs the length of the battery. At the end of the coking period, the doors are removed from each end of the oven and the pushing machine pushes the red hot coke into the quenching car. The quenching car moves to the quenching tower where the coke is cooled with water sprays, and the cooled coke is delivered to handling equipment for subsequent use. Much of the quench water is evaporated in the quench tower. The remainder flows to a settling basin where fine coke particles settle out and are periodically removed. The clarified water is recycled to the quenching tower. The settling basin may overflow if an excess of water is in the system, resulting in a source of wastewater.

In the collection main, the gas produced by the coking process is cooled with water sprays; this water is known as *flushing liquor*. Cooling condenses out most of the tar in the gas, and the liquor, mixed with tar, flows to a decanter where the tar is separated and recovered. The gas then passes through the primary coolers where most of the moisture is condensed and sent to the tar decanter where it is mixed with the flushing liquor. The excess ammonia liquor (flushing liquor or decanter liquor) produced in the coking process must eventually be discarded. Ammonia liquor is the major source of wastewater in most plants.

Following the primary coolers, the gas passes through the exhausters which draw the gas under suction from the collection main and force it under pressure through the by-product plant equipment. The gas then passes through tar extractors where the remaining tar and some additional ammonia liquor are separated and returned to the tar decanter. The ammonia absorber and the ammonia still are discussed later along with dephenolizers. The tar is either sold as the crude product or is further refined.

Following the ammonia absorber, the gas passes through the final coolers in which water sprays dissolve soluble constituents and flush out the insoluble naphthalene which is condensed at this point. The water flows to the naphthalene sump where the naphthalene is recovered by skimming and then to a cooling tower to be recirculated through the final cooler. A properly designed closed recirculation system should have little or no discharged wastewater since the cooling tower evaporation balances the moisture condensation from the gas. When other than a closed system is used, final cooler water can be the largest source of contaminated wastewater.

From the final coolers, the gas passes through gas scrubbers in which the crude light oil is removed by a high-boiling absorbent generally known as *wash oil*. The crude light oil contains materials which are further separated and recovered in the by-product plant. A gas holder stores the gas for underfiring the coke ovens and booster pumps pressurize the remaining gas for fuel use throughout the plant.

Following the gas scrubbers, the light oil is stripped from the wash oil by steam distillation; the wash oil is cooled and recirculated to the gas scrubbers. Vapors leaving the wash oil still are condensed in the light-oil condenser and flow to the light-oil decanter where the light oil and condensed water are separated. Indirect cooling is generally used in the wash-oil cooler and light-oil condenser and no wastewaters are produced. Water from the light oil in the decanter is a major source of contaminated wastewater.

Ammonia is recovered by either indirect or semidirect processes. In the indirect recovery process, a portion of the ammonia is scrubbed from the gas with water. An ammonia still concentrates the ammonia liquor for sale.

In the semidirect ammonia recovery process, the ammonia absorber, or saturator, follows the tar extractor. Here the gas passes through a dilute sulfuric acid solution in a closed system forming ammonium sulfate which is crystallized and dried for sale. Excess ammonia liquor is steam-distilled in the ammonia still where ammonia and other volatile compounds are removed. The steam-distilled products pass to the free leg of the ammonia still and the ammonia, hydrogen sulfide, carbon dioxide, and hydrogen cyanide are steam-distilled and returned to the gas stream. To the liquid leaving the still, milk of lime is added in the fixed leg of the still to decompose ammonium salts; ammonia solution is again steam-distilled and the ammonia returned to the gas stream. The ammonia gas from the ammonia still is recovered from the gas as additional ammonium sulfate in the saturators.

Phenol is recovered by either a liquor extraction or vapor recirculation process. In the liquid extraction process, the ammonia liquor is mixed with benzol or light oil which extracts the phenol. A caustic solution is then added to the phenol solution to extract the phenol as sodium phenolate. The oil is recycled to the process and the dephenolized ammonia liquor goes to the ammonia still. In the vapor recirculation process, the phenol is steam-distilled from the ammonia liquor leaving the free leg of the ammonia still. The steam and vapors are scrubbed with a caustic solution which converts the phenol to sodium phenolate. The steam is reused and the dephenolized liquor is returned to the fixed leg of the still.

The coke-oven gas is sometimes further purified following the light-oil scrubbers to remove hydrogen sulfide. The carbonate process is occasionally used to recover elemental sulfur for sale. Some plants employ no ammonia stills or saturators. The Keystone process recovers anhydrous ammonia through absorption in a recycled solution of ammonium phosphate. In a typical absorption cycle, lean 40 percent phosphate solution is reboiled in a distillation tower from which the ammonia vapor is recovered and the lean phosphate solution is separated for reuse. The nature of the Keystone operation is such that additional light oils are recovered by cooling and compressing the gas following the conventional light-oil scrubbers. The wastewater produced would be similar to the wastewaters from the conventional light-oil decanter and agitator.

The crude coal tar usually is sold as produced. At some plants, however, the tar is refined using a continuous-type distillation unit with multiple columns and reboilers. Ordinarily continuous distillation results in four fractions: light oil, middle or creosote oil, heavy oil, and anthracene oil, which are cuts taken at progressively higher temperatures. The light-oil fraction is agitated with sulfuric acid, then neutralized with caustic soda and redistilled; naphthalene is decanted from the middle fraction before treating this fraction with caustic to remove phenols and other tar acids, then neutralized and fractionally distilled. The wastewaters thus contain a variety of organic compounds from process water uses in addition to the cooling and condenser water from the distillation processes.

There are 51 coke plants in steel mills in the United States with an average of 238 ovens each. The average coke plant cokes 5,328 tons/day of coal and produces 3,705 tons of coke; the average oven thus produces about 15.6 tons/day of coke.

Blast Furnace Operation

Molten iron for subsequent steelmaking operations is normally produced in a blast furnace. The blast furnace is a vertical, quasi-cylindrical structure, ranging from 65 to 106 ft high and 15 to 28 ft in diameter. The blast furnace process consists essentially of charging iron ore, limestone, and coke into the top of the furnace and blowing heated air into the bottom. Combustion of the coke provides the heat necessary to obtain the temperature at which the metallurgical reducing reactions take place. Incandescent carbon of the coke accounts for about 20 percent of the reduction of the iron oxides; carbon monoxide formed between the coke and oxygen of the blast accounts for the remaining reduction. The function of the limestone is to form a slag, fluid at the furnace temperature, which combines with unwanted impurities in the ore. The materials and products bear these relationships: 2 tons of ore, 1 ton or less of coke, ½ ton of limestone, and 3½ tons of air produce approximately 1 ton of iron, ½ ton of slag, and 5 tons of blast furnace gas containing the fines of the burden carried out by the blast; these fines are referred to as *flue dust*. Molten iron is periodically withdrawn from the bottom of the furnace; the fluid slag which floats on top of the iron is also periodically withdrawn from the furnace. Blast furnace flue gas has considerable heating value and is burned to preheat the air blast to the furnace.

The blast furnace auxiliaries consist of the stoves for preheating air, the dry dust catchers which recover the bulk of the flue dust, primary wet cleaners which remove most of the remaining flue dust by washing with water, and secondary cleaners which may be electrostatic precipitators.

Blast furnace flue-gas-washer water contains from 1,000 to 10,000 mg/l of suspended solids, which approximate the composition of the furnace burden. Following a slip in the furnace, the concentration of suspended solids may be as much as 30,000 mg/l. Blast furnace gas-washer water may amount to 600 to 5,000 gal/min per furnace, depending on the type of washer used. The suspended solids from an iron-producing furnace are generally 50 percent finer than 10 microns in diameter and have a specific gravity of about 3.5 on the average; the effluent is red in color. A furnace producing ferromanganese discharges particles which are extremely fine and are lighter in color than those from an iron-producing furnace.

Blast furnace gas-washer water contains significant concentrations of cyanides, phenol, and ammonia in addition to suspended solids. Gas-washer waters from a ferromanganese furnace have much higher concentrations of cyanides than do wash waters from iron furnaces.

These wastewaters result from a gas-cleaning operation, and thus prevent, to a considerable extent, air pollution which would otherwise result. The primary reason for cleaning the gas, however, is to allow its use as a fuel. Cooling blast furnace slag produces quantities of water containing slag particles. The effluent from a slag pit may range from 100 to 200 gal/min and is of a clear appearance. Air-cooled slag is produced by spraying a limited amount of water on molten slag to accelerate cooling into a solid mass which is dug out with power shovels. Granulated slag is produced by pouring molten slag into a water-filled pit and additionally spraying water on the molten stream; the rapid cooling causes the slag to expand and break into small particles.

The blast furnace requires the continuous circulation of cooling water through hollow plates built into the walls of the bosh and stack. Without such cooling, a furnace wall would quickly burn through. Additional water is used in the boiler house, turbine condensers, etc.

The water use in a particular single-furnace shop producing 2,500 tons/day of pig iron is as follows:

	gpm	*gal/ton*
Furnace cooling water	21,000	12,096
Gas-washer water	3,700	2,131
Boiler house and other	21,226	12,226
Totals	45,926	26,453

The suspended solids in blast furnace gas-washer water result from the fines in the burden being carried out in gas. The quantities depend on the operation of the furnace and the nature of the burden, i.e., friability of the ore, pellets, or sinter; particle size of the limestone, etc. Oils can be vaporized and carried into the gas when metal turnings are part of the charge. Phenols, cyanides, and ammonia originate in the coke and are particularly high if the coke has been quenched with wastewaters or if the coke is "green," i.e., has not been completely coked. Cyanides are generated in the blast furnace in the reducing atmosphere from carbon from the coke and nitrogen from the air; cyanide formation is particularly high at the higher temperatures of a ferromanganese furnace.

The number of blast furnaces producing pig iron and ferroalloys in the United

States has decreased from 250 in 1960 to 219 in 1971. Only about 70 percent of the available blast furnaces are operated in any given year. The blast furnaces not in blast are either being relined or being rebuilt or are unnecessary because of age or production capacity. The 1970 production of pig iron and ferroalloys was 93,851,000 net tons and is shown by state in Table 8.

Sinter Plant Operation

Fine ores must be converted to a lump form by some process of agglomeration before they can be used effectively in the blast furnace. Sintering is the principal method used to reclaim flue dust and mill scale for recharging to the blast furnace and to agglomerate fine ores as a part of the blast furnace shop. In sintering, the fine iron-bearing material is mixed with a fuel and burned on a grate under forced draft to a clinker.

Dust produced in the sintering plant is often recovered using wet scrubbers as an air pollution abatement measure. Wet scrubbers are coming into increasing use because of the explosion hazards present with precipitators.

The dust from a sintering plant amounts to about 20 lb of solids per ton of sinter produced. Sinter production averages about 3.35 tons/(day)(sq ft) of grate area. The "average" sinter plant thus produces 4,113 tons/day from a grate area of 1,228 sq ft on two machines. A venturi scrubber using 1,000 gpm of wash water would produce 350 gal of wastewater per ton of sinter containing 6,858 ppm suspended solids. Present practice waste loads result from plain sedimentation and at 95 percent removal amount to about 1.0 lb/ton of sinter. Chemical coagulation as the base level of treatment would reduce the thickener effluent to 15 ppm, corresponding to 0.044 lb/ton. The best practicable treatment at recirculation with 5 percent blowdown would yield a load of 0.0022 lb/ton. The best available treatment probably corresponds to zero discharge since the sinter plant blowdown can usually be disposed of with that from a blast furnace system.

TABLE 8 Blast Furnace Production, 1970

State	Pig iron, tons	Ferroalloys, tons	Total, tons
Pennsylvania	20,768,000	395,000	21,163,000
Ohio	15,554,000	901,000	16,455,000
Indiana	13,348,000		13,348,000
Illinois	7,401,000		7,401,000
New York	5,569,000	69,000	5,638,000
Alabama	4,654,000		4,654,000
Other states	24,141,000	1,051,000	25,192,000
Totals	91,435,000	2,416,000	93,851,000

Assuming that the six single-machine plants of unknown size are of the average size as the machines in the other 33 plants, the total grate area of 44,202 sq ft indicates a daily capacity of 148,077 tons, or 54 million tons/year.

Ferromanganese Blast Furnace Operation

Ferromanganese production in blast furnaces has steadily decreased: less than 50 percent of the total production was produced in 1970. The operation differs from the manufacture of pig iron in that manganese ores or mixtures of manganese and iron ores are used and the furnace temperature is higher. Oxygen enrichments of the blast as high as 30 percent are now used in such furnaces. The suspended solids are much finer than from basic furnaces and the production of cyanide is much greater.

The suspended solids from ferromanganese blast furnaces are light in color and amount to about 300 lb/ton of metal produced. Cyanide protection is about 20 times that from an iron-making blast furnace.

Steelmaking Operations

The principal steelmaking methods in use today are the basic oxygen furnace (BOF or BOP), the open-hearth furnace, and the electric-arc furnace. Little or no steel is now produced in Bessemer converters. The Q-BOP is the newest of the steelmaking processes, developed in Germany and licensed to the United States Steel Corporation in this country. The Q-BOP may well become the steelmaking process of the future.

All the steelmaking processes basically refine the product of the blast furnace blended with scrap, or scrap alone, and alloying elements to required analyses for particular purposes. Steel is any alloy of iron containing less than 1.8 percent carbon. The steelmaking process consists essentially of oxidizing constituents, particularly carbon, down to specified low levels, and then adding various elements to required amounts as determined by the grade of steel to be produced.

The basic raw materials for steelmaking are hot metal or pig iron, steel scrap, limestone, burned lime, dolomite, fluorspar, iron ores, iron-bearing materials (such as pellets or mill scale), and various addition agents which may be the metallic elements or ferrous alloys of such elements as manganese, silicon, chromium, vanadium, nickel, etc.

The steelmaking processes produce fume, smoke, and waste gases as the unwanted impurities are burned off and the process vaporizes or entrains a portion of the molten steel into the off-gases. Other impurities combine with the slag which floats on the surface of the bath and is separately withdrawn. Wastewater results from the steelmaking processes when wet dust collection systems are used on the furnace and in the slag-handling operations.

Dry collection methods require that the gas temperature be reduced to about 500°F or less. This may be accomplished by the use of waste-heat boilers, evaporation chambers, or spray cooling (spark chambers). Waste-heat boilers and evaporation chambers do not result in wastewater effluents. Spray cooling or quenching and/or the use of wet washers result in wastewater containing all or a portion of the particulates in the gas.

Both electric furnace and basic oxygen furnace production have been steadily increasing as open-hearth production has decreased from a high of 93.8 percent of the total steel production in 1950 to 29.5 percent in 1971. For the same period, carbon-grade steel has represented about 89 percent of the total production; alloy steel represents about 10 percent of the total and stainless steel about 1 percent.

Open-hearth furnaces Although declining in recent years, 30 percent of the steel produced in the United States is still made in open-hearth furnaces. Open-hearth furnaces, while similar in design, may vary widely in tonnage capacity. The furnaces found in this country range in capacity from 10 to 600 tons per heat.

The main body of an open-hearth furnace is the hearth itself. Hearths are constructed of refractory brick and are supported by I beams. The steelmaking ingredients (iron, scrap, limestone, alloys, etc.) are charged into the front of the furnace through movable doors. Flame to "cook" the steel is supplied by liquid or gaseous fuel which is ignited by hot air. Continuous hot-air flow is maintained by use of a system of regenerative refractory chambers which are located on either side of the furnace.

As hot air flows horizontally across the hearth, it serves the dual purpose of fuel ignition and heating of the opposite regenerative chamber. Flow is periodically reversed to maintain an even hot-air flow. The molten steel is tapped from the furnace back when the ordered specifications have been reached. In the standard furnace this occurs 10 to 12 hr after the first charge. Many furnaces use oxygen lances which create a more intense heat and reduce charge-to-tap time. These lances (usually two or three) are located in the furnace roof directly over the hearth. The tap-to-tap time for the oxygen-lanced open hearth probably averages about 8 hr, with about 12 hr being the average when oxygen is not used.

The open-hearth furnace allows the operator to, in effect, "cook" the steel to required specifications. The nature of the furnace permits the operator to continually sample the batch contents and make necessary additions. The major drawback of the process is the long time required to produce a "heat." Many basic oxygen furnaces can produce eight times the amount of steel produced by a comparable open-hearth furnace over the same period.

With the use of oxygen lances, the duration of a heat is about 5 to 8 hr. The use of oxygen greatly increases the rate of fume generation and most hearth furnaces are now using oxygen. The rate of fume generation with oxygen lancing has been reported to be from 9.3 to 30 lb/ingot ton. Fume generation rates of about 25 lb/ton with oxygen lancing and about 8 lb/ton without lancing probably best represent current practice. These values are equivalent to the standard raw waste load when venturi scrubbers are used to clean the gas.

The use of precipitators to clean the gas may or may not generate wastewater discharge. When an evaporation chamber is used to cool the gas, no wastewater discharge results since all of the water is evaporated into the gas. When a spark chamber (spray tower) is used to cool the gas, the excess water is discharged as wastewater. The solids may be collected from the precipitators in a completely dry form or as a thick slurry after mixing with water in a pug mill. In either case a wastewater stream results from this operation. In some cases, however, the collected solids have been mixed with the water from the spark chamber and sent to a clarifier. Such a practice results in a raw waste load equal to that of venturi scrubbers.

Basic oxygen furnaces (BOF) BOF steel production first equaled that from open hearths in 1969. The BOP (basic oxygen process) is now clearly the major steelmaking process.

Vessels for the basic oxygen process are generally vertical cylinders mounted on a truncated cone. High-purity oxygen is supplied at high pressure through a water-cooled tube mounted above the center of the vessel. Scrap and molten iron are charged to the vessel and a flux is added. The oxygen lance is lowered and oxygen is admitted. A violent reaction occurs immediately and the resultant turbulence brings the molten metal and the hot gases into intimate contact, causing the impurities to burn off quickly. An oxygen blow of 18 to 22 min is normally sufficient to refine the metal. Alloy additions are made and the steel is ready to be tapped.

A basic oxygen furnace can produce 200 to 300 or more tons of steel per hour and allows very close control of steel quality. A major advantage of the process is the ability to handle a wide range of raw materials. Scrap may be light or heavy, and the oxide may be iron ore, sinter, pellets, or mill scale.

As with the open hearth, the water pollution potential from BOF is in the water used to cool and/or clean the off-gases as an air pollution abatement measure. The particulate matter generated has been reported at 40 to 46 lb/ingot ton, a much narrower range than in the case of open hearths. An average value of 41 lb/ingot ton probably best defines the standard raw waste load. As previously described for the case of the open hearth, such a load results when venturi scrubbers are used or when the solids collected from precipitators are mixed with water from spray cooling. The use of an evaporation chamber and separate solids collection from precipitators should produce no wastewater effluents.

The annual production of steel in the United States by the basic oxygen process has increased from about 600,000 tons in 1957 to 64 million tons in 1971. It is anticipated that basic oxygen production will continue to increase at the expense of open-hearth production. During the past 7 years, alloy steel production in the basic oxygen process has increased steadily from 1 million tons in 1965 to over 4 million tons in 1971. As with the open hearth, however, the principal grade of steel produced in the basic oxygen furnace is carbon steel, accounting for 93 percent of total production.

Electric-arc furnace The electric-arc furnace is uniquely adapted to the production of high-quality steels; however, most of the production is carbon steel. Practically all stainless steel is produced in electric-arc furnaces. Electric furnaces range up to 30 ft in diameter and produce from 2 to 400 tons/cycle in 1.5 to 5 hr.

The cycle in electric furnace steelmaking consists of the meltdown, the molten-metal period, the boil, the refining period, and the pour. The required heat is generated by an electric arc passing from the electrodes to the charge in the furnace. The refining process is similar to that of the open hearth, but more precise control is possible in the electric furnace. Use of oxygen in the electric furnace has been common practice for many years.

Electric-arc furnaces are to be found in almost every integrated steel mill. Many mills operate only electric furnaces, using scrap as the raw materials. In most "cold shops" the electric-arc furnace is the sole steelmaking process.

Wastewater is generated from electric-arc furnaces when excess water is used to cool the gas or when venturi scrubbers are used. Baghouses are predominantly used with electric furnaces and the wastewater potentials are the same as with precipitators. Particulate generation has been reported at from 10 to 15 lb/ingot ton, the average being 11.7 lb/ingot ton. This would be the raw waste load with venturi scrubbers or when solids collected in precipitators or baghouses were mixed with spray cooling water. Particulate emissions are reported about doubled when dirty, subquality scrap is used.

The annual production of steel in the electric-arc furnace has increased from about 8 million tons in 1957 to some 21 million tons in 1971. Although electric furnaces are small in heat capacity as compared to open-hearth or basic oxygen furnaces, a trend toward larger furnaces has recently developed. The largest electric steelmaking furnace in the United States in 1972 had a capacity of 400 tons per heat. The new electric-arc furnaces are not only increasing present plant capacity but are also replacing the fading open-hearth process. It is not expected that the BOF will compete with the electric-arc furnace since the BOF is essentially a hot-metal process and the electric-arc is a scrap-based process. In addition the electric-arc furnace now accounts for nearly all the stainless-steel production. Electric-arc furnaces are the principal steelmaking process utilized by the so-called mini-steel plants which have been built since World War II.

Q-BOP process Recently, the United States Steel Corporation announced the development of a high volume adaptation of the Q-BOP process invented by Maxhutte of West Germany. European experience with this process is limited and has involved relatively small units of 40-ton capacity. Through the United States Steel Corporation's research efforts, the process has been improved so that it can produce a high volume of steel and utilize greater amounts of scrap. The principal difference between the Q-BOP and the BOP lies in the oxygen system. Instead of injecting oxygen at the top of the vessel, oxygen is enveloped in a protective fluid stream and injected into a Q-BOP furnace at the bottom, through gas-cooled tuyeres. It has been estimated that the Q-BOP can be built for half the cost of a conventional BOP and is cheaper to operate. Particulate generation would be expected to be about the same as with the conventional basic oxygen furnace, but no data are as yet available.

Vacuum degassing In the vacuum degassing process, steel is further refined by subjecting the steel in the ladle to a high vacuum in an enclosed refractory-lined chamber. The oxygen, carbon, and some steel in the bath are oxidized further and are emitted as carbon monoxide (CO) gas and iron oxide fumes. A four- or five-stage steam-jet ejector with barometric condensers is used to draw the vacuum.

A means of providing heat is furnished in the process by electric carbon-heating rods to replace the heat lost in the process or in some cases to raise the temperature of the steel bath. Alloys are generally added during this process and the cycle time is approximately 25 to 30 min. The waste products from the vacuum degassing process are condensed steam and waste with iron oxide fumes and CO gases entrained in the discharge effluent.

Teeming (pouring) If the steel is brought to the teeming area, a string of ingot cars with cast-iron ingot molds are stationed in an isle. The mill crane with the steel ladle passes over each ingot mold filling it with molten steel. After the steel is poured, the mill crane dumps slag residue and returns for another heat of steel. The ingots are allowed to cool until a hardened skin forms, then they are taken to a mold-stripper area where the hot ingot is removed from the ingot mold. The ingots are transported to soaking pits for reheating prior to rolling in the rolling mills.

The ingot molds are transported back to a mold preparation area where they are cleaned and prepared for the next cycle. During the teeming operation, some materials are added to the oxidizing agent and lead is used for making leaded steels.

Antisticking treatments are used on the inside of the ingot molds to prevent "stacking" between hot steel and molds. One method is for oil to be sprayed on the inside of the mold; another method is for a powder to be dusted inside the mold. The molds are usually water sprayed to cool them so as to obtain minimum turnaround time.

The waste products from the teeming and mold cycle are generally contaminants that have been spilled, etc., and reach sewers via groundwater.

Continuous casting If the steel is not processed in the teeming area, the steel from the ladle is processed in the continuous-casting area. In the continuous-casting process billets, blooms, and slabs are cast directly from the hot steel, thus eliminating ingots, soaking pits, mold preparation, and stripping facilities. In this process, the molten steel from the ladle is poured into water-cooled, open-ended copper molds. As the steel begins to pass through the copper mold, the outer skin cools and forms a hard steel shell with a liquid center. Water is sprayed on the steel, thus cooling it further. The steel is then cut to definite lengths and transported via "runout tables" to a stacker and storage areas.

The mold and machine cooling systems are usually closed systems and thus water picks up only heat. In the spray zone area where water is sprayed on the steel, the effluent is discharged. This effluent contains steel scale and oil from the machinery.

Slag handling For all of the three steelmaking processes, slag is always generated. The slag generally is deposited in ladles from the furnaces. These ladles are transported to a slag dump where the slag is air-cooled and sometimes sprayed with water to accelerate cooling. The slag is processed to reclaim the iron and the slag is crushed and sold. Pollutants from this process generally are airborne dust, but they become waterborne if wet dust-collecting systems are used. Open-hearth slag contains sulfur and, when wetted, generates hydrogen sulfide gas.

Oxygen generating The oxygen-generating plant produces high-purity (99.5 percent) oxygen in large tonnage for the steelmaking operations. Rates of 500 tons/day are common for the BOF plant. Air is liquefied by means of compression and expansion for separation of the oxygen and nitrogen. Liquid oxygen is stored and the nitrogen and other inert gases are vented from the system. The effluent from an oxygen plant is the heated cooling water from compression equipment.

HOT-ROLLING MILLS

Normally hot-rolling mills are used to transform ingot steel into finished products. Although hot-rolling mills exist in such variety that simple classification and description are difficult, they may be divided into two types whose end products are either semifinished or finished.

Primary Mills—Semifinished Products

In general, primary mills reduce hot ingots into blooms, billets, or slabs which are defined as semifinished products. While it is not possible to apply a precise definition to the terms *bloom, billet,* and *slab,* the following general characteristics normally relate to such terms.

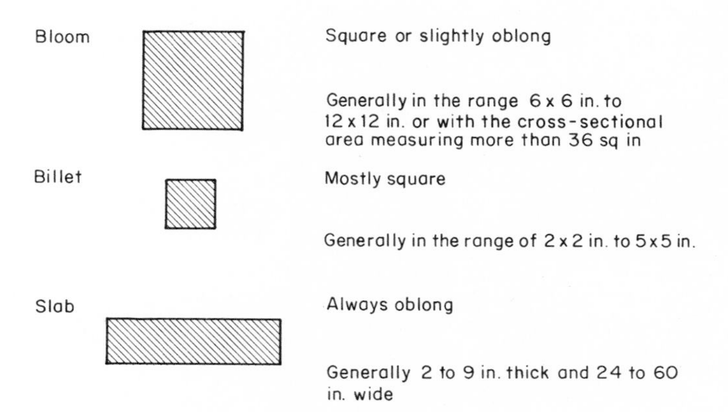

The basic operation in a primary mill is the gradual reduction of the steel ingot between the surface of two rotating rolls. By reversing the rolls and gradually reducing the space between them the ingot is gradually shaped to the desired size.

High-pressure water jets remove surface scale from the ingot as it enters the rolls. As the ingot is passed back and forth between horizontal and vertical rolls, manipulators turn the ingot from time to time so that it is well worked on all sides. When the desired shape has been achieved, the end pieces, or crops, are removed with electric or hydraulic shears. The semifinished pieces are stored or sent to reheating furnaces for subsequent rolling operations.

It is possible, and often economical, to roll ingots in a one-mill continuous operation (frequently without reheating) directly from the bloom, slab, or billet stages into more refined and even finished steel products. Large tonnages of standard rails, beams, and plates are produced regularly in this fashion from medium- and large-sized ingots. Most of the ingot tonnage, however, is rolled into blooms, slabs, or billets in one mill and then cooled, stored, and eventually rolled by other mills and/or forged (hammered) into finished products.

Reheating is necessary throughout the rolling operation whenever the temperature of the worked metal falls below that necessary to retain the required plasticity. Reheating furnaces are of two general classes: batch and continuous. In a *batch furnace* the charged material remains in a fixed position on the hearth until heated to rolling temperature. In a *continuous furnace* the charged material moves through the furnace as it is heated to rolling temperature. Batch furnaces vary in size from those with hearths of only a few feet square to those 20 ft deep by 50 ft long; some modern continuous furnaces have hearths 80 to 90 ft long.

Secondary Mills—Finished Products

Prior to the finishing operations, the semifinished products are inspected for surface defects that would affect the quality of the finished product. These surface defects may be removed by hand chipping, machine chipping, grinding, milling, scarfing, and hot steel scarfing. The various mechanical means of surface preparation are those common in all metalworking and machine shop operations.

Scarfing is a process of utilizing streams of oxygen jets on the surface of the steel being treated. The resulting high surface temperature causes rapid oxidation and localized melting. The process may be either manual or mechanical but in both cases it consists of the continuous motion of an oxyacetylene torch along the length of the piece undergoing treatment. In recent years the so-called hot scarfing machine has come into wide use. This production machine has been adapted to remove a thin layer (⅛ in. or less) of metal from all sides of red-hot steel billets, blooms, or slabs as they travel through the machine in a manner analogous to the motion through rolling mills. After this conditioning operation, the semifinished products are heated in special reheating furnaces prior to rolling in highly specialized mills.

Sheet and strip mills A continuous hot-strip mill is utilized to roll slabs which are brought to rolling temperature in continuous reheating furnaces. Then "conditioned" slabs pass through scale breakers and high-pressure water sprays dislodge the loosened scale. A series of roughing mill stands finish the slab to the proper weight and gage, and the ends are squared with a rotary crop shear. Second scale breakers and high-pressure water sprays precede a finishing mill stand train for final size reduction. Cooling water is sprayed on the *runout table*, and the finished strip is coiled. Such a mill can turn a thick 6-ft slab of steel into a thin strip or sheet ¼ mi long in 3 min or less. Modern hot-strip mills produce a product which may be up to 96 in. wide, although the most common width in newer mills is 80 in.

The product of the hot-strip mill may be sold as produced, or reused within the mill for further processing in cold-reduction mills. The terms *strip* and *sheet* as applied to the finished products refer to width and gage limitations, however these distinctions are not valid when applied to continuous hot-rolling mills. Regardless of whether the end product is strip, sheet, or breakdown (cross rolled), these mills are referred to as *strip mills*.

During 1971 shipment of hot-rolled sheet and strip products amounted to 34,095,289 tons of carbon-grade steel, 1,010,626 tons of alloy-grade steel, and 467,812 tons of stainless steel for a total of 35,573,727 tons or 48 percent of total shipment. Hot-strip mill capacity in the United States is estimated at over 88 million tons/year.

Bar products mills Merchant-bar, rod, and wire mills produce a wide variety of products in continuous operations ranging from small-diameter wire through bars and rods. The designation of the various mills as well as the classification of their products are not very well defined within the industry. In general, the cross-sectional area and length distinguish the products. Raw materials for these mills are reheated billets. Many older mills use hand "looping" operations: material is passed from mill stand to mill stand by hand; newer mills use mechanical methods of transferring the materials. As with other rolling operations, the billet is progressively reduced in size and shape for the desired dimensions.

In 1971, shipments of bar products amounted to 11,810,708 tons of carbon-grade steel, 2,237,892 of alloy-grade steel, and 107,625 tons of stainless steel for a total of 14,156,225 tons or 16 percent of total shipments. Wire production totaled 2,791,343 tons or 3.2 percent of total shipments.

Plate mills Plates are classified, by definition, according to certain size limitations to distinguish them from sheet, strip, and flat bars. According to this classification, plates are generally considered to be those flat hot-rolled products that are more than 8 in. wide and generally ¼ in. or more thick. The sequence of operations for plate mills is heating slabs, descaling, rolling, leveling, cooling, and shearing. Most plate mills use continuous-type heating furnaces. Descaling in a modern plate mill is accomplished with 1,500-psi hydraulic sprays impinging on both top and bottom surfaces. Temperature variation in the plate is a problem of particular importance in rolling plates as is the care that must be exercised in cooling the rolled product to avoid distortion.

Plate-rolling mills generally are divided into two very broad design classifications. One type includes the *universal mills* which are characterized by vertical rolls preceding and following the horizontal rolls; such a mill produces a product of the width conforming to narrow tolerances. The second general type of mill is the *sheared-plate mill* which may or may not include edge-working equipment.

In 1971, shipment of plates amounted to 6,629,968 tons of carbon-grade steel, and 50,828 tons of stainless steel for a total of 7,939,424 tons or 9.1 percent of total shipments.

Structural shapes A wide variety of various steel shapes are rolled from blooms. These shapes include structural sections such as I beams, channels, angles, wide-flanged beams, H beams, sheet piling, rails, and numerous special sections. The heating of the bloom for large sections is usually done in batch-type furnaces, although some newer mills use continuous furnaces. A typical mill consists of a two-high reversing breakdown rolling stand where initial shaping is accomplished followed by a group of three-roll stands in train where the rolling process is completed. These mills are known as *roughing stands, intermediate stands,* and *finishing stands,* respectively. Several passes of the material are made back and forth through the breakdown roughing and intermediate mills; a single pass is usually made through the finishing stand. The sequence of operations then consists of heating blooms, rolling to proper contour dimensions, cutting while hot to lengths that can be handled, cooling to atmospheric temperature, straightening, cutting to ordered lengths, and shipping.

Shipment of shapes, including rails, in 1971 was 7,229,890 tons, of which 6,690,081 tons was carbon-grade steel, 539,633 tons was alloy-grade steel, and 176 tons was stainless steel. The total tonnage represents 8.3 percent of total shipment for 1971.

Pipe and tubing Welded tubular products are made from hot-rolled skelp (sheet steel) with square or slightly beveled edges, the width and thickness of the skelp being selected to suit the various sizes to be made. The coiled skelp is uncoiled, heated, and fed through forming and welding rolls where the edges are pressed together at high temperature to form a weld. Welded pipe or tube can also be made by the electric weld process, where the weld is made by either fusion or resistance welding. Seamless tubular products are made by rotary piercing of a solid round bar or billet followed by various forming operations to produce the required size and wall thickness.

Pipe and tubing shipments for 1971 totaled 7,573,923 tons or 8.7 percent of total shipments; of the total, 6,438,617 tons was carbon-grade steel, 1,108,599 tons was alloy-grade steel, and 26,707 tons was stainless steel.

In general, the effluent (containing mostly scale from the primary and other rolling operations) passes to a catch basin to remove the large particles and prevent sewer clogging. Further treatment is generally some form of sedimentation.

PICKLING

Pickling is the process of chemically removing oxides and scales from the surface of the steel by the action of water solutions of inorganic acids. Depending on the type of product being processed, a number of acids (such as sulfuric, hydrochloric, nitric, hydrofluoric and phosphoric) may be utilized, either individually or in combination, in both batch and continuous equipment. In 1950, sulfuric acid accounted for more than 90 percent of the pickling acid, however, in recent years an increasing number of steel mills have changed to hydrochloric acid. Hydrochloric acid offers several advantages over sulfuric acid: it produces a more even and cleaner surface, requires lower liquor temperatures, and can be regenerated.

Some products such as tubes and wire are pickled in batch operations; that is, the product is immersed in an acid solution and allowed to remain in this solution until the scale or oxide film is removed. The material is lifted from the bath, allowed to drain, and rinsed by sequential immersion in rinse tanks.

Pickling lines for hot-rolled strip operate continuously on coils that are welded together, passed through the pickler countercurrently to the acid, and then sheared and recoiled. Most mild steel is pickled with sulfuric or hydrochloric acid; stainless steels are pickled with hydrochloric, nitric, and hydrofluoric acids. Various organic chemicals are used in pickling to inhibit acid attack on the base metal, while permitting preferential attack on the oxides; wetting agents are used to improve the contact of the acid solution with the metal surfaces. As in the batch operation, the steel passes from the pickling bath through a series of rinse tanks.

The sources of wastewater from pickling operations are the strong spent solutions, the rinse waters, and the water used in fume scrubbers. The latter source generally is found when other than sulfuric or phosphoric acids are used. Due to the volatilities and noxious character of the fumes from hydrochloric, nitric, and hydrofluoric acids, scrubbers are used largely as an industrial hygiene measure.

COLD REDUCTION

Cold rolling of steel strip is divided into two categories: the cold-reduction mill and the temper-pass or skin-pass mill. Cold reduction may be further divided into the tandem four-high mills, the single-stand four-high reversing mills, and also the specialty mills. The principal cold-reduced flat-rolled products are flat bars, cold-rolled strip, cold-rolled sheets, and black plate. Excluding black plate, the products may be made from any of the three main classifications of steel. The four- and five-stand tandem cold mills are generally used for high-volume sheet and tin-plate products while the single-stand reversing mill is more normally associated with small production facilities.

In cold-reduction process, a coil is reduced between 25 and 99 percent of the hot-rolled thickness by one of the above operations. Cold reduction generates heat that is dissipated by a palm-oil lubricant, or synthetic oils are emulsified in water and jetted against the rolls and the steel surface during the rolling operation. Another system involves the spraying of water on the mill rolls as the cooling medium, and a direct application of atomized palm oil to the strip as the lubricant. At the final mill stand, a cleaning agent may be applied to remove the rolling oils. After cleaning and annealing, the product will generally pass through the *temper pass* or *skin pass,* which slightly reduces the thickness but imparts the desired mechanical and surface characteristics.

In general, cold-reduction lubricants and cooling liquids are reused in a closed system.

Electrolytic Tin Plating

Electrolytic tin plating is superior to hot-dipped tin plating. About 96 percent of all tin plating in the United States is produced by the electrolytic process. Prior to 1940, all commercial tin plate was produced by the hot-dip process. The major types of electrolytic tin plate are listed below with estimated capacities.

Horizontal acid, halogen or Weirton line	250,000 tons/year
Vertical or Ferrostan lines	150,000 tons/year
Alkaline solution or alkaline lines	150,000 tons/year

Aside from the differences (such as plating solutions, current densities, and physical arrangements), the following process will generally apply.

1. *Electrolytic cleaning in alkaline solutions.* This step removes those contaminants resulting from prior processing, particularly oil and dirt.
2. *Rinsing.* Water sprays remove carryover from alkaline cleaning.
3. *Pickling.* Removal of iron oxides.
4. *Rinsing.* Water sprays remove carryover from pickling.
5. *Plating.* Solutions, number of cells, and sizes vary according to type of process.
6. *Recovery tank, hot-rinse tank, drier, and melting zone.* In this stage, the tin coating forms a mirrorlike finish.
7. *Chemical treatment.* A chromate solution removes and renders the tin surface resistant to oxidation.
8. *Oiling.* During this step, oil is normally applied electrostatically. Stabilized cottonseed oil or synthetic dioctyl sebacate may be used.

Tin coating by the electrolytic process can range from 0.10 lb/BB* and up. As an example a coating of 11 lb/BB will produce a coating thickness of 0.000060 in.

Chrome-Plated Steel

The development of means to join containers by methods other than soldering and with the rapid increase in the price of tin, the chrome-plated–tin-free steel market has emerged. Chrome-plated steel has successfully been used in applications which involve 40 percent of a 67 billion can market, or over 2 million tons/year in the United States. In Fig. 1 a typical chrome-plating operation is illustrated, showing in detail each major stage of operation. Because of the similarity between chrome plating and tin plating, it can be expected that some present tin lines will be converted to chrome, rather than having new facilities constructed. Both National Steel at Weirton, W. Va., and Bethlehem Steel at Sparrows Point, Md., have completed such conversions.

Wastewaters generated within the chrome-plating process may be divided into two separate types: rinse water and concentrated process solutions. At the Sparrows Point plant a countercurrent system was devised to reuse the rinse water by taking clean, heated water (from the plater and chemical treatment heat exchangers) and using it successively in the final rinse and in the previous chemical treatment stage rinses. Rinse water is collected in a reserve tank and pumped through a strainer to remove particulate matter, through a cation exchanger to remove iron, and then into the evaporation loop. This system eliminates the discharge of chrome-bearing wastewater and recovers the chromium solution for reuse in the plating process. Drag out from the concentrated plating and chemical treatment may be collected in the reverse tank along with the rinse water. This system was chosen over the traditional method of adding barium carbonate to the chromic acid solution to precipitate a sludge of barium chromate.

PRIMARY NONFERROUS METALS

The nonferrous metals are principally aluminum, copper, zinc, and lead, and the product classification is probably the best way of describing the industry. Such a classification cuts across the SIC codes, but is more meaningful for our purposes here.

Aluminum

Aluminum is produced by the electrolytic reduction of alumina in a bath of fused cryolite. Carbon anodes carry the current from overhead bus bars, and the molten aluminum in the bottom of the cell serves as the cathode. Such plants are located near abundant sources of cheap electric power. Plant capacities average about 100,000 tons/year, but range from 40,000 to 250,000 tons/year.

The electrolysis, conducted in a molten bath of alumina and fluorine salts, results in off-gas containing 0.1 to 0.2 percent fluoride as gaseous nitrogen fluoride (NF) and sodium salt particles. These gases are usually scrubbed with water to remove

* BB is the abbreviation for base box, a unit of area equal to 112 sheets of 14 × 20 in. plates.

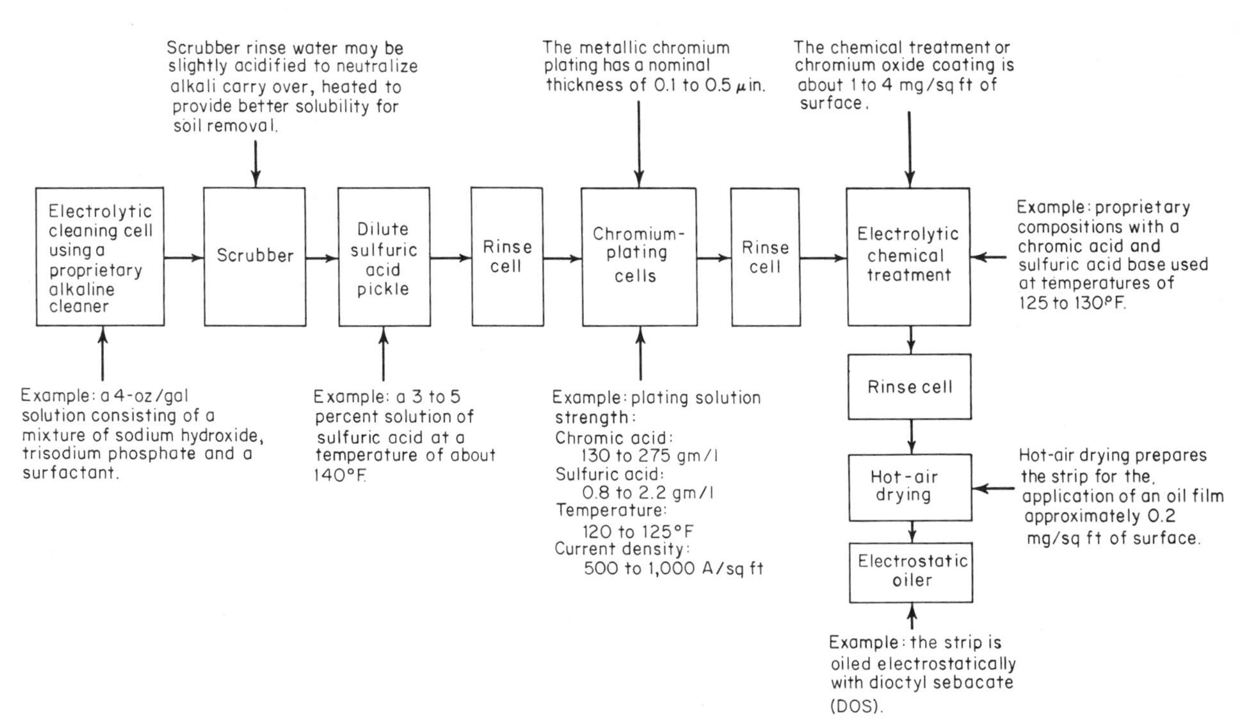

Fig. 1 Production stages of a tin-free steel–chrome-plate line. Line speed 1,000 to 1,600 ft/min.

90 to 99 percent of the contaminants and the scrubber water is the main wastewater source in aluminum refining. Scrubber water use may amount to 28 gal/lb of aluminum; most such water is recirculated.

Aluminum is also produced from scrap in secondary recovery operations. Melting and reverberatory furnaces are used and mostly produce aluminum-based alloys. Furnace fumes such as metal oxides in particulate form and chlorine fumes from chlorine purging are potential wastewater sources if water scrubbing is used.

Aluminum fabrication operations consist of casting, rolling, drawing, and extrusion. Chlorine is used as a purge gas to prevent hydrogen bubbles in castings. The potential wastewater here is from scrubbing water. Lubricant solutions are the major source of wastes from the rolling, drawing, and extrusion. Insoluble oils are used at mild conditions of temperature and pressure. The wastes produced contain oil, solids, and water. Soluble oil emulsions in water are used under conditions of higher temperature and pressure, generally in recycle systems; decomposition of the oils requires periodic dumping.

Copper

Primary copper smelters produce an impure copper metal known as *blister* from concentrated areas. Secondary copper smelters operate on new and old scrap. The major smelter wastes are slag and sulfur dioxide, the latter occurring mostly from smelting sulfide ores. Slag granulation can produce wastewater containing suspended solids, and any water scrubbing to treat off-gases can produce wastewater. Water use at smelters can range from less than 2 to 21 gal/lb of copper.

Copper refineries generally use the electrolytic process, although there are furnace refining processes. Refineries average about 150,000 tons/year of production. An acidic copper solution is used, but no solution need be discarded from the closed system if proper purifying procedures are used. Impurities accumulate in the anode mud from which precious metals are recovered. Most water is used for cooling molds and cast shapes. Suspended solids in the form of scale are potential wastewater contaminants, as is the electrolyte solution if a closed circuit is not maintained.

The major wastes from brass and wire mills, in which 95 percent of copper fabrication occurs, are the spent solutions from the acid baths used to remove oxide scale. These pickling liquors and rinse waters contain sulfuric acid, copper, zinc, and chromium. Oil-bearing wastewaters are generated from lubrication similar to those in aluminum production. Zinc fumes are produced from electrolytic melting furnaces and may appear in wastewater if wet scrubbers are used.

Zinc

Zinc smelting and refining are generally at the same nonmine sites. Smelter capacities average about 50,000 tons/year of zinc, and the roasting furnace wastes are suspended dust and sulfur dioxide. Some plants utilize the waste gases to produce sulfuric acid. Most zinc is refined by the retort process which consists of distillation and condensation by both the batch method and the continuous method. Zinc is almost completely recovered from the fume. In electrolytic refining, the zinc oxide from roasting is leached with acid and the zinc sulfate is purified by precipitation of impurities. The pure solution is then electrolyzed to produce metallic zinc.

Zinc is used principally in die casting, galvanizing, and brass alloying. Wastewater from fabrication primarily contains suspended solids. Wastewater from refining retorts contains suspended solids and sulfur dioxide. It is wet-scrubbed or the sulfur dioxide is oxidized to sulfur trioxide and recovered as sulfuric acid. Electrolytic refining wastes contain spent electrolyte solutions and the impurities in the zinc from roasters.

Lead

Most lead smelters and refineries are located near the mines. Two methods of smelting are used. In the ore hearth method, lead is produced in one step using the high-purity ores found in Missouri. The sintering and blast furnace method produces crude lead oxide. Ore hearthing and blast furnaces produce sulfur dioxide and particulates, much of the former being used to produce sulfuric acid. Wastewaters are produced if wet scrubbers are used. Electrolytic refining is also used to produce lead and produces wastewaters containing spent electrolytes. These solutions are recycled and processed to recover by-products, and the final effluent load is reduced.

Ferroalloys

The ferroalloys, more properly termed *addition agents,* are essential in steelmaking. The principal ferroalloys are ferromanganese, ferrosilicon, silicomanganese, and ferrochrome. Calcium carbide is often included in this industry group as is metallic manganese and chromium. The alloys are made in submerged-arc electric furnaces or by exothermic reactions involving aluminum, metallic manganese, and chromium. Wastewaters result from wet air pollution control devices on the smelting furnace and from spent electrolyte solutions.

Wastewaters from electrolytic processes are of relatively minor importance and are similar to electroplating or spent pickle liquor solutions, i.e., solutions of metallic salts and acids. The primary wastewater sources are effluents from wet scrubbers and from conditioning towers prior to precipitators. The principal determinant of wastewater volume is the degree to which smelting furnaces are covered to reduce inspirated air. Covered and semicovered furnaces require much less water than scrubbers since the off-gas volumes are greatly reduced.

MINI-STEEL PLANT

During the last few years a subtle change has taken place and that is the development of the so-called mini-steel or neighborhood steel plant. Raw steel production from these plants is now in excess of 7 million tons/year and represents a significant part of the steel industry. Production per plant ranges from 50,000 up to 400,000 tons/year and usually serves a marketing area within 250 mi of the plant. Since the electric furnace has become an economical producer of carbon steels and since the successful application of continuous casting of billets has been implemented during the last 10 years, an unprecedented growth of such plants has taken place. Capitalization per annual ton produced amounts to about $100 for the mini-plant compared to about $500 for a completely integrated large-tonnage facility. This modern plant is generally a semi-integrated operation, employing electric furnaces, continuous casting, reheating furnaces, and rolling facilities. Since the majority of these plants are relatively new, they generally contain up-to-date pollution control systems. Usually, process water for the plant is from a closed system with the blowdown being the only discharge. Since the mini-steel plant is a relatively new part of the industry, the available data is scarce and is not available at this time.

WASTEWATER TREATMENT AND CONTROL

The technology of wastewater treatment and control in the metals industries will be considered here for the various manufacturing processes already described. The untreated wastewater volumes and pollutant loads, the raw waste loads, must first be considered in order to define properly the magnitude of the potential problem. Various levels of treatment may then be considered as "present practice" (1973), "base level of treatment," "best practicable treatment," and "best available treatment." The three treatment levels represent decreasing effluent loads in terms of both water flow and pollutant loads. Costs, of course, generally increase as effluent loads are reduced and economic considerations become of increasing importance. The base level of treatment may be considered as the minimum acceptable, while the best practicable treatment (BPCTCA) is that in use to the extent that technological practicality and reasonable costs are readily demonstrable. Best available treatment (BADCT) is that for which technology is available, but for which costs may be considered excessive.

Coke Plant Wastes

Coke plant waste loads are best expressed in terms of unit volumes and quantities per ton of coal coked. Tables 9 to 13 summarize coke plant waste loading and treatment methods.

The raw waste load (RWL) of the "average" coke plant may be estimated on the basis of the following operating conditions:

1. Direct discharge of flushing liquor
2. No ammonia stills or saturators
3. Once-through final cooler
4. Benzol plant

Present practice waste loads (PPWL) in the "average" coke plant may be estimated on the basis of operating practices as follows:

1. Direct discharge of flushing liquor—70 percent of plants, semidirect ammonia recovery—15 percent of plants, indirect ammonia recovery—15 percent of plants
2. Recirculating final cooler with cooling tower blowdown
3. Benzol plant

The base level of treatment (BLT) can most logically be specified as the treatment that has been demonstrated and utilized for 20 years, i.e., the use of free and

TABLE 9 Raw Waste Loads

Parameter	Flushing liquor	Final cooler	Benzol plant	Total effluent
Flow, gal/ton	29.7	1,410.0	375.0	4,255.0
Phenol, lb/ton	0.464	0.073	0.028	0.565
Cyanide, lb/ton	0.024	1.189	0.012	1.225
Ammonia, lb/ton	1.386	5.527	0.008	6.921
Thiocyanate, lb/ton	0.085	4.162	...	>4.247
BOD, lb/ton	0.410	7.171	0.141	7.722
Chlorides, lb/ton	1.353	...	...	>1.353
COD, lb/ton	0.819	...	...	>15.4
Sulfide, lb/ton	0.187	...	...	>0.187
Ferrocyanide, lb/ton	0.005	...	...	>0.005
Pyridine, lb/ton	0.144	...	...	>0.144
Thiosulfate, lb/ton	0.054	...	...	>0.054

TABLE 10 Present Practice Waste Loads

Parameter	Final cooler	Benzol plant	Total effluent
Flow, gal/ton	6.9	375.0	2,862.0
Phenol, lb/ton	0.076	0.028	0.581
Cyanide, lb/ton	0.010	0.012	0.064
Ammonia, lb/ton	0.040	0.008	1.602
Thiocyanate, lb/ton	0.035	...	0.265
BOD, lb/ton	0.235	0.141	1.473
Dissolved solids, lb/ton	...	...	3.802
Oil and tar, lb/ton	...	...	0.563
Chlorides, lb/ton	...	...	1.175
COD, lb/ton	...	...	2.946
Suspended solids, lb/ton	...	...	0.053
Sulfates, lb/ton	...	...	1.278
Sulfides, lb/ton	...	...	0.168

fixed ammonia stills, dephenolizers, and recirculated final coolers with cooling tower blowdown. Assuming the use of a benzol extraction dephenolizer, the basic level of treatment estimated is given in Table 11.

The best practicable treatment (BPT), based on several years of operating experience in coke plants, is probably biological oxidation of the plant effluent. In these plants the effluent volume is reduced to an optimal minimum volume. U.S. Geological Survey (USGS) survey data indicates that 50 percent of the coke plants practicing recirculation of cooling water discharge effluents of less than 311 gal/ton coal, the average being 474 gal/ton of coal. A total effluent volume of 300 gal/ton of coal should be easily achievable. For the average coke plant coking 5,328 tons/

day of coal, the effluent volume would be 1.6 mgd. The concentrations in the effluent would be those shown in Table 12.

The average effluent concentrations or minimum percentage reductions reported for England's Brookehouse plant which treats ammonia still waste rather than flushing liquor provide performance criteria. The criteria for cyanides and suspended solids are taken from the Spencer plant, also in England, and are conservative. Sulfides are assumed converted to sulfates and other inorganics are assumed to be unchanged. The effluent loads for the plant coking 5,328 tons/day of coal per day and treating 1.6 mgd biologically are given in Table 13.

TABLE 11 Base Level of Treatment

Parameter	Still waste	Final cooler	Benzol plant	Total effluent
Flow, gal/ton	39.7	6.9	375.0	2,862.0
Phenol, lb/ton	0.004	0.076	0.028	0.108
Cyanide, lb/ton	0.007	0.010	0.012	0.029
Ammonia, lb/ton	0.027	0.040	0.008	0.075
Thiocyanate, lb/ton	0.085	0.035	...	>0.120
BOD, lb/ton	0.215	0.235	0.141	0.591
Dissolved solids, lb/ton	1.607	...	...	>1.607
Chlorides, lb/ton	1.357	...	...	>1.357
Suspended solids, lb/ton	0.218	...	...	>0.218
Sulfates, lb/ton	0.195	...	...	>0.195
Sulfides, lb/ton	0.037	...	...	>0.037

TABLE 12 BPCTCA Effluent Concentrations

Parameter	Load, lb/day	Concentration, ppm
Phenol	575	43
Cyanide	155	12
Ammonia	400	30
Thiocyanate	639	48
BOD	3,149	236
Dissolved solids	8,562	642
Chlorides	7,230	542
Suspended solids	1,162	87
Sulfates	1,039	78
Sulfides	197	15

TABLE 13

Parameter	Influent, ppm	Effluent, ppm or percent reduction	Effluent, lb/day	Effluent, lb/ton
Phenol	43	1.5 ppm*	20.0	0.004
Cyanide	12	0.3 ppm†	4.0	0.001
Ammonia	30	7%*	372	0.070
Thiocyanate	48	2.5 ppm*	33.3	0.006
BOD	236	86.2%*	434	0.081
Dissolved solids	642	642	8,562	1.607
Chlorides	542	542	7,230	1.357
Suspended solids	87	60 ppm†	800	0.150
Sulfates	78	123 ppm	1,639	0.308
Sulfides	15	0	0	

* Brookehouse.
† Spencer.

The best available treatment is probably a distillation/incineration system like the one installed as a demonstration unit under an Environmental Protection Agency grant to the Alan Wood Steel Company, Conshohocken, Pa. If such treatment were installed, the optimum implementation would obviously be to reduce the wastewater volume to a minimum. USGS data indicates that cooling water effluents can be reduced to 58 gal/ton of coal. The average benzol plant wastewaters for typical large coke plants is 18.9 gal/ton of coal. Adding the still wastes at 39.7 gal/ton and the final cooler bleed at 6.9 gal/ton, a total effluent volume of 123.5 gal/ton of coal should be readily achievable. For a coke plant coking 5,328 tons/day of coal, the effluent volume would be 658,000 gpd. The distillation process would produce an effluent as described below in 96 percent of the original volume, or 632,000 gpd:

Ammonia, ppm	15
Thiocyanates, ppm	10
Oils, ppm	5
Phenols, ppb	10
Cyanides, ppb	10
Total solids, ppm	10

The dissolved solids, concentrated in 26,320 gpd, would be incinerated, spray-dried, land-filled, or disposed of on ore piles, slag quenching, or slag piles.

Blast Furnace Wastes

Based on the data available from 87 blast furnaces with total capacities of 88,327 tons/day of iron, the following figures were obtained:

Washer water volume, gal/ton	3,200
Dry flue dust produced, lb/ton	146
Wet dust produced, lb/ton	58.6

Cooling water use is best estimated from USGS data which indicate an average of 19,100 gal/ton of pig iron. The same source indicates additional uses for boiler feed, sanitary and service, and "other" at 2,900 gal/ton of pig iron. The total use is thus indicated to be 25,200 gal/ton of pig iron. This figure is much higher than previously has been indicated by most sources. The figure most often quoted for total water use in the industry is 40,000 gal/ton of finished steel (Nebolsine) with 25 percent of this used in the blast furnace department. Production data for 1968 are as follows in the year in which the industry used 6,500 billion gal of water (1968 census of manufactures), with corresponding water use rates:

Finished steel (shipments)	91,900 million tons $\simeq$ 70,800 gal/finished ton
Raw steel production	131,500 million tons $\simeq$ 49,500 gal/ingot ton
Pig iron production	89,300 million tons

It is apparent from these data that the water use statistics used in the past have been confused by intake or net use data being used interchangably with gross use data.

The standard raw waste loads (SRWL) of various constituents are estimated on the basis of the available data from 13 plants and are detailed in Table 14.

The present practice waste load (PPWL) probably corresponds to the use of plain sedimentation with 95 percent removal of suspended solids, and no significant removal

TABLE 14 Raw Waste Loads

Flow, gal/ton	3,204.0
Suspended solids, lb/ton	58.6
Phenol, lb/ton	0.021
River water quench	0.001
Cyanide, lb/ton	0.078
Fluorides, lb/ton	0.046
Ammonia, lb/ton	0.545
Alkalinity ($CaCO_3$), lb/ton	5.17

of other contaminants (see Table 15). The base level of treatment (BLT) may be taken as chemical coagulation, alkaline chlorination, and no use of wastewater for coke quenching (see Table 16).

The best practicable treatment (BPT) may be taken as recirculation with a blow-

TABLE 15 Present Practice Waste Loads

Flow, gal/ton	3,204.0
Suspended solids, lb/ton	2.93
Phenol, lb/ton	0.021
Cyanide, lb/ton	0.078
Fluorides, lb/ton	0.046
Ammonia, lb/ton	0.545
Alkalinity, lb/ton	5.17

TABLE 16 Base Level of Treatment

Flow, gal/ton	3,204.0
Suspended solids, lb/ton	0.254
Phenol, lb/ton	0.001
Cyanide, lb/ton	0.0002
Fluorides, lb/ton	0.046
Ammonia, lb/ton	0.036
Alkalinity, lb/ton	5.17

TABLE 17 Best Practicable Treatment

Flow, gal/ton	160.0
Suspended solids, lb/ton	0.013
Phenol, lb/ton	Negligible
Cyanide, lb/ton	Negligible
Fluorides, lb/ton	0.002
Ammonia, lb/ton	0.002
Alkalinity, lb/ton	0.259

TABLE 18 Waste Load Data for Blast Furnaces

Parameter	SRWL	PPWL	BLT	BPT	BAT
Flow, gal/ton	3,204.0	3,204.0	3,204.0	160.0	0
Suspended solids, lb/ton	58.6	2.93	0.254	0.013	0
Phenol, lb/ton	0.021	0.021	0.001	Negligible	
River water quench	0.001				
Cyanide, lb/ton	0.078	0.078	0.0002	Negligible	0
Fluorides, lb/ton	0.046	0.046	0.046	0.002	0
Ammonia, lb/ton	0.545	0.545	0.036	0.002	0
Alkalinity, lb/ton	5.17	5.17	5.17	0.259	0

down of 5 percent of the recirculation rate, treated by alkaline chlorination, and no use of wastewater for quenching (see Table 17).

The best available treatment (BAT) is recirculation with no blowdown, blowdown used in slag quenching, blowdown disposed on ore piles, or blowdown to cotreatment in municipal waste treatment plants. Discharges of pollutants would be zero.

Table 18 summarizes the waste load data for blast furnaces.

Steelmaking Waste Loads

Many present steelmaking operations use only plain sedimentation to treat steelmaking wastewaters. Settling rate curves typically are as shown in Fig. 2, and the sedimentation index (SI) value of the typical thickener is 10 min, indicating an average

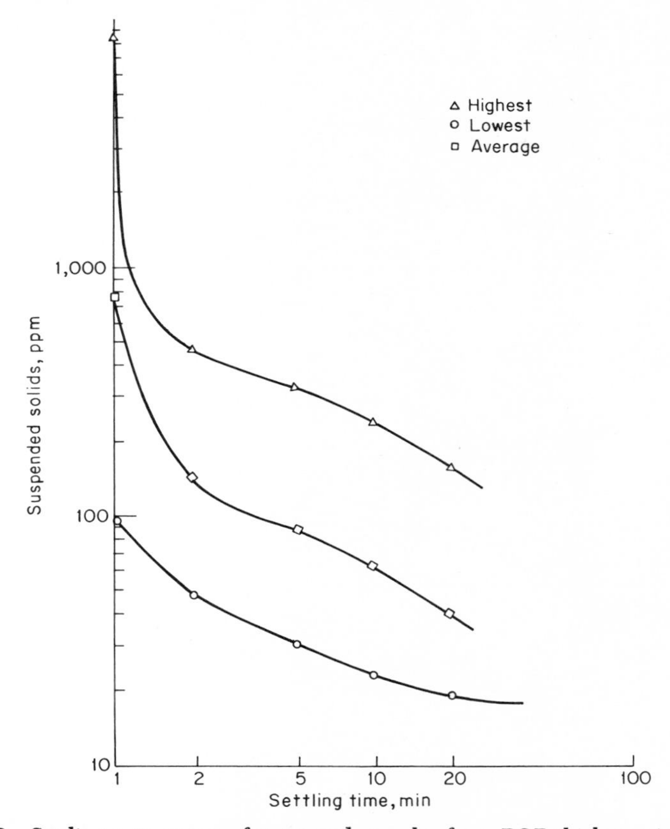

Fig. 2 Settling rate curves of untreated samples from BOP thickener influent.

TABLE 19 Standard Raw Waste Loads

Furnace	System	Flow, gal/ton	Load, lb/ton
BOF	Precipitator-quencher	180	0.097
BOF	Venturi-quencher	540	0.292
BOF	Off-gas system	135	0.073
Electric	Venturi-quencher	1,330	0.720
Open-hearth	Venturi-quencher	1,000	0.541

effluent concentration of 65 ppm. Thus the SRWL for the various steelmaking operations are as shown in Table 19.

No specific data are available, in any usable form, for wastewaters from slab casting. However, since wastewater volumes are essentially the same as for conventional slab mills, the critical finer suspended particle concentrations should be similar.

The fume generated in vacuum degassing should be at least as fine as that of the average from the BOF vessel. That 350 ppm diluted from 260 to 1,060 gal/ton would contribute 86 ppm to the effluent of a scale pit having an SI of 1 min. A typical blooming or billet mill scale pit having an SI of 1 min will have an effluent containing not less than 100 ppm; similar values would be expected from a slab mill. An SRWL then of $1{,}060 \times 8.33 \times 186 \times 10^{-6}$, or 1.64 lb/ton of steel, would be expected.

The best practicable treatment (BPT) without water reuse is sedimentation-flocculation. Effluents of 15 ppm or less are being achieved. Assuming that the effluent from the steelmaking furnace, slab casting, and the vacuum degasser would be combined for treatment in an adequate clarifier, the waste loads would be as shown in Table 20.

The best available treatment (BAT) is recirculation and reuse of the treated effluent. Although the blowdown can probably be much lower, it is clear that it can

TABLE 20 BPT Waste Loads

		Combined		Steelmaking only	
Furnace	System	Flow, gal/ton	Load, lb/ton	Flow, gal/ton	Load, lb/ton
BOF	Precipitator-quencher	1,240	0.155	180	0.022
BOF	Venturi-quencher	1,600	0.200	540	0.067
BOF	Off-gas system	1,195	0.149	135	0.017
Electric	Venturi-quencher	2,390	0.299	1,330	0.166
Open-hearth	Venturi-quencher	2,060	0.257	1,000	0.125

TABLE 21 BAT Waste Loads

		Steelmaking only		Furnace and casting	
Furnace	System	Flow, gal/ton	Load, lb/ton	Flow, gal/ton	Load, lb/ton
BOF	Precipitator-quencher	36	0.004	248	0.031
BOF	Venturi-quencher	108	0.013	320	0.040
BOF	Off-gas system	27	0.003	239	0.030
Electric	Venturi-quencher	266	0.033	478	0.060
Open-hearth	Venturi-quencher	200	0.025	412	0.051

be at least as low as 20 percent. On this basis, the BAT waste loads would be those given by Table 21.

Treatment methods suitable for steelmaking wastes The available wastewater treatment methods include plain sedimentation, sedimentation-flocculation, deep-bed filtration, and reuse of wastewater. Flocculation may be accomplished by the use of chemicals such as ferric sulfate, lime, polyelectrolytes, and/or magnetic agglomeration.

When the gases are passed through a water quenching tower, about 5 to 8 gpm/ton of steel results from this source alone; 35 gpm/ton is required for quenching and scrubbing in a venturi scrubber. About 0.5 gpm/ton is blowdown from such a system (containing 20-ppm suspended solids) and 0.4 gpm/ton is lost as vapor in the gas.* The same reference indicates an average of 13 gpm/1,000 scfm of gas in a venturi scrubber.

Another reference† indicates that for a 160-ton BOF producing 1,200,000 tons/year of steel, a water rate of 700 gpm is given for quenching with 1,400 gpm for

* *Iron and Steel Engineer,* September 1969.
† *Iron and Steel Engineer,* July 1961.

the venturi scrubber. Blowdown (and makeup) rate of 200 gpm is given with the blowdown containing 4 percent suspended solids. The indicated tap-to-tap time is 1.168 hr.

The BOF shop at Interlake Steel Corporation in Chicago has two 75-ton BOF furnaces and uses 1,000 gpm of water for quenching prior to a dry precipitator.

Wet scrubbers on BOFs are normally operated with about 75 percent excess air, while dry precipitators require 150 percent excess air to ensure combustion of carbon monoxide to prevent an explosive mixture from forming. With 75 percent excess air, the total waste gas volume will be 9.33 scf per cu ft of oxygen blown. A venturi scrubber requires 8 gpm of water/1,000 cfm of gas, while a quencher typically requires 4 gpm/1,000 cfm. The gas leaving the furnace will be about 3,000°F.

Table 22 gives reported oxygen rates for several BOF's. An average oxygen-blowing time of 18.5 min is specified and the data indicate an average oxygen rate of 1,775 scf of oxygen per ton of steel. Thus the total gas volume averages about 16,561 scf per ton of steel. A typical wet scrubber operation has gas volume and water flow rates as follows:

Vessel off-gases	65,000 scfm at 3200°F (dry)
Venturi inlet	177,000 cfm at 183°F (saturated)
Stack volume	80,000 cfm at 110°F

The gas volume of the venturi inlet thus averages about 45,000 cu ft per ton of steel. Thus the water uses would be expected to be 360 gal/ton for scrubbing and 180 gal/ton for quenching, totaling 540 gal/ton.

TABLE 22 BOF Oxygen Rates

Plant	Furnace, number-tonnage	O_2 time, min	Off-gas volume rate
Bethlehem, Bethlehem, Pa.	2-250	19	20,000 cfm
Combustion (Nov. 1967)	200		20,000 scfm
Republic, Gadsen	2-190		2,000 cu ft/ton O_2
Alan Wood Steel	2-140	15	12,000 cfm O_2
Bethlehem Burns Harbor	2-250		27,500 scfm O_2
Wheeling-Pgh., Monessen	2-200	18	18,000 cfm O_2
Colorado Fuel & Iron	2-120		10,000 cfm O_2
U.S. Steel, Duquesne	2-220		125,000 scfm, venturi stack
Rowe, et al.	2-300	22	32,000 scfm O_2

Water requirements for a BOF using electrostatic precipitators and an evaporation chamber total 3,200 gpm for two 250-ton vessels producing 2,300,000 tons/year, or 6,300 tons/day, indicating a use of 731 gal/ton. A survey of British plants indicated a mean water use of 2,885 gal/ton in pneumatic steelmaking processes. At least one BOF shop on the Great Lakes uses as much as 4,900 gal/ton for cooling and 438 gal/ton for gas scrubbing.

The BOFs and continuous casters at Weirton use 50 mgd of water producing 9,315 tons/day, i.e., 5,368 gal/ton. Assuming 2,800 gal/ton for the caster and 540 gal/ton for gas cleaning, the BOF cooling water would be 2,028 gal/ton.

An average cooling water use of 2,000 gal/ingot ton for BOF seems to be indicated.

Cooling water use for open-hearth and electric furnaces are best estimated from the USGA survey data at 4,950 and 2,720 gal/ton, respectively. British data tend to confirm these figures.

One electric furnace installation, using venturi scrubbers on very large furnaces, uses about 1,330 gal/ton. This is probably a maximum figure applying to only the largest furnaces. Of the total, 25 percent is used in the quencher and the remainder in the scrubber.

A 200-ton open-hearth furnace at Edgar Thomson Works, United States Steel, used 500 gpm in a venturi scrubber during an 8.5-hr heat. This is equal to 1,275 gal/ton of steel.

The scrubbers on the No. 7 and No. 8 open-hearth furnaces at Youngstown Sheet and Tube, Indiana Harbor, handle gas flows of 70,000 scfm at 1500°F with oxygen rates of 900 cu ft/ton. Each furnace averages 45 tons/hr of production at heat times of 7.2 hr. The exhaust fan for the common cooling tower is rated at 93,000 scfm at 41-in. water suction; the fan outlet volume thus would be about 80,000 cfm. Assuming a total water use of 10 gpm/1,000 scfm, a use here of 930 gal/ton is indicated.

When the off-gas (OG) system is used with a BOF, as shown at Armco, Middletown, the scrubbers are about 25 percent as large and the temperatures are about the same as with the use of 75 percent excess air.

A water quencher will scrub some of the particulate matter from the gas. The cleaning efficiency is, of course, not very good. There is an indication in the data from the Interlake installation that about 25 percent of the particulates generated are relatively large particles which would probably be washed out of the gas by the crudest type of washer.

At Inland Steel in East Chicago, the total water use for a two-furnace shop producing 9,888 tons/day is 70 mgd. The water uses are as follows:

	mgd	*gal/ton*
Hood cooling	23.0	2,330
Lance cooling	5.18	524
Spark box sprays	2.23	226
Scrubbing	39.6	4,003
Final cooling	39.6	4,003

The BOF shop at Lackawanna uses 9,400 gpm when the two furnaces are producing 290-ton heats simultaneously, and 7,000 gpm when one furnace is operating. The oxygen blowing time is 21 min, or 507 gal/ton of steel.

One 300-ton open-hearth furnace at Buffalo uses a minimum of 600 gpm on a venturi scrubber. Assuming a 7-hour heat the water use is 840 gal/ton.

The data for continuous casting and vacuum degassing are taken from a report of NUS Corporation to EPA as shown in Tables 23 and 24.

Hot-Rolling Mill Wastes

The waterborne wastes from hot-rolling operations consist primarily of suspended solids and oil. The solids, of course, are the scale particles which are removed from hot steel by mechanical action and water sprays. The oil originates from that used to lubricate the machinery, and varies particularly with the age and condition of the mill. The quantities of scale vary with the surface condition of the steel at the time of rolling, the type of steel, the stage of finishing, and the type of product.

TABLE 23 Steel Manufacturing Continuous Casting Effluent Standard Raw Waste Load

(Tons/day = 1,000–5,700)

Parameters	Range	Average
Water flow,* cooling water, gal/ton	1,500–2,500	2,000
Process water, gal/ton	600–1,000	800
Total water, gal/ton	2,100–3,500	2,800
Suspended solids:†		
mg/l	3,000–7,500	4,500
lb/ton	20–50	30

* Flow given is circulating water rate. All water is used for cooling. The process water comes in contact with the steel and picks up suspended solids and possibly a trace of oil. The cooling water is indirect cooling water. Generally all water is handled in recirculating cooling towers which would have a total evaporation and blowdown loss of 2 to 3 percent of the circulating rate. Heat removal is about 200 Btu/lb of steel cast.

† Based on process water only.

TABLE 24 Steel Manufacturing Vacuum Degassing Effluent Standard Raw Waste Load

(Tons/day = 1,000–5,700)

Parameters	Range	Average
Water flow, cooling water, gal/ton	100–200	150
Process water, gal/ton	225–300	260
Total water, gal/ton	325–500	410
Suspended solids:		
mg/l	125–700	350
lb/ton*	0.25–1.5	0.75

* Lb/ton calculated from mg/l based on average water flow.

In general, the scale loss of carbon steel is about 3 percent and that of stainless steel is about 1 percent. The various grades of alloy steel have scale losses intermediate between these values, probably averaging 2 percent. Much of this scale is in the form of large particles and drops out in even the crudest scale pit such as the type long used to guard against sewer clogging with no thought of pollution abatement. The only way to measure the gross amount of scale with any accuracy at all is to weigh the scale recovered over a period of time. The resulting number, i.e., 20, 40, or 60 lb/ton, has little significance insofar as potential pollution is concerned. The gross amount of potential effluent oil can likewise only be determined by the oil consumption in a mill over a period of time. The oil, however, constitutes potential pollution in the absence of any recovery method.

Although rolling-oil lubricants are normally associated with cold-rolling operations, recent developments in high-temperature rolling oils have precipitated experimentation of their use in hot mills. Since January 1969, the Sharon Steel Corporation's plant at Farrell has used rolling lubricants on approximately 85 percent of the products rolled on the 60-in. semicontinuous hot-strip mill. Experimentation between July 1968 and January 1969 at the Farrel hot-strip mill showed the following benefits: increased roll life, decreased amount of roll grinding, decreased total roll cost, increased production, decreased labor costs, decreased pickling costs, and an improved product. These developments indicate a possible future for hot-rolling oils and thus an additional pollution parameter for such operations.

The USGS data for the gross water uses in hot-rolling mills is given by Table 25.

It is very difficult to sample a rolling mill effluent (i.e., the scale-pit influent) and arrive at any sort of consistent concentration by analyzing the entire sample for either suspended solids or oil. As has been pointed out, the results means little in terms of potential pollution load. Most steel industry people have accepted the sedimentation index (SI) concept for designing sedimentation basins. The method of sampling and analysis is an integral part of the procedure.

A sample is taken and the solids and oil remaining in suspension after varying periods of time are determined with a standardized test procedure. If the empirical procedure is followed precisely, the time period allowed for sedimentation (flotation

TABLE 25

Primary mills, gal/semifinished ton:	
Median	2,070
Average	3,570
Maximum	11,300
Minimum	637
Secondary mills, gal/finished ton:	
Median	7,640
Average	11,700
Maximum	37,300
Minimum	2,780

in the case of oil) can be related to the performance of a basin which is characterized by an SI number equivalent to that time period in minutes. A crude scale pit suitable only to prevent sewer clogging will have an SI of 0.1 min or less. The best scale pit will usually have an SI of about 1.0 min, ranging up to possibly 10 min for larger pits with relatively lower flow rates or for circular clarifiers.

TABLE 26 Water Use Rates Reported for Specific Rolling Mills

Type of mill	Production, ton/day	Water use, gal/ton				
		Process	Reheat	Roughing	Finishing	Total
Hot-strip	8,400		686	2,923	1,029†	
Hot-strip	1,410	10,213				
Hot-strip	8,630	10,012	2,503			12,515
Hot-strip	9,493	9,101	3,034			12,135
Hot-strip	12,715	13,590	4,530	9,060	4,530	18,120
Hot-strip	1,726				8,201	
Hot-strip	9,205	15,644	6,257			21,901
Hot-strip	8,055	16,447	5,363			21,810
Hot-strip	7,249	7,151				
Plate	2,164	5,989*				
Plate	3,279	10,540	6,587			
Slab and scarfing	11,507	1,502				
Bar	523	9,474				
Blooming	2,589	1,785				
Blooming	8,493	1,187				
Slab	1,726	3,354				
Rod and bar	2,742	788	188			

* Effluent, 50 percent recycled.
† Does not include runout tables.

TABLE 27 Water Uses in Hot-Rolling Mills

(In gallons per ton of rolled products)

Type of mill	Process water	Furnace cooling	Total	Data source
Hot-strip	11,737	3,729	17,296	Table 26
Hot-strip	6,300			NUS report
Hot-strip	6,000			1968 Profile
Plate	11,259	6,587		Table 26
Plate	13,000			NUS report
Bar	9,474			Table 26
Bar	7,500			NUS report
Bar	7,000			1968 Profile
Blooming	1,486			Table 26
Blooming	1,200			NUS report
Blooming	2,300			1968 Profile
Slab	3,354			Table 26
Slab	1,200			NUS report
Slab	720			1968 Profile
Structural	2,000			NUS report
Rod	3,000			NUS report
Seamless pipe	5,000			NUS report
Billet	2,000			NUS report
Billet	1,400			1968 Profile

The data of Table 26 show water use rates for a variety of hot-rolling mills. In Table 27 data are compared for water uses as given in the 1968 Steel Industry Profile, the NUS report to EPA, the examples of Table 26, and the USGS report. The NUS data apparently refer only to process water and apparently do not include water used on strip-mill runout tables.

The best estimates on the basis of the data of Table 27, weighing the NUS report data for an average sample size of 6, and considering that process changes since the 1968 Profile generally tend to increase gross water use, are summarized in Table 28.

The water use in an integrated mill can be approximated by the weighted average use per shipments of the various types of carbon steel products for 1971 (see Table 29).

The total average water use of 15,202 gal/finished ton as shown by the USGS data, considered with the data in Table 28, indicates a cooling water use of 3,155 gal/finished ton. This is very close to the median indicated and to a weighted average of the mills listed, and probably indicates a reasonable value. The indicated wastewater volume of 3,945 gal/ton rolled agrees well with the 1967 Profile estimates of

TABLE 28 Average Water Use per Finished Ton

Rolling mill type	Process water use	Percent of total roll of production	Weighted use, % × use	Percent water use
Hot-strip	11,000	16.8	1,848	46.7
Plate	13,000	2.7	351	8.9
Bar	9,000	4.8	432	11.0
Blooming	1,500	39.7	596	15.1
Slab	1,500	19.6	294	7.5
Structural	2,000	2.7	54	1.4
Rod	3,000	1.8	54	1.4
Pipe	5,000	2.6	130	3.3
Billet	2,000	9.3	186	4.7

$$\text{Water use per finished ton} = \left(\frac{243.547}{79.306}\right) \times 3{,}945 = 12{,}115 \text{ gal/ton}$$

TABLE 29

Steel products	Shipments, tons
Blooming mills: (107,700,000 − 11,000,000) (ingot tons less continuous casting)	96,700,000
Structural mills (plus rails and accessories)	6,690,081
Plates	6,629,968
Rod mills (wire and wire rods)	4,292,629
Bar mills	11,810,708
Pipe and tubing	6,438,617
Billet mills (wire plus bars plus tube and pipes)	22,541,954
Slab mills (plate plus strip mills)	47,536,416
Strip mills (sheet plus tin plate and black plate)	40,906,488
Total finished and semifinished	243,547,000
Total finished production, 1971 tons	79,306,000

3,160 gal/ton rolled in typical production technology and 4,268 gal/ton rolled in advanced technology.

The raw waste loads on the basis of sampled rolling mill effluents (i.e., prior to scale pits) may be approximated (see Table 31) from the NUS report concentrations, the flows of Table 30, and the percentage of water uses by mill as previously calculated. The total use is 12,115 gal/ton of finished steel.

The raw waste load of suspended solids is very close to the generally accepted scale loss of 3 percent and that of oil agrees with the value of the NUS report, arrived at by an entirely different calculation. Expressed in average concentrations for all hot-rolling:

SS = 672 ppm
Oil = 37 ppm

The data of Fig. 3 show settling rate curves, determined by the SI procedure, for 123 samples of various rolling mill effluents. It is apparent that for the purpose here an average can be used to define levels of treatment. A crude scale pit can thus be expected to have an effluent of about 215 ppm, a fairly good scale pit about 130 ppm, and the best plain secondary settling basin about 50 ppm. Oil in the effluents of the former two would be about equal to the raw waste load (37 ppm), and oil in the latter would be about 15 ppm, assuming efficient oil skimming.

Properly designed and operated deep-bed filters produce an effluent of 15 ppm or less suspended solids, and 5 ppm oil recycling of the treated effluent with 5 percent blowdown is readily achievable. Thus this level of treatment would give waste loads as follows:

$$SS = 12{,}155 \times 8.33 \times 10^{-6} \times 15 \times 0.05 = 0.08 \text{ lb/ton}$$
$$Oil = 12{,}155 \times 8.33 \times 10^{-6} \times 5 \times 0.05 = 0.03 \text{ lb/ton}$$

TABLE 30 Summary of Hot-Rolling Water Uses

Type of mill	Process water, gal/ton rolled products
Hot-strip	11,000
Plate	13,000
Bar	9,000
Blooming	1,500
Slab	1,500
Structural	2,000
Rod	3,000
Seamless pipe	5,000
Billet	2,000

Table 31 Standard Raw Waste Loads per Ton Finished Steel

Type of mill	Wastewater, gal/ton	Concentration, ppm		Load, lb/ton	
		SS	Oil	SS	Oil
Hot-strip	5,657	575	40	27.1	1.88
Plate	1,078	185	45	1.66	0.40
Bar	1,333	200	15	2.22	0.17
Blooming	1,829	1,000	10	15.2	0.46
Slab	909	2,000	30	15.1	0.23
Structural	170	900	200	1.27	0.28
Rod	170	120	30	0.17	0.04
Pipe	400	840	7	2.80	0.02
Billet	569	480	55	2.28	0.26
Totals				67.8	3.74

The waste load from hot-rolling operations at various levels of treatment may be summarized as below and as in Table 32.

STANDARD RAW WASTE LOAD. Suspended solids and oil in mill effluent

BASE LEVEL OF TREATMENT. Scale pit with SI = 0.1 min

PRESENT PRACTICE. Scale pit with SI = 1.0 min

BEST PRACTICABLE TREATMENT. Scale pit and deep-bed filters, once-through use

BEST AVAILABLE TREATMENT. Scale pit and deep-bed filters, 5 percent blowdown

Pickling Wastes

Carbon steel

Sulfuric Pickling. Of all the steel products produced, pickling operations are performed on 50 percent of carbon steel, almost all alloy steels, and all stainless steels.

In 1967, SIC 3312 establishments used 1.089 million tons of sulfuric acid, com-

TABLE 32 Levels of Treatment for Hot-Rolling Wastewaters

Level of treatment	gal/ton	Suspended solids (SS) lb/ton	Oil lb/ton
Standard raw waste	12,115	67.8	3.74
Base level	12,115	21.7	3.74
Present practice	12,115	13.1	3.74
Best practicable	12,115	1.51	0.50
Best available	606	0.08	0.03

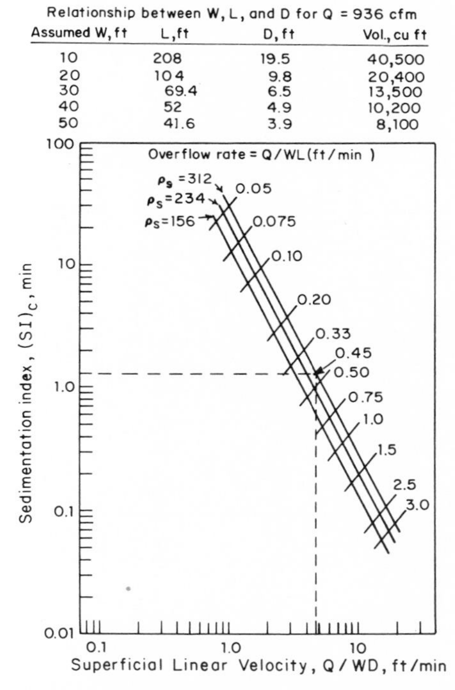

Relationship between W, L, and D for Q = 936 cfm

Assumed W, ft	L, ft	D, ft	Vol., cu ft
10	208	19.5	40,500
20	104	9.8	20,400
30	69.4	6.5	13,500
40	52	4.9	10,200
50	41.6	3.9	8,100

Fig. 3 Lines of optimum performance for mill scale, silica sand, and flue dust at different overflow rates.

pared with 1.176 million tons in 1963. Carbon-steel products totaled 76.042 million tons in 1967 and 69.510 million tons in 1963. The sulfuric acid used in pickling presently is estimated at about 22 lb of acid per ton of carbon-steel products. The typical spent liquor from a continuous-strip pickler contains 8.5 percent free H_2SO_4 and 13.0 percent $FeSO_4$, weighing about 10 lb/gal; the liquor is typically made up of 20 percent H_2SO_4 (specific gravity = 1.14). About 12.5 percent of the free and combined acid in spent liquor is lost in the rinse water. Expressed then in terms of total carbon-steel products, raw waste loads are as follow:

SPENT LIQUOR:

Basis = 1.000 gal pickle liquor

0.875 gal × 10 lb/gal. = 8.75 lb

$8.75 \times 0.085 = 0.744$ lb H_2SO_4

$8.75 \times 0.130 = 1.138$ lb $FeSO_4 \left(\frac{98}{152}\right) \times 1.138 = 0.734$ lb H_2SO_4

Original acid equivalent in waste pickle liquor (WPL) = 1.478 lb H_2SO_4

RINSE WATER:

$$\left(\frac{0.125}{0.875}\right) \times 0.744 = 0.106 \text{ lb } H_2SO_4$$

$$\left(\frac{0.125}{0.875}\right) \times 1.138 = 0.163 \text{ lb } FeSO_4,\ 0.105 \text{ lb } H_2SO_4$$

Original acid equivalent in rinse water = 0.211 lb H_2SO_4

The original liquor thus contained 1.689 lb H_2SO_4/gal, equivalent to about an 18 percent solution at 20°C:

$$1.1243 \times 8.33 \times 0.18 = 1.686 \text{ lb/gal}$$

The raw waste loads for the spent liquor are thus:

$$\frac{0.875 \times 22}{1.686} = 11.4 \text{ gal/ton}$$

$$(11.4 \times 10) \times 0.085 = 9.69 \text{ lb } H_2SO_4 \text{ per ton}$$

$$(11.4 \times 10) \times 0.130 = 14.82 \text{ lb } FeSO_4 \text{ per ton, } 5.46 \text{ lb Fe per ton}$$

The constituent raw waste loads for the rinse water are:

$$\left(\frac{0.125}{0.875}\right) \times 9.69 = 1.38 \text{ lb } H_2SO_4 \text{ per ton}$$

$$\left(\frac{0.125}{0.875}\right) \times 5.46 = 0.78 \text{ lb Fe per ton, } 2.12 \text{ lb } FeSO_4 \text{ per ton}$$

The above data are in terms of production of carbon-steel products. Since sulfuric acid pickling generally requires 45 lb of acid per ton of steel pickled, the values above can be multiplied by 45/22 or 2.05 for expression in terms of ton of steel pickled. Rinse-water volumes are given in the NUS report at 500 gal/ton of steel. This is about right on the basis of the N. H. Robertson plant at Ambridge, Pa. The rinse-water rate there was 110 gpm at a throughput of 150 ft/min. At 1 lb/sq ft for a 36-in. sheet, the rinse-water rate is 489 gal/ton.

Converting all of the above to the basis of tons of steel pickled, we have the following.

STRONG SPENT LIQUOR:

Volume = 11.4 × 2.05 = 23.4 gal/ton

Iron = 5.46 × 2.05 = 11.19 lb/ton

FREE ACIDITY AS $CaCO_3$:

$$1.38 \times 2.05 \times \left(\frac{100}{98}\right) = 2.89 \text{ lb/ton}$$

TOTAL ACIDITY AS $CaCO_3$:

$$1.38 \times 2.05 \times \left(\frac{100}{98}\right) = 2.89$$

$$2.12 \times 2.05 \times \left(\frac{100}{152}\right) = \frac{2.86}{5.75} \text{ lb/ton}$$

Iron in the rinse water as above would be 384 ppm, well within the 300- to 700-ppm range experienced at the Ambridge plant. The spent-liquor volume of 75 gpm at National Steel, Midwest Division is equivalent to about 16 gal/ton pickled, assuming that the 2,360,000 ton/year cold-reduction capacity is pickled. The spent liquor there contains 16 percent $FeSO_4$, and the volume thus would be expected to be somewhat lower; the indicated iron waste load is 9.43 lb/ton. The available data thus seem to substantiate these raw waste loads.

Hydrochloric Pickling. The 100-gpm spent liquor from Armco's new (1969) facilities at Middleton, Ohio, presumably results from processing about 1,680,000 tons/year and is equivalent to 29.8 gal/ton. The 130-gpm flow at J & L's Hennepin works is about 52 gal/ton on the basis of the 1,250,000 tons/year tandem mill. Armco reports 20 to 25 percent $FeCl_2$ in the WPL; J & L 16 to 21 percent. Both indicate 0 to 1 percent free acid; Watkins gives an average value of 0.25 percent free acid. On the basis of the above, a WPL volume of 41 gal/ton is indicated with an $FeCl_2$ concentration of 20 percent and a free-acid concentration of 0.5 percent. The specific gravity would be about 1.21. The data at Armco indicate a rinse-water volume of about 7.75 times that of the strong liquor volume, containing an average of 190-ppm Fe and 510-ppm acidity. The raw waste loads are estimated as follows:

STRONG SPENT LIQUOR

Volume = 41 gal/ton

$$\text{Iron} = 41 \times 8.33 \times 1.21 \times 0.20 \times \left(\frac{56}{127}\right) = 36.4 \text{ lb/ton}$$

FREE ACIDITY AS $CaCO_3$:

$$0.005 \times 41 \times 8.33 \times 1.21 \times \left(\frac{100}{2 \times 36.5}\right) = 2.83 \text{ lb/ton}$$

TOTAL ACIDITY AS $CaCO_3$:

$$0.005 \times 41 \times 8.33 \times 1.21 \times \left(\frac{100}{2 \times 36.5}\right) = 2.83$$

$$41 \times 8.33 \times 1.21 \times 0.20 \times \left(\frac{100}{127}\right) = \frac{65.1}{67.93} \text{ lb/ton}$$

RINSEWATER:

Volume = 7.75 × 41 = 3.18 gal/ton

Iron = $218 \times 8.33 \times 10^{-6} \times 190 = 0.50$ lb/ton

TOTAL ACIDITY AS HCl:

$318 \times 8.33 \times 10^{-6} \times 510 = 1.35$ lb/ton

COMBINED ACIDITY AS HCl:

$$0.50 \times \left(\frac{36.5 \times 2}{56}\right) = 0.65 \text{ lb/ton}$$

FREE ACIDITY AS HCl:

1.35 − 0.65 = 0.70 lb/ton

FREE ACIDITY AS $CaCO_3$:

$$0.70 \times \left(\frac{100}{2 \times 36.5}\right) = 0.96 \text{ lb/ton}$$

TOTAL ACIDITY AS $CaCO_3$:

$$1.35 \times \left(\frac{100}{2 \times 36.5}\right) = 1.85 \text{ lb/ton}$$

The capital costs for treatment are probably best estimated on the basis of the Armco data for the rinse-water system, accepting the Armco statement that the rinse-water system would be built as a standby for future operational changes.

$$\frac{\$1,070,000}{780,000 \text{ tons/year}} = \$1.37 \text{ per annual ton}$$

Operating costs for the intermediate level of treatment above are about 6 cents/ton of steel rolled and should be about the same for the best practicable treatment. Operating costs for the best available treatment are about 7 cents/ton of steel rolled.

The Steel Company of Canada at Hamilton, Ontario, reported* an HCl spent-liquor volume of 40 gpm at a pickling rate of 500,000 tons/year. At 20 shifts per week, this is equal to 40 gal/ton as estimated above.

Alloy and stainless-steel pickling The production of stainless-steel strip typically proceeds as follows:

1. Hot-rolled strip (0.125 in.), annealed, and pickled in two 35-ft long tanks containing 15 percent hydrochloric acid at 160°F, followed by a single similar tank containing 4 percent hydrofluoric acid and 10 percent nitric acid at 150 to 170°F.
2. Cold reduction to 0.060 in. using soluble oils, followed by annealing and pickling in HNO_3–HF.
3. Cold reduction to 0.030 in. using soluble oils, followed by annealing and pickling in HNO_3–HF.
4. Cold reduction to 0.013 to 0.015 in. using soluble oils, followed by annealing and pickling in HNO_3–HF.
5. Temper mill finishing to 0.010 in. using a kerosene-type solution such as Stanisol.

The production of stainless-steel billets, bars, and plates typically involves a single

* *Iron and Steel Engineer,* August 1971.

pickling operation in a 10 percent sulfuric acid solution at 140 to 160°F, followed by a 10 percent HNO_3–4 percent HF bath at 130 to 150°F.

The alloy steels, depending on the grade, are pickled in a great variety of acids and combinations of acids. Sulfuric acid alone is usually ineffective. Various combinations of sulfuric, hydrochloric, nitric, and phosphoric acid are used.

According to Shreve,[20] about 27 percent of the hydrofluoric acid produced in 1963 was used in the metal and petroleum industries. According to the 1963 Petroleum Industry Profile about 42 percent of alkylation units used HF, and this operation had a capacity equal to 6 percent of the typical refinery throughput. On the basis of the 1963 throughput of 3.156 billion bbl, HF alkylation capacity was 79.53 million bbl/year. According to Nelson,[21] about 0.55 lb of acid is consumed or lost per barrel. The indicated 1963 use in the petroleum industry was thus about 22,000 tons. Of the 105,000-ton production in 1963 then, about 6,000 tons presumably was used in the steel industry.

Stainless-steel shipments in 1963 were 667,701 tons, indicating an overall use of HF of about 18 lb/ton. Nitric acid use would thus be expected to be about 18 × 2.5, or 45 lb/ton. Cold-rolled sheet and strip totaled 359,217 tons and hot-rolled sheet and strip totaled 36,016 tons. The use of HCl and H_2SO_4 is thus estimated as follows on the basis of 59 percent hot-rolling of sheets and strip and 41 percent production of other products:

$$0.59 \times 18 \times \left(\frac{2 \times 15}{4}\right) = 79.7 \text{ lb HCl per ton}$$

$$0.41 \times 18 \times \left(\frac{10}{4}\right) = 18.5 \text{ lb } H_2SO_4 \text{ per ton}$$

The total indicated volumes of pickle liquor per ton then (assuming a density of 10 lb/gal) are:

$$\left(\frac{18}{0.04}\right) \times 10 = 45 \text{ gal } HNO_3\text{–HF liquor per ton of stainless steel}$$

$$\frac{79.7}{0.15 \times 10} = 53 \text{ gal HCl liquor per ton hot-rolled sheet strip}$$

$$\frac{18.5}{0.10 \times 10} = 18.5 \text{ gal } H_2SO_4 \text{ liquor per ton bars, plates, and billets}$$

The practice in cold-rolled sheet and strip production in 1963 probably averaged that indicated on p. 1119 of "The Making, Shaping and Treating of Steel" (1964)[1], i.e., one pickling following cold-rolling. With two additional picklings now used during cold-rolling of sheet and strip, about twice as much HNO_3–HF pickle liquor would be expected to be used for that portion of the stainless steel production. The HNO_3–HF liquor may now amount to 50 percent more than the above estimates. The production of hydrofluoric acid increased by about 43 percent from 1963 to 1967, indicating, at least, that this conclusion is not impossible.

Raw waste loads for stainless pickling are estimated assuming that the rinse-water volumes and free-acid concentrations are the same as for HCL and H_2SO_4 carbon-steel pickling and as for that of HCl carbon-steel pickling for HNO_3–HF solutions. Free-acid concentrations in the strong liquors are similarly assumed.

HNO_3–HF Pickling (per Ton of Stainless Production)

CARBON STEEL HCl ACIDITIES AS $CaCO_3$:

Total acidity in HCl spent liquor and rinse = 67.93 + 1.85 = 69.78
Free acid in HCl spent liquor = 2.83; in rinse water = 0.96
Combined acid in HCl spent liquor = 65.10; in rinse water = 0.89

STRONG SPENT LIQUOR:

$$\text{Free HF} = \left(\frac{2.83}{69.78}\right) \times 1.5 \times 18 = 1.10 \text{ lb HF}$$

$$\text{Free } HNO_3 = \left(\frac{2.83}{69.78}\right) \times 1.5 \times 45 = 2.74 \text{ lb } HNO_3$$

$$\text{Combined acid} = \left(\frac{65.10}{69.78}\right) \times 1.5 \times 418 = 25.19 \text{ lb HF}$$

$$\text{Combined acid} = \left(\frac{65.10}{69.78}\right) \times 1.5 \times 45 = 62.97 \text{ lb } HNO_3$$

$$\text{Iron} = 25.19 \times \left(\frac{56}{2 \times 20}\right) = 63.3 \text{ lb Fe}$$

TOTAL ACIDITY AS $CaCO_3$:

$$(1.10 + 25.19) \times \left(\frac{100}{2 \times 20}\right) = 65.73$$

$$(2.74 + 62.97) \times \left(\frac{100}{2 \times 63}\right) = \frac{52.15}{117.88} \text{ lb } CaCO_3$$

FREE ACIDITY AS $CaCO_3$:

$$1.10 \times \left(\frac{100}{2 \times 20}\right) + 2.74 \times \left(\frac{100}{2 \times 63}\right) = 4.92 \text{ lb } CaCO_3$$

Volume = 45 × 1.5 = 67.5 gal

RINSE WATER:

$$\text{Free HF} = \left(\frac{0.96}{69.78}\right) \times 1.5 \times 18 = 0.37 \text{ lb HF}$$

$$\text{Free } HNO_3 = \left(\frac{0.96}{69.78}\right) \times 1.5 \times 45 = 0.93 \text{ lb } HNO_3$$

$$\text{Combined acid} = \left(\frac{0.89}{69.78}\right) \times 1.5 \times 18 = 0.34 \text{ lb HF}$$

$$\text{Combined acid} = \left(\frac{0.89}{69.78}\right) \times 1.5 \times 45 = 0.86 \text{ lb } HNO_3$$

$$\text{Iron} = \left[0.34 \times \left(\frac{56}{2 \times 20}\right)\right] = \left[0.86 \times \left(\frac{56}{2 \times 63}\right)\right] = 0.86 \text{ lb Fe}$$

TOTAL ACIDITY AS $CaCO_3$:

$$(0.37 \times 0.34) \times \left(\frac{100}{2 \times 20}\right) = 1.78$$

$$(0.93 + 0.86) \times \left(\frac{100}{2 \times 63}\right) = \frac{1.42}{3.20} \text{ lb } CaCO_3$$

FREE ACIDITY AS $CaCO_3$:

$$\left[0.37 \times \left(\frac{100}{2 \times 20}\right)\right] + \left[0.93 \times \left(\frac{100}{2 \times 63}\right)\right] = 1.67 \text{ lb } CaCO_3$$

Volume = 7.75 × 67.5 = 523 gal

HCl Pickling (per Ton Hot-Rolled Sheet and Strip)

$$\text{HCl carbon steel pickling} = 69.78 \times \left(\frac{36.5}{100}\right) = 25.47 \text{ lb HCl/ton}$$

STRONG SPENT LIQUOR:

Volume = 53 gal

$$\text{Iron} = \left(\frac{79.7}{25.5}\right) \times 36.4 = 113.8 \text{ lb}$$

FREE ACIDITY AS $CaCO_3$:

$$\left(\frac{79.7}{25.5}\right) \times 2.83 = 8.85 \text{ lb}$$

TOTAL ACIDITY AS $CaCO_3$:

$$\left(\frac{79.7}{25.5}\right) \times 67.93 = 212 \text{ lb}$$

RINSE WATER:

Volume = 7.75 × 53 = 411 gal

$$\text{Iron} = \left(\frac{79.7}{25.5}\right) \times 0.50 = 1.56 \text{ lb}$$

FREE ACIDITY AS $CaCO_3$:

$$\left(\frac{79.7}{25.5}\right) \times 0.70 = 2.19 \text{ lb}$$

TOTAL ACIDITY AS $CaCO_3$:

$$\left(\frac{79.7}{25.5}\right) \times 1.85 = 5.78 \text{ lb}$$

H_2SO_4 Pickling (per Ton Bars, Plates and Billets)

H_2SO_4 carbon-steel pickling = 45 lb H_2SO_4 per ton

STRONG SPENT LIQUOR:

Volume = 18.5 gal

Iron = $\left(\frac{18.5}{45}\right) \times 11.19 = 4.60$ lb

FREE ACIDITY AS $CaCO_3$:

$\left(\frac{18.5}{45}\right) \times 20.27 = 8.33$ lb

TOTAL ACIDITY AS $CaCO_3$:

$\left(\frac{18.5}{45}\right) \times 40.26 = 15.66$ lb

RINSE WATER:

Volume = $\left(\frac{18.5}{23.4}\right) \times 500 = 395$ gal

Iron = $\left(\frac{18.5}{45}\right) \times 1.60 = 0.66$ lb

FREE ACIDITY AS $CaCO_3$:

$\left(\frac{18.5}{45}\right) \times 2.89 = 1.19$ lb

TOTAL ACIDITY AS $CaCO_3$:

$\left(\frac{18.5}{45}\right) \times 5.75 = 2.36$ lb

Raw waste loads for pickling are thus estimated on the basis of units per ton of steel pickled, averaging those for alloy-steel production on the basis of 50 percent for stainless steel, 0.50 (22/45) for sulfuric pickling of carbon steel, and 0.50 (45—22)/45 for hydrochloric pickling of carbon steel. The data are summarized in Table 33.

Alloy-steel pickling, as previously indicated, uses such a variety of procedures that general raw waste loads cannot be estimated on the basis of any hard data. A reasonable approximation, however, can be made on the basis of the averages of carbon and stainless practice.

One recent estimate indicates that about one-half of the spent pickle liquor produced by the steel industry is discharged without treatment. This occurs despite the fact that spent pickle liquor has been the subject of research and development studies for more than 40 years. The various processes which have been developed are too numerous to tabulate; there are well over 150 patented processes alone. The following list includes the major processes.

- Neutralization processes:
  - High calcium lime
  - Dolomitic lime
  - Limestone
  - Limestone and lime
  - Dry lime
  - Molten blast furnace slag
- Neutralization with air oxidation (Mellon, A. O. Smith, Du Pont)
- Recovery processes:
  - Copperas (cooling, evaporation, differential solubility)
  - Ferrous sulfate monohydrate (Martin, Chemico)
  - Ferric sulfate
  - Coke-oven gas processes (Elzi, Tiddy, Mellon, Williputte)
  - Ammonium sulfate (pure ammonia)
- Construction material production (Ferron)
- Extraction processes:
  - Manganese from low-grade ores
  - Magnesia from dolomite
- Regeneration processes:
  - Electrolytic regeneration
  - Lurgi fluidized-bed process

TABLE 33 Raw Waste Loads for Pickling

	Raw waste loads, lb/ton pickled		
	Carbon steel	Stainless	Alloy
H_2SO_4 pickling:			
Volume, gal	23.4	18.5	14.9
Iron, lb Fe	11.2	4.60	4.99
Free acidity, lb $CaCO_3$	20.3	8.33	9.04
Total acidity, lb $CaCO_3$	40.3	16.6	18.0
Sulfate, lb SO_4	38.7	15.9	17.2
HCL pickling:			
Volume, gal	41.0	53.0	37.2
Iron, lb Fe	36.4	114	66.5
Free acidity, lb $CaCO_3$	2.83	8.85	5.17
Total acidity, lb $CaCO_3$	67.9	212	124
Chloride, lb Cl	48.2	151	88.0
HNO_3–HF pickling:			
Volume, gal		67.5	33.8
Iron, lb Fe		63.3	31.7
Free acidity, lb $CaCO_3$		4.92	2.46
Total acidity, lb $CaCO_3$		118	59.0
Fluoride, lb F		25.0	12.5
Nitrate, lb NO_3		64.7	32.4
H_2SO_4 rinse water:			
Volume, gal	500	395	318
Iron, lb Fe	1.60	0.66	0.17
Free acidity, lb $CaCO_3$	2.89	1.19	1.29
Total acidity, lb $CaCO_3$	5.75	2.36	2.56
Sulfate, lb SO_4	5.52	2.27	2.46
HCL rinse water:			
Volume, gal	318	411	282
Iron, lb Fe	0.50	1.56	0.90
Free acidity, lb $CaCO_3$	0.96	2.19	1.33
Total acidity, lb $CaCO_3$	1.85	5.78	3.33
Chloride, lb Cl	1.31	1.40	1.01
HNO_3–HF rinse water:			
Volume, gal		523	262
Iron, lb Fe		0.86	0.43
Free acidity, lb $CaCO_3$		1.67	0.84
Total acidity, lb $CaCO_3$		3.20	1.60
Fluoride, lb F		0.68	0.34
Nitrate, lb NO_3		1.76	0.88

- Lurgi refrigeration process
- Blaw-Knox Ruthner processes (H_2SO_4)
- Haveg turbulator process
- Chemical separations ion-exchange process (Higgins)
- Dravo-Ruthner process (HCl)

Deepwell disposal

Cotreatment:

- Rolling-mill effluent clarification
- Wool scouring wastes
- Coke plant wastes

Contract hauling

Sale:

- For water treatment
- For waste treatment
- For manufacturing uses

Barging to sea

Treatment methods The usual treatment methods for strong spent pickle liquors are contract hauling, lime neutralization, and deep-well disposal. Regeneration of HCl liquors is practiced at the Steel Company of Canada, Ontario, and at Republic Steel Corporation, Gadsden, Ala. Some portion of the strong liquor can be used as a source of iron salts for the clarification of rolling-mill wastes. A maximum use at an integrated mill is probably about 20 percent of the total volume of the strong liquor produced.

Rinse waters generally are treated by neutralization in a separate facility or are combined with the total mill effluent, with or without the addition of an alkaline agent. The latter methods of treatment can be considered a type of cotreatment.

Cold-Reduction Raw Waste Loads

Water use on cold-reduction mills was given as from 1,675 to 3,000 gal/ton in the 1967 Profile. The NUS report gives an average value of 1,700 gal/ton. A water use of 10,000 gpm for a modern five-stand tandem mill is given by both Bowman and Houston[6] and Gronbech.[13] The five-stand tandem mills at Weirton Steel in Weirton have capacities of 600,000 and 660,000 tons/year. A similar mill at J & L's Aliquippa works has a capacity of 637,200 tons/year and one of Armco's Ashland Works has a capacity of 720,000 tons/year. At an average of say 650,000 tons/year, a water use of about 8,000 gal/ton is indicated, or about 1,600 gal/ton per stand.

The 1967 Profile gives oil and solids concentrations at 150 and 50 ppm, respectively, in the effluent. The NUS report gives ranges of 5 to 185 ppm suspended solids and 15 to 1,500 ppm oil, with averages of 125 and 300 ppm, respectively. Other reported concentration areas follow in cases where varying degrees of coolant recirculation are practiced:

Plant	*Oil, ppm*	*Solids, ppm*
J & L, Hennepin works	200	50
Bethlehem, Lackawanna	230	100
National Steel, Midwest	200	
National Steel, Weirton	376	111*

* Total Iron.

The most reasonable values from the above appear to be 109 ppm suspended solids and 200 ppm oil. Assuming recirculation of the coolant solution with discharge only from the final stands as the base conditions, raw waste loads are 1.33 lb solids and 2.67 lb oil per ton of steel in an effluent volume of 1,600 gal/ton of steel. The spent emulsions are additionally dumped on a batch basis. Recovery of most of the oil in the spent emulsions has long been practiced; recovery plants are operated in many steel mills on a contract basis by such independent companies as Palm Oil Recovery, Inc., who process the oil for sale.

On the basis of the data from Armco's Ashland Works, the concentrated coolant amounts to about 11.1 gal/ton of steel and has the following composition:

Suspended solids, ppm	1,025
COD, ppm	31,600
Total oil, ppm	14,600
Emulsified oil, ppm	3,494

The contribution to the raw waste load is as follows, and the total raw waste load is calculated below on the basis of the same percent total and emulsified oil in the rinse water as in the concentrated coolant with COD in proportion to total oil (see Table 34).

The best practicable treatment probably corresponds to the demonstration program results at Ashland. During the test period, average results were reported as follows in an effluent of 350 gpm resulting from the treatment of combined rinsewater and coolant:

pH	6.0–7.6
Turbidity, JTU	37
COD, ppm	441
BOD, ppm	57
Total oil, ppm	76
Suspended solids, ppm	51

TABLE 34 Raw Waste Loads for Cold Rolling

	Raw waste loads, lb/ton of steel		
	Coolant	Rinse water	Total
Volume, gal/ton	11.1	1,600	1,611
Suspended solids	0.09	1.33	1.42
COD	2.91	5.78	8.69
Total oil	1.34	2.67	4.01
Emulsified oil	0.32	0.64	0.96

The effluent load then is 1,611 gal/ton and would not be more than with treatment similar to the Armco system at Ashland as shown in Fig. 4. Somewhat lower loads are probable on the basis of the few operating data available when the coolant/rinsewater ratio approximated 11/1,600.

The raw waste loads for tin plating and chrome plating are best estimated from the Weirton Steel Company data. The four tin mills there have a combined capacity of 1,135 tons/shift or 3,405 tons/day. The chrome-plating line operates at 1,500 ft/min as compared with the tin lines at 1,800 ft/min. Chrome-plating capacity is thus about 700 tons. The total plating capacity is 4,114 tons/day and the total effluent is 15 million gpd, equivalent to 3,646 gal/ton. This plant includes two continuous annealing lines, a water demineralization plant, and two so-called Weirlite mills which function to further reduce strip to the desired thickness prior to plating. Average effluent analyses are given in Table 35.

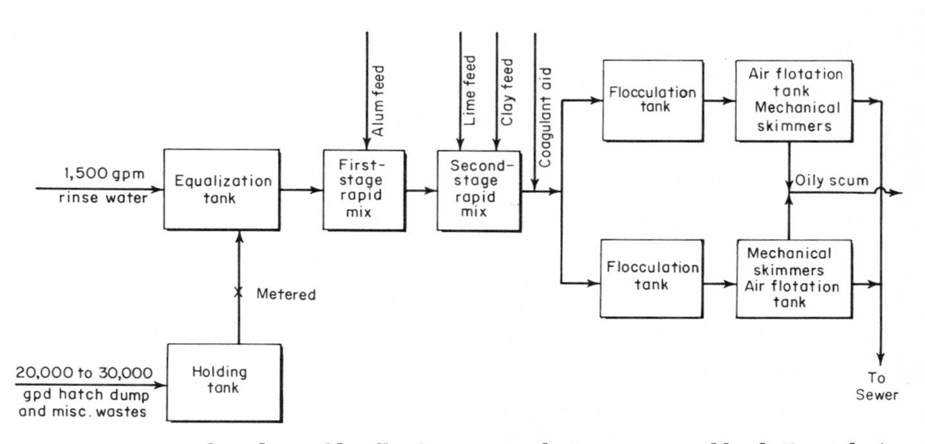

Fig. 4 Five-stand tandem cold mill. (*Armco Steel Corporation, Ashland, Kentucky.*)

Influent Analytical Data

Analysis	Concentration	
	Average	Range
SS	80	16–280
COD	5,556	1,040–37,600
Total oil	895	113–3,034
Emulsified oil	244	30–850
BOD	383	165–540
pH		6.1–8.2

The average plating line at Weirton has an effluent of 2.56 mgd, equivalent to 3,000 gal/ton, which is an appropriate volume to use with the above concentrations to calculate raw waste loads, as are summarized in Table 36.

Detinning facilities The principal function of a detinning plant is to recover for reuse metallic tin from both tin-plate scrap and electrolytic sodium fluorostannate acid sludge. In the detinning operation tin-bearing scrap is rotated in a tank containing sodium nitrate and caustic soda at temperatures of about 205°F until the solution absorbs sodium stannate. Excess sodium stannate precipitates out of solution and settles on the bottom. The detinned scrap is returned to the steelmaking facilities and the sodium stannate precipitate is subjected to a sulfuric acid treatment

TABLE 35 Average Effluent Analyses for Plating Operations

	Tin lines			Average tin line and calculated chrome lines		
Parameter	4	5	6	Tin line	Chrome line	Chrome line
pH	6.40	4.60	3.90	4.60	6.70	±8.8
Chloride, ppm	39.10	207.00	45.5	97.2	111.00	124.8
Sulfate, ppm	104.60	152.00	250.7	169.1	130.50	91.9
Suspended solids, ppm	80.20	129.10	146.0	118.4	457.50	797.0
Total iron, ppm	4.40	21.60	29.0	18.3	30.60	42.9
Total chromium, ppm	20.20	15.50	2.1	12.6	49.00	85.4
Hexavalent chromium, ppm	10.40	0.34	0.0	3.58	5.50	7.42
Cyanide, ppm	0.74	1.06	1.04	0.95	0.15	
Tin, ppm	48.90	122.90	12.4	61.4		
Fluoride, ppm	27.00	30.48	8.6	22.0		

TABLE 36 Raw Waste Loads for Plating

	Raw waste loads, lb/ton plated	
Constituent	Tin plating	Chrome plating
pH	6.7	8.8
Chloride	2.43	3.12
Sulfate	4.23	2.30
Suspended solids	2.96	19.9
Total iron	0.46	1.07
Total chromium	0.32	2.14
Hexavalent chromium	0.09	0.19
Cyanide	0.02	
Tin	1.54	
Fluoride	0.55	

which converts it to stannic hydroxide. The stannic hydroxide is then filtered, dried, mixed with anthracite coal and reduced to metallic tin. The electrolytic sodium fluorostannate acid sludge is reacted with sodium carbonate to form stannic hydroxide and treated in the same manner as the wastewaters in the detinning operation evolved from filtering, rinsing, and spills. Wastewaters from the detinning scrap operation may amount to 280 gal/ton of scrap processed. Pollutant levels for such an operation are shown in Table 37.

Wastewater from the detinning operation may amount to 9 gal/ton of tin-plate product. Pollutant levels for such an operation are given in Table 38. Additional pollution parameters which may exist in the discharge are nitrates and dissolved solids.

Galvanizing Total galvanizing capacity in the United States is estimated at 8,400,000 net tons/year.* In 1971, shipments of galvanized sheet and strip amounted to 5,067,609 net tons or 5.82 percent of total net shipments. Of the total galvanized shipments in 1942, 4,742,493 net tons or 93.6 percent of total shipments were produced by the hot-dip method while 325,115 net tons or 6.4 percent of the total were produced by the electroplating process. With the exception of 4,707 net tons of galvanized shipments of alloy steel, all other shipments were carbon-grade steel.

In 1961, 368,773 tons of slab zinc were consumed by the galvanizing industry. Of this amount, 209,606 tons were used for the galvanizing of 3,330,000 net tons of sheet and strip or 125.9 lb of zinc per ton of product. Assuming the same proportion for 1971, it would require 309,006 tons of slab zinc for galvanizing.

TABLE 37 Raw Waste Loads for Scrap Detinning

Parameter	Concentration, ppm			Waste load, lb/ton of scrap
	High	Low	Average	
pH	9.3	7.8	9.0	
Pht alkalinity*	352.0	4.0	108.5	0.4254
Mo alkalinity†	1,072.0	64.0	540.6	2.1200
Chlorides	422.0	24.0	128.1	0.5023
Sulfates	6,996.0	110.4	1,490.5	5.8450
SS	2,397.0	64.5	390.8	1.5325
Total iron	14.2	3.7	6.9	0.0270
Cyanide	0.96	0.46	0.73	0.0028
Tin	1,440.0	9.7	191.5	0.7509
Total chromium	0.15	0	0.06	0.0002

* Phenolphthalein (endpoint at pH 8.0)
† Methyl orange (endpoint at pH 4.5)

TABLE 38 Raw Waste Loads for Sludge Detinning

Parameter	Concentration, ppm			Waste load, lb/ton of tin plate
	High	Low	Average	
pH	10.9	7.1	8.6	
Mo alkalinity	3,850.0	76.0	1,932.0	0.1361
Chlorides	275.0	50.0	135.8	0.0095
Sulfates	14,400.0	1,080.0	5,580.0	0.3932
Suspended solids	1,287.0	90.0	633.0	0.0446
Total iron	36.6	2.0	13.3	0.0009
Total chromium	6.4	0	1.8	0.0001
Fluorides	920.0	430.0	571.2	0.0402
Tin	540.0	24.8	137.8	0.0097
Cyanide	6.5	0.13	3.3	0.0002

In the hot-dip process, a zinc coating is applied by passing the material through a molten bath of the metal. Several designs of continuous hot-dip galvanizing lines in commercial use are listed below.

1. *The Cook-Norteman process.* This process takes strip that has been annealed separately, cleans the surface by chemical means, and then applies a zinc-ammonium-chloride flux prior to the zinc bath.

2. *The Sendzimir process.* Uses the advantages of continuous pretreatment and annealing with the aluminum in the zinc bath.

* Developments in the Iron & Steel Industry During 1970, "Iron and Steel Engineer Year Book," Association of Iron and Steel Engineers, Pittsburgh, 1970.

3. *The United States Steel Corporation process.* Rolling oil residues are removed by anodic cleaning, followed by annealing and cooling in an atmosphere of cracked ammonia.

4. *The Weirton Steel Company process.* Batch annealed strip is precleaned by chemical methods and preheated in a reducing atmosphere prior to the zinc bath.

5. *The Sharon Steel Corporation process.* To clean the strip prior to galvanizing, gaseous hydrogen chloride is used at temperatures where iron chloride is volatilized.

Zinc coatings are electroplated from two types of solutions: the acid bath and the alkaline cyanide bath. The acid bath process is used widely for coating strip and wire, while the alkaline cyanide process may be more generally applicable for coating hardware, iron and steel castings, and small manufactured parts. Steel strip widths up to 60 in. are electrogalvanized with coating as low as 0.015 to 0.020 oz/sq ft. Because of the very thin coating, several proprietary phosphates are used for corrosion protection and paint bonding characteristic. Preparation of the base metal is very important, thus great care is used to provide a clean surface for coating. Normally an alkaline cleaning bath made up of mixtures of sodium hydroxide, sodium carbonate, phosphates, and silicates is used to remove oil and grease. This is followed by acid baths of sufficient strength to remove oxide films. The acid baths would normally contain a solution of either 5 to 10 wt % sulfuric acid or 20 wt % hydrochloric acid. During 1970, only one new galvanizing line went into operation, the 72-in. continuous galvanizing line at the Midwest Steel Division of National Steel Corporation. This line is designed to have an optimum capacity of 60 tons/hr while producing 18 gage by 42-in. wide product with a maximum capacity of 100 tons/hr on the full hard-cycle steel.

TABLE 39 Total Galvanizing Department Discharge Flow 4,320,000 gpd

(Volume = 2,700 gal/ton)

Parameter	Concentration, ppm			Waste load, lb/ton galvanized
	High	Low	Average	
pH	10.2	2.9	8.9	
Pht alkalinity	62	10	27.6	0.62
Mo alkalinity	104	42	65.8	1.48
Mineral acidity			118	2.65
Total iron	25.5	4.8	17.1	0.38
Chlorides	48	20	32.5	0.73
Suspended solids	218	99	198.5	4.47
Phosphates	6.4	1.2	4.3	0.097
Silicon	20.9	13.8	17.9	0.38
Zinc	1.1	0.31	0.6	0.014
Total chromium	3.3	0.56	1.5	0.030
Hexavalent chromium	2.9	0.42	1.0	0.023

The galvanizing department of the Weirton Steel Division of National Steel Corporation consists of four continuous galvanizing lines. Wastewaters from the galvanizing operation consist primarily of orthosil tank overflow, scrubber waters, and rinses. Total discharge from all four lines is about 4,320,000 gal/day (see Table 39). Examples of the discharges are reported in the publication entitled "Combined Steel Mill and Municipal Wastewaters Treatment."[19]

The values in Table 39 may be taken as the best available data on raw waste loads from hot-dip galvanizing. Electrogalvanizing in the steel industry utilizes the acid process so that cyanides are not a problem from this source. The only information on electrogalvanizing wastes is in United Nations data which indicate 100 ppm zinc in approximately 31,600 gal/day of rinse water in a plant galvanizing 10,000 tons/year. The indicated raw waste loads are approximately 2,000 gal rinse water and 0.91 lb of zinc per ton electrogalvanized.

The treatment methods available for wastewaters from tin or chrome plating, electrogalvanizing, and galvanizing are chromate reduction, sedimentation with chemical flocculation, and rinse-water reuse. The H. H. Robertson Company, Ambridge, Pa., reported effluent concentrations of the galvanizing operation as follows:

pH	7.82
Suspended solids, ppm	5.0
Dissolved iron, ppm	0
Manganese, ppm	0.01
Total zinc, ppm	0.3
Total chromium, ppm	0.07
Oil, ppm	0.1

In an average wastewater volume of 3,000 gal/ton of galvanized steel, the corresponding loads would be:

Suspended solids, lb/ton	0.125
Dissolved iron, lb/ton	0
Manganese, lb/ton	0.0003
Total zinc, lb/ton	0.008
Total chromium, lb/ton	0.002
Oil, lb/ton	0.003

While these values have been attained at this relatively small plant, in a new treatment facility, they are probably excessively stringent for general application. Table 40 compares this data and the "A" level treatment standards proposed by American Iron and Steel Institute.

TABLE 40 Levels of Treatment for Galvanizing Wastes

	Concentration, ppm		
Parameter	AISI tin plating	AISI other coating	H. H. Robertson
Suspended solids	15.6	15.0	5.0
Dissolved solids	1.17	1.2	0
Manganese			0.01
Total zinc		1.2	0.3
Total chromium	0.7	0.05	0.07
Oil			0.01
Tin	7.0		
Cyanide	0.78	0.18	

TABLE 41 BPT and BAT for Galvanizing Wastes

Constituent	Concentration, ppm	BPT, lb/ton	BAT, lb/ton
Suspended solids	10.0	0.250	0.125
Dissolved iron	0.6	0.015	0.008
Manganese	0.2	0.005	0.003
Total zinc	0.7	0.018	0.009
Total chromium	0.3	0.008	0.004
Oil	5.0	0.125	0.063
Tin	3.0	0.075	0.038
Cyanide	0.40	0.010	0.005

The most reasonable values would appear to be averages of the concentrations given in Table 40 with the value for tin based on the tin/chromium ratio as indicated by the AISI tin-plating data and oil equal to the best observed in rolling-mill operations. Best practicable treatment (BPT) is based on the use of 3,000 gal/ton and best available treatment (BAT) on a reuse factor of 50 percent; the latter seems to be conservative in view of H. H. Robertson's reuse of 80 percent. These levels of treatment are summarized in Table 41.

Temper and skin-pass mills After the cold-rolled strip has been cleaned and annealed, the final mechanical properties are developed by the temper or skin-pass mills. The principal purpose of this process is to acquire the proper stiffness or hardness by cold-working the strip. Additionally, tempering tends to improve the flatness of annealed strip which is of great importance. Most modern temper mills utilize heavy rolls and operate at high speed. From a report published in the U.S. Environmental Protection Agency's Water Pollution Control Research Series, the discharge data of Table 42 were acquired.

Since temper passing is performed dry, wastewater results from machine cooling water and the major pollutant parameter is equipment lubricating oils (Table 43).

TABLE 42 Discharge from Temper Mill
(Flow: 2,880,000 gpd)

Parameter	High	Low	Average
pH	9.4	8.6	9.1
Pht alkalinity, mg/l	140	6	70
Mo alkalinity, mg/l	200	32	96
Hexavalent chromium, mg/l	0.1	0	0.03
Total chromium, mg/l	0.2	0.0	0.10
Suspended solids, mg/l	40	25	33
Oils, mg/l	58	14	31

TABLE 43 Best Practicable Effluent Loads for Cold Rolling

Volume, gal/ton	1,611
COD, lb/ton	5.92
BOD, lb/ton	0.76
Total oil, lb/ton	1.02
Suspended solids, lb/ton	0.68

TABLE 44 Best Available Treatment for Cold Rolling

Parameter	Raw load, lb/ton	Percent removal	Effluent load, lb/ton
Volume, gal	11		11
Suspended solids	0.09	74	0.02
COD	2.91	92	0.23
Total oil	1.34	95	0.07
Emulsified oil	0.32	95	0.02

Cold Rolling Wastewater Treatment

The best available treatment should correspond to the batch treatment of coolant with recirculation on all stands, i.e., the effluent is concentrated coolant only. On the basis of the Armco data, the effluent loads would be as in Table 44.

Intermediate between these levels of treatment would be that corresponding to the Armco rinse-water treatment scheme in which 2,360,000 gal of wastewater was generated in rolling 9,000 tons of steel. On this basis, effluent waste loading would be as shown in Table 45.

Treatment methods The wastewater effluents from cold-reduction rolling mills contain concentrations of emulsified oil and suspended solids. In addition, a detergent is often used at the final stand to remove all traces of oil from the sheet. Oils used may be of mineral, animal, or vegetable origin and may be soluble or insoluble. These oils may be found in the wastewater in varying degrees of being free or emulsified, saponified or unsaponified. Depending on the nature of the product being

TABLE 45 Intermediate Level Treatment for Cold Rolling

Parameter	Effluent, ppm	Waste load, lb/ton
Volume, gal/ton	262	262
COD	441	0.95
BOD	57	0.12
Total oil	76	0.17
Suspended solids	51	0.11

rolled, lubrication and cooling may be applied on a once-through basis or recycled. However, even with a recycle system, batch dumps will occur when the quality of the solution falls below minimum. For example, a 10,000-gal solution is dumped every 7- to 10-day period at the five-stand tandem mill facility of Midwest Steel Division of National Steel Corporation.

An example of both systems is the Weirton Steel Division of National Steel Corporation. At this point the rolling solutions are recycled at tandem mills 6 and 7 and periodically dumped while a once-through system is utilized at tandem mills 5 and 8. In both cases the wastewater is pumped to a treatment plant operated by a private firm. Here the wastes are subjected to treatment including chemical additions, air flotation, sedimentation, and skimming. The recovered oil either may be returned to the plant for other uses or may be hauled away.

COSTS OF WASTEWATER TREATMENT METHODS

Coke Plant Wastewaters

There is considerable doubt as to whether or not the costs associated with the operation of ammonia stills should be considered to be pollution abatement costs. Stills were operated for many years as part of normal production and have only been eliminated or not operated because of the dwindling market for ammonium sulfate, principally due to competition from synthetic ammonia. Many plants still produce and sell ammonium sulfate and at least one plant produces anhydrous ammonia.

In 1955, ammonium sulfate sold for $42 per ton f.o.b. and sulfuric acid cost about $23.50 per ton. Ammonium sulfate production at that time was at least marginally profitable. It can be inferred from the reported work by Bethlehem Steel Corporation that ammonia stills for a plant coking 4,800 tons/day of coal would cost less than $700,000 (1972).

Assuming the production of 25 lb of ammonium sulfate per ton of coal, the "average" coke plant would produce 133,200 lb/day or 67 tons/day of ammonium sulfate using 50 tons of sulfuric acid. The net daily cost would have been $1,639 in 1955. On the basis of the M&S equipment cost index, 1972 comparative costs would be about $2,810 per day (1955 = 190.6; 1972 = 326.8), or $1,026,000 per year.

The ammonia in the flushing liquor is about 20 percent of the total. The cost associated with the operation at the ammonia stills would thus be about $562 per day, or $205,130 per year. Taking the capital cost of the stills at 5,328/4,800 × $700,000 or $777,000 at 10 percent for 20 years, the annualized capital cost would be $91,266, or $250 per day.

Base level of treatment Costs may be estimated for a plant coking 5,328 tons/day of coal.

Capital costs = $777,000 = $146 per ton of coal per day

Operating costs = $113,880 per year = $0.06 per ton of coal coked

A dephenolizer, in 1950, for a plant carbonizing 3,600 tons/day of coal costs $225,000. Based on the M&S Index,* the 1972 (1950 = 167.9 + 1972 = 326.8) cost for a plant coking 5,328 tons/day of coal would be:

$$\left(\frac{5{,}328}{3{,}600}\right)^{0.6} \times \left(\frac{326.8}{167.9}\right) \times \$225{,}000 = \$554{,}000$$

or $104 per ton of coal per day.

* "Comparative Replacement Cost Multipliers," the series of cost indexes published by Marshall & Swift Publication Co.

Given the fact that the value of sodium phenolate has decreased over the years, the value of the produce should at least cover the operating costs other than depreciation, i.e., be zero.

Best practicable treatment The Bethlehem Steel biooxidation plant at Bethlehem, Pa., cost \$310,000 and has a hydraulic capacity of 450,000 gpd. On the basis of the EN-R Construction Cost Index (1962 = 900; 1972 = 1,700) and a size exponent of 0.6, a plant to handle 1.6 mgd would cost:

$$\left(\frac{1,600,000}{450,000}\right)^{0.6} \times \left(\frac{1,700}{900}\right) \times \$310,000 = \$1,171,000$$

The operating costs of such a facility costing \$732 per 1,000 gpd would be about \$116 per year per 1,000 gpd, or \$185,600 per year (organic profile).

Costs then for a plant coking 5,328 tons/day of coal would be:

Capital costs = \$1,171,000 = \$220 per ton of coal per day

Operating costs = \$185,600 per year = \$0.095 per ton of coal coked

Best available treatment The cost of the distillation/incineration system installed at Alan Wood Steel Company was \$1.8 million. This plant handles 180,000 gpd. The comparable cost for the "average" coke plant would be:

$$\left(\frac{658,000}{180,000}\right)^{0.6} \times (\$1.8 \times 10^6) = \$3.92 \times 10^6$$

This is a maximum figure based on the first, nonoptimized plant. Operating costs are estimated at \$1.75 per 1,000 gal, or \$1,152 per day, taking no credit for product water.

Costs for a plant coking 5,328 tons/day of coal would be:

Capital costs = \$736 per ton of coal per day

Operating costs = \$420,300 per year = \$0.216 per ton of coal coked.

Blast Furnace and Sinter Plant Treatment Costs

The costs of wastewater treatment are estimated from the 1967 Steel Industry Profile. Sinter plant production in 1966 was 54.3 million tons and pig iron production was 91.5 million tons. The total water use, using the present study figures, would have been

$$\frac{(3,204 \times 9.5) + (54.3 \times 350)}{91.5} = 3,412 \text{ gal/ton of pig iron}$$

This is essentially the same as the Profile estimate of water use, so that the costs per unit of water treated may be used.

Direct costs (labor, supervision, maintenance, chemicals) in 1966 dollars are:

PLAIN SEDIMENTATION:

$\$0.138$ per 1,000 gal $\times$ 3.412 = \$0.471 per ton of iron

COAGULATION-SEDIMENTATION:

$\$0.214$ per 1,000 gal $\times$ 3.412 = \$0.730 per ton of iron

DIFFERENCE IN OPERATING COSTS, in 1972 dollars at 3.5 percent per year:

$(\$0.730 - \$0.471) \times (1.035)^6 = \$0.319$ per ton of iron

Operating costs, in 1972 dollars

PLAIN SEDIMENTATION:

$\$0.471 \times (1.035)^6 = \$0.579$ per ton of iron

COAGULATION-SEDIMENTATION:

$\$0.731 \times (1.035)^6 = \$0.898$ per ton of iron

The capital costs of various wastewater treatment methods for blast furnaces and sinter plants together are given in Table 46.

Steelmaking and Rolling Mill Treatment Costs

The costs of treating steelmaking wastewaters are similar, on a unit cost basis, to those for treating blast furnace and sinter plant effluents. These costs are best given in terms of wastewater volumes of representative flow rates, since various combinations of processes can be found in steelmaking operations.

Gas cleaning and wastewater treatment systems for steelmaking furnaces are illustrated in Figs. 5 to 7, and treatment costs are given in Table 47.

TABLE 46 Blast Furnace and Sinter Plant Treatment Costs

Treatment method	Blast furnace, dollars per ton of iron per year	Sinter plant, dollars per ton of sinter per year
Plain sedimentation	2.21	0.58
Coagulation-sedimentation	2.44	0.65
Recirculation and		
Plain sedimentation	2.65	0.70
Coagulation-sedimentation	3.18	0.84

TABLE 47 Steelmaking Treatment Costs

(In 1972 dollars per annual ton)

Type of treatment	Wastewater volume, gal/ton				
	500	1,000	1,500	2,000	2,500
	CAPITAL COSTS				
Plain sedimentation	$0.71	$1.09	$1.39	$1.65	$1.89
Coagulation-sedimentation	0.79	1.22	1.56	1.85	2.11
Recirculation and					
Plain sedimentation	0.85	1.32	1.68	2.00	2.29
Coagulation-sedimentation	1.02	1.58	2.02	2.39	2.74
	OPERATING COSTS				
Plain sedimentation	$0.18	$0.28	$0.35	$0.42	$0.48
Coagulation-sedimentation	0.28	0.43	0.55	0.66	0.75
Recirculation and					
Plain sedimentation	0.18	0.28	0.35	0.42	0.48
Coagulation-sedimentation	0.28	0.43	0.55	0.66	0.75

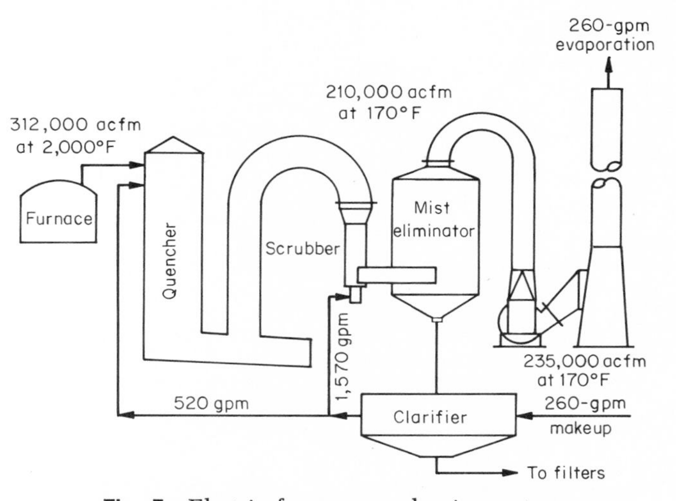

Fig. 5 Electric furnace gas-cleaning system.

The cost of plain sedimentation in a scale pit with an SI of 0.1 min is zero, particularly insofar as pollution control is concerned. The value of the recovered scale exceeds at least the operating cost, and the scale pit itself is constructed primarily to protect the sewer system.

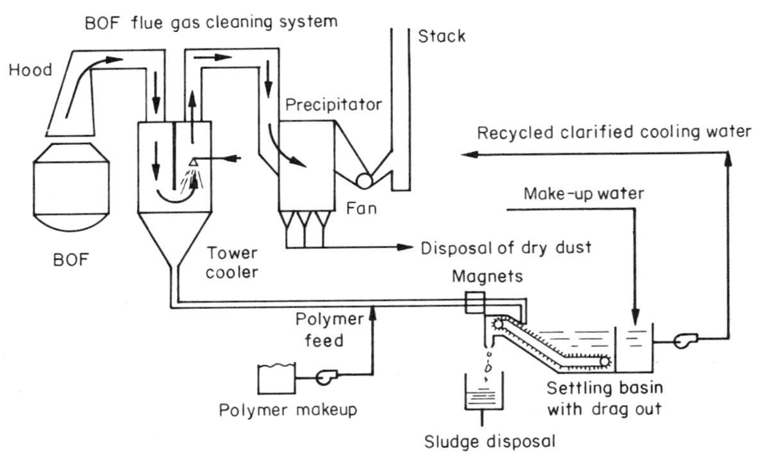

Fig. 6 Schematic diagram of polymer and magnetic flocculation of basic oxygen furnace wastewater.

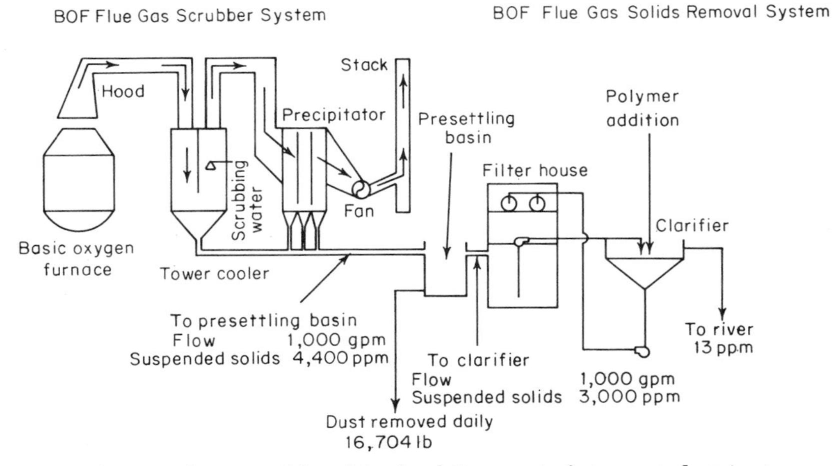

Fig. 7 Schematic diagram of Interlake Steel Corporation's integrated air/water waste treatment system for the basic oxygen furnace shop.

A scale pit with an SI of 1 min or more has been designed for pollution control although performance does not meet 1972 standards. The capital costs can be estimated as the difference between the lowest and highest unit costs reported in the 1967 Profile and updated to 1972 dollars:

$$(\$2.50 - \$1.11) \times (1.035)^6 = \$1.71 \text{ per annual ingot ton}$$

$$\$1.71 \times \left(\frac{107{,}000}{79{,}306}\right) = \$2.32 \text{ per annual finished ton}$$

Direct operating costs in 1966 dollars were $0.023 per 1,000 gal. These costs are presently

$$\$0.023 \times 12.115 \times (1.035)^6 = \$0.34 \text{ per finished ton}$$

The approximate maximum costs of deep-bed filters are $50 per gpm and that of flocculator-clarifiers about $40 per gpm. Costs as low as $20 per gpm and $33 per gpm (in 1968 dollars) have been estimated for 9,000-gpm filters and flocculator-clarifiers, respectively (Lukens Steel Company).

$$12{,}115 \text{ gal/ton} \times 79{,}306{,}000 \text{ tons/year} = 960.792 \times 10^9 \text{ gal/year}$$

$$\frac{12{,}115 \text{ gal/ton}}{365 \text{ days/year} \times 1{,}440 \text{ min/day} \times 20/21 \text{ shifts}} = 0.0242 \text{ gpm/annual ton}$$

$$\text{Deep-bed filters} = 0.0242 \times \$50 = \$1.21 \text{ per annual finished ton}$$

$$\text{Flocculator-clarifiers} = 0.0242 \times \$40 = \$0.97 \text{ per annual finished ton}$$

On the basis of 1966 costs, direct costs for flocculation-sedimentation are $0.122 per 1,000 gal:

$$\$0.122 \times 12.115 \times (1.035)^6 = \$1.81 \text{ per annual finished ton}$$

Operating labor for filters is about one-third of that for flocculation-sedimentation and chemical costs for the former are nil (Lukens Steel Company). The direct operating costs for filters are thus about 50 percent of those of flocculation-sedimentation or about $0.90 per annual finished ton.

TABLE 48 Summary of Estimated Costs for Rolling Mill Wastes

	Costs, dollars per annual finished ton	
Treatment	Capital costs, dollars	Direct operating costs, dollars/year
Base level (crude pit)	Nil	Nil
Present practice (SI = 1.0)	1.71	0.34
Best practicable (filters)	1.21	0.90
Best available (recirculation)	1.21	0.90

The 25,000-gpm filtration-recirculation system at Colorado Fuel and Iron, Pueblo, Colo., cost $2 million, or $80 per gpm. That particular installation utilizes a gravity system that is significantly less expensive than a pressure system. The indicated costs of filtration and recirculation here are $40 per gpm for each. The operating costs are probably equal, totaling about $1.80 per annual finished ton. Estimated costs are summarized in Table 48.

Pickling Wastewater Treatment Costs

The waste treatment methods for wastewaters from pickling may be grouped as follows:

- Strong spent liquor
  - Contract hauling
  - Deep-well disposal
  - Lime neutralization
  - Regeneration
    - Hydrochloric liquor
    - Sulfuric liquor
- Rinsewaters
  - Cotreatment
  - Neutralization

The listings above are in the order of preferred utilization insofar as the industry is concerned.

Contract hauling Contract hauling is used whenever possible because there are no capital costs aside from collection and storage facilities; the flat charge per gallon is a wholly tax deductible operating expense, and the plant operator has a minimum of bother with the problem. The average cost is probably about 2 cents/gal.

Deep-well disposal Deep-well disposal is the next preferred method because both capital and operating costs are the lowest of in-plant methods before credits. The plant operator has little bother with what is essentially an automated operation.

One of the most critical factors in this disposal method is the required injection pressure which ranges from 0 to 3,000 psig. The following three cases cover the range experienced:

Plant	*Location*	*Injection pressure, psi*	*Rate, gpm*
Jones & Laughlin	Alliquippa, Pa	3,000	
Armco Steel	Middletown, Ohio	500	100
National Steel	Portage, Ind.	0	75

The capital costs for deep-well disposal at 100 gpm are not much affected by injection pressure and for average geological conditions such a well would cost about $200,000 (1969) with minimum pretreatment by filtration (Inorganic Chemical Profile). With the 1972 ENR Index approaching 1800 (1969 = 1285), 1972 costs are probably about $280,000. Collection facilities and auxiliary equipment probably give a total cost of about $500,000.

Operating costs at Portage were $5,182 per month in 1966. About 23 million gal had been injected in 18 months. The operating costs were thus 0.4 cents/gal not including capital charges. At 3.5 percent per year, 1972 costs are probably about 0.5 cents/gal.

It should be noted that standby lime neutralization facilities have been installed with some deep-well installations such as at Portage. Total capital costs must thus be looked at carefully to determine whether or not this type of cost is included.

Neutralization Lime neutralization for strong spent liquor is basically of two types: conventional lime neutralization which produces a bulky, permanently wet sludge and air oxidation to produce a settleable, filterable sludge which can be used to produce a dry fill material. The latter include the Mellon magnetic iron oxide, the Eimco, and the Du Pont processes; all are essentially the same.

The differences in capital costs between the conventional and air oxidation processes are relatively little. The operating costs for the air oxidation processes are lower because of savings in sludge disposal costs. Costs in 1959 were as follows for 100,000 gpd of H_2SO_4 waste pickle liquor WPL:

	Eimco process	*Conventional*
Capital costs	$935,000	$900,000
Annual operating costs	$673,200	$953,650

On the basis of the ENR Cost Index, the 1972 capital costs for this type of facility are probably about double the above. The operating costs in 1972 at 3.5 percent per year would be about 3.1 and 4.3 cents/gal for the air oxidation and conventional processes, respectively.

The performance of such treatment systems can best be estimated from the work reported by Keystone Steel and Wire, Peoria, Ill. Iron in the supernatant liquor after lime neutralization can probably be reduced to 15 ppm. With air oxidation at elevated temperatures (80°C), iron in the effluent can be reduced essentially to zero. The pH of the reaction, and hence the effluent, must be above 8.0 for the above results. The solubility of calcium sulfate is about 2,000 ppm and would be expected in the effluent. Calcium nitrate is 1,000 × more soluble than calcium sulfate. Calcium chloride has 112 × the solubility of calcium nitrate. Calcium fluoride is about 1/100th as soluble as calcium sulfate.

The effluents from lime neutralization of WPL are thus estimated in Table 49, assuming that air oxidation will be less than 100 percent efficient, but at least equivalent to results with rinse water:

TABLE 49 Concentrations of Constituents in Treated WPL

	Conventional	Air oxidation
Iron, ppm	15	4
pH	8.0	9.0
Calcium sulfate, ppm	2,000	2,000
Calcium nitrate	Raw load	Raw load
Calcium chloride	Raw load	Raw load
Calcium fluoride, ppm	20	20

For the case of pickling rinsewaters, costs are best estimated on the basis of the Armco demonstration project at Middletown, Ohio. Total Fe in the effluent averaged 4.0 ppm, turbidity 10 ppm, and pH 6.9. Even a superficial perusal of the data for April, 1970 shows that pH below 6.8 and temperatures below 115°F are less than optimum. The other constituents in the effluent may be deduced from the above data for the strong spent liquor up to the limits of the raw waste loads.

Iron, ppm	4
pH	6.9
Turbidity, ppm	10
Calcium sulfate, ppm	2,000
Calcium nitrate	Raw load
Calcium chloride	Raw load
Calcium fluoride, ppm	20

In the recommended operation of the Du Pont process, calcium lime is added as a 25 percent slurry. This added volume need not be considered as an addition to the total waste volume since treated rinse water can be used to make up slurry. Effluent suspended solids should probably be taken at 15 ppm for the total pickling operation since this can be achieved according to the Armco data in treating rinse water. The treated pickle liquor effluent should be the vacuum filter filtrate. The latter, in the worst case, could be discharged through the rinse-water clarifiers. Cotreatment of rinse water would produce a similar effluent if the total wastes were sand filtered, i.e., received the best available treatment.

The Armco data indicate operating costs of 24 cents/1,000 gal of rinse water. The capital costs of a facility to treat 1,500 gpm, or 2.16 mgd, were $1,360,000.

Regeneration of spent liquor Of the many technically feasible processes, the Lurgi and Dravo-Ruthner processes for hydrochloric liquors and the Higgins and Blaw-Knox Ruthner processes for sulfuric acid liquors are probably best representative of the costs involved. Effluent waste loads would be essentially zero. The Dravo-Ruthner process is installed and in operation at Republic Steel, Gadsden, Ala., at the Steel Company of Canada, Ontario, and at McClouth Steel Corporation, Detroit, Mich. Republic reportedly plans another installation in Cleveland, Ohio. The Higgins process has been demonstrated under an EPA grant and was at one time enthusiastically regarded by industry representatives as the best solution for sulfuric acid spent-liquor treatment. The Blaw-Knox Ruthner process was demonstrated in a large-scale pilot plant by a steel industry consortium in the early 1950s.

The Steel Company of Canada plant cost $2 million in 1966 to treat 30 gpm of spent HCl liquor. In 1969, they reported an operating cost of 60 cents/ton of steel pickled. The Lurgi fluidized-bed process for HCl regeneration operates on the same chemical principle as the Dravo-Ruthner process. A battery-limits plant to treat 13.9 gpm of spent liquor reportedly cost $480,000 in 1972, and an operating cost of $.50 to $1 per ton of steel pickled was quoted in 1966. The process was commercialized in Germany in 1966 and some 25 plants have been built around the world—none in the United States.

Plants to treat 100,000 gpd, or 69.4 gpm, would thus cost

$$\$2{,}000{,}000 \times \left(\frac{140}{110}\right) \times \left(\frac{69.4}{30.0}\right)^{0.6} \times = \$4{,}208{,}000 \qquad \text{(Dravo-Ruthner)}$$

$$(2 \times \$480{,}000) \times \left(\frac{69.4}{13.9}\right)^{0.6} \times = \$2{,}525{,}000 \qquad \text{(Lurgi)}$$

These figures are based on the M & S Equipment Cost Index and assume double the battery-limits cost for a complete plant.

A capital cost of $4 million for a 100,000 gpd HCl regeneration plant thus seems to be a conservative estimate. An operating cost of 60 cents/ton of steel pickled is indicated.

The direct operating costs for a 100,000 gpd Higgins process plant for sulfuric acid regeneration have been estimated at $893 per day or $326,000 per year. A 100,000 gpd Blaw-Knox Ruthner plant was estimated at $4,113,000 in 1959 with total direct operating costs of $821,330 per year. On the basis of the M & S Equipment Cost Index, 1972 costs for a 100,000 gpd Blaw-Knox Ruthner plant would be about 1.4 × $4,113,000, or $5,758,000. Had operating costs increased proportionately, 1972 direct annual costs would be $1,150,000.

A conservative estimate of the 1972 cost of a sulfuric acid regeneration plant for 100,000 gpd thus appears to be about $6 million with direct operating costs of about $1 million.

TABLE 50 Treated Pickling Effluent Waste Loads per Ton of Steel Pickled

	BPCTCA			BADCT		
	Carbon	Stainless	Alloy	Carbon	Stainless	Alloy
H_2SO_4 WPL:						
Volume, gal	23.4	18.5	14.9	0	0	0
Iron, lb Fe	0.0008	0.0006	0.0005			
$CaCO_4$, lb	0.39	0.31	0.25			
pH	9.0	9.0	9.0			
Suspended solids, lb	0.003	0.002	0.002			
HCl WPL:						
Volume, gal	41.0	53.0	37.2	0	0	0
Iron, lb Fe	0.001	0.002	0.001			
$CaCO_2$, lb	0.17	0.22	0.15			
pH	9.0	9.0	9.0			
Suspended solids, lb	0.004	0.008	0.008			
HNO_3–HF WPL:						
Volume, gal		67.5	33.8		67.5	33.8
Iron, lb Fe		0.002	0.001		0.002	0.001
pH		9.0	9.0		9.0	9.0
CaF, lb		0.011	0.006		0.011	0.006
$Ca(NO_3)_2$, lb		265	133		265	133
Suspended solids, lb		0.008	0.004		0.008	0.004
H_2SO_4 rinse water:						
Volume, gal	500	395	318	500	395	318
Iron, lb Fe	0.017	0.013	0.011	0.017	0.013	0.011
$CaSO_4$, lb	7.8	3.2	3.5	7.8	3.2	3.5
pH	6.9	6.9	6.9	6.9	6.9	6.9
Suspended solids, lb	0.06	0.05	0.04	0.06	0.05	0.04
HCl rinse water:						
Volume, gal	3.8	411	282	318	411	282
Iron, lb Fe	0.011	0.014	0.009	0.011	0.014	0.009
$CaCl_2$, lb	2.1	2.2	1.6	2.1	2.2	1.6
pH	6.9	6.9	6.9	6.9	6.9	6.9
Suspended solids, lb	0.04	0.05	0.04	0.06	0.05	0.04
HNO_3–HF rinse water:						
Volume, gal		523	262		523	262
Iron, lb Fe		0.017	0.009		0.017	0.009
pH		6.9	6.9		6.9	6.9
CaF_2, lb		0.09	0.04		0.09	0.04
$Ca(NO_3)_2$, lb		2.33	1.16		2.33	1.16
Suspended solids, lb		0.07	0.03		0.07	0.03

The regeneration processes generate at least enough credits in recovered acid and iron oxide to cover direct operating costs. Operating costs, as used herein, are thus essentially zero; capital charges and other indirect costs must, of course, be considered.

Assuming then that neutralization with air oxidation and vacuum filtration of the sludge is the best practicable treatment (BPT) for strong spent liquors and is also the best available treatment (BAT) for HNO_3–HF liquors, that regeneration is the best available treatment (BAT) for H_2SO_4 and HCl liquors, and that co-treatment or neutralization with air oxidation is the sole treatment for rinse waters, effluent waste loads for pickling are as shown in Table 50.

The treatment costs for steel coating wastewaters should be approximately the same as for pickling rinse water, i.e., \$630 per 1,000 gpd capital costs and 24 cents per 1,000 gal operating costs. On the basis of the typical line at Weirton, capital costs are

$$823 \text{ ton/day} \times 3{,}646 \text{ gal/ton} \times \$0.630 \text{ per gpd} = \$1{,}890{,}415$$

which is \$2,297 per daily ton or \$6.29 per annual ton
At 3,000 gal/ton, operating costs equal 8 cents/ton.

REFERENCES

1. "The Making, Shaping and Treating of Steel," 9th ed., U.S. Steel Corporation, Pittsburgh, Pa., 1971.
2. Bramer, H. C.: Iron and Steel, in "Industrial Wastewater Control," Academic, New York, 1965.
3. Bramer, H. C.: Design Criteria for Sedimentation Basins, *I & EC Process Design and Development*, vol. 3, pp. 46–48, 1964.
4. Bramer, H. C.: Pollution Control in the Steel Industry, *Environmental Sci. and Tech.*, vol. 5, p. 1004, 1971.
5. Baker, E. C.: "Estimated Costs of Steel Slag Disposal," U.S. Department of Mines Information Circ. 8440, 1970.
6. Bowman, G. A., and R. B. Houston: "AISI Yearbook," 1966.
7. U.S. Department of Interior: The Cost of Clean Water, Vol. III, Industrial Waste Profile No. 1—Blast Furnaces and Steel Mills, Federal Water Pollution Control Administration, 1970.
8. Burns Harbor Wastewater Treatment Plant, *Water & Sewage Works*, vol. 113, pp. 468–470, 1966.
9. Coleman, F. S.: Ohio Seamless Invests \$232,000 in Pickle Liquor Treatment, *Water & Waste Engrg.*, vol. 5, no. 9, pp. I-33-3, September 1968.
10. Donovan, E. J., Jr.: Treatment of Wastewater for Steel Cold Finishing Mills, *Water & Waste Engrg.*, vol. 7, no. 11, pp. 722–725, November 1970.
11. "Reducing Phenol Wastes from Coke Plants," Ohio River Valley Water Sanitation Commission, Cincinnati, Ohio, 1953.
12. Elliott, A. C.: Regeneration of Steel HCl Pickle Liquor, *Effluent & Water Treatment J.*, vol. 10, no. 7, pp. 385–390, July 1970.
13. Gronbech, R. N.: "Water Systems for Cooling and Cleaning in Rolling Mills," ISI Publication 128, p. 81, The Iron and Steel Institute, London, 1970.
14. High-Rate Sedimentation and Filtration, *Water & Waste Engrg.*, vol. 7, no. 6, pp. 37–40, June 1970.
15. Kramer, C. G.: Armco Steel Facility Features Pollution Control, *Civil Engrg.*, vol. 40, no. 6, pp. 37–40, June 1970.
16. Smith, R. D.: Steel Company Builds Flexible Wastewater Treatment System, *Water & Waste Engrg.*, vol. 6, no. 3, pp. Bi-4, March 1969.
17. Water Pollution Control in The Iron and Steel Industry, *Water Pollution Conf. (London)*, vol. 68, pp. 569–573, 1969.
18. "Watkins Cyclopedia of the Steel Industry," 11th ed., Steel Publications, Inc., Pittsburgh, 1967.
19. "Combined Steel Mill and Municipal Wastewaters Treatment," U.S. Environmental Protection Agency, February, 1972.
20. Shreve, R. Norris: "Chemical Process Industries," 3rd ed., McGraw-Hill, New York, 1967.
21. Nelson, W. L.: "Petroleum Refining Engineering," 4th ed., McGraw-Hill, New York, 1969.

Chapter 10

Water Pollution Control in the Power Generation Industry

JAMES H. WRIGHT

General Manager, Environmental Systems Department, Westinghouse Electric Corporation, Pittsburgh, Pennsylvania

and

STANLEY J. DEA

Manager, Environmental Process Engineering Department, NUS Corporation, Rockville, Maryland

INTRODUCTION

The power generation industry is by far the greatest user of cooling water in the United States. The industry uses 81 percent of the total, or approximately 10 percent of the annual total flow of waters in rivers and streams (Table 1).[1] In the early years of the industry, wastewater produced by electric power generation created relatively few problems. The rapid growth of the power industry, however, and the direct discharge of waste into streams, lakes, or estuaries by industries and municipalities soon challenged the natural assimilative capacity of many waterways. Legislation designed to assure protection of the aquatic environment first resulted on a state level. Federal controls then came into effect in 1948 with the Federal Water Pollution Con-

TABLE 1 Industrial Users of Cooling Water

Industry	Cooling water intake, billions of gallons	% of total
Electric power generation	40,680	81.3
Primary metals	3,387	6.8
Chemical and allied products	3,120	6.2
Petroleum and coal products	1,212	2.4
Paper and allied products	607	1.2
Food products	392	0.8
Machinery	164	0.3
Rubber and plastics	128	0.3
Transportation equipment	102	0.2
Others	273	0.5
Total	50,065	100.0

trol Act. The amendments added in 1956 and 1961 extended federal authority to all interstate and navigable waters and governed most types of pollution including thermal pollution. More recently, the nation has reemphasized its commitment to the protection of the total environment with passage of the National Environmental Policy Act (NEPA) of 1969 and the Federal Water Pollution Control Act Amendments of 1972. This last law mandates a sweeping federal and state campaign to reduce and eliminate water pollution. It sets forth two general goals: (1) to achieve, wherever possible, by July 1, 1983, water fit for recreational, fish and wildlife use, and (2) by 1985, to have no discharges of pollutants into the nation's waters. These goals set the stage for a coordinated series of specific actions that must be taken, with strict deadlines and strong enforcement provisions. For the first time, the law extends the federal pollution control program to all United States waters. Also for the first time, the law authorizes the federal government to seek an immediate court injunction against water polluters when water pollution presents an "imminent and substantial endangerment" to public health or when it endangers someone's livelihood.

To summarize the 1972 law, the deadlines which must be met are:

July 1, 1977 Best practicable control technology currently available (BPCTCA)
July 1, 1983 Best available technology economically achievable (BATEA)
July 1, 1985 Zero pollutant discharge

Whether or not these dates can, or should, be met and how terms are defined have been the subject of intense, on-going debate that has moved from the Congress to the Environmental Protection Agency (EPA) and now to the courts. The Agency has evaluated the "best practicable" and "best available" control technologies for various industries. The results were used to develop effluent limitation guidelines for the various industrial categories. The guidelines in turn determine what standards will be imposed on industrial discharges. Furthermore, any industrial discharge including storm water runoff currently requires a National Pollutant Discharge Elimination System (NPDES) permit. Limitations and controls were issued for the "steam-electric power generating point source category" in March, 1974 as draft guidelines and finalized in October, 1974.

Looking back over the past 3 years it has become more and more evident that the implications of zero discharge are staggering as facts and cost information are accumulated by responsible scientists and engineers. Long-term documentation will show that complete environmental purity is an impossible task to achieve economically. That is because the differential cost of removing a unit of pollutant increases exponentially as the concentration approaches zero. This more than offsets the advantages in cost gained by savings realized from increases in scale factor or combination of functions. On the other hand, while we may not achieve the zero discharge objective, it will not be any easier in the future to discharge even small amounts of pollutant loads into surface waters. Long lead times of 5 to 10 years in the power industry from go-ahead to production place the pressure of planning for a minimum of best available technology now with the expectation that technological advancement will reduce cost when the facilities are actually designed. These stringent legal requirements coupled with localized shortages of "conventional" water resources create a strong inducement for process modifications to reduce water usage and/or to increase the reuse of treated wastewaters. In many cases this will bring about a substantial volume reduction of effluent and increased volumes of sludges and brines.

The conventional approach to wastewater treatment consists of controlling plant discharges so that concentrations of pollutants meet specific state and federal standards. This simple approach cannot be used to treat wastewater produced by power generation because of the complexity of the industry's pollution problem. Power plant operation has an impact on water quality and the aquatic ecosystem in three ways: it pollutes the water thermally; it subjects aquatic organisms to a variety of physical stresses as they are transported through the plant; and it pollutes the water chemically. Of these three, thermal pollution and plant transport effects are of greatest concern.

In evaluating any cooling system to comply with NEPA, environmental impacts must be carefully weighed against economic costs. Full compliance with present and pending legislation will necessitate site-specific ecological studies to fulfill this requirement as provided in NEPA 1969 and the Federal Water Pollution Control Act of 1972. Standards for evaluating water quality and environmental impact with respect to these thermal discharges and plant transport impacts, however, are not easily identified and traditionally have been based on site-specific environmental evaluations. The result is that identification, evaluation, and solution of wastewater treatment problems in the power industry are significantly different from other industries.

Concern about thermal pollution is not new. Regulatory and research communities have long voiced strong concern regarding potential ecological impact of thermal pollution on the fish, planktonic, and benthic organisms inhabiting the lakes, streams, and estuaries used as cooling water sources. While many of these concerns are theoretically sound, significant adverse impacts are generally limited to relatively few immobile benthic organisms, those incapable of avoiding the direct thermal discharge. Chronic exposure of these immobile benthic organisms to supraambient discharge results in limited zones of benthic degradation routinely encountered at many sites. These adverse effects, however, are normally restricted to the immediate discharge area and considerable recolonization usually occurs with the onset of cooler seasonal ambient water temperatures. The fish and plankton components of the ecosystem are generally unaffected by the thermal discharge.

Until recently, the problem of discharge did not grow as rapidly as did power production because of improvements in unit heat rates of thermal plants. Now, however, fossil-fired power plants are reaching a plateau of thermal efficiency, and the use of nuclear plants, which reject 50 percent more heat to cooling water than equivalent fossil plants, is growing. At the same time, concern for the impact of water transport and chemical pollution on the aquatic ecosystem has grown and is now demanding much attention.

For any potential power plant site, only a few cooling system alternatives are available. Basically, these are once-through (direct) cooling, a variety of cooling towers, and cooling ponds. Once-through cooling, where the heat is discharged into natural water bodies, is the system most commonly used in the United States and elsewhere. When environmentally acceptable, it is the preferred system because it provides high plant efficiency and low cost. The alternative cooling methods are typically more expensive and have their own unique set of environmental advantages and liabilities.

We will examine briefly the cooling systems available to the power generation industry and the thermal, chemical, and water transport impacts of each of these systems on both the aquatic environment and the atmosphere.

THE POWER GENERATION INDUSTRY

To understand, evaluate, and solve the wastewater problems of the power generation industry, it is as important to consider the industry's projected growth as it is to understand the actual processes which produce the waste water. Our energy requirements will keep growing; the only question is how we will meet our needs.

Electric Energy Growth

Although the depletion of both United States and world oil and natural gas reserves is within sight, these two fuels still provide about 76 percent of the current energy needs of the United States. The disparity between available reserves of fuels and the present usage pattern is shown in Fig. 1.[2] While natural gas accounts for only 1.5 percent of the United States energy resource, it supplies about 32 percent of the nation's requirements. Oil, at just over 2 percent of our energy resource, supplies 44 percent of the energy requirements. On the other hand, while coal accounts for 63 percent of the energy resource, it fills only 22 percent of the demand. Imports are not the answer either, for, apart from economic and political implications, world production of oil is expected to peak out before the year 2000 and world natural gas supplies will also dwindle.

Our long-term energy problem, then, can be summarized as follows: demand for energy will continue to grow, yet oil and gas, which now supply 76 percent of United States energy needs, have already reached peak production levels in the United States and will soon do so in the world. Obviously, if we are to satisfy our energy needs in

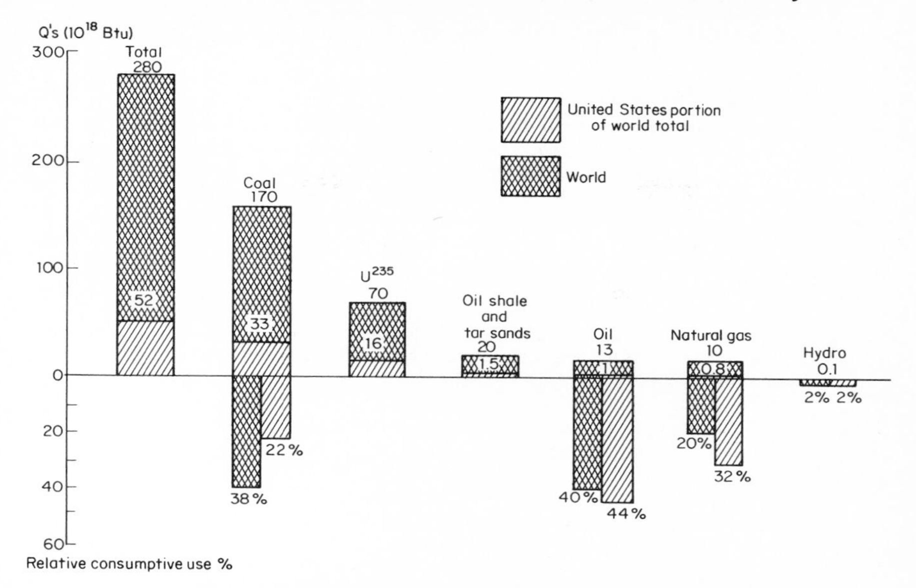

Fig. 1 World's ultimate supply of fossil fuels and U^{235}.[2]

the future, either energy usage must be curtailed sharply or alternatives to oil and gas as energy sources must be developed and used.

Conservation, though justifiable and advisable, is only a small factor; it is not a long-term solution to the energy crisis. Fortunately, the United States does have another answer: alternative fuel sources, rich coal and uranium reserves. But to be usable in many areas, these fuels require conversion to electricity. Present energy consumption patterns are shown in Fig. 2.[3] To substitute electrical usage for only the

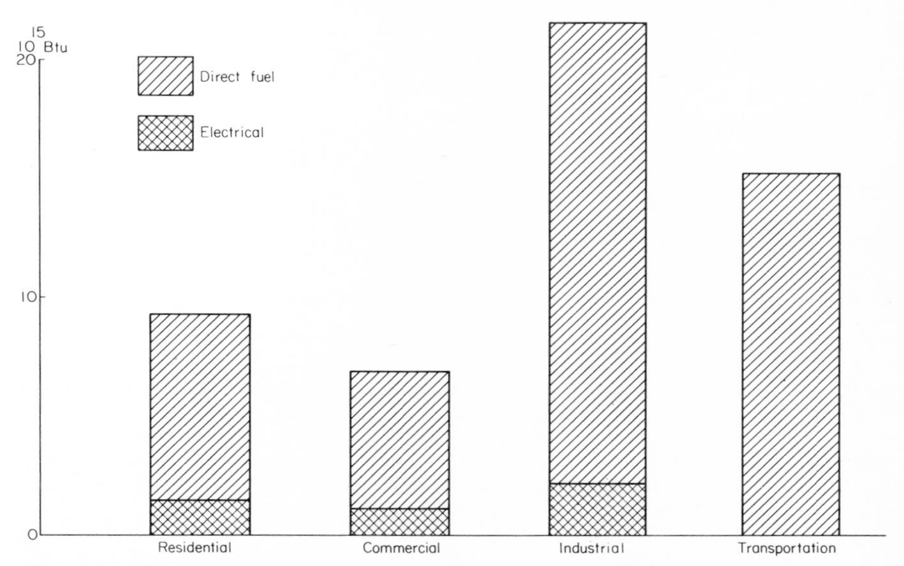

Fig. 2 1968 United States energy—total energy use by sector from electricity and direct fuel.[3]

direct consumption of oil and natural gas in a portion of these areas will necessarily require a significant increase in this country's electrical power generation capacity.

Present Power Generation Facilities

At present, our electrical energy is generated in fossil-fired or nuclear plants, hydroelectric plants, and by gas turbines. The percentage of power produced hydroelectrically is expected to fall from 14.4 percent in 1970 to about 5.2 percent by 1990, since the hydroelectric sites that can be developed economically are already in use. Remaining sites will be used primarily for flood control, irrigation, water supply, and recreational development. Although gas turbines will continue to be a significant factor in power production, their output is only about 0.5 percent of the annual electrical requirements and is not expected to increase dramatically. By 1990 fossil-fired power plants will produce almost twice as much electric energy as they did in 1970 even though their output as a percentage of total electric output will decrease from 84 to only 34 percent. On the other hand, by 1990 nuclear power plants should produce more than 60 percent of all electric energy in the United States.

Neither hydroelectric nor gas-turbine-generated power contributes to the wastewater problem. The bulk of wastewater is associated with steam plants, both fossil and nuclear, for now and in the future.

Future Developments

The most promising new sources of energy are breeder and fusion reactors, both of which have heat-rejection requirements which may require significant volumes of cooling water. Of the other new methods of generating electrical power, solar energy will not require extensive use of cooling water, nor will fuel cells, magnetohydrodynamics (MHD), or electrogasdynamics (EGD). None of these methods, however, are expected to contribute significantly to meeting our projected power requirements during the next decade or so.

THE NATURE OF THE WASTEWATER PROBLEM

Since wastewater from power generation is likely to be a problem for some years, the problem and possible solutions must be examined.

All existing steam power plants, whether nuclear or fossil-fueled, are variations of the Rankine steam power cycle. Steam expands through a turbine and turns the turbine shaft which is coupled to an electrical generator. Spent steam at the turbine exhaust enters a condenser (Fig. 3). To increase cycle efficiency, two common variations are used: (1) several turbines with steam reheated between turbines, and (2) a multiple-stage turbine in which some steam is withdrawn between stages to preheat the water before it reenters the boiler.

A large, efficient fossil-fired generating plant will consume approximately 8800 Btu of energy to produce 3412 Btu of electric energy or 1 kwh. For each kilowatt hour of electricity then, 5388 Btu of heat is rejected to the environment. Of this, about 880 Btu is rejected directly to the atmosphere through the emission of the stack gases from the boiler and about 4500 Btu/kwh is rejected through the steam condenser. To dissipate this amount of heat for a 1,000-MW fossil plant, a cooling water flow of approximately 450,000 gpm is required, producing a temperature rise at 20 F° at the condenser. For *all* this heat to be dissipated by evaporation of 90°F water in a cooling tower, 8,600 gpm of water would be consumed.

Heat-rejection losses for nuclear-generating plants are even larger than for fossil plants: heat cannot be rejected into the atmosphere during the thermal cycle as it can through stack gases in a fossil-fired boiler; and nuclear plants currently operate at lower, less efficient steam temperatures, causing higher heat rates. A large, modern, pressurized water reactor (PWR) plant, for example, might have a turbine heat rate of 10,050 Btu/kwh output, leaving approximately 6600 Btu to be rejected through the steam condenser. Such a heat exchange would require 660,000 gpm of cooling water and produce a 20 F° temperature rise. If *all* the heat were to be transferred to the atmosphere by evaporating 90°F water in a cooling tower, 12,650 gpm of cooling water would be consumed by evaporation.

Water Intake

Power plants which take their cooling water supply from lakes, rivers, or estuaries containing considerable floating debris usually have trash racks to remove large objects which might clog the system and cause a plant shutdown. Such coarse screens or bars are ineffective in preventing fish transit. To collect smaller debris and prevent fish entrainment, nearly all power plants currently operating in the United States also employ finer vertical traveling screens, usually 3/8-in. mesh, for the final screening of cooling water. These traveling screens may be controlled manually or automatically; the manually controlled screens are completely washed of accumulated debris on a regular schedule; the automatically controlled screens are backwashed whenever the pressure drop across the screen exceeds a predetermined level.

The nature and magnitude of fish collection or entrapment on the intake screens depend on many environmental, design, and operational factors. Of paramount importance are the size and species of fish involved and the species' physiological and behavioral response to ambient illumination, water temperature, and intake water

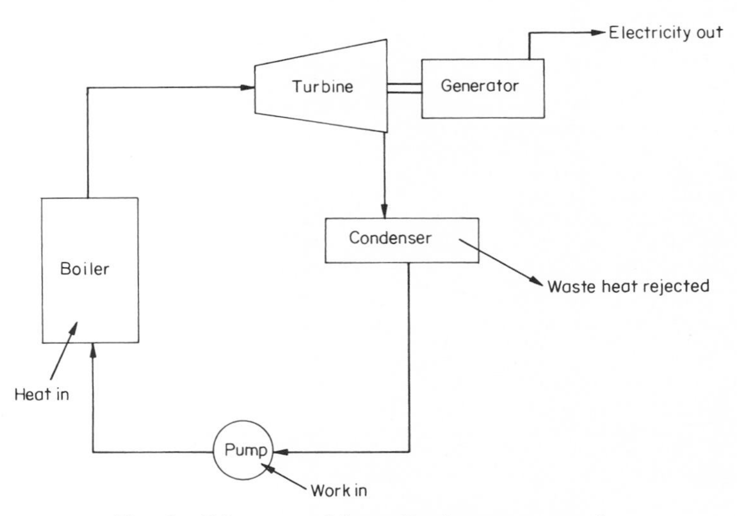

Fig. 3 Schematic of basic Rankine power cycle.

velocity. At most power plants, fish entrapment losses tend to fall into three nonrelated patterns:

1. Daily losses, independent of season, which generally involve small numbers of fish of several different species
2. Regular seasonal losses, which reflect the type of fish movement or congregation usually associated with natural migratory or spawning activities
3. Losses due to unusual changes in natural environment, such as abnormally warm or cold weather, or drought

Condenser and Internal Piping

All aquatic organisms small enough to pass through vertical traveling screens (entrained organisms) will be directly exposed to the physical and chemical stresses imposed by the circulating water pumps, condensers, and internal piping. In a once-through cooling tower system, organisms would also experience the additional physical stress of increased velocity, pressure, and associated turbulence. In all systems, the major chemical stress is imposed by the biocides, usually chlorine, injected into the cooling water system to keep it free of undesirable biological growth which could cause clogging, poor heat transfer, and materials pitting.

Discharge

After the cooling water has passed through the condenser, it is either discharged directly into the primary cooling water supply through a discharge canal which varies considerably in design from site to site (once-through open system) or it is passed through a cooling pond or cooling tower prior to discharge into the primary cooling water source (once-through cooling pond or cooling tower system) or through a cooling pond or cooling tower prior to recirculation (closed-loop system).

For most once-through open cooling systems, a discharge canal from a few hundred feet to many miles long has been routinely designed to minimize recirculation of discharged cooling water. These canals are usually 10 to 15 ft deep and 30 to 50 ft wide, with a discharge velocity seldom above 2 to 3 ft/sec. Only recently has the length of discharge canals become a subject for concern. While some sites need long canals to prevent recirculation of cooling water, the temperature drop of the cooling water is generally only 1 to 2 F°. Since survival of many entrained species depends on the length of time they are exposed to elevated discharge temperatures, use of these long canals with their long "residence times" is now open to question.

Effluent Limitation Guidelines

The limitations contained in the Effluent Limitation Guidelines for the Steam Electric Power Generating Point Source Category issued by the EPA[4] are summarized in Tables 2 and 3 covering thermal and nonthermal (chemical) limitations. The following three significant points apply to the tables:

1. All power-generating stations are subject to chemical effluent limitations. Cooling tower blowdown was exempted from any limitations on total suspended solids (TSS) or oil and grease for 1977, 1983 and Standards of Performance for New Sources (SPNS). The 1977 best practicable control technology currently available (BPCTCA) limits are only slightly different from the 1983 best available technology economically achievable (BATEA). The differences are principally in the limitations for bottom ash discharge and in limitations for corrosion inhibitors in cooling tower blowdown.

In view of the differences, it is likely that most power plants that have to do any significant amount of pollution control installation in order to meet 1977 limits will take the option of going all the way to meet 1983 limits by the 1977 deadline. This course is most probable for oil- and gas-fired plants that have relatively small treatment facilities compared to those required for coal-fired plants with their ash ponds.

2. The provisions of Section 316(b) of the Act apply to any cooling water intake even if the cooling water discharge from the plant is exempted categorically from thermal discharge limitations. Section 316(b) of the Act requires that the location, design, construction, and capacity of the cooling water intake structures reflect the best technology available for minimizing any adverse environmental impact. This technology is not as clearly defined as in the case of closed-cycle cooling system.

3. All discharges from power plants, whether thermal or chemical, must comply with state water quality standards. State standards may be more stringent than the federal guidelines. Thus, exemption categorically from effluent limitations, as is the case for plants smaller than 500 MW capacity, many times will still require the plant to proceed to off-stream cooling in order to meet state water quality standards.

The 316(a) variance Section 316(a) of the Act covers thermal discharges. This section provides that the EPA Regional Administrator or the state may impose a thermal effluent limitation that is less stringent than that required by the guidelines under the following condition: whenever the owner or operator of a power plant can demonstrate to the satisfaction of the EPA Regional Administrator or the state (where the state is the appropriate agency) that any effluent limitation proposed for the control of the thermal component of a discharge requires effluent limitations more stringent than necessary to assure the protection and propagation of a balanced indigenous population of shellfish, fish, and wildlife in and on the body of water in which the discharge is made (taking into account the interaction of such thermal component with other pollutants). Any such lesser limitations must still assure the protection and propagation of a balanced indigenous population of aquatic life.

It is well to note that state water quality standards must be met by July 1, 1977, and that all heat may be discharged where a cooling pond or cooling lake is used or is under construction as of November 7, 1974. Only cooling ponds (not lakes) can be employed for new sources, construction of which commenced after November 7, 1974. Definitions are important here. The term *cooling lake* means any manufactured water impoundment which impedes the flow of a navigable stream.

It is of interest to note in connection with thermal discharges that there is no provision or regulation to allow for ocean discharge that is any different from discharge into any other body of water.

The current guidelines for chemical discharges regulate 11 specific pollutants from 7 specific sources within a power plant. A significant requirement is the separation of bottom ash transport water from fly ash transport water, and the imposition of different limits for 1983 (BATEA) for each. In the case of bottom ash transport water, it is proposed that for 1983 the bottom ash sluice water system be closed and recycled with an estimated maximum blowdown of 8 percent of the recycle rate. The TSS, pH, and oil and grease limitations are then imposed on this blowdown. The regulation, however, continues to permit once-through discharge of fly ash transport water with limits for TSS, oil and grease, and pH. Thus, an ash transport system that would meet the 1977 BPCTCA limits for total suspended solids (for example, 30 mg/l average) would have to either (1) separate the systems into bottom ash and fly ash and apply the recycle to bottom ash in order to meet BATEA, or (2) install a system for increased removal efficiency on the combined ash transport in order to achieve the 1983 limits that would now be weighted by a 12.5 factor.

It is notable that no recycling of fly ash transport water is proposed for BATEA. Presumably this is because of the substantial leaching of soluble matter that can occur with many fly ash systems that makes such recycling an impossibility, or at least an impractical solution. The limits proposed for standards of performance for new sources, however, do not permit the discharge of any fly ash transport total suspended solids or oil and grease. The very apparent intention is that some system other than wet transport be employed for all new sources; namely, dry fly ash handling.

Here the real point of concern is the possibility of heavy metals being leached from the fly ash and an inability at this date in specifying reasonable effluent limitations for the many different heavy metals that might be involved. Bottom ash transport water for new sources is required to be recycled, but with a maximum of 5 percent blowdown or an effluent mass limitation one-twentieth of that for discharge from a once-through system.

COOLING SYSTEMS

Basically, there are three ways of dissipating heat: once-through cooling systems, cooling towers, and cooling ponds. With the exception of the dry cooling tower, all the cooling systems discharge some volume of water which is polluted thermally, chemically, or both thermally and chemically. In evaluating any of the cooling systems, system costs, effects on plant operating efficiency, and effects on the environment must be considered. Similar attention must also be given other cooling system components such as the water intake structure and discharge system.

Once-Through Cooling

Once-through cooling, the most common and least expensive method for removing heat from power plant condensers in the United States, diverts water from a large-volume source such as a river or ocean, pumps it through the condenser tubes where it is heated by steam condensing on the outer surface of the tubes, and discharges it to the water source at a point sufficiently distant from the intake to prevent recirculation. No attempt is made to cool the heated effluent prior to discharge. Since the plant must be adjacent to a water source of high-flow capacity, the number of sites where this system can be used is limited.

Capital and installation costs for once-through cooling are usually low, although seawater installations require a slightly more expensive condenser and longer intake and outlet piping. Although operating and maintenance costs are low, environmental costs are high. Of all cooling systems, once-through cooling has the largest water flow requirement, needs the largest intake structures, and has the largest environmental impact. Various forms of aquatic life are forced through the condenser tubes, often

TABLE 2 Steam Electric Power Generating Point Source Category Thermal Limitations[a]

Category	Best practicable control technology currently available (BPCTCA)	Best available technology economically achievable[b] (BATEA)	Standards of performance for new sources (SPNS)
Small unit[c]	No limitation	No limitation	No discharge of heat except: ■ Heat may be discharged in blowdown from recirculated cooling water systems provided the temperature does not exceed the lowest temperature prior to the addition of the makeup water. ■ Heat may be discharged in blowdown from cooling ponds provided the temperature does not exceed the lowest temperature prior to the addition of the makeup water.
Old unit[d]	No limitation	No limitation	
Generating unit	No limitation	No discharge of heat except: ■ Heat may be discharged in blowdown from recirculated cooling water systems provided the temperature does not exceed the lowest temperature prior to the addition of the makeup water. ■ Heat may be discharged in blowdown from recirculated cooling water systems designed to discharge blowdown at a temperature above the lowest temperature prior to the addition of makeup water providing such systems were in operation or under construction prior to November 7, 1974.	No discharge of heat except: ■ Heat may be discharged in blowdown from recirculated cooling water systems provided the temperature does not exceed the lowest temperature prior to the addition of the makeup water. ■ Heat may be discharged in blowdown from cooling ponds provided the temperature does not exceed the lowest temperature prior to the addition of the makeup water.

Generating unit	No limitation	■ Heat may be discharged where a cooling pond or cooling lake is used or is under construction as of November 7, 1974. ■ Heat may be discharged where sufficient[e] land for the construction and operation of mechanical draft evaporative cooling towers is not available on property owned or controlled as of March 4, 1974, and no alternate recirculating cooling system is practicable.[f] ■ Heat may be discharged where the total dissolved solids concentration in blowdown exceeds 30,000 mg/l and land not owned or controlled as of March 4, 1974 is located within 130 m (500 ft) in the prevailing downwind direction of every practicable location for mechanical-draft cooling towers and no alternative recirculating cooling system is practicable.[f] ■ Heat may be discharged where the cooling tower plume would cause a substantial hazard to commercial aviation and no alternate recirculating cooling water system is practicable.[f]

[a] All units must meet state water quality standards by July 1, 1977 [Section 301(b)(1)(c)]. Applies only to discharge of heat from the main condensers.

[b] These limitations are effective on July 1, 1981. However, where reliability would be seriously impacted by compliance with the effective date, an alternative schedule of compliance may be adopted providing that 50 percent of capacity shall meet the compliance date, that an additional 30 percent of capacity shall comply by July 1, 1982, and the balance shall comply by July 1, 1983.

[c] Any generating unit not an "old unit" which is less than 25 MW or any unit a part of a system of less than 150 MW.

[d] Any generating unit, of 500 MW or greater which was first placed in service on or before January 1. 1970, and any generating unit of less than 500 MW which was first placed in service on or before January 1, 1974.

[e] 100 M^2/MW or 1,000 ft^2/MW.

[f] This exception requires a "demonstration by the discharger."

TABLE 3 Steam Electric Power Generating Point Source Category Non-thermal Limitations[a,b]

Waste streams and pollutants	Best practicable control technology currently available (BPCTCA)		Best available technology economically achievable (BATEA)		Standards of performance for new sources (SPNS)	
	Max, mg/l[c]	Avg, mg/l[d]	Max, mg/l[c]	Avg, mg/l[d]	Max, mg/l[c]	Avg, mg/l[d]
All waste streams:						
pH (except once-through cooling)	6.0–9.0		6.0–9.0		6.0–9.0	
PCB's	No discharge		No discharge		No discharge	
Low volume waste streams:						
TSS	100	30	100	30	100	30
Oil and grease	20	15	20	15	20	15
Ash transport water:						
TSS	100	30				
Oil and grease	20	15				
Bottom ash transport water:						
TSS			100[e]	30[e]	100[f]	30[f]
Oil and grease			20	15	20	15
Fly ash transport water:						
TSS			100	30	No discharge	
Oil and grease			20	15	No discharge	
Metal cleaning wastes:						
TSS	100	30	100	30	100	30
Oil and grease	20	15	20	15	20	15
Copper (total)	1	1	1	1	1	1
Iron (total)	1	1	1	1	1	1
Boiler blowdown:						
TSS	100	30	100	30	100	30
Oil and grease	20	15	20	15	20	15
Copper (total)	1	1	1	1	1	1
Iron (total)	1	1	1	1	1	1
Once-through cooling water:						
Free available chlorine[g]	0.5	0.2	0.5	0.2	0.5	0.2
Cooling tower blowdown:						
Free available chlorine[g]	0.5	0.2	0.5	0.2	0.5	0.2
Zinc			1	1		
Chromium			0.2	0.2		
Phosphorus			5	5		
Other corrosion inhibitors			Case by Case Limit			
Area run off subcategory[h]						
TSS	≤50		≤50		≤50	
pH	6.0–9.0		6.0–9.0		6.0–9.0	
Pretreatment standards[i]						
Free available chlorine	No limitation		No limitation		No limitation	
Total residual chlorine	No limitation		No limitation		No limitation	

[a]Except where specified otherwise, the allowable discharge equals flow multiplied by the concentration limitation. Where waste streams from various sources are combined for treatment or discharge, the quantity of each pollutant attributable to each waste source shall not exceed the specified limitation for that waste source.

[b]All sources must meet state water quality standards by 1977 [Section 301 (b) (1)(c)].

[c]Maximum for any one day.

[d]Average of daily values for 30 consecutive days.

[e]Allowable discharge equals flow multiplied by concentration divided by 12.5.

[f]Allowable discharge equals flow multiplied by concentration divided by 20.0.

[g]Limits given are maximum and average concentration. Neither free available chlorine nor total residual chlorine may be discharged from any unit for more than 2 hrs. in any one day; and not more than one unit in any plant may discharge free available or total residual chlorine at any one time, unless the utility can demonstrate that the units in a particular location cannot operate at or below this level of chlorination.

[h]Only the runoff flow from material storage piles associated with a 10-year, 24-hr. rainfall is subject to these limitations.

[i]Applies only to sources which discharge to publicly owned treatment works. These discharges are also subject to the provisions of 40 CFR 128.

resulting in high mortality rates. The 10 to 20 F° warmer discharge water upsets the ecology by lowering the oxygen content of the water, increasing the metabolic rate of the fish, and enhancing growth of undesirable bacteria. And, because of the very slow cooling process, this upset may persist for many miles before the water temperature returns to normal.

Heat dissipation in coastal waters. The impact of heated effluent discharged into seawater is substantially more difficult to calculate than for lakes or rivers because of complex circulation patterns involving ocean currents generated by winds, waves, and tides. Occasionally intense freshwater runoff from the land may result in stratification that involves both temperature and salinity gradients.

In semiconfined coastal areas, depending on tidal stages, an effluent may be discharged into (1) relatively quiet water, (2) a tidal current traveling in one direction, or (3) a tidal current traveling in the opposite direction, (4) or even a rotary tidal motion. In the absence of other major circulation patterns, the net movement of the water mass over a complete tidal cycle may still be relatively small, but current shear and turbulence caused by the tides will generally reduce the area of stratification occupied by heated effluents to less than that for equivalent heat loads discharged to open lakes and reservoirs.

The behavior of the discharge may also depend on the intake. In coastal waters where stratification might exist the greater the depth from which the seawater is drawn, the more saline it will be. And as the temperature of this saline water is increased, its density decreases to less than that of the surface water. The net result is that the heated effluent stratifies on top. But as it cools, the high-salinity water sinks, complicating predictions of the time and place of heat dissipation. Clearly, all marine intake/discharge sites require extensive investigation and systems need to be designed carefully to avoid recirculating a stratified discharge. Condenser water usually is taken from a minimum depth of 30 to 40 ft to avoid the recirculation effect and to minimize ecological impact. Since the beach gradient of most available sites is relatively low, intake siphons and effluent lines from 2,500 to 4,000 ft long are often required to reach such depths.

Factors governing the size and dispersion of thermal plumes are complex. The thermal plume of one particular, large [2,000 megawatt electric (MWe)] nuclear plant could occasionally affect an area within a 6,000-yd radius. Beyond this, the temperature differential between the stratified and underlying layers became too low to maintain stratification (less than 1½ F°). With changing tides and wind conditions, the thermal plume could be forced landward and might reach the shoreline.

Heat dissipation in estuaries The behavior of heated effluents discharged into estuaries can be even more complex than in freshwater or marine environments and usually requires in-depth studies at individual sites, followed by computer modeling. In one particular type of estuary (a "salt wedge" estuary) typical estuarine conditions involve well-established stratification with instrusion of a saltwater wedge at the bottom and fresh or brackish water at the surface. Although the net movement of water will obviously be out of the estuary because of the river flow, tidal action may regularly reverse the direction of flow, further complicating the interface between the surface and deeper waters. The tendency for warm effluents to stratify on the surface will be reinforced by the natural characteristics of estuaries.

Cooling Towers

With the increased emphasis on reducing or eliminating thermal discharge to natural bodies of water, cooling towers are rapidly becoming more important. The different types of towers offer variations in heat exchange by evaporation and in economics. Natural-draft cooling towers rely on natural air circulation to dissipate waste heat to the atmosphere. Mechanical-draft cooling towers use induced drafts to promote sensible and evaporative heat transfer. Both natural- and mechanical-draft cooling towers rely on an overall enthalpy drawing force to promote heat transfer between water and air. Dry cooling towers use a temperature driving force between the water inside the tubes and air flowing past the tubes. The wet/dry cooling tower is a relatively new breed of tower which offers a compromise between the efficiency of wet cooling towers and the environmental advantages of dry cooling towers. Depending on atmospheric conditions, it uses varying portions of air-cooled heat exchangers and conventional evaporative cooling sections.

Natural-draft cooling towers A natural-draft cooling tower is basically a tall, hollow chimney which creates a draft for air circulation. Circulation is maintained by the difference between the heated, essentially saturated air within the tower and the atmosphere. The actual cooling takes place in the lower part of the tower. The capital cost of a natural-draft tower system for a 1,000 MWe nuclear power plant is approximately $7 to $10 million more than a comparable-duty, once-through cooling system.

The reinforced-concrete, thin-shelled towers are hyperboloid in shape to provide a venturi effect, increasing the draft velocity and tending to stabilize the draft. The shape also provides maximum shell strength at minimum cost (Fig. 4).[5] The height of the towers minimizes local ground fogging and prevents the effluent from recirculating to the tower intake. Water draining from grid structures in the lower part of the towers collects in a concrete basin which serves as a reservoir for the recirculating condenser cooling water system.

Depending on the method by which air/water contact is accomplished, natural-draft towers can be subdivided further into one of three categories:

1. *The spray tower.* The incoming water is sprayed directly into the airspace within the tower to fall through the rising air. At higher loadings, these towers suffer from poor volumetric efficiency.

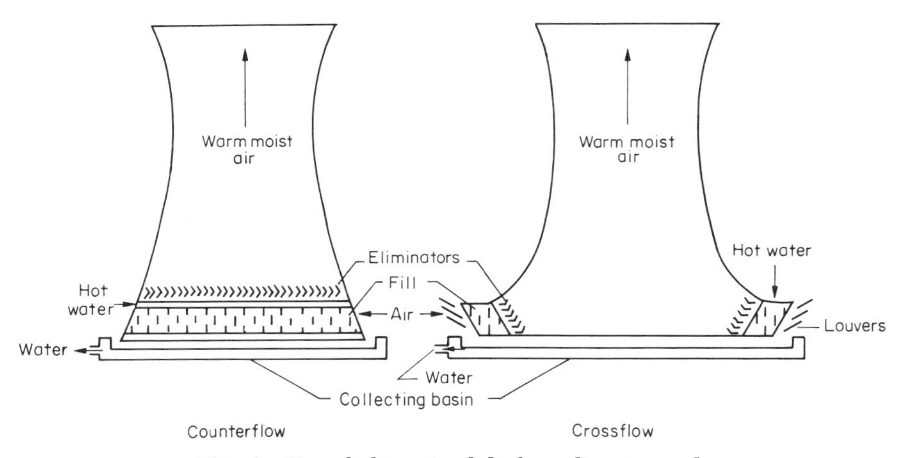

Fig. 4 Hyperbolic natural-draft cooling towers.[5]

2. *The counterflow tower.* The lower section of the shell is filled with a packing which extends the surface over which the water cascades. A commonly used packing is a gridwork of thin slats of asbestos cement sheets. This arrangement provides the most efficient heat transfer through continuous contact of air and water over the full temperature range.

3. *The cross-flow packed tower.* The packing surrounds the base of the tower but is outside the shell proper. Air is drawn horizontally through the packing and into the tower. An advantage of these towers is that the effective packing area is not limited by the cross-sectional area of the tower. Within reasonable limits, additional packing area can be provided by increasing the height of the packing while maintaining low resistance to airflow.

Cooling towers dissipate waste heat by evaporation of recirculated water and by convective transference of heat from the water to air. The ratio between evaporative and convective heat loss varies with the temperature and humidity of the ambient air. An increase in ambient air temperature, or a decrease in humidity, will increase the proportion of water removed by evaporation.

Since temperature and humidity changes also affect the natural draft, they have an effect on a tower's cooling capability. In warmer, dryer weather, the density difference between the air inside and outside the tower drops, reducing the efficiency of the natural-draft cooling. Higher ambient air temperatures also limit the temperature to which the water may be cooled. For these reasons, natural-draft cooling towers are often impractical in hot and dry climates typical of regions east of the Cascade Mountains and in the Southwest.

Mechanical-draft cooling towers Mechanical-draft cooling towers from 20 to 60 ft high have been used in the United States for several years (Fig. 5).[6] Characteristically, mechanical-draft towers comprise rows of individual counterflow or crossflow tower cells, each limited in size to about 35 to 40 ft by the fan capacity. For a 1,000-MWe nuclear power plant, an induced-draft cooling tower might contain 32 to 36 cells which would be arranged in widely spaced rows to minimize air recirculation.

As in natural-draft towers, cooling in a mechanical-draft wet cooling tower is achieved by both convective and evaporative heat transfer; but because airflow is mechanically induced, such towers are more compact. Like the natural-draft cooling tower, the mechanical-draft wet cooling tower also discharges large volumes of water to the atmosphere and generates a fog plume as well as drifts of water droplets. And

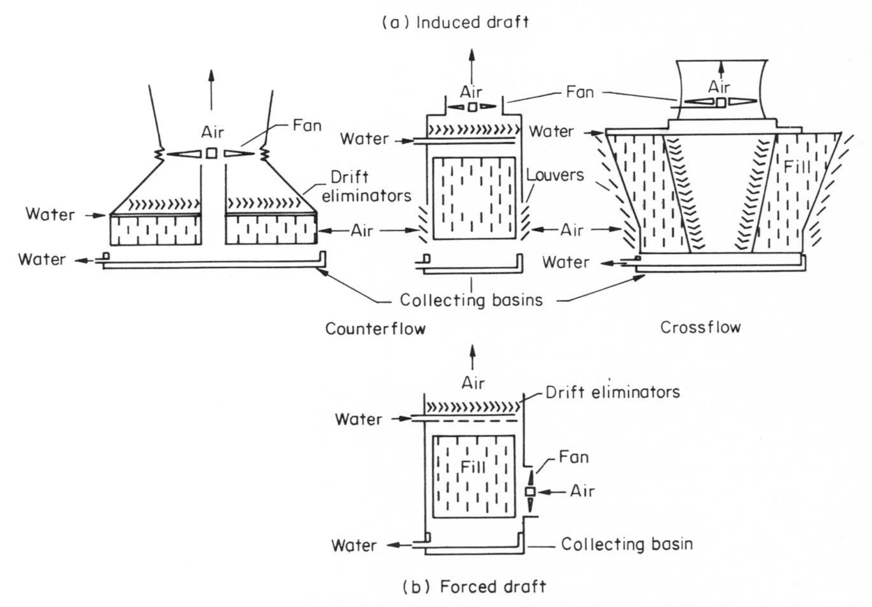

Fig. 5 Mechanical-draft cooling towers.[6]

because these towers are lower, the plumes often present a significant ground visibility problem. The low-level discharge also makes these towers more susceptible to recirculation of the exhausted air, reducing their efficiency.

The induced-draft tower allows improved operating flexibility: water and airflow rates may be varied according to operating conditions. It also costs less initially: $6 million for a 1,000-MWe nuclear plant, as compared with about $10 million for natural-draft towers. But these advantages are partially offset by the following cost factors:

- Higher operating costs, caused in part by the added power requirements for fan operation—some 4,800 hp required for a 1,000-MWe-sized tower
- Increased cost of the circulating water system piping that connects towers and condensers—a result of the large area requirement of the induced-draft towers
- Higher overall maintenance costs

In general, if atmospheric humidity at a site permits efficient operation of natural draft towers, the overall costs of these towers will prove less over the life of the plant.

Dry cooling towers Unlike the wet cooling towers, dry towers dissipate heat by conduction and convection. Heated cooling water from the plant's condensers is pumped through banks of finned-tube, heat-exchanger surfaces. Heat is transferred by conduction to the metal walls of the tubing, then by convection to air. Because the heat transfer does not include the latent heat of evaporation, dry cooling towers require both greater airflows and larger air temperature increases in order to dissipate the same amount of heat as a comparable evaporative cooling system. But since water and air never come into direct contact, no water is lost by evaporation. Two types of dry cooling systems can be considered: (1) steam directly condensed in air coolers with supplemental spray cooling provided, and (2) substitution of dry cooling units for evaporative cooling units.

Dry cooling is generally considered only when water availability is severely limited and significant net power generation losses can be accepted. Environmental costs in terms of land and fuel are high, and system performance and reliability are questionable. The technology of dry cooling has not been demonstrated in large-sized units and specially modified turbine designs would have to be developed to accommodate the high back pressure. As long as a reasonable selection of cooling-system alternatives is available, dry cooling is not a viable solution.

Cooling Ponds

A second alternative for heat dissipation in a closed-loop process is the cooling pond. Heated water from the condenser is discharged into one side of a natural or artificial lake or pond, where it partially mixes with the receiving water, producing a drop in temperature but no heat loss. As the water proceeds through the pond, heat is transferred from the pond's surface to the atmosphere by evaporation, conduction, and long-wave radiation. The effective pond surface area must be adequate for heat-load dissipation, and the pond's configuration should permit the warm circulating water to reach all areas of the pond to maximize heat dissipation and minimize the short-circuiting of warm water.

Water loss from a closed-cycle cooling pond results from natural and forced evaporation, seepage, blowdown losses, etc., and varies from 1 to 3 percent of the pumping rate. Depending primarily on wind and water temperature, heat loss due to forced evaporation accounts for 40 to 80 percent of the waste heat with the higher figures being more typical. The remaining waste heat, usually about 30 percent, is dissipated from the surface by conduction or long-wave radiation.

Surface evaporation is attributable to both natural evaporation and dissipation of the plant heat load. In an existing pond used for cooling purposes, natural evaporation would be supplemented by water losses attributable to the dissipation of plant load. In an artificial cooling pond, all water losses would be attributable to the operation of the power plant.

A major disadvantage of cooling ponds is the large amount of land required. Typically, ponds require 1 to 2 acres/MW. Even efficient ponds in low-humidity regions require about 0.75 acres/MW. The cooling pond site must also offer a location for the dam and pond containment, appropriately situated for the plant condensers.

On the other hand, these aesthetically pleasing cooling pond alternatives have the advantage of simplicity, low maintenance, recreational value, ability to operate for extended periods without makeup water, low power requirements, and most important, high thermal inertia. High thermal inertia means that in a properly designed pond, the temperature of the intake water will not reflect short-term changes in meteorological conditions or plant loadings. In addition, fogging is minimal; 200 m downwind is typically the limit of the affected area, although this distance can increase substantially with an increase in the pond's size and heat load.

Spray-supplemented cooling ponds An important outgrowth of the conventional cooling pond is the spray-supplemented pond. In a spray-supplemented cooling pond, natural evaporation is enhanced by spraying the warm water into the air above the pond. This effectively increases the surface area of water exposed to the air and the relative velocity between the water droplets and the air. The spray-supplemented cooling pond needs about 5 percent of the land required for a conventional cooling pond, and the economics of a spray pond are comparable to those of a mechanical-draft wet cooling tower system.

The disadvantages of spray ponds are threefold. First, for efficient evaporative cooling, the water spray must be in contact with cool, dry ambient air. Second, the spray modules must provide proper water distribution without interfering with adjacent modules. And third, the water spray can drift quite severely beyond the site, increasing the probability of fogging and icing.

To date, operating experience with spray ponds at power stations larger than 250 MWe is extremely limited, but, already, fouling of the spray equipment has proved to be a problem. For this reason alone, continuous operation of spray cooling units using water with high solids content is not feasible. Spray units do, however, offer valuable part-time supplemental cooling for a conventional cooling pond system. A pond with high thermal loading could be used without spray cooling during cool periods, but have sufficient supplemental spray cooling to reduce the thermal loading on the pond to reasonable levels during hot periods.

Saltwater Cooling Systems

In the near future, many new power-generating plants will have to use cooling waters that contain various concentrations of salt—from brackish inland waters to seawater. This will result partly from the decreasing availability of freshwater for cooling purposes and partly from the location of new plants in coastal areas.

The substitution of saltwater for freshwater in any type of cooling system will result in minor differences in the cooling system discharges. While the heat rejected will be the same, the mass and volumetric flow rates of saltwater coolant are 2 to 5 percent higher due to the reduced heat capacity of saltwater. In condenser cooling systems, the salt concentration in the coolant and in the blowdown stream will be 50 to 100 percent higher than the intake saltwater due to evaporation. Blowdown discharges containing these high salt concentrations will be more dense than the receiving water and will tend to sink, bringing the heated salt-rich effluent closer to the benthic community. For this reason alone, saltwater system discharges will require additional water treatment.

A state-of-the-art review of the design, performance, cost, and environmental impact of saltwater cooling towers is available from the U.S. Atomic Energy Commission.[7]

Comparative Economic Costs

Since the cost of the cooling water system is sensitive to environmental conditions, it is not feasible to develop absolute costs for each type of cooling system. By considering typical site conditions, however, it is possible to develop relative cost increments. Such a comparison of capital costs for various water cooling systems for a 1,000-MWe nuclear station is given in Table 4.[8] These costs, based on an extensive cost analysis, were validated against a similar study performed for the Westinghouse

TABLE 4 Comparison of Capital Costs for Various Methods of Cooling Water Supply, (For 1,000-MWe nuclear station) *,[8]

Cooling water supply	Circulating water system (civil works, pumps, etc.)	Condensers	Total	Incremental capital cost, dollars/kW
Freshwater (lakes, rivers)	2,909	2,246	5,155	Base
Estuaries—salt water once-through	3,111	2,627	5,738	0.583
Cooling ponds, recirculated freshwater	3,247	3,562	6,809	1.654
Seacoast, once-through	4,222	2,615	6,837	1.682
Wet cooling towers:				
Mechanical-draft	5,589	3,493	9,082	3.927
Natural-draft	7,760	3,570	11,330	6.175
Dry cooling towers:				
Natural-draft			25,000	19.855
Mechanical-draft			27,000	21.845

*Typical plant sites were used. Costs could vary substantially due to local conditions.

Electric Utility Headquarters Department by United Engineers in 1965. Base costs for freshwater systems were within 5 percent. Estimated costs for dry cooling systems are based on published data for specific installations.

A reasonably accurate economic ladder comparing the relationships in power generation cost increments from various sources of cooling water supply can be developed. The incremental capital cost per kilowatt must be converted to mils per kilowatthour using conventional calculations and annual operating costs developed for such terms as pumping and fan power, water treatment chemical costs, and maintenance on the tower systems. These costs must also be converted to mils per kilowatthour using an 80 percent capacity factor.

The loss in generating capacity due to the different types of cooling systems is summarized in Table 5.[8] Cooling ponds and wet cooling towers cause a 2 percent loss of capacity on large nuclear plants, and dry cooling towers cause a 10.6 percent loss in the turbine capacity. Maximum derating would occur during periods of high temperature. The total power-generating cost penalty of the various systems indicates that the once-through freshwater cooling system is the most economical.

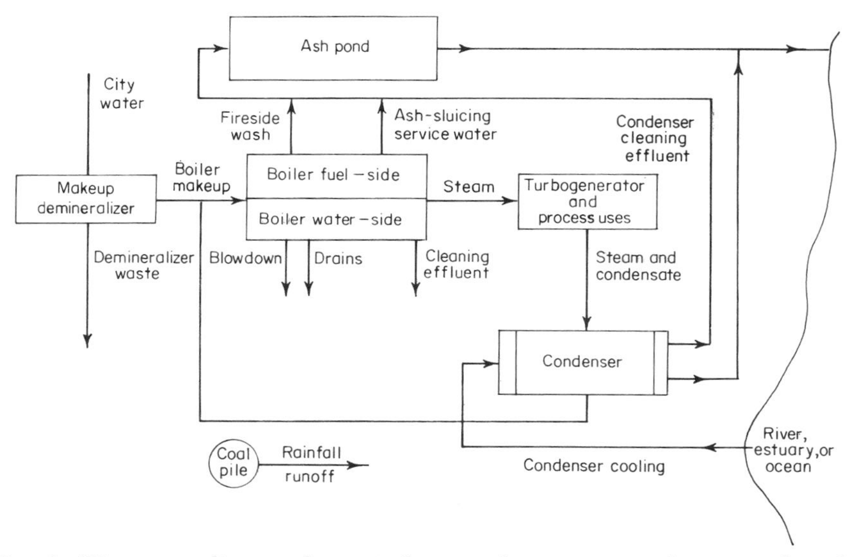

Fig. 6 Water use diagram for typical steam-electric power plant once-through cooling.

In addition, useful siting information can be developed by comparing power generation cost penalties, translated into distance penalties expressed in miles, with power transmission cost penalties. For example, all other factors being equal, it would be an economic trade-off to transmit power generated with a freshwater once-through cooling supply for 82½ mi compared to generating the power locally using a mechanical-draft wet cooling tower. Since the difference in power-generating cost penalties between mechanical-draft and natural-draft towers is very small, the choice between these two systems will depend entirely on the weather conditions and the expected load factors.

CHEMICAL DISCHARGES AND THEIR CONTROL

Chemical effluents from a steam-electric power plant result from makeup water treatment; chemicals added to plant cooling water or steam generator; products of corrosion, erosion, wear, or chemical reaction from plant systems; combustion products; residuals from pollution control equipment; and rainfall runoff. Figure 6 depicts a typical schematic of power plant water use. The EPA effluent limitations are based

TABLE 5 Total Economic Impact of Cooling Water Supply on Plant Location (For 1,000-MWe nuclear plant)*,[8]

Cooling water supply	Increase costs, mils/kWh	Plant capability loss, kW	Incremental kW capacity capital cost, mils/kWh†	Additional fuel cost due to higher heat rate, mils/kWh	Total power-generating cost penalties, mils/kWh	Distance penalties, (mi)‡
Freshwater	Base	Base	Base	Base	Base	
Estuaries	0.01166	Base	Base	Base	0.01166	4.6
Cooling ponds	0.03308	20,000	0.03000	0.02400	0.08708	34.3
Seacoast	0.03364	Base	Base	Base	0.03364	13.2
Wet cooling towers:						
Mechanical draft	0.15568	20,000	0.03000	0.02400	0.20968	82.5
Natural-draft	0.14464	20,000	0.03000	0.02400	0.19864	78.2
Dry cooling towers:						
Natural-draft	0.42650	106,000	0.15900	0.12720	0.71270	280.6
Mechanical draft	0.53060	106,000	0.15900	0.12720	0.81680	321.6

* Based on 14 percent annual charge, 80 percent capacity factor.

† Plant capability loss is assumed as peaking loss which is replaced at $75 per kW capital cost.

‡ Trade-off between electrical transmission distance and penalties associated with various cooling water supplies, incremental transmission costs at 0.00254 mils/(kWh)(mi).

on minimizing the "quantities" of chemical pollutants discharged in various waste streams that are considered of major environmental consequence. (Pollutant quantities are defined as flow multiplied by concentration.)

The quantity and characteristics of chemical constituents of discharges from steam-electric power-generating units are highly variable and should be examined on a case-by-case basis. Table 6 summarizes the factors which influence the type of chemical discharges that can occur for a power plant. Since most utilities have not had a need to monitor and record in-plant waste streams, a waste characterization study is usually needed to define the quantities and qualities. EPA chemical effluent limitations for specific source streams have been outlined in the section on the nature of the problem. In the past, the major emphasis has been on recording data for end-of-pipe treatment systems and compliance with site effluent limitations at the discharge point. Current emphasis, however, is on water reuse, but from a somewhat different perspective. Since treatment technology can produce an effluent quality high enough to allow cascading uses and in-plant reuse, an intelligent water management evaluation can uncover the better cost-effective solutions.

TABLE 6 Factors Affecting Type of Chemical Discharges from Steam-Electric Power-Generating Facilities

Fuel type
Type of combustion
Type of fuel storage facilities
Unit capacity
Capacity factor
Type of operation
Makeup water quality
Pretreatment requirements
In-plant treatment requirements
System water chemistry control programs
Materials of construction
Age of facility
Extent of reuse of water
Type of cooling
Type of air pollution control equipment
Type of waste treatment systems used
Meteorological and environmental influences
Economics
Regulatory and licensing constraints

The chemical parameters or pollutants listed for control in the EPA effluent guidelines are:

pH
Polychlorinated biphenols
Total suspended solids
Oil and grease
Copper
Iron
Free available chlorine and total residual chlorine
Zinc
Chromium
Phosphorus
Other corrosion inhibitors

Descriptions of the waste streams as categorized in the EPA effluent limitations are described in the following sections. Average flow data for a 100-MW coal-fired, freshwater makeup plant are presented in Table 7.[13] Most of the data represent highly variable conditions and a wide range of values.

Some of the effluent discharges are generated on a regular basis, and the chemical compounds are present in somewhat predictable quantities at somewhat predictable intervals for a given plant. Other chemical discharges are not as regular and

TABLE 7

	gpd/MW	Continuous flow, gpm
Boiler cleaning	4	0.3
Fireside cleaning	5	0.4
Air preheater cleaning	100	6.9
Laboratory drains	10	0.7
Boiler blowdown	100	6.9
Recirculating ash, handling	300	20.8
Recirculating wet, scrubber	20	1.4
Ion-exchange Regeneration	88	6.1
Evaporator	—	—
Miscellaneous	3.22	0.2
Floor drains	30	2.1
Total	660	45.8

are not readily predictable as to frequency and chemical composition. This distinction is presented in Table 8.

Low-Volume Wastes

Sources of low-volume wastes include, but are not limited to, the following:

- Water treatment
  - Ion-exchange regeneration
  - Filter backflush
  - Clarifier blowdown
  - Evaporator blowdown
  - Softener regenerant
  - Reverse osmosis reject
  - Condensate
- Cooling tower basin cleaning
- Boiler blowdown
- Closed cooling water system drains
- Floor drains
- Stack cleaning
- Wet scrubber
- Miscellaneous equipment cleaning
- Laboratory and sampling streams

Periods of high turbidity in the makeup water or high plant rates for makeup water requirements can result in more frequent blowdown, backflush, and regeneration of makeup water treatment equipment. For plants using evaporators, an increase in

TABLE 8

Stream	Discharge character	
	Regular	Irregular
Low-volume waste streams	Mixed	
Ash transport water	X	
Bottom ash transport water	X	
Fly ash transport water	X	
Metal cleaning wastes		X
Boiler blowdown	X	
Once-through cooling water	X	
Cooling tower blowdown	X	
Rainfall runoff		X

blowdown rate is required. Condenser tube leak would cause an increase in frequency of regeneration for condensate polishing demineralizers. Increased evaporator blowdown rates are required for unusually high feed dissolved solids concentration or production rates.

Several of the waste streams listed (for example, floor drainage and cooling tower basin cleaning wastes) may be treated sufficiently by directing them to the ash pond, where chemical neutralization and settling afforded by the pond can be utilized, or they may otherwise be redirected for reuse. Elimination of these streams from the duty imposed on the central chemical treatment plant will reduce the capital and operating costs of the facility since the design volumes are significantly reduced. Moreover, the remaining combination of streams can be more efficiently dealt with since dilution by the segregated stream will be lessened. Floor-drain wastewater should frequently be put through an oil separator with waste oil collected for reuse of incineration.

Ash Transport Water

The quantity and chemical characteristics of ash transport water and liquid effluent from transport and storage facilities is influenced by the following factors:

Type of fuel
Unit capacity
Ash content of fuel
Mode of firing
Design of combustion chamber
Fraction of fly ash vs. bottom ash
Type and efficiency of air pollution control equipment
Quantity of transport water used
Availability of land for holdup or treatment

In the operation of a typical coal-fired electric power generating plant, one of the major wastes is ash. Since many ash-handling systems in use today depend on water to transfer the ash at one stage or another away from the point of generation, the effect of these ash-bearing waters on the plant effluent must be considered.

Coal-fueled power generation produces large amounts of ash from the combusted coal. A typical power station with a rated capacity in the 600-MW range could generate somewhere in the neighborhood of 1,000 tons/day of ash, depending on ash content in the coal. Of this total, approximately 80 percent or 800 tons/day would be fly ash, the remaining 200 tons/day would be bottom ash.

Fly ash is first collected at the boilers, dry, in stack hoppers, preheater hoppers, and economizer hoppers. Many power plant operations then employ a semicontinuous wet slurry transport operation to pneumatically remove the fly ash from the storage hoppers with water eductors. Other approaches do not use a wet slurry, but do use water to create a vacuum. Others are completed dry except for small amounts of water used to wet the ash before loading on trucks before disposal, and perhaps air washers. The slurry systems are specifically regulated by the effluent guidelines. Generally, in wet slurry transport, the fly ash is sucked dry out of a hopper and then mixed and conveyed in the eductor water stream to the sump. Once in the sump, the fly ash is pumped to the ash storage and disposal facilities. This wet ash transfer is usually at a rate of 3,000 to 6,000 gpm, depending on the amount of water used to slurry the ash, and the frequency and rate of eductor operation. The fly ash–water slurry is typically discharged to an ash settling pond for treatment.

Bottom ash typically is collected in a water-filled bottom ash hopper at the base of the boiler. Sluice gates at the hopper are periodically opened and the bottom ash sluiced or educted (or both) through clinker grinders to reduce the particle size of the clinkers. The bottom ash is then sluiced to a sump via a floor drain system and pumped to the ash ponds for further treatment. Transfer to the ash ponds is also in the 3,000- to 6,000-gpm range, depending on the amount of water used in sluicing and the frequency and rate of sluicing.

As mentioned previously, a typical current method of treatment of ash transfer wastewater is to employ ash settling ponds for removal of suspended matter. The quality of the treated effluent discharged from these typically once-through systems depends heavily on pond hydraulic design, influent water distribution, frequency of cleaning and the quality of the ash. Many ashes contain considerable soluble matter (through leaching) and also fines which are not susceptible to ready settling. A hydraulically well-designed ash pond, providing for uniform wastewater influent distribution, sufficient retention time, and avoiding bottom scour can generally be expected to produce effluent suspended solids levels in the 20- to 30-mg/l range. In some cases, pH control is necessary to prevent acid or alkaline discharges.

Although the primary item of concern in ash pond effluents is suspended matter, dissolved salts may increase across the ash pond. This is due to the leachability of mineral salts in the fly ash while it is in contact with water. Depending on sluice rate, pond detention, etc., dissolved solids may increase anywhere from 100 to 300 mg/l across the system. The leached dissolved salts vary considerably depending on the area where the coal is mined and the particular mineral constituents that predominate in that area. The final effluent may require treatment for heavy metal removal depending on local and state regulatory requirements. If so, special provisions will be required.

Leaching of the ash pond water through the ground to contaminate ground water supplies is another problem to consider. Where the soil is not adequate to contain the water, ponds must be lined with nonporous materials such as rubber, vinyl, or bentonite. Some of the ash systems may even contain self-sealing materials that will form a natural impervious barrier on the soil.

Current studies on the use of fly ash for construction materials (such as concrete, asphalt, etc.), for land reclamation, and for road building are generating significant interest. In the near future there will be tremendous quantities of this type of material available—a 300-MW unit with 8 percent ash, for example, will produce 900 cu-ft/hr of ash. While recovery uses would represent a highly desirable disposal method, it is doubtful that the market can absorb a very significant portion of the total amount of fly ash generated.[9]

The addition of stack gas scrubbers to the system further compounds wastewater problems. Many SO_2 removal systems produce suspended solids in the form of calcium sulfate or calcium sufite precipitate (5 to 15 wt percent slurry) plus varying quantities of fly ash. Some systems use the scrubber wastes to wet down dry fly ash. Another approach is to increase the solids content by mechanical separation and then truck the solids off site to a suitable disposal area. All scrubber waste systems are in their infancy, and since they present severe leaching problems, they must be handled carefully. In general, enormous quantities of waste are produced, greater than fly ash quantities.

Metal-Cleaning Wastes

Deposits accumulate on metal surfaces, raising water wall temperatures in steam generators, reducing heat transfer in condensers, and thereby reducing cycle efficiency. Periodic cleaning is required. Mechanical and manual cleaning methods in large, modern steam generators have not been found to be feasible or practical. Chemicals that have been used in metal-cleaning processes for power plant components include a wide range of cleaning compounds and neutralizing agents. The frequency of cleaning and, thus, the quantity of pollutants discharged depend on the following factors:

Plant reliability requirements
Materials of construction
Use of corrosion inhibitors
Use of antifoulants
Use of biocides (condenser cooling)
Compliance with equipment water quality control requirements
Mode of operation of unit and equipment
Economics of cleaning processes
Extent of degradation of performance
Type of chemicals permitted for cleaning process

Metal-cleaning effluents are difficult to treat because they occur intermittently in large batches. Table 9 presents examples of the frequency of cleaning various equipment and the corresponding volume from such cleaning processes. The chemical effluents not only depend on the basic chemicals used in the process, but on the type

TABLE 9 Typical Plant Equipment Which May Require Periodic Cleaning

Equipment	Materials	Waste volume per cleaning gal/(MW)/ (cleaning or wash)	Typical frequency per year
Boiler, steam generators	Stainless steel Carbon steel Inconel	50–400	0.2–1
Feedwater heaters	Carbon steel Stainless steel Admiralty brass 90/10, 80/10, 70/10 CU-Ni Monel Arsenical copper		Only preopera-tional
Condenser tubes	Admiralty brass 90/10 Cu-Ni Stainless steel		
Air preheaters	Carbon steel	100–1500	4–24
Boiler fireside		100–1000	2–8
Miscellaneous equipment, Piping	Carbon steel Stainless steel Copper alloys		

of corrosion or fouling existing on the equipment surfaces and the extent of metal removal from surfaces during the cleaning process. Any specific treatment plant will require a system in which the effluent can be neutralized and the metals can be precipitated and removed from the system as sludge. The liquid phase might then be bled into the main discharge, incinerated, or evaporated to a disposable solid. A problem with any specific treatment system will be its relatively high cost considering its infrequent use in plants with only a few boilers to clean. Contingent upon the company system, an intracompany or even intercompany facility to which the cleaning effluents could be transported by truck, rail car, or barge could be the most efficient approach. It should be noted that with respect to the current copper limitations of 1 mg/l, neutralization, precipitation, and TSS removal will probably not produce a satisfactory effluent concentration for acid boiler cleaning solvents in many situations.[10]

Boiler Blowdown

Boiler blowdown varies with:

- Allowable boiler water solids content
- Condenser leakage
- Makeup water quality
- Boiler operating conditions

Most modern boilers will have a blowdown range of 0.1 to 1 percent of steam flow or about 20 to 200 gpd/MW. Old plants operate at lower pressures than new plants and hence can tolerate a higher boiler total dissolved solids (TDS) content. The chemical composition of boiler blowdown is such that suspended solids, copper, and iron are minimal for most operations. However, the pH will likely be on the basic side because of the type of chemical water treatment. Although there is a wide disparity in boiler blowdown dissolved solids levels ($<$ 50 to 2,500 mg/l), their effect on plant effluent is insignificant because of their low volume compared to the total plant effluent. Chemical characteristics depend on materials for construction of the systems involved, the feedwater chemical control program, and the type of plant operation. In many cases boiler blowdown can be used after cooling as a supplement to ash sluicing makeup, to the cooling tower system, or it can be recycled to the makeup supply system.

Once-Through Cooling Water

Most steam-electric power plants use a biocide in the circulating water system to control microbial growths (mainly bacterial slimes) on condenser exchange surfaces. Unless these growths are minimized, they can seriously reduce heat transfer and adversely affect overall generating efficiency. The predominant biocides used are sodium hypochlorite and gaseous chlorine. Generally, no corrosion inhibitors are used in the once-through circulating water system. However, pH control is sometimes used in the range of 6.0 to 9.0 to mitigate deposition on condenser tubes of salts from high alkalinity water.

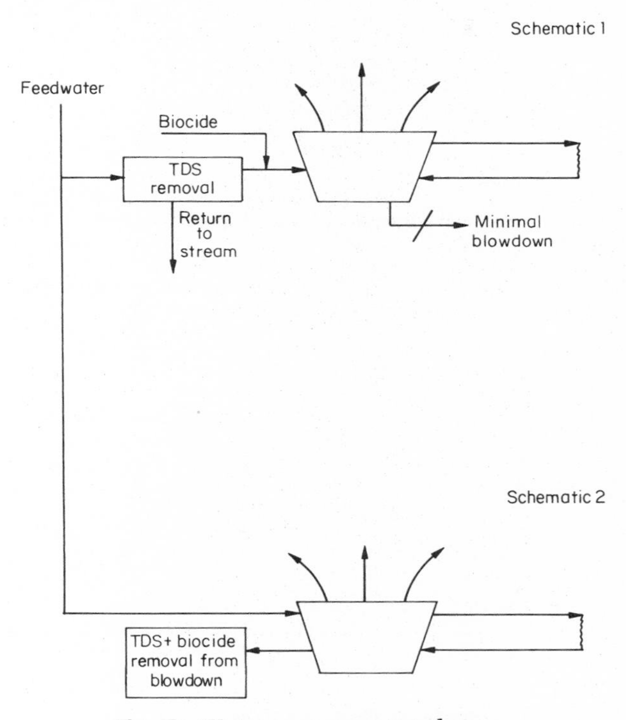

Fig. 7 Water management techniques.

Typically, the chlorine is added at a predetermined fixed rate until a free chlorine residual has been established at the condenser outlet, indicating that sufficient chlorine is present for microbiocidal action. The effluent limitations can be achieved by means of available feedback control systems presently in wide use in other applications. Chlorination for biological control can be applied intermittently on a "shock" basis. It should be applied to one unit at a time at the same plant in order to minimize the maximum concentration of total residual chlorine at any time in the combined cooling water discharged from the plant.

Cooling Tower Blowdown

During operation, the cooling tower concentrates salts and biocides in the circulating water, including any added corrosion/scaling inhibitors, sometimes making disposal of tower blowdown a serious problem. Since all these chemical constituents build up to high levels in blowdown streams, some water quality management is clearly desirable and sometimes necessary to meet local requirements.

There are essentially two places in the cooling tower schematic where water management techniques may be applied (Fig. 7). Water management techniques employed at the front of the tower (schematic 1 of Fig. 7) will reduce the effect of concentration difference and eliminate biocide effects on the environment. Dissolved solids will be returned to the stream at a concentration only double that of the feed stream (assuming a 50 percent water recovery rate) with no biocide addition or thermal effects. The biocide is retained in the tower and the tower will rarely, if ever, have to be blown down. Mud and silt buildup in the tower will require periodic removal. A distinct disadvantage of this system is the high cost of providing water to the tower that is free of total dissolved solids (TDS).

Water management techniques designed for the blowdown (schematic 2, Fig. 7) would have to operate on a much more highly concentrated feedstock but would involve substantially lower volumes. A 5:1 concentration factor, for example, would reduce stream flow by an order of magnitude. However, biocide and corrosion inhibitors must also be removed from the water flow. Addition of inhibitors for deposit control is necessary to maintain heat-transfer surfaces and efficient operation of equipment. Deposit formation in cooling systems originates from the feedwater, from the air being scrubbed in the cooling tower, from reactions with water treatment, and from corrosion in the system.

The blowdown rate depends on the quality of makeup water and the permissible concentration factor for cooling tower operation. It is chosen to produce concentrations of all salts in the circulating water which are below their saturation points under the worst prevailing conditions. Blowdown is costly since it wastes water and treatment chemicals and requires treatment, so analysis is needed to minimize the rate. Blowdown rates as a percentage of circulating water flow may range from 0.1 percent for high-quality makeup to 5 percent for severely brackish water.

TABLE 10 Chemicals for Control of Corrosion, Deposition, and Biological Growth[12]

Biocide:	Corrosion and scale inhibitors:
Hypochlorites	Chromate-based compounds
Gaseous chlorine	Phosphate and polyphosphate compounds
Hypochlorous acid	Zinc salts
Bromine	Polyelectrolytes
Chlorophenates	Organic phosphonates
Quaternary ammonium compounds	pH control reagents
Organotin compounds	
Organic thiocyanates	
Organic thiocarbonates	

Chemicals added to cooling tower systems are summarized in Table 10. The marginal effectiveness of "nonpolluting" inhibitors is likely to motivate continued usage of zinc- and chromium-based inhibitors and consequently will require the installation of waste treatment systems for inhibitor removal.[10] Various process schemes are available in arid areas to achieve zero discharge by concentrating tower blowdown for discharge to solar ponds.[11]

Blowdown treatment systems are being advanced on a large scale to enable use of more adequate inhibitors. Chromate reduction with subsequent precipitation is the present method employed to remove this toxic material from blowdown. Zinc is removed by selective ion exchange but can also be removed by precipitation. The adequacy of these approaches is questionable, since toxic treatment chemicals will be discharged by windage and possible leaks at process areas.

A current issue related to treatment of chemical constituents in cooling tower blowdown is differentiating between "gross" and "net" pollutants. The current effluent limitations are interpreted to be based on a gross basis, i.e., the discharge stream can contain no more than the established concentration for a particular pollutant. In many cases this would require the removal of a pollutant which was present in the intake or makeup waters and subsequently concentrated in the circulating water system. Similarly, the towers "scrub" dust and particles from the air flowing through the towers—not only the ambient air pollutants, but also those present as a result of plant operation. Responsibility for the removal of only the "net" contribution added to the incoming water can be allowed, but the burden of proof rests on the particular utility and each case is handled separately.

Rainfall Runoff

Limitations on the quality of rainfall runoff have been established for material storage areas and construction areas. Requirements for control of rainfall runoff from material storage areas are applicable to coal-fueled power plants, but the requirements imposed on construction sites are applicable to all power plants under construction or proposed for the future and to all plant modifications.

Runoff volumes and characteristics from coal pile storage depend on the following factors:

Average and maximum rainfall (maximum design rainfall for 10-year, 24-hr event)
Quantity of coal stored
Type of coal
Cleanliness of coal
Storage area
Seasonal temperatures

Surge control, ph control, and clarification are required to meet the current limitations. Coal particles which constitute the sludge can be further dewatered and returned to the coal pile.

The quantity and chemical characteristics of rainfall runoff from a construction site depend on the following factors:

Average and maximum rainfall (design rainfall of 10-year, 24-hr event)
Area of construction site
Type of soil
Slope and slope length
Soil erodibility
Erosion control techniques

The application of the same design event and minimal control limits to runoff from major construction activities is difficult.[10] Plant sites can entail development of large land areas, where impoundments and other erosion control measures represent an integral part of the project. Achievement of the suspended solids limitation value in a cost-effective manner is problematic.

Process Technology

Water systems in electric power-generating plants should be considered as one system, although with discrete, individual parts. Such a concept allows management to confront the modern goals of conservation, reclamation, reuse, and pollution control in the most cost-effective manner. Ultimately, it is the only approach to implement the most efficient, economical, and environmentally suitable operating conditions. Thus, if the makeup system, the preboiler, boiler and steam system, condensate return system, cooling and process water system, blowdown, and wastewater systems each are treated as one part of an interrelated larger system, one can abandon some of the less-imaginative stereotypical methods which formerly characterized the water/wastewater industry.

In order to take full advantage of this single-system concept of water management, it is necessary to know the technical and economic facts of each individual part. Some of the total process considerations in power plants which should be evaluated are:

Makeup water systems
Condensate treatment
Causes and control of corrosion, deposits, and carryover in steam generation systems
Chemical cleaning technology
Control of corrosion, scaling, fouling, and biological growth in cooling systems
Wastewater treatment systems
Reuse and recovery
Operational change

Usually, process or equipment redesign in a power plant to avoid production of the pollutants is very complex and not feasible.

After the systems approach has been taken, the selection of process treatment steps to remove specific pollutants from intermediate or end-of-pipe waste streams must be made. Removal systems can be introduced at any point to treat any defined waste stream. To meet the EPA effluent limitations, nine pollutants must be controlled prior to discharge: suspended solids, oil and grease, copper, iron, chromium, phosphorus, zinc, and total dissolved solids. The first seven are specified under "best practicable" and "best available" standards. New source performance standards require "no detectible amount" of "materials added for corrosion inhibition" for cooling tower blowdown. Control of total dissolved solids is a general requirement in some state limitations.

Table 11 presents a review of process technology available for abatement and removal systems for each pollutant. Sludge processing is also involved. These unit operations or processes are either in use, demonstrated, or presently contemplated as viable alternatives. Engineering judgment is the basis for differentiating those processes that are (1) "common practice" (generally in use today, perhaps in other industries), (2) "established technology" (where technical feasibility has been demonstrated and costs reasonably well defined), or (3) "developmental" (where technical and/or economic feasibility has not yet been satisfactorily demonstrated). This method of presenting the technology is, of course, a great simplification since it ignores the many and important variants of each unit process, process sequence, and a host of plant-specific factors. Only a detailed waste characterization, treatability, and process design effort will yield the optimum overall treatment system for a particular application. However, a general perspective is provided.

Recovery and Reuse

The stringent effluent limitation requirements for existing and new plants coupled with localized shortages of "conventional" water resources create a strong inducement for process modifications to reduce water usage and/or to increase reuse of treated wastewaters. In many cases this will bring about a substantial volume reduction of effluent and increased volumes of sludges and brines. The basic economic considerations for pollution control revolve around cost comparisons between waste treatment and other "conventional" water supply sources. These costs in turn must be compared with use of concentrating systems within the plant (such as waste-heat boilers and water cooling towers) as a means of achieving reduction in blowdown flows.[13]

Regardless of the extent of reuse, some makeup water will be required, either from seawater, "conventional" sources, or renovated municipal/industrial effluents. A demand on the order of 17,500 gpd/MW (12 gpm/MW) (closed-cycle cooling, oil-fired plant)[14] often creates severe strain on conventional sources of available water supply. This factor must be evaluated seriously on an annual basis in terms of both quantity and reliability. The efficiency of water use can be optimized both by "cascading" the water supplies in series from high-quality demands to lower-quality demands and by combining streams to achieve more cost effectiveness. Wastewater streams requiring treatment total approximately 660 gpd/MW for a coal-fired, fresh-water makeup plant.[15] In addition, cooling blowdown is approximately 170 gpd/MW. If reused, these streams become a substitute for raw-water makeup.

Technical considerations in planning for wastewater treatment and reuse are, to a large extent, a function of the planned use of the water. Total system considerations of treatment and maximum reuse are shown in Fig. 8, a block flow diagram indicating the sources, uses, consumption, treatment, renovation, and reuse relationship. Process selection and water quality criteria are perhaps the most important technical considerations. The goal of process selection is to determine those treatment steps which will convert a wastewater of quality X to a product water of quality Y suitable for reuse.

Recycling wastewaters, most likely for cooling water makeup, will cause buildup of dissolved solids in the system, creating the need for more complex corrosion and deposit control schemes and a means for disposal of concentrated brines. Cooling towers do not need water of potable quality. Concentrated waste streams will remain concentrated, whereas dilute streams will remain dilute, be treated, reused, and in turn, concentrated. Extensive work has been done in the use of cooling

TABLE 11 Treatment Processes Alternatives

Suspended solids	Oil and grease	Copper	Iron	Chromium	Phosphorus	Zinc	Total dissolved solids	Sludge dewatering
Sedimentation	Gravity separation	Coagulation and precipitation	Aeration and sedimentation	Reduction and precipitation	Chemical precipitation	Chemical precipitation	Reverse osmosis	Flotation
Clarification	Skimming	Ion exchange	Coagulation and sedimentation	Ion exchange	Ion exchange	Ion exchange	Ion exchange	Thickening
Flotation	Dissolved air flotation		Ion exchange	Electrochemical			Evaporation	Evaporation
Coagulation and flocculation	Adsorption		Softening				Electrodialysis	Coagulation and flocculation
Filtration	Filtration		Filtration				Distillation	Centrifugation
Microscreening								Vacuum filtration

Common practice (single box) — Established technology (double box) — Development technology (dashed box) towers and boilers to concentrate waste for ultimate disposal as solid residue. Under this approach, refractory inorganic salts are removed as a dry solid, or, if desired, as a concentrated solution for ultimate disposal.[13] Current technology is pushing TDS concentrations up to saline levels, 35,000 ppm. Most likely these levels will be doubled by application of emerging technology. This will require common use of corrosion and scale inhibiting materials (currently zinc- and chromium-based), and the installation of waste treatment systems for inhibitor removal.

Storm water runoff control implies impoundment on site, treatment, and then release at a controlled rate later. For reasons given earlier, attention should be given to reuse of this water in the process or cooling cycles.

Planning for the handling of wastewater will be increasingly important in view of current and projected regulatory requirements. This is primarily true because of the dual benefits, i.e., pollution control and water supply, of such projects. The high degree of treatment required for discharge renders the product too valuable to throw

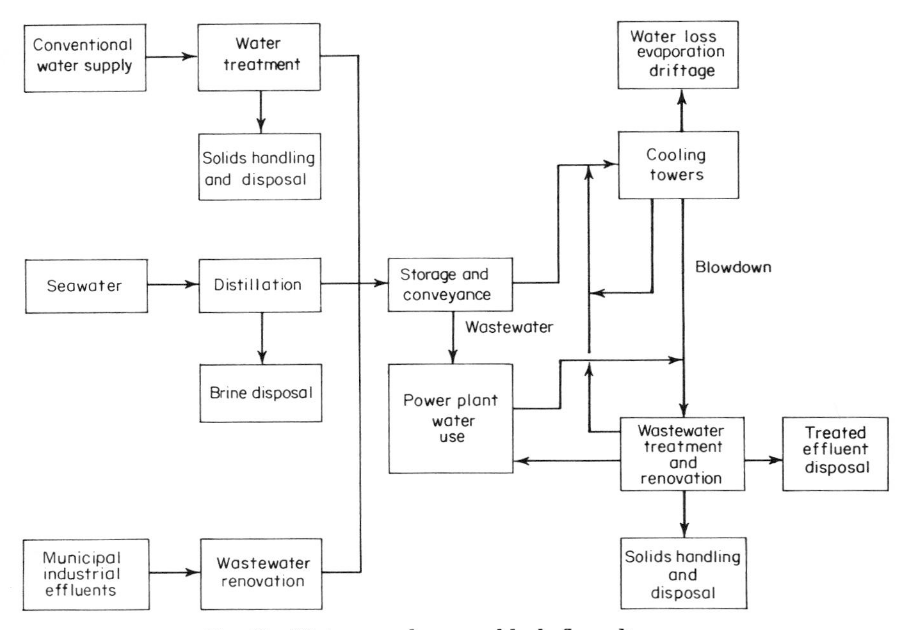

Fig. 8 Water supply-reuse block flow diagram.

away; reuse is thus inherently advantageous. Taking the systems approach toward all use, reuse, and disposal cycles of water will be necessary to achieve effective management. An important side benefit also results—freedom from outside wastewater regulation, whether local, state, or federal. This freedom allows management flexibility for in-plant process and water use changes without filing for revised NPDES permits. There is no doubt that the concept of water reuse will play a dominant role depending on the type of water supply envisioned, the project location, and the specific effluent limitations to be met.

ENVIRONMENTAL EFFECTS

By far the most important effect that wastewater has on the environment is the aquatic impact. The withdrawal, use, and discharge of large or small volumes of cooling water directly or indirectly subject a variety of aquatic organisms to physical, chemical, or thermal stresses which they may or may not be able to survive. The major physical stresses imposed on aquatic organisms are attributable to the intake system and passage through internal piping and condensers. Thermal stresses occur at the condenser and may persist through discharge. Chemical stresses are applied if biocides and corrosion inhibitors are injected into the system.

Atmospheric effects resulting from the discharge of moist air to the local atmosphere will also occur, particularly when mechanical-draft cooling towers are used for waste-heat dissipation.

Economics, land use, water consumption, performance and efficiency, aesthetics, and social factors must also be considered and these factors vary considerably with location.

Aquatic Impact

An in-depth review of the aquatic impact of cooling systems is obviously beyond the scope of this chapter. But to suggest the magnitude and complexity of the problems involved, the aquatic impact has been summarized briefly on a quantitative basis.

Entrainment effects Entrainment studies conducted at a variety of power plants indicate that observed mortality may be extrapolated from laboratory bioassay studies. Such studies indicate that the thermal tolerance of any species depends on the stage of development of the organism, ambient temperatures, and duration of the entrainment.[14,15]

The effect of transport may be classified as lethal and sublethal. Lethal effects would result in the total destruction of all organisms of a particular species; sublethal effects would result in a temporary alteration, within the zone of tolerance, in the physiological state of the organism. Studies performed at the Yorktown, Virginia plant of the Virginia Electric and Power Company indicated that while phytoplankton were not killed during transport, the photosynthetic rate was significantly increased, and that this increase depended on the ambient temperature of the stream as well as on the thermal shock imposed by the condensers. Increased photosynthesis prevailed when ambient temperatures were low, but was markedly depressed during summer months when ambient temperatures were high. The greater the temperature rise in the summer, the greater the depression of the photosynthetic rate.

Indirect effects of entrainment must also be considered. Exposure to cooling-system stress may not affect the transported organism directly but may affect its reproductive cycle. Studies of the Patuxent Estuary, for example, show a significant decrease in hatchability of embryos of zooplankton after passage through a thermal power plant.[16] In this instance, the species affected were major food organisms of fish in the estuary.

Despite an increase in research efforts during the last 25 years, the effects of temperature on specific ecological relationships are still not well understood. Upper temperature limits have been established for most valuable types of marine life, but there is still dispute concerning long-range changes and imbalances attributable to incremental increases in the temperature of natural bodies of water. It is quite likely that utilities will be required to undertake extensive studies before discharging waste heat into natural bodies of water. Future studies must determine the significance of an observed plant-induced impact with respect to the continued functioning of the aquatic ecosystem in question. Quantification of impact through descriptive/predictive mathematical modeling technology will be required to assess the significance of ecological impact of both once-through and cooling tower cooling systems.

Water quality effects

Physical Composition. As water absorbs waste heat in the power plant cooling system, the resulting temperature increase often leads to a decrease in the quantity of oxygen dissolved in the water (dissolved oxygen). The maximum amounts of dissolved oxygen that water can hold at various temperatures (saturation values) are given in Table 12. These higher water temperatures also tend to stimulate the growth of biological organisms: specifically, their respiratory rate increases. As dissolved oxygen becomes less available, then, the demand for it increases. In practice, though, unless the cooling water contains a significant amount of oxygen-demanding organic matter, it is unlikely that a reduction in dissolved oxygen due to increased water temperature would kill many aquatic organisms. Nor is the situation as bad as the theory implies. The dissolved oxygen content of discharge water from many operating power plants remains relatively unchanged and sometimes even increases.[17] And even where dissolved oxygen levels are reduced, these reductions are rarely critical in terms of fish survival.

TABLE 12 Saturation Values of Dissolved Oxygen at Various Temperatures

Temperature		
°F	°C	Dissolved oxygen, ppm*
32	0	14.5
41	5	12.8
50	10	11.3
59	15	10.1
68	20	9.2
77	25	8.3
86	30	7.6

*Equivalent to mg/l.

Perhaps a more real threat to aquatic life is an overabundance of dissolved gases. While most fish can survive in water supersaturated with oxygen (up to 300 percent), an increase in nitrogen content as small as 25 percent above the supersaturation level may result in significant mortalities.

Chemical Composition. Residual chlorine species (mono-, di-, and trichloramine) represent perhaps the most common, though not thoroughly studied, chemical threat to fish and the lower phyla.

Several laboratory studies relating to the effects of residual chlorine on the lower aquatic organisms have been performed, but few field observations have been made. Field data, where available,[15,18] indicate that although all phytoplankton passing through a power plant are destroyed during chlorination, no significant overall population changes can be attributed to this mortality.

A second source of potential chemical stress arises from the chemicals commonly injected into cooling tower recirculating water to protect against scaling, fouling, and corrosion. The concentrations of these chemicals (zinc, chromates, phosphates, and organics) are summarized in Table 13.[19] The gap between typical cooling tower concentrations and concentrations considered appropriate for discharge to receiving waters by various regulatory agencies clearly indicates that blowdown streams require substantial treatment prior to discharge.

The toxicity of zinc is well known: 4.29 mg/l will reduce the population growth of *Nitzschia linearis*[20] in the presence of 44 mg/l Ca-Mg by 50 percent. The degree of toxicity, however, is virtually impossible to characterize because it depends so much on the pH and on the calcium and magnesium concentrations of water—parameters which vary widely from water body to water body.

Chromium, particularly in the hexavalent (chromate) state, is a major current concern because data are beginning to indicate a toxic effect on both plants and animals. Although bluegills have survived for 20 days at concentrations of 45 mg/l,[21] a cumulative toxicity to trout and salmon has been demonstrated.[22] *Daphnia* and *Microregma* show a preliminary reaction to hexavalent chromium at concentrations of 16 to 700 ppm. And even though sublethal chromium concentrations can stimulate algae growth in receiving streams, chromium can also inhibit growth.[20,23] For example, 50 percent reductions in population growth of *Nitzschia linearis* have been observed at Cr^{+6} concentrations of 0.2 mg/l.

Phosphorus is probably the most publicized water pollutant of this decade and, as in the case of many pollutants, its environmental influence is complex and poorly understood. An essential element for both plant and animal growth, phosphorus can also stimulate growth to an unacceptable degree. At least 50 μg/l of phosphorus or more in a receiving stream can result in the undesirable appearance of algae.

Perhaps more complex still is the influence of, or median tolerance limit of, the large number of organic compounds used as fungicides and algicides. The 48-hr median tolerance limits for various species in milligrams per liter are summarized in Table 14.[20] Generally, one one-hundredth of the limit is a conservative estimate of a safe continuous exposure level.

Thermal effects The effects of temperature changes on aquatic organisms have been studied extensively and several comprehensive bibliographies are available[24–26] Theoretically, any species can exist over a wide temperature range. This range, de-

TABLE 13 Waste Disposal Characteristics of Cooling Tower Inhibitor—Biocide Systems[18]

Inhibitor system	Concentration in recirculating water	Stream standards	Ratio blowdown concentrated stream standard
Chromate only	200–500 as CrO_4	0.05 as CrO_4*	10,000
		3.0 as Cr*	80§
Zinc	8–35 as Zn	5.0 as Zn*	7
		0.05 as Zn†	35
Chromate	17–65 as CrO_4	0.05 as CrO_4*	1,300
		3.0 as Cr*	10§
Chromate	10–15 as CrO_4	0.05 as CrO_4*	300
		3.0 as Cr*	2§
Phosphate	30–45 as PO_4	0.3 as PO_4 †,¶	150
Zinc	8–35 as Zn	5.0 as Zn*	7
		0.05 as Zn†	35
Phosphate	15–60 as PO_4	0.3 as PO_4†,¶	200
Zinc	8–35 as Zn	5.0 as Zn*	7
		0.05 as Zn†	35
Phosphate	15–60 as PO_4	0.3 as PO_4†,¶	200
Phosphate	15–60 as PO_4	0.3 as PO_4†,¶	200
Organic	3–10 as organic	(See below)	
Organic only	100–200 as organic		
	10 est. as BOD	20 as BOD*	
	100 est. as COD	40 as COD	2.5
	50 est. as CCl_4 extract	0.2 as exotic organic*	250
	5 est. as MBAS	0.5†	10
Organic Biocide	30 as chlorophenol	0.2 as phenol	100
	5 as sulfone	0.1 as is (est.)	50
	1 as thiocynate	5.0 as SCN (est.)	

* Pennsylvania Industrial Waste Manual, San. Engr. Publication No. 14.
† Pennsylvania Rules and Regulations.
‡ California Water Quality Criteria WPCB Publication No. 3.
§ Ratio for equivalent amount of reduced chrome.
¶ Illinois Technical Release 20-22, San. Water Board 20-22 (April 1, 1968).

fined by "upper" and "lower" lethal levels beyond which normal development and survival will be impaired, is called the *zone of thermal tolerance*. Laboratory studies have been concerned primarily with delineating upper and lower lethal developmental temperatures for a variety of different species, but few studies have attempted to define thermal tolerance with respect to sudden and brief exposure. The ambient water temperature to which organisms have become acclimated or acclimatized is of extreme importance in establishing the ultimate upper lethal temperature for the species.

The temperatures of the effluent may fluctuate over a daily cycle, for example, and these fluctuations may be more stressful for aquatic life than constant high temperatures. Acclimation not only raises the upper lethal temperature, it also raises the lower lethal temperature. Thus, shutdown of a plant or displacement of a discharge plume may spell death to fish if this reduces the water temperature below the fish's new lower lethal temperature.

Aquatic organisms exposed to a thermal plume may display a preference for a water temperature of their choice. In evaluating the impact of thermal plumes on the various characteristics of biological life, three factors should be considered:[27] temperature tolerance, ability to accommodate to changes in the ambient environ-

TABLE 14 Fourty-eight hour Median Tolerance Limits for Herbicides, Fungicides, Defoliants, Algicides[20]

Pesticide	Stream invertebrate*		*Cladocerans*†		Fish‡		*Gammarus lacustris*, TLm[3]
	Species	TLm	Species	TLm	Species	TLm	
Ametryne					Rainbow trout	3,400	
Aminotriazole							
Aquathol					Bluegill	257	
Atrazine			*Daphnia magna*	3,600	Rainbow t.	12,600	
Azide, potassium					Bluegill	1,400	10,000
Azide, sodium					Bluegill	980	9,000
Copper chloride					Bluegill	1,100	
Copper sulfate					Bluegill	150	
Dichlobenil	*Pteronarcys californica*	44,000	*Daphnia pulex*	3,700	Bluegill	20,000	1,500
2,4-D PGBEE			*D. pulex*	3,200	Rainbow t.	960	1,800
2,4-D BEE	*P. californica*	1,800			Bluegill	2,100	760
2,4-D isopropyl					Bluegill	800	
2,4-D butyl ester					Bluegill	1,300	
2,4-D butyl + isopropyl ester.					Bluegill	1,500	
2,4,5-T isooctyl ester					Bluegill	16,700	
2,4,5-T isopropyl ester					Bluegill	1,700	
2,4,5-T PGBE					Bluegill	560	
2(2,4-DP) BEE					Bluegill	1,100	
Dalapon	*P. californica* Very low toxicity		*D. magna*	6,000		Very low toxicity	
Dead-X	*P. californica*	5,000	*D. pulex*	3,700	Rainbow t.	9,400	5,600
DEF	*P. californica*	2,300			Bluegill	36	230
Dexon	*P. californica*	42,000			Bluegill	23,000	6,000
Dicamba					Nontoxic		5,800
Dichlone			*D. magna*	26	Rainbow t.	48	11,500
Difolitan	*P. californica*	150			Channel cat	31	6,500

Dinitrocresol	*P. californica*	560			Rainbow t.	210	
Diquat					Rainbow t.	12,300	
Diuron	*P. californica*	2,800	*D. pulex*	1,400	Rainbow t.	4,300	380
Du-ter					Bluegill	33	
Dyrene			*D. magna*	490		15	
Endothal, copper					Rainbow t.	290	
Endothal, dimethylamine					Rainbow t.	1,150	
Fenac, acid	*P. californica*	70,000			Rainbow t.	16,500	
Fenac, sodium	*P. californica*	80,000	*D. pulex*	4,500	Rainbow t.	7,500	18,000
Hydram (molinate)	*P. californica*	3,500			Rainbow t.	290	
Hydrothol 191					Rainbow t.	690	1,000
Lanstan (korax)					Rainbow t.	100	5,500
LFN					Rainbow t.	79	
Paraquat	*P. californica*		*D. pulex*	3,700	Very low toxicity		18,000
	Very low toxicity						
Propazine					Rainbow t.	7,800	
Silvex, PGBEE			*D. pulex*	2,000	Rainbow t.	650	
Silvex, isoctyl					Bluegill	1,400	
Silvex, BEE					Bluegill	1,200	
Simazine	*P. californica*	50,000			Rainbow t.	5,000	21,000
Sodium arsenite	*P. californica*		*Simocephalus serrulatus*	1,400	Rainbow t.	36,500	
	Very low toxicity						
Tordon (picloram)					Rainbow t.	2,500	48,000
Trifuralin	*P. californica*	4,200	*D. pulex*	240	Rainbow t.	11	5,600
Vernam¶ (vernolate)					Rainbow t.	5,900	25,000

*Stonefly bioassay was done at Denver, Colo., and at Salt Lake City, Utah. Denver tests were in soft water (35 mg/l TDS), nonaerated, 60°F. Salt Lake City tests were in hard water (150 mg/l TDS), aerated, 48 to 50°F. Response was death.

† *Daphnia pulex* and *Simocephalus serrulatus* bioassay was done at Denver, Colo., in soft water (35 mg/l TDS), nonaerated, 60°F. *Daphnia magna* bioassay was done at Pennsylvania State University in hard water (146 mg/l TDS), nonareated, 68°F. Response was immobilization.

‡ Fish bioassay was done at Denver, Colo., and at Rome, N.Y. Denver tests were with 2-in. fish in soft water (35 mg/l TDS), nonaerated; trout at 55°F. other species at 65°F. Rome tests were with 2- to 2½-in. fish in soft water (6 mg/l TA: pH 5.85 to 6.4), 60°F. Response was death.

; *Gammarus* bioassay was done at Denver, Colo., in soft water (35 mg/l TDS), nonaerated, 60°F. Response was death.

¶ Becomes bound to soil when used according to directions, but highly toxic (reflected in numbers) when added directly to water.

ment, and avoidance reactions. Fish kills due solely to thermal addition occur only when these three protective mechanisms fail.

A temperature increase does not necessarily have to result in immediate death; it can be detrimental to aquatic organisms in a variety of ways. The organisms could die as a direct result of exposure to very high temperatures. Alternatively, the elevated temperature may alter the physical environment, thus indirectly killing the organism. These indirect effects may include a change in dissolved gas content, elimination of a food source, the inability of the organism to catch available food, a lowering of reproductive potential, an increased susceptibility to disease or poisoning, or stimulated growth and reproduction in otherwise unproductive winter waters.

Observations made at a number of operating power plants indicate that fish tend to move toward a thermal discharge in colder months and away from it during summer months. And it is well established that most aquatic organisms, when free to move in a gradient of temperature, tend to congregate in areas where a relatively narrow range of temperature exists. Movement of organisms to avoid dangerous temperatures has been documented at many power plants operating with saltwater, as well as fresh cooling water.[24]

In the presence of a thermal plume, the number and species composition of benthic organisms partially or completely lacking the avoidance reaction (such as rooted aquatic plants, insect larvae, and oysters) would generally be altered.[24] More mobile benthic invertebrates (such as crabs and lobsters) would be less affected. Although these effects have been documented, their ecological significance is seriously contested since only relatively small bottom areas are adversely affected and then primarily during the warmer months of the year. Also, during winter months when discharge water temperatures are more favorable, considerable regrowth and recolonization occur. For example, at the Turkey Point site of the Florida Power and Light Company, the zone of complete or partial benthic degradation consisted of several hundred acres during the warmer summer months but less than 100 acres during the winter.

Surface Plume Discharge. Surface plume discharges primarily affect fish. Depending on the preferred temperature range for a particular species, fish confronted with a thermal discharge may elect to stay within the warmer areas or may avoid the thermal discharge entirely. With this mobility, adult fish should not be affected adversely provided that deleterious temperatures do not extend throughout the entire water mass.

Accumulated data on thermal responses of fish show a discernible upper and lower zone of thermal resistance and a central zone of thermal tolerance bonded respectively above and below by an upper and lower *incipient lethal temperature*.[28] This incipient lethal temperature is defined as the temperature which, when fish are brought instantaneously to it from a different temperature, will kill a stated fraction of the population (generally, 50 percent is used) within an indefinitely prolonged exposure.

Effect of Deep Discharges of Heated Effluent. An attractive alternative to a shoreline discharge is a submerged effluent pipe which carries the discharge into deep water some distance from shore or, in the case of rivers, at the bottom of midchannel. This is biologically advantageous because it minimizes shoreline effects and the contact of hot water with bottom communities.

Delivery of the heated effluent to the "mainstream" of river flow or tidal water currents enhances mixing and dispersion, which rapidly lowers temperatures. One disadvantage, however, is that rapid mixing by deep discharge reduces the net temperature difference between the surface water and air, decreasing the heat-transfer rate and causing the heat effects in the river to persist longer. Deep water discharges may also cause other problems such as thermal blocks or dams.

Polluted receiving waters Several thermal power stations have demonstrated that when condenser cooling water is discharged to a stream heavily polluted with organic wastes, the results are dramatic and often fatal to the majority of aquatic organisms. Decomposition of organic matter (such as sewage or pulp mill waste) increases with temperature. This decomposition also uses dissolved oxygen, the availability of which drops as the water temperature rises. For about each 10°C (18°F) rise in temperature, the rate of dissolved oxygen consumption doubles. When the rate of decomposition exceeds the diffusion rate of oxygen from the atmosphere, the dissolved oxygen in the water will be entirely consumed; the result is an area of decomposing material unable to support anything other than the most tolerant species of worms.

Atmospheric Impact

Visible plume To evaluate the potential impact of the various cooling systems on the atmosphere, it is necessary to consider a number of physical parameters. Effluents from natural-draft towers are released at high elevations. This, coupled with the low degree of initial turbulence and high buoyancy and high momentum, results in a relatively high plume rise. Mechanical-draft tower plumes originate at much lower elevations, have a higher degree of initial turbulence and much less buoyancy. The result is a much lower plume rise and a higher probability for the plume to intercept ground. The length of the natural-draft visible plume is usually greater than the plume of a mechanical-draft tower, however. With cooling lakes, cooling ponds, spray canals, and spray ponds, heat and water vapor are released over much larger areas with lower degrees of turbulence at ground level and forced convection. The ground-level extent of these vapor plumes is usually less than those from mechanical-draft towers but more than those from natural-draft towers. The vertical extent of the plumes depends on the degree of convection and may reach several hundred meters. The new wet/dry cooling tower offers a novel method of reducing the size and frequency of occurrence of the visible vapor plume characteristic of a mechanical-draft tower.

Fog and ice Fogging and icing attributable to cooling systems occur when ambient temperatures are low and humidity is high. Fogging and icing with natural-draft towers are minimal; they occur more frequently with mechanical-draft towers. In both cases, fog persistence typically will be 2 to 4 hr. With mechanical-draft towers, fog episodes attributable to the cooling system can be expected up to 100 to 150 days per year and with natural-draft towers up to about 20 to 40 days per year, depending on ambient atmospheric conditions at the selected site.

Most tower-related fog is produced in the winter and early spring between 2 and 10 A.M. In extreme cases, visibility can be reduced to 300 m or less. At near- or below-freezing ambient temperatures, the fog droplets freeze, creating layers of low-density rime ice when the vapor plume intercepts vertical or ground surfaces.

While ground fog from cooling ponds[29] can extend up to about 2 km downwind, 50 m is a more common figure. Stratus fog, when it occurs, can extend more than 16 km. Ice buildup on vertical surfaces ranges from about 0.2 to about 1.6 mm/hr and can extend 10 to 60 m downwind.

To date, no major environmental problems associated with fog, icing, or cloud formation from spray canals have been observed.[30] Spray-induced fog can rise up to about 60 to 80 m and will extend in the form of thin fog up to a maximum of 3 to 4 km downwind.

Comparative effects of cooling systems A comparison of the various environmental effects created by the cooling systems used by electric power plants to dissipate waste heat is summarized in Table 15.

TABLE 15 Summary of the Atmospheric Effects of Cooling Systems

Cooling system	Extent of visible plume	Extent of Ground fog	Ice	Drift deposition
Cooling towers:				
Natural-draft	High	Low	Low	Low
Mechanical-draft	Moderate to high	Moderate to high	Moderate to high	Moderate to high
Wet dry	Minimal	Minimal	Minimal	Minimal
Dry	None	None	None	None
Cooling lake or pond	Moderate to low	Moderate to low	High but localized	None
Spray systems	Moderate to low	Moderate to low	High but localized	Moderate to high but localized

BENEFICIAL USES OF POWER PLANT DISCHARGES

The physical and biological changes induced by discharging heated cooling water to bodies of water are not all detrimental. Indeed, it should be possible to turn waste heat into a valuable resource. At present capacity levels, for example, there is already more than enough waste heat to heat all the homes in the United States. But because of the relatively low intensity level of this heat, the most promising uses appear to be biological and biochemical processes and, perhaps, some chemical and physical processes.

Urban Applications

The viability of using waste heat for heating and air-conditioning systems has been demonstrated in Iceland where 187°F water from geothermal discharges is transported 10 mi to Reykjavik. The key to waste-heat utilization for air conditioning is an ammonia or lithium bromide absorption refrigeration mechanism. The ammonia-water system uses an air-cooled condenser and absorber that requires a heat supply at 250°F. The lithium bromide, which requires a heat supply at 220°F, is about 50 percent more efficient. These heat-driven air conditioners are easily modified to supply hot water at 150 to 170°F for space heating during the cold seasons.

For a new city, thermal energy could be transmitted underground to substations throughout the city, each of which would contain absorption refrigeration equipment. From the substation, the thermal energy would be distributed to the living and working spaces for one or more large buildings or for a cluster of single residences or townhouses. Within each building or residence, a very simple system would control the environmental temperature. Unused energy would be discharged to the air via heat exchangers on the roofs of the substations or large buildings. This form of heat dissipation is superior to the dry cooling tower approach since the rate of discharge per unit area is much less.

The temperature of the average thermal discharge could be raised to the 220°F required for a lithium bromide air-conditioning system by extracting supplemental heat from the plant's turbine cycle. For a 1,000-MWe nuclear plant, this would take about 20 percent of the electrical generating capacity, or about 200 MWe—a small cost compared with the saving of 2,000 MW of heat which would otherwise be wasted in a once-through cooling system.

Using waste heat to deice and defog airports has also been considered. Although technically feasible, this use of waste heat is not economical.

Sewage Treatment

Condenser discharge could also be used in the aeration system designed to improve the water quality of a river by increasing its oxygen content. These aeration systems are being used more and more to improve water quality and are being viewed increasingly as an alternative to tertiary sewage treatment facilities. A small percentage of the condenser discharge would be diverted into separate loops where it would be pressurized with pure oxygen. The oxygen-rich stream would then be returned to the condenser discharge and ultimately to the river. The resultant increase in dissolved oxygen should improve the aquatic environment.

The heated discharge could also improve the rate and effectiveness of secondary sewage treatment processes which are strongly temperature-dependent. The most common form of secondary sewage treatment used in the United States is the activated sludge process. Sewage, prescreened for grit removal and subjected to preliminary settling, is fed into an aeration tank where it reacts with water, carbon dioxide, and sludge. The average temperature of domestic and most industrial sewage in the United States is approximately 70°F with usually not more than a 5 F° seasonal variation. A 10 C° (18 F°) rise in temperature will approximately double the biochemical reaction rate. The increase in temperature also decreases the water viscosity, thereby enhancing the sedimentation of activated sludge particles. If the sewage temperature could be raised from 70 to 95°F, then, theoretically, the sewage treatment rate could be doubled.

Transferring waste heat to the sewage would be done most efficiently by routing prefiltered sewage through a portion of the power plant condenser. The water header would, of course, be modified to keep the flows separate.

For a fossil-fuel plant, not only the heat but the fuel could be used in sewage treatment. A system in which raw sewage or secondary-treated sewage is filtered through coal has successfully been demonstrated in pilot-plant operation. Filtering secondary-treated waste through a coal filter reduces the biochemical oxygen demand (BOD) of the effluent to about 5 percent. Such a system would require only 1 ton of coal per 1 million gal of sewage, and the sludge accumulated on the coal filter bed would burn easily in any high-temperature boiler.

Aquaculture

One of the most promising ways of using waste heat is in aquacultural projects, particularly fish or invertebrate "farms." Warm-water aquaculture is attractive for many reasons. The metabolic and growth rate of poikilothermic or cold-blooded aquatic organisms increases dramatically with temperature, provided the chosen temperature lies within the thermal tolerance range for the species being cultured. The North American lobster, for example, which normally takes 5 to 8 years to reach marketable size, can be reared to maturity within 18 to 36 months at optimum temperatures.

But accelerated growth does not result from increased temperature alone. The increased metabolic rate requires an increased food supply, and more dissolved oxygen is required for respiration. In addition to warm water, the power plant can provide, on a continuous basis, great volumes of oxygen-laden water. This same water would also transport toxic metabolic waste products from the rearing facility.

Some work still needs to be done on the use of thermal effluents for aquaculture. Many materials used in the construction of power plant cooling systems are toxic to aquatic life, particularly in immature stages.

More research needs to be done on "optimum" temperature requirements for particular selected species. The food consumption of the brown trout, for example, is highest when the fish are held between 50 and 60°F. But within this range, fish are so active that the energy derived from a relatively large portion of food intake is required just to maintain the increased level of activity of bodily function.

Food is, in fact, a major problem confronting the fledgling American aquaculture industry. The quality of feed is of extreme importance. The great differences in food conversion ratios of various feeds are closely correlated with nutritive compositions. As well as the composition of the feed, the form is of considerable importance, particularly in the rearing of marine and freshwater crustaceans.

Despite these difficulties, a number of power-plant-associated aquaculture programs are in existence. In the United States, Long Island Lighting Company and Northeast Utilities are experimenting with oysters; Texas Electric Service Company with catfish; a Louisiana utility is studying the freshwater crayfish; and several utlities (Boston Edison Company, Central Maine Power Company, New England Electric Systems, Northeast Utilities, and San Diego Gas and Electric Company) are involved to various degrees in lobster farming.

Agriculture

In several areas, the use of waste heat for agricultural purposes extends growing seasons and gives the farmer greater control in planning his harvest.

In an Oregon demonstration project sponsored by the Eugene Water and Electric Board, crops and fruit trees were spray-irrigated with warm effluent from a paper plant to prevent frost and extend the growing season. By providing protection against temperatures down to 27°F, farmers were able to introduce strawberries to the market 10 days earlier than normal, resulting in a 25 percent increase in profit. A 1,000-MWe nuclear plant could irrigate about 100,000 acres with heated water.

Alternatively, warm effluent could be pumped through buried piping systems to heat greenhouse soil and improve growth of root crops. Most root crops do best at soil temperatures about 70°F, with optimum temperature about 75°F. Experiments are currently under way at Oregon State University on a laboratory scale.

REFERENCES

1. Boyle, R. R.: Cooling Water Requirements, presented at 1971 Electric Utility Conf., March 14–26, 1971.
2. Ross, Philip N.: Implications of the Nuclear-Electric Economy, presented by the panel on Possible Impact of Research on the Electric Power Industry at the Conf. on Research for the Electric Power Industry, Washington, D.C., December 11, 1972, p. 2.
3. Ibid., p. 5.
4. U.S. Environmental Protection Agency: Effluent Limitation Guidelines for Steam-Electric Power-generating Point Source Category, 40 CFR 423; 39 FR 36186, October 8, 1974, effective November 7, 1974; 40 FR 7095, February 19, 1975; 40 FR 23987, June 4, 1975.
5. Roffman, A., et al.: "The State of the Art of Saltwater Cooling Towers for Steam Electric Generating Plants," Westinghouse Electric Corp., Environmental Systems Dept., prepared for the U.S. Atomic Energy Commission, Division of Reactor Development and Technology under Contract No. AT[11-1]-2221, February 1973.
6. Ibid., p. 9.
7. Ibid., p. 10.
8. Hauser, L. G.: Waste Heat Management in the Electric Utility Industry, Eng. Rept. GEN68-002, Westinghouse Electric Corp., Electric Utility Dept., March 1968.
9. Atwood, K. E., and W. R. Greenaway: "Flyash Handling Systems Study," submitted to Utility Water Act Group, June 1975.
10. Goldstein, P.: Control of Chemical Discharges for the Steam Electric Power Industry, presented at Conf. Water Quality—Considerations for Steam-Electric Power Plants, Atomic Industrial Forum, Inc., Phoenix, Ariz., January 1975.
11. Rice, J. K.: Zero Aqueous Discharge Steam Electric Power Plant Cooling Systems, presented at International Energy Eng. Congress, Chicago, November 1975.
12. McKee and Wolf: Publication 96–3, 2d ed., The Resources Agency of California State Water Quality Control Board, Sacramento, Calif.
13. Rice, J. K.: Water Management to Eliminate Water Waste, presented at Petroleum Mechanical Eng. Conf., American Society of Mechanical Engineers, New Orleans, September 1966.
14. U.S. Environmental Protection Agency: "Development Document for Effluent Limitations Guidelines and New Source Performance Standards for the Steam-Electric Power-generating Point Source Category," October 1974.
15. "Comments on EPA's proposed SS 304 Guidelines and SS 306 Standards of Performance for Steam Electric Power Plants," Utility Water Act Group, Vol. 3, June 1974.
16. Marcy, B. C.: Survival of Young Fish in the Discharge Canal of a Nuclear Power Plant, *J. Fish Res. Board of Canada,* vol. 28, no. 7, pp. 1057–1060, 1971.
17. Lauer, G., and P. N. Bibko: Effects of Acute Thermal Shock upon Various Embryonic and Larval Stages of the Striped Bass (*Morone saxitalis*), *Proc. 3d Ann. Workshop on Entrainment and Entrapment Effects,* The Johns Hopkins University, Baltimore, Md., March 1973.
18. Heinle, D. R.: Temperature and Zooplankton, *Proc. 2d Thermal Workshop of the U.S. International Biological Program, reprinted in Chesapeake Science,* vol. 19, no. 3–4, pp. 96–209 (1969).
19. Markowski, S.: The Cooling Water of Power Stations. A New Factor in the Environment of Marine and Freshwater Invertebrates, *J. Animal Ecology,* vol. 28, no. 2, pp. 243–248 (1959).
20. Hamilton, D. H., et al.: Power Plants: Effects on Estuarine Primary Production, *Science,* vol. 169, pp. 197–198 (1970).
21. "Industrial Process Design for Water Pollution Control," American Institute of Chemical Engineers, Houston, Texas, 1969.
22. "Water Quality Criteria," Report of the National Technical Advisory Committee to the Secretary of the Interior, April 1968.
23. Doudoroff, P., and M. Katz: Critical Review of Literature on the Toxicity of Industrial Wastes and Their Components on Fish. II. Metal as Salts, *Sew. Ind. Wastes,* vol. 25, no. 7, pp. 802–839, 1953.
24. Olson, P. A., and R. F. Foster: Effect of Chronic Exposure to Sodium Dichromate on Young Chinook Salmon and Rainbow Trout, in Hanford Biological Res. Ann. Rep. for 1955, HW-41500, unclassified, Hanford Atomic Products Operation, Richland, Wash., pp. 35–47, 1956.
25. Hervey, R. K.: Effect of Chromium on the Growth of Unicellular Chlorophyceae and Diatoms, *Bot. Gaz.,* vol. 111, no. 1, pp. 1–11, 1949.

26. Trembley, F. J.: 1960 Research Projection, Effects of Condenser Discharge Water on Aquatic Life, Lehigh University, Bethlehem, Pa., *Inst. Res. Prog. Rept.*, 1956–1959.
27. Kennedy, V. S., and J. A. Mihursky: "A Bibliography on the Effects of Temperature on the Aquatic Environment," University of Maryland, Nat. Res. Inst., Contract No. 326, mimeo. 1969.
28. Raney, E. C., B. W. Menzel, and E. C. Weller: Heated Effluents and Effects on Aquatic Life with Emphasis on Fishes, *Ichthyological Assoc. Bull. No.* 9, U.S. Atomic Energy Commission, Office of Information Services, Technical Information Center, Washington, D.C., 1969.
29. Krenkel, P. A., and F. L. Parker (eds.): *Biological Aspects of Thermal Pollution,* Vanderbilt University Press, Nashville, Tenn., 1969.
30. Fry, F. E., J. S. Hart, and K. F. Walker: Lethal Temperature Relations for a Sample of Young Speckled Trout, *Salvelinus frontinalis, University of Toronto, Stud. Biol. Serv. 54,* vol. 66, pp. 1–35, 1946.
31. Currier, E. L., J. B. Knox, and T. V. Crawford: Cooling Pond Steam Fog, paper 73–126, 66th Ann. Mtg. Air Pollution Control Assoc., Chicago, June 24–28, 1973.
32. Carson, J. E.: The Atmospheric Consequences of Thermal Discharges from Power Generating Stations, Ann. Rept., Radiological Physics Div., Argonne National Laboratory, 1971.

Chapter 11

Effluent Guidelines and Standards

LEE HENRY

Director of Laboratories, The Mogul Corporation,
Chagrin Falls, Ohio

INTRODUCTION

The effluent guidelines and standards table has been placed in this chapter for the convenience of the reader. This table will cover the Best Practicable Control Technology Currently Available, Best Available Technology Economically Achievable plus the New Source Standards of Performance.

The units of each industry are presented (Table 1) prior to the table to give meaning to the numbers.

Two descriptions of products and processes involving the Organic Chemicals Manufacturing category are included prior to the table. The purpose is to give a better understanding of that section of the table.

TABLE 1 Effluent Guidelines and Standards Units

Point source category	Metric	English
1. Pulp, paper, and paperboard	kg/1,000 kg of product	lb/ton of product
2. Builders paper and roofing felt segment of the builders paper and board mills	kg/1,000 kg of product	lb/ton of product
3a. Meat products General	kg/1,000 kg LWK*	lb/1,000 lb LWK
3b. Meat products Small processor	kg/1,000 kg of finished product	lb/1,000 lb of finished product
4. Dairy products	kg/1,000 kg of BOD_5 input	lb/100 lb of BOD_5 input
5. Grain mills	kg/1,000 kg of corn, wheat, rice, or other product	lb/1,000 stdbu† corn lb/1,000 stdbu wheat lb/100 cwt of rice lb/1,000 lb cereal lb/1,000 lb of raw material (wheat flour)
6. Canned and preserved fruits and vegetables processing industry	kg/1,000 kg of raw material	lb/1,000 lb of raw material

TABLE 1 Effluent Guidelines and Standards Units (Continued)

Point source category	Metric	English
7. Canned and preserved fruits and vegetables processing industry	kg/1,000 kg of raw material	lb/1,000 lb of raw material
8a. Beet sugar processing	kg/1,000 kg of product	lb/1,000 lb of product
8b. Liquid and crystalline cane sugar refining	kg/1,000 kg of melt	lb/ton of melt
9. Textile industry	kg/1,000 kg of product	lb/1,000 lb of product
10. Cement manufacturing		
Subpart A	kg/1,000 kg of product	lb/1,000 lb of product
Subpart B	kg/1,000 kg of dust leached	lb/1,000 lb of dust leached
11. Feedlots, Subpart B	kg/1,000 ducks	lb/1,000 ducks
12. Electroplating copper, nickel, chromium, and zinc on ferrous and nonferrous materials	mg/m^2 per operation	lb/million sq ft per operation
13. Organic chemicals	kg/1,000 kg of product	lb/1,000 lb of product
14. Inorganic chemicals		
Subpart B	mg/l	ppm
Subpart D	kg/1,000 kg of product	lb/1,000 lb of product
15. Plastics and synthetics	kg/1,000 kg of product	lb/1,000 lb of product
16. Soap and detergent manufacturing	kg/1,000 kg of anhydrous product	lb/1,000 lb of anhydrous product
17. Fertilizer manufacturing		
Subpart A	mg/l	ppm
Subparts B to E	kg/1,000 kg of product	lb/1,000 lb of product
18. Petroleum refining	kg/1,000 m^3 of feedstock Ballast (only) kg/m^3 of flow	lb/1,000 bbl of feedstock lb/1,000 gal of flow
19. Iron and steel manufacturing	kg/1,000 kg of product	lb/1,000 lb of product
20. Nonferrous metals manufacturing	kg/1,000 kg of product	lb/1,000 lb of product
21. Phosphate manufacturing	kg/1,000 kg of product	lb/1,000 lb of product
22. Steam electric power generating	mg/l	None
23. Ferroalloy manufacturing		
Subparts A, B	kg/MWh‡	lb/MWh
Subpart C	kg/1,000 kg processed	lb/ton processed

TABLE 1 Effluent Guidelines and Standards Units (Continued)

Point source category	Metric	English
24. Leather tanning and finishing	kg/1,000 kg of raw material	lb/1,000 lb of raw material
25a. Glass manufacturing		
Subpart A	kg/1,000 kg of product	lb/1,000 lb of product
Subpart E to G	g/1,000 kg of product	lb/ton of product
Subpart H to L	g/1,000 kg of furnace pull	lb/1,000 lb of furnace pull
Subpart M	mg/l	None
25b. Asbestos manufacturing	kg/1,000 kg of product	lb/ton of product
Subpart G	kg/mpc§ of product	lb/mpc of product
26. Rubber processing	kg/1,000 kg of product	lb/1,000 lb of product
27. Timber processing		
Subpart A, B	kg/cu m of product	lb/cu ft of product
Subpart E	kg/1,000 kg of product	lb/2,000 lb of product
Subpart G	kg/1,000 m^3 of product	lb/1,000 ft^3 of product
Subpart I	centimeter	inch
Subpart N, O	kg/1,000 kg of product	lb/2,000 lb of product

* LWK = live weight killed.
† stdbu = standard bushel.
‡ MWh = megawatt hours.
§ mpc = 1,000 pieces of floor tile.

ORGANIC CHEMICALS MANUFACTURING

The following is a description of products and processes involved in Organic Chemicals Manufacturing. Series I represents "nonaqueous processes subcategory" as noted in Subpart A of the Organic Chemicals Manufacturing title.

Series II represents "processes with process water contact as steam diluent or absorbent subcategory," as noted in Subpart B of the Organic Chemicals Manufacturing title.

Series I

The provisions of this subpart are applicable to discharge of process wastewater resulting from the manufacture of the following products:

Product	*Process Description*
BTX aromatics	Hydrotreatment of pyrolysis gasoline
BTX aromatics	Solvent extraction from reformate
Cyclohexane	Hydrogenation of benzene
Vinyl chloride	Addition of hydrochloric acid to acetylene

Series II

The provisions of this subpart are applicable to discharges of process wastewater resulting from the manufacture of the following products:

B1 Product	*B1 Process Description*
Acetone	Dehydrogenation of isopropanol
Butadiene	Coproduct of ethylene
Ethyl benzene	Alkylation of benzene with ethylene
Ethyl and propylene	Pyrolysis of naphtha or liquid petroleum gas
Ethylene dichloride	Direct chlorination of ethylene
Ethylene oxide	Catalytic oxidation of ethylene
Formaldehyde	Oxidation of methanol
Methanol	Steam reforming of natural gas
Methyl amines	Addition of ammonia to methane
Vinyl acetate	Synthesis of ethylene and acetic acid
Vinyl chloride	Cracking of ethylene dichloride

B2 Product	*B2 Process Description*
Acetaldehyde	Dehydrogenation of ethanol
Acetylene	Partial oxidation of methane
Butadiene	Dehydrogenation of *n*-butane
Butadiene	Oxidative-dehydrogenation of *n*-butane
Styrene	Dehydrogenation of ethyl benzene

TABLE 2 Effluent Guidelines and Standards

Category	Subpart	Effluent characteristic	BPCTCA effluent limitations: Maximum for any 1 day M[a]	E[a]	BPCTCA: Average of daily values for 30 consecutive days shall not exceed M	E	BATEA effluent limitations: Maximum for any 1 day M	E	BATEA: Average of daily values for 30 consecutive days shall not exceed M	E	New source standards of performance: Maximum for any 1 day M	E	New source: Average of daily values for 30 consecutive days shall not exceed M	E
1. Pulp, paper and paperboard	Subpart A	BOD_5	5.6	11.2	2.8	5.6	2.7	5.4	1.35	2.7	3.1	6.2	1.55	3.1
Subpart A Unbleached Kraft[1]		TSS	12.0	24.0	6.0	12.0	3.7	7.4	1.85	3.7	7.5	15.0	3.75	7.5
		pH	6.0–9.0		6.0–9.0		6.0–9.0		6.0–9.0		6.0–9.0		6.0–9.0	
		Color					15.0	30.0	10.0	20.0	15.0	30.0	10.0	20.0
Subpart B Sodium-based neutral sulfite semichemical	Subpart B	BOD_5	8.7	17.4	4.35	8.7	4.5	9.0	2.25	4.5	5.2	10.4	2.6	5.2
		TSS	11.0	22.0	5.5	11.0	5.0	10.0	2.5	5.0	7.7	15.4	3.85	7.7
		pH	6.0–9.0		6.0–9.0		6.0–9.0		6.0–9.0		6.0–9.0		6.0–9.0	
		Color					75% removal							
Subpart C Ammonia-based neutral sulfite semichemical	Subpart C	BOD_5	8.0	16.0	4.0	8.0	6.4	12.8	3.2	6.4	7.5	15.0	3.75	7.5
		TSS	10.0	20.0	5.0	10.0	5.2	10.4	2.6	5.2	7.5	15.0	3.75	7.5
		pH	6.0–9.0		6.0–9.0		6.0–9.0		6.0–9.0		6.0–9.0		6.0–9.0	
		Color					75% removal							
Subpart D Unbleached Kraft neutral sulfite semichemical (cross-recovery)	Subpart D	BOD_5	8.0	16.0	4.0	8.0	3.2	6.4	1.6	3.2	3.8	7.6	1.9	3.8
		TSS	12.5	25.0	6.25	12.5	4.2	8.4	2.1	4.2	8.0	16.0	4.0	8.0
		pH	6.0–9.0		6.0–9.0		6.0–9.0		6.0–9.0		6.0–9.0		6.0–9.0	
		Color					25.0	37.5	12.5	25.0	25.0	37.5	12.5	25.0
Subpart E Paperboard from waste paper	Subpart E	BOD_5	3.0	6.0	1.5	3.0	1.3	2.6	0.65	1.3	1.5	3.0	0.75	1.5
		TSS	5.0	10.0	2.5	5.0	1.6	3.2	0.8	1.6	4.0	8.0	2.0	4.0
		pH	6.0–9.0		6.0–9.0		6.0–9.0		6.0–9.0		6.0–9.0		6.0–9.0	
2a. Builders paper and roofing felt segment of the builders paper and board mills[2,3]	Subpart A	BOD_5	5.0	10.0	3.0	6.0	1.75	3.5	1.0	2.0	1.75	3.5	1.0	2.0
		TSS	5.0	10.0	3.0	6.0	1.75	3.5	1.0	2.0	1.75	3.5	1.0	2.0
		Settable solids	Less than 0.2mg/l	1	Less than 0.2mg/l	1	Less than 0.2mg/l	1	Less than 0.2mg/l	1	Less than 0.2mg/l	1	Less than 0.2mg/l	1

Industry	Subpart	Parameter												
Subpart A Builders paper and roofing felt		pH	6.0–9.0		6.0–9.0		6.0–9.0		6.0–9.0		6.0–9.0		6.0–9.0	
2b. Builders paper and board manufacturing[2,3]	Subpart A	BOD	1.4	2.8	1.0	2.0	1.4	2.8	1.0	2.0	1.4	2.8	1.0	2.0
Subpart A Builders paper and roofing felt		TSS	1.55	3.1	1.0	2.0	1.55	3.1	1.0	2.0	1.55	3.1	1.0	2.0
		pH	6.0–9.0		6.0–9.0		6.0–9.0		6.0–9.0		6.0–9.0		6.0–9.0	
3. Meat products[4,5]	Subpart Aa	BOD_5	0.24	0.24	0.12	0.12	0.06	0.06	0.03	0.03				
Subpart Aa Simple slaughterhouse on-site slaughter		TSS	0.40	0.40	0.20	0.20	0.10	0.10	0.05	0.05				
		Oil and grease	0.12	0.12	0.06	0.06	10 mg/l							
		Fecal coliform	Maximum at any time 400 MPN*/100 ml		Maximum at any time 400 MPN/100 ml		Maximum at any time 400 MPN/100 ml		Maximum at any time 400 MPN/100 ml					
		Ammonia					8.0 mg/l		4.0 mg/l		0.34	0.34	0.17	0.17
		pH	6.0–9.0		6.0–9.0		6.0–9.0		6.0–9.0					
Subpart Ab Simple slaughterhouse defleshing washing and curing	Subpart Ab	BOD_5	0.04	0.04	0.02	0.02								
		TSS	0.08	0.08	0.04	0.04								
Subpart Ac Slaughterhouse blood processing	Subpart Ac	BOD_5	0.04	0.04	0.02	0.02	0.014	0.014	0.007	0.007				
		TSS	0.08	0.08	0.04	0.04	0.026	0.026	0.013	0.013				
		Ammonia									0.06	0.06	0.03	0.03
Subpart Ad Wet or low-temperature rendering of animals slaughtered elsewhere	Subpart Ad	BOD_5	0.06	0.06	0.03	0.03	0.02	0.02	0.01	0.01				
		TSS	0.12	0.12	0.06	0.06	0.04	0.04	0.02	0.02				
		Ammonia									0.01	0.01	0.05	0.05
Subpart Ae Dry rendering of animals slaughtered elsewhere	Subpart Ae	BOD_5	0.02	0.02	0.01	0.01	0.006	0.006	0.003	0.003				
		TSS	0.04	0.04	0.02	0.02	0.014	0.014	0.007	0.007				
		pH	6.0–9.0		6.0–9.0									
		Ammonia									0.04	0.04	0.02	0.02

[a] Metric and English units, see Table 1.

* Most probable number.

TABLE 2 Effluent Guidelines and Standards (Continued)

Category	Subpart	Effluent characteristic	BPCTCA effluent limitations				BATEA effluent limitations				New source standards of performance			
			Maximum for any 1 day		Average of daily values for 30 consecutive days shall not exceed		Maximum for any 1 day		Average of daily values for 30 consecutive days shall not exceed		Maximum for any 1 day		Average of daily values for 30 consecutive days shall not exceed	
			M[a]	E[a]	M	E	M	E	M	E	M	E	M	E
3. Meat products (*cont.*)	Sub-	BOD_5	0.42	0.42	0.21	0.21	0.08	0.08	0.04	0.04				
Subpart Ba	part	TSS	0.50	0.50	0.25	0.25	0.14	0.14	0.07	0.07				
Complex slaughterhouse	Ba	Oil and grease	0.16	0.16	0.08	0.08	10 mg/l							
on-site slaughtering		Fecal coliform	Maximum at any time 400 MPN/100 ml		Maximum at any time 400 MPN/100 ml		Maximum at any time 400 MPN/100 ml		Maximum at any time 400 MPN/100 ml					
		pH	6.0–9.0		6.0–9.0		6.0–9.0		6.0–9.0					
		Ammonia									0.48	0.48	0.24	0.24
Subpart Bb	Sub-	BOD_5	0.04	0.04	0.02	0.02								
Defleshing washing and	part	TSS	0.08	0.08	0.04	0.04								
curing	Bb													
Subpart Bc	Sub-	BOD_5	0.04	0.033	0.02	0.02	0.014	0.014	0.007	0.007				
Blood processing	part	TSS	0.08	0.066	0.04	0.04	0.026	0.026	0.013	0.013				
	Bc	Ammonia									0.06	0.06	0.03	0.03
Subpart Bd	Sub-	BOD_5	0.06	0.06	0.03	0.03	0.02	0.02	0.01	0.01				
Wet and low-temperature	part	TSS	0.12	0.12	0.06	0.06	0.04	0.04	0.02	0.02				
rendering	Bd	Ammonia									0.10	0.10	0.05	0.05
Subpart Be	Sub-	BOD_5	0.02	0.02	0.01	0.01	0.006	0.006	0.003	0.003				
Dry rendering	part	TSS	0.04	0.04	0.02	0.02	0.014	0.014	0.007	0.007				
	Be	Ammonia									0.04	0.04	0.02	0.02
Subpart C	Sub-	BOD_5	0.34	0.34	0.17	0.17	0.08	0.08	0.04	0.04				
Low processing	part	TSS	0.48	0.48	0.24	0.24	0.12	0.12	0.06	0.06				
packinghouse	Ca	Oil and grease	0.16	0.16	0.08	0.08	10 mg/l							

Subpart Ca On-site slaughtering		Fecal coliform	Maximum at any one time 400 MPN/100 ml		Maximum at any one time 400 MPN/100 ml		Maximum at any one time 400 MPN/100 ml		Maximum at any one time 400 MPN/100 ml					
		Ammonia					8.0 mg/l		4.0 mg/l		0.48	0.24	0.48	0.24
		pH	6.0–9.0		6.0–9.0		6.0–9.0		6.0–9.0					
Subpart Cb Defleshing washing and curing	Subpart Cb	BOD_5	0.04	0.04	0.02	0.02								
		TSS	0.08	0.08	0.04	0.04								
Subpart Cc Blood processing	Subpart Cc	BOD_5	0.04	0.04	0.02	0.02	0.014	0.014	0.007	0.007				
		TSS	0.08	0.08	0.04	0.04	0.026	0.026	0.013	0.013				
		Ammonia									0.06	0.06	0.03	0.03
Subpart Cd Wet or low-temperature rendering	Subpart Cd	BOD_5	0.06	0.06	0.03	0.03	0.02	0.02	0.01	0.01				
		TSS	0.12	0.12	0.06	0.06	0.04	0.04	0.02	0.02				
		Ammonia									0.10	0.10	0.05	0.05
Subpart Ce Dry rendering	Subpart Ce	BOD_5	0.02	0.02	0.01	0.01	0.006	0.006	0.003	0.003				
		TSS	0.04	0.04	0.02	0.02	0.014	0.014	0.007	0.007				
		Ammonia									0.04	0.04	0.02	0.02
Subpart D High processing packing house	Subpart Da	BOD_5[b]	0.48	0.48	0.24	0.24	0.16	0.16	0.08	0.08				
		TSS[b]	0.62	0.62	0.31	0.31	0.20	0.20	0.10	0.10				
		Oil and grease	0.26	0.26	0.13	0.13	10.0 mg/l							
Subpart Da On-site slaughter		Fecal coliform	Maximum at any one time 400 MPN/100 ml		Maximum at any one time 400 MPN/100 ml		Maximum at any one time 400 MPN/100 ml		Maximum at any one time 400 MPN/100 ml					
		Ammonia									0.80	0.80	0.40	0.40
		pH	6.0–9.0		6.0–9.0		6.0–9.0		6.0–9.0					
Subpart Db Defleshing washing and curing	Subpart Db	BOD_5	0.04	0.04	0.02	0.02								
		TSS	0.08	0.08	0.04	0.04								
Subpart Dc Blood processing	Subpart Dc	BOD_5	0.04	0.04	0.02	0.02	0.014	0.014	0.007	0.007				
		TSS	0.08	0.08	0.04	0.04	0.026	0.026	0.013	0.013				
		Ammonia									0.06	0.06	0.03	0.03

[b] Average plants, i.e., plants with ratio of average weight of processed meat products to average LWK = 0.55. Adjustments can be made for other ratios according to formulas: kg BOD_5/1,000 kg LWK = 0.21 + 0.23 (V–0.4). kg TSS/1,000 kg LWK = 0.28 + 0.30 (V–0.4), where V = kg processed meat products per kg LWK.

TABLE 2 Effluent Guidelines and Standards (Continued)

Category	Sub-part	Effluent characteristic	BPCTCA effluent limitations				BATEA effluent limitations				New source standards of performance			
			Maximum for any 1 day		Average of daily values for 30 consecutive days shall not exceed		Maximum for any 1 day		Average of daily values for 30 consecutive days shall not exceed		Maximum for any 1 day		Average of daily values for 30 consecutive days shall not exceed	
			M[a]	E[a]	M	E	M	E	M	E	M	E	M	E
3. Meat products (*cont.*)	Sub-	BOD_5	0.02	0.02	0.01	0.01	0.006	0.006	0.003	0.003				
Subpart De	part	TSS	0.04	0.04	0.02	0.02	0.014	0.014	0.007	0.007				
Dry rendering	De	Ammonia									0.04	0.04	0.02	0.02
4. Dairy products[6]	Sub-	BOD_5	0.475	0.048	0.190	0.019	0.100	0.010	0.050	0.005	0.100	0.010	0.050	0.005
Subpart A	part	TSS	0.713	0.071	0.285	0.029	0.126	0.013	0.063	0.006	0.126	0.013	0.063	0.006
Receiving stations	Aa	pH	6.0–9.0		6.0–9.0		6.0–9.0		6.0–9.0		6.0–9.0		6.0–9.0	
Subpart Aa Receiving more than 150,000 lb/day of milk														
Subpart Ab	Sub-	BOD_5	0.625	0.063	0.313	0.031	0.150	0.015	0.075	0.008	0.100	0.010	0.050	0.005
Receiving 150,000 lb/day	part	TSS	0.938	0.094	0.469	0.047	0.188	0.019	0.094	0.009	0.126	0.013	0.063	0.006
or less of milk	Ab	pH	6.0–9.0		6.0–9.0		6.0–9.0		6.0–9.0		6.0–9.0		6.0–9.0	
Subpart B	Sub-	BOD_5	3.375	0.338	1.350	0.135	0.740	0.074	0.370	0.037	0.740	0.074	0.370	0.037
Fluid products	part	TSS	5.506	0.551	2.025	0.203	0.925	0.093	0.463	0.046	0.925	0.093	0.463	0.046
Subpart Ba Receiving more than 250,000 lb/day of milk	Ba	pH	6.0–9.0		6.0–9.0		6.0–9.0		6.0–9.0		6.0–9.0		6.0–9.0	
Subpart Bb	Sub-	BOD_5	4.50	0.450	2.250	0.225	1.10	0.110	0.550	0.055	0.740	0.074	0.370	0.037
Receiving 250,000 lb/day	part	TSS	6.750	0.675	3.375	0.338	1.375	0.138	0.688	0.069	0.925	0.093	0.463	0.046
or less of milk equivalent	Bb	pH	6.0–9.0		6.0–9.0		6.0–9.0		6.0–9.0		6.0–9.0		6.0–9.0	

Subpart C Cultured products	Sub-part Ca	BOD_5	3.375	0.338	1.350	0.135	0.740	0.074	0.370	0.037	0.740	0.074	0.370	0.037
Subpart Ca Receiving more than 60,000 lb/day of milk equivalent (>6,200 lb/day BOD_5 input)		TSS	5.063	0.506	2.025	0.203	0.926	0.093	0.463	0.046	0.926	0.093	0.463	0.046
		pH	6.0–9.0		6.0–9.0		6.0–9.0		6.0–9.0		6.0–9.0		6.0–9.0	
Subpart Cb Receiving 60,000 lb/day or less of milk equivalent (<6,200 lb/day of BOD_5 input)	Sub-part Cb	BOD_5	4.50	0.450	2.250	0.225	1.10	0.110	0.550	0.055	0.740	0.074	0.370	0.037
		TSS	6.750	0.675	3.375	0.338	1.375	0.138	0.688	0.069	0.926	0.093	0.463	0.046
		pH	6.0–9.0		6.0–9.0		6.0–9.0		6.0–9.0		6.0–9.0		6.0–9.0	
Subpart D Butter	Sub-part Da	BOD_5	1.375	0.138	0.550	0.055	0.160	0.016	0.080	0.008	0.160	0.016	0.080	0.008
Subpart Da Processing 175,000 lb/day milk equivalent (>18,180 lb/day BOD_5 input)		TSS	2.063	0.206	0.825	0.083	0.20	0.020	0.100	0.010	0.200	0.020	0.100	0.010
		pH	6.0–9.0		6.0–9.0		6.0–9.0		6.0–9.0		6.0–9.0		6.0–9.0	
Subpart Db Processing 175,000 lb/day milk equivalent or less (<18,180 lb/day BOD_5 input)	Sub-part Db	BOD_5	1.825	0.183	0.913	0.091	0.250	0.025	0.125	0.013	0.160	0.016	0.080	0.008
		TSS	2.738	0.274	1.369	0.137	0.313	0.031	0.156	0.016	0.200	0.020	0.100	0.010
		pH	6.0–9.0		6.0–9.0		6.0–9.0		6.0–9.0		6.0–9.0		6.0–9.0	
Subpart E Cottage cheese and cultured cheese	Sub-part Ea	BOD_5	6.70	0.670	2.680	0.268	1.480	0.148	0.740	0.074	1.480	0.148	0.740	0.074
Subpart Ea Processing more than 25,000 lb/day of milk equivalent (>2,600 lb/day of BOD_5 input)		TSS	10.050	1.005	4.020	0.402	1.850	0.185	0.925	0.093	1.850	0.185	0.925	0.093
		pH	6.0–9.0		6.0–9.0		6.0–9.0		6.0–9.0		6.0–9.0		6.0–9.0	
Subpart Eb Processing 25,000 lb/day or less of milk equivalent (<2,600 lb/day of BOD_5 input)	Sub-part Eb	BOD_5	8.926	0.893	4.463	0.446	2.226	0.223	1.113	0.111	1.480	0.148	0.740	0.074
		TSS	13.388	1.339	6.694	0.669	2.782	0.278	1.391	0.139	1.850	0.185	0.925	0.093
		pH	6.0–9.0		6.0–9.0		6.0–9.0		6.0–9.0		6.0–9.0		6.0–9.0	

TABLE 2 Effluent Guidelines and Standards (Continued)

Category	Sub-part	Effluent characteristic	BPCTCA effluent limitations				BATEA effluent limitations				New source standards of performance			
			Maximum for any 1 day		Average of daily values for 30 consecutive days shall not exceed		Maximum for any 1 day		Average of daily values for 30 consecutive days shall not exceed		Maximum for any 1 day		Average of daily values for 30 consecutive days shall not exceed	
			M[a]	E[a]	M	E	M	E	M	E	M	E	M	E
4. Dairy products (*cont.*) Subpart F Natural and processed	Sub-part Fa	BOD_5	0.715	0.072	0.290	0.029	0.160	0.016	0.080	0.008	0.160	0.016	0.080	0.008
		TSS	1.088	0.109	0.435	0.044	0.200	0.020	0.100	0.010	0.200	0.020	0.100	0.010
		pH	6.0–9.0		6.0–9.0		6.0–9.0		6.0–9.0		6.0–9.0		6.0–9.0	
Subpart Fa Processing more than 100,000 lb/day of milk equivalent (>10,390 lb/day of BOD_5 input)														
Subpart Fb Processing 100,000 lb/day or less of milk equivalent (<10,390 lb/day of BOD_5 input)	Sub-part Fb	BOD_5	0.976	0.098	0.488	0.049	0.250	0.025	0.125	0.013	0.160	0.016	0.080	0.008
		TSS	1.462	0.146	0.731	0.073	0.312	0.031	0.156	0.016	0.200	0.020	0.100	0.010
		pH	6.0–9.0		6.0–9.0		6.0–9.0		6.0–9.0		6.0–9.0		6.0–9.0	
Subpart G Fluid mix for ice cream and other frozen desserts	Sub-part Ga	BOD_5	2.20	0.220	0.880	0.088	0.480	0.048	0.240	0.024	0.480	0.048	0.240	0.024
		TSS	2.640	0.264	1.320	0.132	0.600	0.060	0.300	0.030	0.600	0.060	0.300	0.030
		pH	6.0–9.0		6.0–9.0		6.0–9.0		6.0–9.0		6.0–9.0		6.0–9.0	
Subpart Ga More than 85,000 lb/day of milk equivalent (>8,830 lb/day of BOD_5 input)														
Subpart Gb Products of 85,000 lb/day or less of milk equivalent (<8,830 lb/day of BOD_5 input)	Sub-part Gb	BOD_5	2.926	0.293	1.463	0.146	0.726	0.073	0.363	0.036	0.480	0.048	0.240	0.024
		TSS	4.388	0.439	2.194	0.219	0.908	0.091	0.454	0.045	0.600	0.060	0.300	0.030
		pH	6.0–9.0		6.0–9.0		6.0–9.0		6.0–9.0		6.0–9.0		6.0–9.0	

Subpart H Ice cream, frozen desserts novelties, and other dairy desserts	Subpart Ha	BOD_5	4.60	0.460	1.840	0.184	0.940	0.094	0.470	0.047	0.940	0.094	0.470	0.047
		TSS	6.90	0.690	2.760	0.276	1.175	0.118	0.588	0.059	1.175	0.118	0.588	0.059
		pH	6.0–9.0		6.0–9.0		6.0–9.0		6.0–9.0		6.0–9.0		6.0–9.0	
Subpart Ha More than 85,000 lb/day of milk equivalent (>8,830 lb/day of BOD_5 input)														
Subpart Hb Products of 85,000 lb/day or less of milk equivalent (<8,830 lb/day of BOD_5 input)	Subpart Hb	BOD_5	6.126	0.613	3.063	0.306	1.40	0.140	0.700	0.070	0.940	0.094	0.470	0.047
		TSS	9.188	0.919	4.594	0.459	1.750	0.175	0.875	0.088	1.175	0.118	0.588	0.059
		pH	6.0–9.0		6.0–9.0		6.0–9.0		6.0–9.0		6.0–9.0		6.0–9.0	
Subpart I Condensed milk	Subpart Ia	BOD_5	3.450	0.345	1.380	0.138	0.760	0.076	0.380	0.038	0.760	0.076	0.380	0.038
		TSS	5.175	0.518	2.070	0.207	0.950	0.095	0.475	0.048	0.950	0.095	0.475	0.048
		pH	6.0–9.0		6.0–9.0		6.0–9.0		6.0–9.0		6.0–9.0		6.0–9.0	
Subpart Ia More than 100,000 lb/day of milk equvalent (>10,390 lb/day of BOD_5 input)														
Subpart Ib 100,000 lb/day or less of milk equivalent (<10,390 lb/day of BOD_5 input)	Subpart Ib	BOD_5	4.60	0.460	2.30	0.230	1.150	0.115	0.575	0.058	0.760	0.076	0.380	0.038
		TSS	6.90	0.690	3.450	0.345	1.438	0.144	0.719	0.072	0.950	0.095	0.475	0.048
		pH	6.0–9.0		6.0–9.0		6.0–9.0		6.0–9.0		6.0–9.0		6.0–9.0	
Subpart J Dry milk	Subpart Ja	BOD_5	1.625	0.163	0.650	0.065	0.360	0.036	0.180	0.018	0.360	0.036	0.180	0.018
		TSS	2.438	0.244	0.975	0.098	0.450	0.045	0.225	0.023	0.450	0.045	0.225	0.023
		pH	6.0–9.0		6.0–9.0		6.0–9.0		6.0–9.0		6.0–9.0		6.0–9.0	
Subpart Ja More than 145,000 lb/day of milk equivalent (>15,070 lb/day of BOD_5 input)														
Subpart Jb 145,000 lb/day or less of milk equivalent (<15,070 lb/day of BOD_5 input)	Subpart Jb	BOD_5	2.176	0.218	1.088	0.109	0.550	0.055	0.275	0.028	0.360	0.036	0.180	0.018
		TSS	3.276	0.328	1.638	0.164	0.688	0.069	0.344	0.034	0.450	0.045	0.225	0.023
		pH	6.0–9.0		6.0–9.0		6.0–9.0		6.0–9.0		6.0–9.0		6.0–9.0	

TABLE 2 Effluent Guidelines and Standards (Continued)

Category	Subpart	Effluent characteristic	BPCTCA effluent limitations				BATEA effluent limitations				New source standards of performance			
			Maximum for any 1 day		Average of daily values for 30 consecutive days shall not exceed		Maximum for any 1 day		Average of daily values for 30 consecutive days shall not exceed		Maximum for any 1 day		Average of daily values for 30 consecutive days shall not exceed	
			M[a]	E[a]	M	E	M	E	M	E	M	E	M	E
4. Dairy products (*cont.*) Subpart K Condensed whey Subpart Ka More than 300,000 lb/day of fluid raw whey input (>20,700 lb/day of solids or 14,160 lb/day of BOD_5 input)	Subpart Ka	BOD_5	1.00	0.100	0.400	0.040	0.220	0.022	0.110	0.011	0.220	0.022	0.110	0.011
		TSS	1.50	0.150	0.600	0.060	0.276	0.028	0.138	0.014	0.276	0.028	0.138	0.014
		pH	6.0–9.0		6.0–9.0		6.0–9.0		6.0–9.0		6.0–9.0		6.0–9.0	
Subpart Kb 300,000 lb/day or less of raw fluid whey input (<20,700 lb/day of solids or 14,160 lb/day of BOD_5 input)	Subpart Kb	BOD_5	1.300	0.130	0.650	0.065	0.326	0.033	0.163	0.016	0.220	0.022	0.110	0.011
		TSS	1.950	0.195	0.975	0.098	0.408	0.041	0.204	0.020	0.276	0.028	0.138	0.014
		pH	6.0–9.0		6.0–9.0		6.0–9.0		6.0–9.0		6.0–9.0		6.0–9.0	
Subpart L Dry whey Subpart La More than 57,000 lb/day of 40% solids whey (22,800 lb/day solids or 15,260 lb/day of BOD_5 input)	Subpart La	BOD_5	1.00	0.100	0.400	0.040	0.220	0.022	0.110	0.011	0.220	0.022	0.110	0.011
		TSS	1.50	0.150	0.600	0.060	0.275	0.028	0.138	0.014	0.275	0.028	0.138	0.014
		pH	6.0–9.0		6.0–9.0		6.0–9.0		6.0–9.0		6.0–9.0		6.0–9.0	

Subpart Lb 57,000 lb/day or less of 40% solids whey (<22,800 lb/day solids or 15,620 lb/day of BOD_5 input)	Sub-part Lb	BOD_5	1.30	0.130	0.650	0.065	0.326	0.033	0.163	0.016	0.220	0.022	0.110	0.011
		TSS	1.95	0.195	0.975	0.098	0.408	0.041	0.204	0.020	0.275	0.028	0.138	0.014
		pH	6.0–9.0		6.0–9.0		6.0–9.0		6.0–9.0		6.0–9.0		6.0–9.0	
5. Grain mills[7,8] Subpart A Corn wet mlling	Sub-part A	BOD_5	2.67	1.50	0.89	50	1.08	60	0.36	20	1.08	60	0.36	20
		TSS	2.67	1.50	0.89	50	0.54	30	0.18	10	0.54	30	0.18	10
		pH	6.0–9.0		6.0–9.0		6.0–9.0		6.0–9.0		6.0–9.0		6.0–9.0	
Subpart B Corn dry milling	Sub-part B	BOD_5	0.21	12.0	0.07	4.0	0.11	6.0	0.036	2.0	0.110	6.0	0.036	2.0
		TSS	0.18	10.5	0.06	3.5	0.054	3.0	0.018	1.0	0.054	3.0	0.018	1.0
		pH	6.0–9.0		6.0–9.0		6.0–9.0		6.0–9.0		6.0–9.0		6.0–9.0	
Subpart C Normal wheat flour milling	Sub-part C		There shall be no discharge of process wastewater pollutants to navigable waters											
Subpart D Bulgar wheat flour milling	Sub-part D	BOD_5	0.025	1.50	0.0083	0.50	0.015	0.90	0.005	0.30	0.015	0.90	0.005	0.30
		TSS	0.025	1.50	0.0083	0.50	0.0099	0.60	0.0033	0.20	0.0099	0.60	0.0033	0.20
		pH	6.0–9.0		6.0–9.0		6.0–9.0		6.0–9.0		6.0–9.0		6.0–9.0	
Subpart E Normal rice milling	Sub-part E		There shall be no discharge of process wastewater pollutants to navigable waters											
Subpart F Parboiled rice processing	Sub-part F	BOD_5	0.42	0.042	0.14	0.014	0.21	0.021	0.07	0.007	0.21	0.021	0.07	0.007
		TSS	0.24	0.024	0.08	0.008	0.09	0.009	0.03	0.003	0.09	0.009	0.03	0.003
		pH	6.0–9.0		6.0–9.0		6.0–9.0		6.0–9.0		6.0–9.0		6.0–9.0	
Subpart G Animal feed	Sub-part G		There shall be no discharge of process wastewater pollutants to navigable waters											
Subpart H Hot cereal	Sub-part H		There shall be no discharge of process wastewater pollutants to navigable waters											
Subpart I Ready-to-eat cereal	Sub-part I	BOD_5	1.2	1.2	0.40	0.40	0.60	0.60	0.20	0.20	0.60	0.60	0.20	0.20
		TSS	1.2	1.2	0.40	0.40	0.45	0.45	0.15	0.15	0.45	0.45	0.15	0.15
		pH	6.0–9.0		6.0–9.0		6.0–9.0		6.0–9.0		6.0–9.0		6.0–9.0	

TABLE 2 Effluent Guidelines and Standards (Continued)

Category	Subpart	Effluent characteristic	BPCTCA effluent limitations				BATEA effluent limitations				New source standards of performance			
			Maximum for any 1 day		Average of daily values for 30 consecutive days shall not exceed		Maximum for any 1 day		Average of daily values for 30 consecutive days shall not exceed		Maximum for any 1 day		Average of daily values for 30 consecutive days shall not exceed	
			M[a]	E[a]	M	E	M	E	M	E	M	E	M	E
5. Grain mills (*cont.*)	Sub-	BOD_5	6.0	6.0	2.0	2.0	1.5	1.5	0.50	0.50	3.0	3.0	1.0	1.0
Subpart J	part	TSS	6.0	6.0	2.0	2.0	1.2	1.2	0.40	0.40	3.0	3.0	1.0	1.0
Wheat starch and gluten	J	pH	6.0–9.0		6.0–9.0		6.0–9.0		6.0–9.0		6.0–9.0		6.0–9.0	
6. Canned and preserved fruits and vegetables[9]	Sub-	BOD_5	0.60	0.60	0.30	0.30	0.20	0.20	0.10	0.10	0.20	0.20	0.10	0.10
Subpart A	part	TSS	0.80	0.80	0.40	0.40	0.20	0.20	0.10	0.10	0.20	0.20	0.10	0.10
Apple juice	A	pH	6.0–9.0		6.0–9.0		6.0–9.0		6.0–9.0		6.0–9.0		6.0–9.0	
Subpart B	Sub-	BOD_5	0.10	0.10	0.55	0.55	0.20	0.20	0.10	0.10	0.20	0.20	0.10	0.10
Apple products	part	TSS	1.40	1.40	0.70	0.70	0.20	0.20	0.10	0.10	0.20	0.20	0.10	0.10
	B	Fecal coliform					Maximum at any one time of 400 MPN/100 ml				Maximum at any one time of 400 MPN/100 ml			
		pH	6.0–9.0		6.0–9.0		6.0–9.0		6.0–9.0		6.0–9.0		6.0–9.0	
Subpart C	Sub-	BOD_5	0.80	0.80	0.40	0.40	0.14	0.14	0.07	0.07	0.14	0.14	0.07	0.07
Citrus products	part	TSS	1.70	1.70	0.85	0.85	0.20	0.20	0.10	0.10	0.20	0.20	0.10	0.10
	C	Fecal coliform					Maximum at any one time of 400 MPN/100 ml				Maximum at any one time of 400 MPN/100 ml			
		pH	6.0–9.0		6.0–9.0		6.0–9.0		6.0–9.0		6.0–9.0		6.0–9.0	
Subpart D	Sub-	BOD_5	2.80	2.80	1.40	1.40	0.34	0.34	0.17	0.17	0.34	0.34	0.17	0.17
Frozen potato products	part	TSS	2.80	2.80	1.40	1.40	1.10	1.10	0.55	0.55	1.10	1.10	0.55	0.55
	D	Fecal coliform					Maximum at any one time of 400 MPN/100 ml				Maximum at any one time of 400 MPN/100 ml			
		pH	6.0–9.0		6.0–9.0		6.0–9.0		6.0–9.0		6.0–9.0		6.0–9.0	
Subpart E	Sub-	BOD_5	2.40	2.40	1.20	1.20	0.34	0.34	0.17	0.17	0.34	0.34	0.17	0.17
Dehydrated potato	part	TSS	2.80	2.80	1.40	1.40	1.10	1.10	0.55	0.55	1.10	1.10	0.55	0.55
products	E	Fecal coliform					Maximum at any one time of 400 MPN/100 ml				Maximum at any one time of 400 MPN/100 ml			
		pH	6.0–9.0		6.0–9.0		6.0–9.0		6.0–9.0		6.0–9.0		6.0–9.0	

7. Canned and preserved seafood processing[10,11]	Sub-	BOD_5					4.6	4.6	2.3	2.3	4.6	4.6	2.3	2.3
	part	TSS	28	28	9.2	9.2	11	11	5.7	5.7	11	11	5.7	5.7
Subpart A	A	Oil and grease	10	10	3.4	3.4	0.90	0.90	0.45	0.45	0.90	0.90	0.45	0.45
Farm-raised catfish processing		pH	6.0–9.0		6.0–9.0		6.0–9.0		6.0–9.0		6.0–9.0		6.0–9.0	
Subpart B	Sub-	BOD_5					0.30	0.30	0.15	0.15	0.30	0.30	0.15	0.15
Conventional blue crab	part	TSS	2.2	2.2	0.74	0.74	0.90	0.90	0.45	0.45	0.90	0.90	0.45	0.45
processing	B	Oil and grease	0.60	0.60	0.20	0.20	0.13	0.13	0.065	0.065	0.13	0.13	0.065	0.065
		pH	6.0–9.0		6.0–9.0		6.0–9.0		6.0–9.0		6.0–9.0		6.0–9.0	
Subpart C	Sub-	BOD_5					5.0	5.0	2.5	2.5	5.0	5.0	2.5	2.5
Mechanized blue crab	part	TSS	36	36	12.0	12.0	13	13	6.3	6.3	13	13	6.3	6.3
processing	C	Oil and grease	13	13	4.2	4.2	2.6	2.6	1.3	1.3	2.6	2.6	1.3	1.3
		pH	6.0–9.0		6.0–9.0		6.0–9.0		6.0–9.0		6.0–9.0		6.0–9.0	
Subpart D	Sub-	BOD_5					5.0	5.0	2.0	2.0				
Nonremote Alaskan	part	TSS	19	19	6.2	6.2	1.3	1.3	0.53	0.53	16	16	5.3	5.3
crab processing	D	Oil and grease	1.8	1.8	0.61	0.61	0.21	0.21	0.082	0.082	1.6	1.6	0.52	0.52
		pH	6.0–9.0		6.0–9.0		6.0–9.0		6.0–9.0		6.0–9.0		6.0–9.0	
Subpart E	Sub-	TSS					16	16	5.3	5.3	16	16	5.3	5.3
Remote Alaskan crab	part	Oil and grease	[c]	[c]	[c]	[c]	1.6	1.6	0.52	0.52	1.6	1.6	0.52	0.52
meat processing	E	pH					6.0–9.0		6.0–9.0		6.0–9.0		6.0–9.0	
Subpart F	Sub-	BOD_5					3.3	3.3	1.3	1.3				
Nonremote Alaskan crab	part	TSS	12	12	3.9	3.9	0.83	0.83	0.33	0.33	9.9	9.9	3.3	3.3
meat processing	F	Oil and grease	1.3	1.3	0.42	0.42	0.12	0.12	0.048	0.048	1.1	1.1	0.36	0.36
		pH	6.0–9.0		6.0–9.0		6.0–9.0		6.0–9.0		6.0–9.0		6.0–9.0	
Subpart G	Sub-	TSS					9.9	9.9	3.3	3.3	9.9	9.9	3.3	3.3
Remote Alaskan whole	part	Oil and grease	[c]	[c]	[c]	[c]	1.1	1.1	0.36	0.36	1.1	1.1	0.36	0.36
crab and crab section processing	G	pH					6.0–9.0		6.0–9.0		6.0–9.0		6.0–9.0	
Subpart H	Sub-	BOD_5					4.3	4.3	1.7	1.7	10	10	4.1	4.1
Dungeness and tanner	part	TSS	8.1	8.1	2.7	2.7	0.58	0.58	0.23	0.23	1.7	1.7	0.69	0.69
crab processing in the	H	Oil and grease	1.8	1.8	0.61	0.61	0.18	0.18	0.07	0.07	0.25	0.25	0.10	0.10
contiguous states		pH	6.0–9.0		6.0–9.0		6.0–9.0		6.0–9.0		6.0–9.0		6.0–9.0	

[c] No pollutants may be discharged which exceed 1.27 cm (0.5 in.) in any dimension.

TABLE 2 Effluent Guidelines and Standards (Continued)

Category	Subpart	Effluent characteristic	BPCTCA effluent limitations				BATEA effluent limitations				New source standards of performance			
			Maximum for any 1 day		Average of daily values for 30 consecutive days shall not exceed		Maximum for any 1 day		Average of daily values for 30 consecutive days shall not exceed		Maximum for any 1 day		Average of daily values for 30 consecutive days shall not exceed	
			M[a]	E[a]	M	E	M	E	M	E	M	E	M	E
7. Canned and preserved seafood processing (*cont.*)	Sub-	BOD_5					70	70	28	28				
Subpart I	part	TSS	320	320	210	210	45	45	18	18	270	270	180	180
Nonremote Alaskan	I	Oil and grease	51	51	17	17	3.8	3.8	1.5	1.5	45	45	15	15
shrimp processing		pH	6.0–9.0		6.0–9.0		6.0–9.0		6.0–9.0		6.0–9.0		6.0–9.0	
Subpart J	Sub-	TSS	[c]	[c]	[c]	[c]	270	270	180	180	270	270	180	180
Remote Alaskan shrimp	part	Oil and grease					45	45	15	15	45	45	15	15
processing	J	pH	6.0–9.0		6.0–9.0		6.0–9.0		6.0–9.0		6.0–9.0		6.0–9.0	
Subpart K	Sub-	BOD_5					68	68	27.0	27.0	155	155	62	62
Northern shrimp pro-	part	TSS	160	160	54	54	12	12	4.9	4.9	38	38	15	15
cessing in the contiguous	K	Oil and grease	126	126	42	42	9.5	9.5	3.8	3.8	14	14	5.7	5.7
states		pH	6.0–9.0		6.0–9.0		6.0–9.0		6.0–9.0		6.0–9.0		6.0–9.0	
Subpart L	Sub-	BOD_5					25	25	10	10	63	63	25	25
Southern non-breaded	part	TSS	110	110	38	38	8.5	8.5	3.4	3.4	25	25	10	10
shrimp processing in	L	Oil and grease	36	36	12	12	2.8	2.8	1.1	1.1	4.0	4.0	1.6	1.6
contiguous states		pH	6.0–9.0		6.0–9.0		6.0–9.0		6.0–9.0		6.0–9.0		6.0–9.0	
Subpart M	Sub-	BOD_5					43	43	17.0	17.0	100	100	40	40
Breaded shrimp pro-	part	TSS	280	280	93	93	19	19	7.4	7.4	55	55	22	22
cessing in contiguous	M	Oil and grease	36	36	12	12	2.5	2.5	1.0	1.0	3.8	3.8	1.5	1.5
states		pH	6.0–9.0		6.0–9.0		6.0–9.0		6.0–9.0		6.0–9.0		6.0–9.0	
Subpart N	Sub-	BOD_5	23	23	9.0	9.0	2.2	2.2	0.62	0.62	20	20	8.1	8.1
Tuna processing	part	TSS	8.3	8.3	3.3	3.3	2.2	2.2	0.62	0.62	7.5	7.5	3.0	3.0
	N	Oil and grease	2.1	2.1	0.84	0.84	0.27	0.27	0.077	0.077	1.9	1.9	0.76	0.76
		pH	6.0–9.0		6.0–9.0		6.0–9.0		6.0–9.0		6.0–9.0		6.0–9.0	

8. Beet sugar processing[12,13]														
Subpart A Beet sugar processing														
Subpart Aa Barometric condensing operations only	Sub- part Aa	BOD_5	3.3	3.3	2.2	2.2	2.0	2.0	1.3	1.3	There shall be no discharge of process waste-water to navigable waters			
		pH	6.0–9.0		6.0–9.0		6.0–9.0		6.0–9.0					
		Temperature	[d]	[e]	[d]	[e]	[d]	[e]	[d]	[e]				
Subpart Ab Barometric condensing operations and any other beet sugar operation	Sub- part Ab	BOD_5	3.3	3.3	2.2	2.2	2.0	2.0	1.3	1.3	There shall be no discharge of process waste-water to navigable waters			
		TSS	3.3	3.3	2.2	2.2	2.0	2.0	1.3	1.3				
		pH	6.0–9.0		6.0–9.0		6.0–9.0		6.0–9.0					
		Fecal coliform	Not to exceed 400 MPN/100 ml at any time				Not to exceed 400 MPN/100 ml at any time							
		Temperature	[f]	[g]	[f]	[g]								
9. Textile industry[14]														
Subpart A Wool scouring	Sub- part A	BOD_5	10.6	10.6	5.3	5.3	4.8	4.8	2.4	2.4	10.6	10.6	5.3	5.3
		TSS	32.2	32.2	16.1	16.1	4.0	4.0	2.0	2.0	10.6	10.6	5.3	5.3
		COD	138.0	138.0	69.0	69.0	36.0	36.0	18.0	18.0	138.0	138.0	69.0	69.0
		Oil and grease	7.2	7.2	3.6	3.6	2.0	2.0	1.0	1.0	7.2	7.2	3.6	3.6
	(Total)	Chromium	0.10	0.10	0.05	0.05	0.05	0.05	0.025	0.025	0.10	0.10	0.05	0.05
		Phenol	0.10	0.10	0.05	0.05	0.05	0.05	0.025	0.025	0.10	0.10	0.05	0.05
		Sulfide	0.20	0.20	0.10	0.10	0.10	0.10	0.05	0.05	0.20	0.20	0.10	0.10
		pH	6.0–9.0		6.0–9.0		6.0–9.0		6.0–9.0		6.0–9.0		6.0–9.0	
		Color					Shall not exceed 600 APHA units		Shall not exceed 600 APHA units					
		Fecal coliform					Shall not exceed 400 MPN/100 ml		Shall not exceed 400 MPN/100 ml					
Subpart B Wool finishing	Sub- part B	BOD_5	22.4	22.4	11.2	11.2	9.2	9.2	4.6	4.6	22.4	22.4	11.2	11.2
		TSS	35.2	35.2	17.6	17.6	5.0	5.0	2.5	2.5	22.4	22.4	11.2	11.2
		COD	163.0	163.0	81.5	81.5	54.2	54.2	27.1	27.1	163.0	163.0	81.5	81.5
	(Total)	Chromium	0.14	0.14	0.07	0.07	0.05	0.05	0.025	0.025	0.14	0.14	0.07	0.07
		Phenol	0.14	0.14	0.07	0.07	0.05	0.05	0.025	0.025	0.28	0.28	0.14	0.14
		Sulfide	0.28	0.28	0.14	0.14	0.10	0.10	0.05	0.05	0.28	0.28	0.14	0.14
		pH	6.0–9.0		6.0–9.0		6.0–9.0		6.0–9.0		6.0–9.0		6.0–9.0	
		Color					Shall not exceed 600 APHA units		Shall not exceed 600 APHA units					
		Fecal coliform					Shall not exceed 400 MPN/100 ml		Shall not exceed 400 MPN/100 ml					

[d] Not to exceed the temperature of cooled water acceptable for return to the heat producing process and in no event greater than 32°C.

[e] Not to exceed the temperature of cooled water acceptable for return to the heat producing process and in no event greater than 90°F.

[f] Not to exceed 32°C.

[g] Not to exceed 90°F.

TABLE 2 Effluent Guidelines and Standards (Continued)

Category	Subpart	Effluent characteristic	BPCTCA effluent limitations				BATEA effluent limitations				New source standards of performance			
			Maximum for any 1 day		Average of daily values for 30 consecutive days shall not exceed		Maximum for any 1 day		Average of daily values for 30 consecutive days shall not exceed		Maximum for any 1 day		Average of daily values for 30 consecutive days shall not exceed	
			M[a]	E[a]	M	E	M	E	M	E	M	E	M	E
9. Textile industry (*cont.*) Subpart C Dry processing (yard manufacturing, texterizing, unfinished fabric manufacturing, fabric coating, fabric laminating, tire cord and fabric dipping, carpet tufting and backing	Subpart C	BOD_5	1.4	1.4	0.7	0.7	0.4	0.4	0.2	0.2	1.4	1.4	0.7	0.7
		TSS	1.4	1.4	0.7	0.7	0.4	0.4	0.2	0.2	1.4	1.4	0.7	0.7
		COD	2.8	2.8	1.4	1.4	0.8	0.8	0.4	0.4	2.8	2.8	1.4	1.4
		Fecal coliform	Shall not exceed 400 MPN/100 ml		Shall not exceed 400 MPN/100 ml		Shall not exceed 400 MPN/100 ml		Shall not exceed 400 MPN/100 ml		Shall not exceed 400 MPN/100 ml		Shall not excede 400 MPN/100 ml	
		pH	6.0–9.0		6.0–9.0		6.0–9.0		6.0–9.0		6.0–9.0		6.0–7.0	
							(*Rubber or rubber coated fabrics are specifically excluded*)							
Subpart D Woven fabric finishing (desizing, bleaching, mercerizing, dyeing, printing, resin treatment, waterproofing, flameproofing, soil repellency	Subpart Da (Total)	BOD_5	6.6	6.6	3.3	3.3	4.4	4.4	2.2	2.2	6.6	6.6	3.3	3.3
		TSS	17.8	17.8	8.9	8.9	3.0	3.0	1.5	1.5	6.6	6.6	3.3	3.3
		COD	60.0	60.0	30.0	30.0	20.0	20.0	10.0	10.0	60.0	60.0	30.0	30.0
		Chromium	0.10	0.10	0.05	0.05	0.10	0.10	0.05	0.05	0.10	0.10	0.05	0.05
		Phenol	0.10	0.10	0.05	0.05	0.10	0.10	0.05	0.05	0.10	0.10	0.05	0.05
		Sulfide	0.20	0.20	0.10	0.10	0.20	0.20	0.10	0.10	0.20	0.20	0.10	0.10
		pH	6.0–9.0		6.0–9.0		6.0–9.0		6.0–9.0		6.0–9.0		6.0–9.0	
Subpart Da Natural fiber, a synthetic fiber or a natural and synthetic fiber blend		Color					Shall not exceed 300 APHA units		Shall not exceed 300 APHA units					
		Fecal coliform					Shall not exceed 400 MPN/100 ml		Shall not exceed 400 MPN/100 ml					
Subpart Db Natural fiber, a synthetic fiber or a natural and synthetic fiber blend	Subpart Db	Same as Da except COD	20	20	10	10	6.6	6.6	3.3	3.3	20	20	10	10

Subpart Dc Natural and synthetic fiber blend or through complex manufacturing operations, employing a synthetic fiber	Subpart Dc	Same as Da except COD	40	40	20	20	13.4	13.4	6.7	6.7	40	40	20	20
Subpart Dd Natural and synthetic fiber blend	Subpart Dd	Same as Da except COD	60	60	30	30	20	20	10	10	60	60	30	30
10. Cement manufacturing[15] Subpart A Nonleaching	Subpart A	TSS Temperature pH	0.005 [h] 6.0–9.0	0.005 [h]			0.005 [h] 6.0–9.0	0.005 [h]			0.005 [h] 6.0–9.0	0.005 [h]		
Subpart B Leaching	Subpart B	TSS Temperature pH	0.4 [h] 6.0–9.0	0.4 [h]			0.005 [h] 6.0–9.0	0.005 [h]			0.4 [h] 6.0–9.0	0.4 [h]		
Subpart C Materials storage piles runoff	Subpart C	TSS pH	50 mg/l 6.0–9.0				50 mg/l 6.0–9.0				50 mg/l 6.0–9.0			
11. Feed lots[16] Subpart A All subcategories except ducks	Subpart A						Same as [i] but substitute 25-yr, 24-hr rainfall for 10-yr, 24-hr rainfall				No discharge of pollutants			
Subpart B Ducks	Subpart B	BOD Fecal coliform	1.66 Not to exceed 400 MPN/100 ml at any time	3.66	0.91 Not to exceed 400 MPN/100 ml at any time	2.00	Same as [i] but substitute 25-yr, 24-hr rainfall for 10-yr, 24-hr rainfall				No discharge of pollutants			

[h] Not to exceed 3°C rise above inlet temperature.

[i] There shall be no discharge of process wastewater pollutants to navigable waters. (Subject to provision: Process waste pollutants in the overflow may be discharged to navigable waters whenever rainfall events, either chronic or catastrophic, cause an overflow of process wastewater from a facility designed, constructed and operated to contain all process-generated wastewaters plus the runoff from a 10-yr, 24-hr rainfall event for the location of the point source.)

TABLE 2 Effluent Guidelines and Standards (Continued)

Category	Subpart	Effluent characteristic	BPCTCA effluent limitations				BATEA effluent limitations				New source standards of performance			
			Maximum for any 1 day		Average of daily values for 30 consecutive days shall not exceed		Maximum for any 1 day		Average of daily values for 30 consecutive days shall not exceed		Maximum for any 1 day		Average of daily values for 30 consecutive days shall not exceed	
			M[a]	E[a]	M	E	M	E	M	E	M	E	M	E
12. Electroplating copper, nickel, chromium, and zinc on ferrous and nonferrous materials[17]	Subpart Aa	Copper	160	32.7	80	16.4	No discharge of process wastewater pollutants to navigable waters (with a production of less than 120 sq m/hr a variation from Aa (BPCTCA) may be necessary). If necessary, the source shall be subject to effluent limitations no less stringent than those required by new sources.				80	16.4	40	8.2
		Nickel	160	32.7	80	16.4					80	16.4	40	8.2
		Chromium (VI)	16	3.3	8	1.6					8	1.6	4	0.8
		Chromium (total)	160	32.7	80	16.4					80	16.4	40	4.2
Subpart A Electroplating copper, nickel, chromium, and zinc on ferrous and nonferrous materials Aa		Zinc	160	32.7	80	16.4					80	16.2	40	4.2
		Cyanide-A[j]	16	3.3	8	1.6					8	1.6	4	0.8
		Cyanide-(total)	160	32.7	80	16.4					80	16.2	40	4.7
		TSS	4,800	982	3,200	654					2,400	491	1,600	327
		pH	6.0–9.5		6.0–9.5						6.0–9.5		6.0–9.5	
Subpart Ab Alternate	Subpart Ab	For the purpose of complying with the requirements, a discharger may establish a correlation between area plated and another parameter, such as ampere-hours used in plating												
Subpart Ac Alternate	Subpart Ac	Application of the factors listed in Sec. 304(b) of the Federal Water Pollution Control Act Amendments of 1972, requires variation from the effluent limitations set forth in Aa (above) for any point source subject to such effluent limitations with production less than 33 sq m/hr or an installed direct-current capacity less than 2,000 A. For such sources, the BPCTCA consists of cyanide destruction, if any, equalization, and pH adjustment to a range of 6.0–9.0 prior to discharge.												
13. Organic chemicals manufacturing[18]	Subpart A	BOD_5	0.045	0.045	0.02	0.02	0.015	0.015	0.0085	0.0085	0.037	0.037	0.017	0.017
		TSS	0.067	0.067	0.03	0.03	0.022	0.022	0.013	0.013	0.034	0.034	0.015	0.015
Subpart A Non-Aqueous Processes[k]		pH	6.0–9.0		6.0–9.0		6.0–9.0		6.0–9.0		6.0–9.0		6.0–9.0	
		COD					0.062	0.062	0.045	0.045				
Subpart B Processes with water contact as steam diluent or absorbent[k] Ba	Subpart Ba	BOD_5	0.13	0.13	0.058	0.058	0.044	0.044	0.025	0.025	0.11	0.11	0.048	0.048
		TSS	0.20	0.20	0.088	0.088	0.066	0.066	0.040	0.040	0.10	0.10	0.044	0.044
		pH	6.0–9.0		6.0–9.0		6.0–9.0		6.0–9.0		6.0–9.0		6.0–9.0	
		COD					0.80	0.80	0.58	0.58				

Subpart Bb[k]	Sub-part Bb	BOD_5	0.95	0.95	0.42	0.42	0.32	0.32	0.18	0.18	0.76	0.76	0.34	0.34
		TSS	1.42	1.42	0.64	0.64	0.48	0.48	0.29	0.29	0.72	0.72	0.32	0.32
		pH	6.0–9.0		6.0–9.0		6.0–9.0		6.0–9.0		6.0–9.0		6.0–9.0	
		COD					1.32	1.32	0.95	0.95				
Subpart C Aqueous liquid phase reaction systems[k] Ca	Sub-part Ca	BOD_5	0.28	0.28	0.12	0.12	0.093	0.093	0.053	0.053	0.23	0.23	0.10	0.10
		TSS	0.42	0.42	0.19	0.19	0.14	0.14	0.085	0.085	0.21	0.21	0.94	0.94
		pH	6.0–9.0		6.0–9.0		6.0–9.0		6.0–9.0		6.0–9.0		6.0–9.0	
		COD					0.52	0.52	0.37	0.37				
Subpart Cb[k]	Sub-part Cb	BOD_5	0.55	0.55	0.25	0.25	0.12	0.12	0.068	0.068	0.45	0.45	0.20	0.20
		TSS	0.56	0.56	0.25	0.25	0.19	0.19	0.11	0.11	0.28	0.28	0.12	0.12
		pH	6.0–9.0		6.0–9.0		6.0–9.0		6.0–9.0		6.0–9.0		6.0–9.0	
		COD					1.75	1.75	0.98	0.98				
Subpart Cc[k]	Sub-part Cc	BOD_5	1.15	1.15	0.51	0.51	0.067	0.067	0.043	0.043	0.94	0.94	0.42	0.42
		TSS	0.15	0.15	0.068	0.068	0.05	0.05	0.03	0.03	0.076	0.076	0.034	0.034
		pH	6.0–9.0		6.0–9.0		6.0–9.0		6.0–9.0		6.0–9.0		6.0–9.0	
		COD					6.07	6.07	4.37	4.37				
Subpart Cd[k]	Sub-part Cd	BOD_5	3.08	3.08	1.37	1.37	0.62	0.62	0.35	0.35	2.56	2.56	1.14	1.14
		TSS	2.80	2.80	1.25	1.25	0.94	0.94	0.57	0.57	1.40	1.40	0.63	0.63
		pH	6.0–9.0		6.0–9.0		6.0–9.0		6.0–9.0		6.0–9.0		6.0–9.0	
		COD					39.25	39.25	28.26	28.26				
Subpart Ce[k]	Sub-part Ce	Phenols	0.045	0.045	0.020	0.020	0.003	0.003	0.017	0.017	0.045	0.045	0.02	0.02
14. Inorganic chemicals manufacturing[19] — Subpart A Aluminum chloride production	Sub-part A	There shall be no discharge of process wastewater pollutants to navigable waters												
Subpart B Aluminum sulfate production[l]	Sub-part B	There shall be no discharge of process wastewater pollutants to navigable waters												

[j] A = Those cyanides amenable to chlorination as described in 1972 annual book of ASTM standards, Standard D2036-72, Method B, p 553.

[k] See p. 11-4 for description of products involved.

[l] A process wastewater impoundment which is designed, constructed, and operated so as to contain the precipitation from the 10-yr, 24-hr rainfall event may discharge that volume of process wastewater which is equivalent to the volume of precipitation that falls within the impoundment in excess of that attributable to the 10-yr, 24-hr rainfall event, when such event occurs.

TABLE 2 Effluent Guidelines and Standards (Continued)

Category	Sub-part	Effluent characteristic	BPCTCA effluent limitations				BATEA effluent limitations				New source standards of performance			
			Maximum for any 1 day		Average of daily values for 30 consecutive days shall not exceed		Maximum for any 1 day		Average of daily values for 30 consecutive days shall not exceed		Maximum for any 1 day		Average of daily values for 30 consecutive days shall not exceed	
			M[a]	E[a]	M	E	M	E	M	E	M	E	M	E
14. Inorganic chemicals manufacturing (*cont.*) Subpart C Calcium carbide production	Subpart C		There shall be no discharge of process wastewater pollutants to navigable waters											
Subpart D Calcium chloride production	Subpart D	TSS	0.016	0.016	0.0082	0.0082	There shall be no discharge of process wastewater pollutants to navigable waters							
		pH	6.0–9.0		6.0–9.0									
Subpart E Calcium oxide and calcium hydroxide production[l]	Subpart Ea, b, c		There shall be no discharge of process wastewater pollutants to navigable waters											
			mg/l	ppm	mg/l	ppm								
	Subpart Ed[m]	TSS	50	50	25	25								
		pH	6.0–9.0		6.0–9.0									
Subpart F Chlorine and sodium or potassium hydroxide production	Subpart Fa	TSS	0.64	0.64	0.32	0.32	Subject to provisions (see [n] below), there shall be no discharge of process wastewater pollutants to navigable waters				0.64	0.64	0.32	0.32
		Mercury	0.00028	0.00028	0.00014	0.00014					0.00014	0.00014	0.00007	0.00007
		pH	6.0–9.0		6.0–9.0						6.0–9.0		6.0–9.0	
Subpart Fa Mercury cell process														
Subpart Fb Diaphragm cell process	Subpart Fb	TSS	0.64	0.64	0.32	0.32	There shall be no discharge of process wastewater pollutants to navigable waters				0.64	0.64	0.32	0.32
		Lead	0.005	0.005	0.0025	0.0025					0.00008	0.00008	0.00004	0.00004
		pH	6.0–9.0		6.0–9.0						6.0–9.0		6.0–9.0	

Subpart	Subpart	Parameter	mg/l	ppm	mg/l	ppm	Requirement
Subpart G Hydrochloric acid	Subpart G						There shall be no discharge of process wastewater pollutants to navigable waters
Subpart H Hydrofluoric acid	Subpart Ha,b,c						Subject to provisions[l] of Eb, Ec, Ed, there shall be no discharge of process wastewater pollutants to navigable waters
	Subpart Hd	Fluoride	30	30	15	15	Subject to provisions (see [n] below), there shall be no discharge of process wastewater pollutants to navigable waters
		TSS	50	50	25	25	
		pH	6.0–9.0		6.0–9.0		
Subpart I Hydrogen peroxide production	Subpart Ia	TSS	0.8	0.8	0.4	0.4	There shall be no discharge of process wastewater pollutants to navigable waters
		TOC	0.44	0.44	0.22	0.22	
		pH	6.0–9.0		6.0–9.0		
Subpart Ia By the oxidation of alkyl hydroanthraquinous							
Subpart Ib By the electrolytic process	Subpart Ib	TSS	0.005	0.005	0.0025	0.0025	Subject to provisions[n], there shall be no discharge of process wastewater pollutants to navigable waters
		Cyanide-A[o]	0.0004	0.0004	0.0002	0.0002	
		pH	6.0–9.0		6.0–9.0		
Subpart J Nitric acid production	Subpart J						There shall be no discharge of process wastewater pollutants to navigable waters
Subpart K Potassium metal production	Subpart K						There shall be no discharge of process wastewater pollutants to navigable waters
Subpart L	Subpart L						There shall be no discharge of process wastewater pollutants to navigable waters

[m] During any calendar month there may be discharge from a process wastewater impoundment, wastewater equivalent to the precipitation minus evaporation for the month. If greater, a volume of process wastewater may be discharged equivalent to the mean precipitation minus the mean evaporation.

[n] A process wastewater impoundment which is designed, constructed, and operated so as to contain the precipitation from the 25-yr, 24-hr rainfall event may discharge that volume of process wastewater which is equivalent to the volume of precipitation that falls within the impoundment in excess of that attributable to the 25-yr, 24-hr rainfall event, when such event occurs.

[o] Cyanide A = Those cyanides amenable to chlorination as described in 1972 annual book of ASTM Standards D-2036-72 Method B, page 553.

TABLE 2 Effluent Guidelines and Standards (Continued)

Category	Subpart	Effluent characteristic	BPCTCA effluent limitations				BATEA effluent limitations				New source standards of performance			
			Maximum for any 1 day		Average of daily values for 30 consecutive days shall not exceed		Maximum for any 1 day		Average of daily values for 30 consecutive days shall not exceed		Maximum for any 1 day		Average of daily values for 30 consecutive days shall not exceed	
			M[a]	E[a]	M	E	M	E	M	E	M	E	M	E
14. Inorganic chemicals manufacturing (*cont.*)	Subpart Ma,b,c		Subject to provisions[l] of Mb, Mc, Md, there shall be no discharge of process wastewater pollutants to navigable waters											
Subpart M Potassium sulfate production			mg/l	ppm	mg/l	ppm								
	Subpart Md	TSS	50	50	25	25								
		pH	6.0–9.0		6.0–9.0									
Subpart N Sodium bicarbonate production	Subpart N		There shall be no discharge of process wastewater pollutants to navigable waters											
Subpart O Sodium carbonate	Subpart O	TSS	0.34	0.34	0.17	0.17	0.20	0.20	0.10	0.10	There shall be no discharge of process wastewater pollutants to navigable waters			
		pH	6.0–9.0		6.0–9.0		6.0–9.0		6.0–9.0					
Subpart P Sodium chloride	Subpart Pa		There shall be no discharge of process wastewater pollutants to navigable waters, except that unused bitterns may be removed to the body of water from which the process brine solution was originally withdrawn, provided no additional pollutants are added to the bitterns during the production of sodium chloride											
Subpart Pa Solar evaporation process														
Subpart Pb Solution brine mining process	Subpart Pb	TSS	0.34	0.34	0.17	0.17	There shall be no discharge of process wastewater pollutants to navigable waters							
		pH	6.0–9.0		6.0–9.0									

Category	Subpart	Pollutant	1	2	3	4	5	6	7	8	9	10	11	12
Subpart Q Sodium dichromate and sodium sulfate	Subpart Q	TSS	0.44	0.44	0.22	0.22	Subject to provisions[n], there shall be no discharge of process wastewater pollutants to navigable waters				0.30	0.30	0.15	0.15
		Chromium VI	0.009	0.009	0.0005	0.0005					0.009	0.009	0.0005	0.0005
		Chromium (total)	0.0088	0.0088	0.0044	0.0044					0.0088	0.0088	0.0044	0.0044
		pH	6.0–9.0		6.0–9.0						6.0–9.0		6.0–9.0	
Subpart R Sodium metal production	Subpart R	TSS	0.46	0.46	0.23	0.23	Subject to provisions[n]							
		pH	6.0–9.0		6.0–9.0									
Subpart S Sodium silicate	Subpart S	TSS	0.01	0.01	0.005	0.005	Subject to provisions[n]							
		pH	6.0–9.0		6.0–9.0									
Subpart T Sodium sulfate	Subpart T	TSS	0.032	0.032	0.016	0.016	Subject to provisions[n], there shall be no discharge of process wastewater pollutants to navigable waters							
		COD	3.4	3.4	1.7	1.7								
		pH	6.0–9.0		6.0–9.0									
Subpart U Sulfuric acid production	Subpart U		There shall be no discharge of process wastewater pollutants to navigable waters											
Subpart V Titanium dioxide production	Subpart Va	TSS	4.6	4.6	2.3	2.3	2.6	2.6	1.3	1.3	2.6	2.6	1.3	1.3
		Iron	0.72	0.72	0.36	0.36	0.36	0.36	0.18	0.18	0.36	0.36	0.18	0.18
		pH	6.0–9.0		6.0–9.0		6.0–9.0		6.0–9.0		6.0–9.0		6.0–9.0	
Subpart Va Chloride process														
Subpart Vb Sulfate process	Subpart Vb	TSS	21.0	21.0	10.5	10.5	10.6	10.6	5.3	5.3	10.6	10.6	5.3	5.3
		Iron	1.7	1.7	0.84	0.84	0.84	0.84	0.42	0.42	0.84	0.84	0.42	0.42
		pH	6.0–9.0		6.0–9.0		6.0–9.0		6.0–9.0		6.0–9.0		6.0–9.0	
15. Plastic and synthetics[20,21]	Subpart Aa	BOD_5	0.70	0.70	0.36	0.36	0.41	0.41	0.28	0.28	0.37	0.37	0.19	0.19
Subpart A Polyvinyl chloride		COD	7.0	7.0	3.6	3.6	1.92	1.92	1.28	1.28	1.70	1.70	0.89	0.89
		TSS	1.8	1.8	0.99	0.99	0.23	0.23	0.19	0.19	0.19	0.19	0.13	0.13
		pH	6.0–9.0		6.0–9.0		6.0–9.0		6.0–9.0		6.0–9.0		6.0–9.0	
Subpart Aa Suspension polymerization														

TABLE 2 Effluent Guidelines and Standards (Continued)

Category	Subpart	Effluent characteristic	BPCTCA effluent limitations				BATEA effluent limitations				New source standards of performance			
			Maximum for any 1 day		Average of daily values for 30 consecutive days shall not exceed		Maximum for any 1 day		Average of daily values for 30 consecutive days shall not exceed		Maximum for any 1 day		Average of daily values for 30 consecutive days shall not exceed	
			M[a]	E[a]	M	E	M	E	M	E	M	E	M	E
15. Plastic and synthetics (*cont.*) Subpart Ab Emulsion polymerization	Subpart Ab	BOD_5	0.26	0.26	0.13	0.13	0.20	0.20	0.13	0.13	0.26	0.26	0.13	0.13
		COD	2.6	2.6	1.3	1.3	0.92	0.92	0.61	0.61	1.20	1.20	0.61	0.61
		TSS	0.65	0.65	0.36	0.36	0.11	0.11	0.092	0.092	0.14	0.14	0.092	0.092
		pH	6.0–9.0		6.0–9.0		6.0–9.0		6.0–9.0		6.0–9.0		6.0–9.0	
Subpart Ac Bulk polymerization	Subpart Ac	BOD_5	0.12	0.12	0.06	0.06	0.09	0.09	0.06	0.06	0.12	0.12	0.06	0.06
		COD	1.2	1.2	0.60	0.60	0.42	0.42	0.28	0.28	0.54	0.54	0.28	0.28
		TSS	0.29	0.29	0.16	0.16	0.05	0.05	0.042	0.042	0.06	0.06	0.042	0.042
		pH	6.0–9.0		6.0–9.0		6.0–9.0		6.0–9.0		6.0–9.0		6.0–9.0	
Subpart B Polyvinyl acetate	Subpart B	BOD_5	0.39	0.39	0.20	0.20	0.29	0.29	0.19	0.19	0.35	0.35	0.18	0.18
		COD	3.9	3.9	2.0	2.0	1.33	1.33	0.89	0.89	1.6	1.6	0.84	0.84
		TSS	1.0	1.0	0.55	0.55	0.16	0.16	0.14	0.14	0.19	0.19	0.13	0.13
		pH	6.0–9.0		6.0–9.0		6.0–9.0		6.0–9.0		6.0–9.0		6.0–9.0	
Subpart C Polystyrene	Subpart Ca	BOD_5	0.43	0.43	0.22	0.22	0.33	0.33	0.22	0.22	0.43	0.43	0.22	0.22
		COD	4.3	4.3	2.20	2.20	1.55	1.55	1.03	1.03	2.0	2.0	1.03	1.03
Subpart Ca Suspension polymerization		Chromium (total)	0.0046	0.0046	0.0023	0.0023	0.0046	0.0046	0.0023	0.0023	0.0046	0.0046	0.0023	0.0023
		TSS	1.1	1.1	0.61	0.61	0.18	0.18	0.18	0.18	0.24	0.24	0.16	0.16
		pH	6.0–9.0		6.0–9.0		6.0–9.0		6.0–9.0		6.0–9.0		6.0–9.0	
Subpart Cb Bulk polymerization	Subpart Cb	BOD_5	0.08	0.08	0.04	0.04	0.06	0.06	0.04	0.04	0.08	0.08	0.04	0.04
		COD	0.80	0.80	0.40	0.40	0.29	0.29	0.19	0.19	0.37	0.37	0.19	0.19
		TSS	0.20	0.20	0.11	0.11	0.033	0.033	0.028	0.028	0.04	0.04	0.028	0.028
		pH	6.0–9.0		6.0–9.0		6.0–9.0		6.0–9.0		6.0–9.0		6.0–9.0	
Subpart D Polypropylene	Subpart D	BOD_5	0.81	0.81	0.42	0.42	0.48	0.48	0.32	0.32	0.43	0.43	0.22	0.22
		COD	4.1	4.1	2.1	2.1	3.21	3.21	2.14	2.14	2.9	2.9	1.47	1.47
		TSS	2.1	2.1	1.16	1.16	0.27	0.27	0.23	0.23	0.24	0.24	0.16	0.16
		pH	6.0–9.0		6.0–9.0		6.0–9.0		6.0–9.0		6.0–9.0		6.0–9.0	

Subpart E Polyethylene / Subpart Ea Low density	Subpart Ea	BOD_5	0.39	0.39	0.20	0.20	0.29	0.29	0.19	0.19	0.35	0.35	0.18	0.18
		COD	3.9	3.9	2.0	2.0	2.48	2.48	1.65	1.65	3.5	3.5	1.80	1.80
		TSS	1.0	1.0	0.55	0.55	0.16	0.16	0.14	0.14	0.19	0.19	0.13	0.13
		pH	6.0–9.0		6.0–9.0		6.0–9.0		6.0–9.0		6.0–9.0		6.0–9.0	
Subpart Eb High density (solvent process)	Subpart Eb	BOD_5	0.58	0.58	0.30	0.30	0.45	0.45	0.30	0.30	0.58	0.58	0.3	0.3
		COD	5.8	5.8	3.0	3.0	2.40	2.40	1.60	1.60	3.1	3.1	1.6	1.6
		Chromium (total)	0.0062	0.0062	0.0031	0.0031	0.0062	0.0062	0.0031	0.0031	0.0062	0.0062	0.0031	0.0031
		TSS	1.5	1.5	0.83	0.83	0.25	0.25	0.21	0.21	0.31	0.31	0.31	0.31
		pH	6.0–9.0		6.0–9.0		6.0–9.0		6.0–9.0		6.0–9.0		6.0–9.0	
Subpart Ec High density (polyform process)	Subpart Ec	BOD_5	0.01	0.01	0.052	0.052	0.078	0.078	0.052	0.052	0.10	0.10	0.054	0.054
		COD	1.0	1.0	0.52	0.52	0.42	0.42	0.28	0.28	0.54	0.54	0.28	0.28
		TSS	0.25	0.25	0.14	0.14	0.043	0.043	0.037	0.037	0.05	0.05	0.036	0.036
		pH	6.0–9.0		6.0–9.0		6.0–9.0		6.0–9.0		6.0–9.0		6.0–9.0	
Subpart F Cellophane	Subpart F	BOD_5	17.8	17.8	8.7	8.7	6.75	6.75	4.5	4.5	6.2	6.2	3.2	3.2
		COD	178.0	178.0	87.0	87.0	58.5	58.5	39.0	39.0	83.0	83.0	42.7	42.7
		TSS	29.1	29.1	16.0	16.0	3.75	3.75	3.19	3.19	3.3	3.3	2.27	2.27
		pH	6.0–9.0		6.0–9.0		6.0–9.0		6.0–9.0		6.0–9.0		6.0–9.0	
Subpart G Rayon	Subpart G	BOD_5	10	10	4.8	4.8	3.75	3.75	2.50	2.50	3.5	3.5	1.8	1.8
		COD	150	150	72	72	32.3	32.3	21.7	21.7	81	81	42.0	42.0
		Zinc	0.91	0.91	0.534	0.534	0.210	0.210	0.105	0.105	0.15	0.15	0.075	0.075
		TSS	16	16	8.8	8.8	2.08	2.08	1.77	1.77	1.9	1.9	1.28	1.28
		pH	6.0–9.0		6.0–9.0		6.0–9.0		6.0–9.0		6.0–9.0		6.0–9.0	
Subpart H Acrylonitrile butadiene styrene (ABS) and styrene acrylonitrile (SAN) resin copolymers	Subpart H	BOD_5	1.3	1.3	0.63	0.63	0.60	0.60	0.40	0.40	0.74	0.74	0.38	0.38
		COD	13	13	6.3	6.3	4.35	4.35	2.9	2.9	5.4	5.4	2.79	2.79
		TSS	2.1	2.1	1.16	1.16	0.33	0.33	0.28	0.28	0.40	0.40	0.27	0.27
		Chromium (total)	0.0088	0.0088	0.0044	0.0044	0.0084	0.0084	0.0042	0.0042	0.0080	0.0080	0.0040	0.0040
		pH	6.0–9.0		6.0–9.0		6.0–9.0		6.0–9.0		6.0–9.0		6.0–9.0	
Subpart I Polyester / Subpart Ia Resin by batch processing	Subpart Ia	BOD_5	1.4	1.4	0.78	0.78	0.48	0.48	0.32	0.32	0.62	0.62	0.32	0.32
		COD	21.5	21.5	11.7	11.7	2.46	2.46	1.64	1.64	5.7	5.7	2.92	2.92
		TSS	0.95	0.95	0.52	0.52	0.16	0.16	0.13	0.13	0.19	0.19	0.13	0.13
		pH	6.0–9.0		6.0–9.0		6.0–9.0		6.0–9.0		6.0–9.0		6.0–9.0	

TABLE 2 Effluent Guidelines and Standards (Continued)

Category	Sub-part	Effluent characteristic	BPCTCA effluent limitations: Maximum for any 1 day		BPCTCA: Average of daily values for 30 consecutive days shall not exceed		BATEA effluent limitations: Maximum for any 1 day		BATEA: Average of daily values for 30 consecutive days shall not exceed		New source standards of performance: Maximum for any 1 day		New source: Average of daily values for 30 consecutive days shall not exceed	
			M[a]	E[a]	M	E	M	E	M	E	M	E	M	E
15. Plastic and	Sub-	BOD_5	1.4	1.4	0.78	0.78	0.48	0.48	0.32	0.32	0.62	0.62	0.32	0.32
synthetics (*cont.*)	part	COD	21.5	21.5	11.7	11.7	2.46	2.46	1.64	1.64	5.7	5.7	2.92	2.92
Subpart Ib	Ib	TSS	0.95	0.95	0.52	0.52	0.16	0.16	0.13	0.13	0.19	0.19	0.13	0.13
Fiber by batch processing		pH	6.0–9.0		6.0–9.0		6.0–9.0		6.0–9.0		6.0–9.0		6.0–9.0	
Subpart Ic	Sub-	BOD_5	1.4	1.4	0.78	0.78	0.95	0.95	0.63	0.63	0.35	0.35	0.18	0.18
Resin and fiber by	part	COD	21.5	21.5	11.7	11.7	4.95	4.95	3.30	3.30	3.2	3.2	1.67	1.67
continuous processing	Ic	TSS	0.95	0.95	0.52	0.52	0.32	0.32	0.27	0.27	0.12	0.12	0.078	0.078
		pH	6.0–9.0		6.0–9.0		6.0–9.0		6.0–9.0		6.0–9.0		6.0–9.0	
Subpart Id	Sub-	BOD_5	2.8	2.8	1.56	1.56	0.38	0.38	0.25	0.25	1.2	1.2	0.63	0.63
Polyester resin and fiber	part	COD	43.0	43.0	23.4	23.4	1.95	1.95	1.30	1.30	11.3	11.3	5.84	5.84
by continuous processing	Id	TSS	1.9	1.9	1.04	1.04	0.13	0.13	0.11	0.11	0.4	0.4	0.27	0.27
		pH	6.0–9.0		6.0–9.0		6.0–9.0		6.0–9.0		6.0–9.0		6.0–9.0	
Subpart J	Sub-	BOD_5	1.2	1.2	0.66	0.66	0.40	0.40	0.27	0.27	0.53	0.53	0.27	0.27
Nylon 66	part	COD	6.0	6.0	3.3	3.3	2.09	2.09	1.39	1.39	3.7	3.7	1.92	1.92
Subpart Ja	Ja	TSS	0.80	0.80	0.44	0.44	0.13	0.13	0.11	0.11	0.16	0.16	0.11	0.11
Resin		pH	6.0–9.0		6.0–9.0		6.0–9.0		6.0–9.0		6.0–9.0		6.0–9.0	
Subpart Jb	Sub-	BOD_5	1.1	1.1	0.58	0.58	0.35	0.35	0.23	0.23	0.45	0.45	0.23	0.23
Fiber	part	COD	5.3	5.3	3.0	3.0	1.82	1.82	1.21	1.21	3.3	3.3	1.68	1.68
	Jb	TSS	0.70	0.70	0.39	0.39	0.12	0.12	0.10	0.10	0.15	0.15	0.10	0.10
		pH	6.0–9.0		6.0–9.0		6.0–9.0		6.0–9.0		6.0–9.0		6.0–9.0	
Subpart Jc	Sub-	BOD_5	2.3	2.3	1.24	1.24	0.75	0.75	0.50	0.50	0.98	0.98	0.50	0.50
Resin and fiber	part	COD	11.3	11.3	6.2	6.2	3.90	3.90	2.60	2.60	7.0	7.0	3.60	3.60
	Jc	TSS	1.5	1.5	0.83	0.83	0.25	0.25	0.21	0.21	0.31	0.31	0.21	0.21
		pH	6.0–9.0		6.0–9.0		6.0–9.0		6.0–9.0		6.0–9.0		6.0–9.0	

Subpart K	Sub-	BOD_5	6.8	6.8	3.71	3.71	1.95	1.95	1.30	1.30	2.1	2.1	1.10	1.10
Nylon 6	part	COD	68.0	68.0	37.1	37.1	10.2	10.2	6.77	6.77	22.0	22.0	11.4	11.4
Subpart Ka	Ka	TSS	4.5	4.5	2.48	2.48	0.65	0.65	0.55	0.55	0.69	0.69	0.47	0.47
Resin		pH	6.0–9.0		6.0–9.0		6.0–9.0		6.0–9.0		6.0–9.0		6.0–9.0	
Subpart Kb	Sub-	BOD_5	3.5	3.5	1.90	1.90	1.00	1.00	0.67	0.67	1.1	1.1	0.57	0.57
Fiber	part	COD	35.0	35.0	19.0	19.0	5.21	5.21	3.44	3.44	11.0	11.0	5.90	5.90
	Kb	TSS	2.3	2.3	1.27	1.27	0.33	0.33	0.28	0.28	0.35	0.35	0.24	0.24
		pH	6.0–9.0		6.0–9.0		6.0–9.0		6.0–9.0		6.0–9.0		6.0–9.0	
Subpart Kc	Sub-	BOD_5	10.3	10.3	5.61	5.61	2.95	2.95	1.97	1.97	3.2	3.2	1.67	1.67
Resin and fiber	part	COD	103.0	103.0	56.1	56.1	15.3	15.3	10.2	10.2	33.0	33.0	17.4	17.4
	Kc	TSS	6.8	6.8	3.75	3.75	0.98	0.98	0.84	0.84	1.1	1.1	0.71	0.71
		pH	6.0–9.0		6.0–9.0		6.0–9.0		6.0–9.0		6.0–9.0		6.0–9.0	
Subpart L	Sub-	BOD_5	7.5	7.5	4.13	4.13	1.88	1.88	1.25	1.25	1.6	1.6	0.83	0.83
Cellulose acetate	part	COD	75.0	75.0	41.3	41.3	9.75	9.75	6.5	6.5	15.5	15.5	8.0	8.0
Subpart La	La	TSS	5.0	5.0	2.75	2.75	0.63	0.63	0.53	0.53	0.51	0.51	0.35	0.35
Resin		pH	6.0–9.0		6.0–9.0		6.0–9.0		6.0–9.0		6.0–9.0		6.0–9.0	
Subpart Lb	Sub-	BOD_5	7.5	7.5	4.13	4.13	1.88	1.88	1.25	1.25	1.6	1.6	0.83	0.83
Fiber	part	COD	75.0	75.0	41.3	41.3	9.75	9.75	6.5	6.5	15.5	15.5	8.0	8.0
	Lb	TSS	5.0	5.0	2.75	2.75	0.63	0.63	0.53	0.53	0.51	0.51	0.35	0.35
		pH	6.0–9.0		6.0–9.0		6.0–9.0		6.0–9.0		6.0–9.0		6.0–9.0	
Subpart Lc	Sub-	BOD_5	15	15	8.26	8.26	3.75	3.75	2.50	2.50	3.2	3.2	1.67	1.67
Resin and fiber	part	COD	150	150	82.6	82.6	19.5	19.5	13.0	13.0	31.0	31.0	16.0	16.0
	Lc	TSS	10	10	5.50	5.50	1.26	1.26	1.06	1.06	1.1	1.1	0.71	0.71
		pH	6.0–9.0		6.0–9.0		6.0–9.0		6.0–9.0		6.0–9.0		6.0–9.0	
Subpart M	Sub-	BOD_5	5	5	2.75	2.75	0.98	0.98	0.65	0.65	1.2	1.2	0.63	0.63
Acrylics	part	COD	25	25	13.8	13.8	5.07	5.07	3.38	3.38	24	24	12.2	12.2
	M	TSS	2	2	1.1	1.1	0.33	0.33	0.27	0.27	0.4	0.4	0.27	0.27
		Phenolic compounds	0.017	0.017	0.0083	0.0083	0.0032	0.0032	0.0016	0.0016	0.0032	0.0032	0.0016	0.0016
		pH	6.0–9.0		6.0–9.0		6.0–9.0		6.0–9.0		6.0–9.0		6.0–9.0	
Subpart N	Sub-	BOD_5	0.14	0.14	0.07	0.07	0.09	0.09	0.06	0.06	0.10	0.10	0.05	0.05
Ethylene vinyl	part	COD	0.70	0.70	0.35	0.35	0.29	0.29	0.19	0.19	0.40	0.40	0.22	0.22
	N	TSS	0.35	0.35	0.19	0.19	0.05	0.05	0.04	0.04	0.05	0.05	0.04	0.04
		pH	6.0–9.0		6.0–9.0		6.0–9.0		6.0–9.0		6.0–9.0		6.0–9.0	

TABLE 2 Effluent Guidelines and Standards (Continued)

Category	Sub-part	Effluent characteristic	BPCTCA effluent limitations				BATEA effluent limitations				New source standards of performance			
			Maximum for any 1 day		Average of daily values for 30 consecutive days shall not exceed		Maximum for any 1 day		Average of daily values for 30 consecutive days shall not exceed		Maximum for any 1 day		Average of daily values for 30 consecutive days shall not exceed	
			M[a]	E[a]	M	E	M	E	M	E	M	E	M	E
15. Plastic and	Sub-	BOD_5	7.0	7.0	3.6	3.6	3.3	3.3	2.2	2.2	1.6	1.6	0.80	0.80
synthetics (*cont.*)	part	COD	13.0	13.0	6.7	6.7	5.9	5.9	4.0	4.0	2.9	2.9	1.4	1.4
	O	TSS	18.0	18.0	9.9	9.9	1.8	1.8	1.6	1.6	0.83	0.83	0.57	0.57
Subpart O		Fluorides	1.2	1.2	0.6	0.6	1.2	1.2	0.6	0.6	1.2	1.2	0.6	0.6
Fluorocarbons		pH	6.0–9.0		6.0–9.0		6.0–9.0		6.0–9.0		6.0–9.0		6.0–9.0	
Subpart P	Sub-	BOD_5	0.78	0.78	0.40	0.40	0.33	0.33	0.22	0.22	0.08	0.08	0.04	0.04
Polypropylene fiber	part	COD	3.9	3.9	2.0	2.0	0.59	0.59	0.40	0.40	0.14	0.14	0.07	0.07
	P	TSS	2.0	2.0	1.1	1.1	0.18	0.18	0.16	0.16	0.04	0.04	0.03	0.03
		Oil and grease	1.0	1.0	0.5	0.5	0.18	0.18	0.092	0.092	0.033	0.033	0.017	0.017
		pH	6.0–9.0		6.0–9.0		6.0–9.0		6.0–9.0		6.0–9.0		6.0–9.0	
Subpart Q	Sub-	BOD_5	0.60	0.60	0.33	0.33	0.14	0.14	0.10	0.10	0.03	0.03	0.02	0.02
Alkyds and unsaturated	part	COD	3.0	3.0	1.7	1.7	0.74	0.74	0.52	0.52	0.20	0.20	0.11	0.11
polyester resins	Q	TSS	0.40	0.40	0.22	0.22	0.04	0.04	0.03	0.03	0.008	0.008	0.006	0.006
		pH	6.0–9.0		6.0–9.0		6.0–9.0		6.0–9.0		6.0–9.0		6.0–9.0	
Subpart R	Sub-	BOD_5	26	26	14.0	14.0	9.4	9.4	6.9	6.9	11.0	11.0	6.0	6.0
Cellulose nitrate	part	COD	85	85	46.0	46.0	47.0	47.0	34.0	34.0	54.0	54.0	30.0	30.0
	R	TSS	17	17	9.4	9.4	2.5	2.5	2.1	2.1	2.7	2.7	1.8	1.8
		pH	6.0–9.0		6.0–9.0		6.0–9.0		6.0–9.0		6.0–9.0		6.0–9.0	
Subpart S	Sub-	BOD_5	1.2	1.2	0.66	0.66	0.50	0.50	0.37	0.37	0.67	0.67	0.37	0.37
Polyamide (nylon 6/12)	part	COD	6.0	6.0	3.3	3.3	2.6	2.6	1.9	1.9	3.4	3.4	1.9	1.9
	S	TSS	0.80	0.80	0.44	0.44	0.13	0.13	0.11	0.11	0.17	0.17	0.11	0.11
		pH	6.0–9.0		6.0–9.0		6.0–9.0		6.0–9.0		6.0–9.0		6.0–9.0	
Subpart T	Sub-	BOD_5	1.4	1.4	0.78	0.78	0.59	0.59	0.44	0.44	0.80	0.80	0.44	0.44
Polyester resins	part	COD	22	22	12	12	3.1	3.1	2.3	2.3	12	12	6.5	6.5
	T	TSS	0.95	0.95	0.52	0.52	0.16	0.16	0.14	0.14	0.20	0.20	0.14	0.14
		pH	6.0–9.0		6.0–9.0		6.0–9.0		6.0–9.0		6.0–9.0		6.0–9.0	

Subpart U	Sub-	BOD_5	26	26	14	14	9.1	9.1	6.7	6.7	10	10	5.5	5.5
Silicones	part	COD	127	127	70	70	47	47	35	35	82	82	46	46
Subpart Ua1	Ua1	TSS	17	17	9.1	9.1	2.4	2.4	2.0	2.0	2.5	2.5	1.7	1.7
Multiproduct plants		Cu	0.14	0.14	0.071	0.071	0.06	0.06	0.03	0.03	0.050	0.050	0.025	0.025
(general)		pH	6.0–9.0		6.0–9.0		6.0–9.0		6.0–9.0		6.0–9.0		6.0–9.0	
Subpart Ua2	Sub-	BOD_5	15	15	8.2	8.2								
Multiproduct plants	part	COD	75	75	41	41								
(coupling agents	Ua2	TSS	10	10	5.4	5.4								
manufacturing)		Cu	0.083	0.083	0.042	0.042								
		pH	6.0–9.0		6.0–9.0									
Subpart Ub	Sub-	BOD_5	6.0	6.0	3.3	3.3	1.6	1.6	1.2	1.2	1.0	1.0	0.57	0.57
Fluid product plant	part	COD	30	30	17	17	8.5	8.5	6.3	6.3	8.5	8.5	4.7	4.7
	Ub	TSS	4.0	4.0	2.2	2.2	0.44	0.44	0.37	0.37	0.26	0.26	0.18	0.18
		Cu	0.034	0.034	0.017	0.017	0.011	0.011	0.0055	0.0055	0.0052	0.0052	0.0026	0.0026
		pH	6.0–9.0		6.0–9.0		6.0–9.0		6.0–9.0		6.0–9.0		6.0–9.0	
Subpart V	Sub-	BOD_5	3.9	3.9	2.1	2.1	1.3	1.3	0.95	0.95	1.2	1.2	0.67	0.67
Epoxy resin	part	COD	58	58	32	32	6.5	6.5	4.8	4.8	12.9	12.9	9.2	9.2
Subpart Va	Va	TSS	2.6	2.6	1.4	1.4	0.33	0.33	0.28	0.28	0.30	0.30	0.20	0.20
Batch and continuous epoxy resin (liquid,		Phenolic compounds	0.0022	0.0022	0.011	0.011	0.0033	0.0033	0.0017	0.0017	0.0024	0.0024	0.0012	0.0012
solid solution)		pH	6.0–9.0		6.0–9.0		6.0–9.0		6.0–9.0		6.0–9.0		6.0–9.0	
Subpart Vb	Sub-	BOD_5	0.45	0.45	0.25	0.25	0.17	0.17	0.12	0.12	0.19	0.19	0.11	0.11
Epoxy resins by batch	part	COD	6.7	6.7	3.9	3.9	0.88	0.88	0.65	0.65	2.1	2.1	1.5	1.5
fusion (solid and solution)	Vb	TSS	0.30	0.30	0.17	0.17	0.05	0.05	0.04	0.04	0.05	0.05	0.03	0.03
		Phenolic compounds	0.0025	0.0025	0.0013	0.0013	0.0044	0.0044	0.0022	0.0022	0.0038	0.0038	0.0019	0.0019
		pH	6.0–9.0		6.0–9.0		6.0–9.0		6.0–9.0		6.0–9.0		6.0–9.0	
Subpart W	Sub-	BOD_5	6.7	6.7	3.7	3.7	1.3	1.3	0.96	0.96	1.3	1.3	0.69	0.69
Phenolic resins	part	COD	34	34	19	19	6.8	6.8	5	5	34	34	19	19
	W	TSS	2.7	2.7	1.5	1.5	0.35	0.35	0.30	0.30	0.31	0.31	0.21	0.21
		Phenolic compounds	0.23	0.23	0.11	0.11	0.0035	0.0035	0.0018	0.0018	0.0025	0.0025	0.0013	0.0013
		pH	6.0–9.0		6.0–9.0		6.0–9.0		6.0–9.0		6.0–9.0		6.0–9.0	
Subpart X	Sub-	BOD_5	0.38	0.38	0.20	0.20	0.08	0.08	0.06	0.06	0.11	0.11	0.06	0.06
Urea and melamine	part	COD	5.5	5.5	3.2	3.2	0.13	0.13	0.09	0.09	0.18	0.18	0.10	0.10
resins	X	TSS	0.25	0.25	0.13	0.13	0.021	0.021	0.017	0.017	0.04	0.04	0.02	0.02
		pH	6.0–9.0		6.0–9.0		6.0–9.0		6.0–9.0		6.0–9.0		6.0–9.0	

TABLE 2 Effluent Guidelines and Standards (Continued)

Category	Sub-part	Effluent characteristic	BPCTCA effluent limitations				BATEA effluent limitations				New source standards of performance			
			Maximum for any 1 day		Average of daily values for 30 consecutive days shall not exceed		Maximum for any 1 day		Average of daily values for 30 consecutive days shall not exceed		Maximum for any 1 day		Average of daily values for 30 consecutive days shall not exceed	
			M[a]	E[a]	M	E	M	E	M	E	M	E	M	E
16. Soap and detergent manufacturing[22]	Sub-part A	BOD_5	1.80	1.80	0.60	0.60	0.80	0.80	0.40	0.40	0.80	0.80	0.40	0.40
		COD	4.50	4.50	1.50	1.50	2.10	2.10	1.05	1.05	2.10	2.10	1.05	1.05
Subpart A Soap manufacturing by batch kettle		TSS	1.20	1.20	0.40	0.40	0.80	0.80	0.40	0.40	0.80	0.80	0.40	0.40
		Oil and grease	0.30	0.30	0.10	0.10	0.10	0.10	0.05	0.05	0.10	0.10	0.05	0.05
		pH	6.0–9.0		6.0–9.0		6.0–9.0		6.0–9.0		6.0–9.0		6.0–9.0	
Subpart B Fatty acid manufacturing by fat splitting	Sub-part Ba	BOD_5	3.60	3.60	1.20	1.20	0.50	0.50	0.25	0.25	0.50	0.50	0.25	0.25
		COD	9.90	9.90	3.30	3.30	1.80	1.80	0.90	0.90	1.80	1.80	0.90	0.90
		TSS	6.60	6.60	2.20	2.20	0.40	0.40	0.20	0.20	0.40	0.40	0.20	0.20
Subpart Ba Fatty acid manufacturing		Oil and grease	0.90	0.90	0.30	0.30	0.30	0.30	0.15	0.15	0.30	0.30	0.15	0.15
		pH	6.0–9.0		6.0–9.0		6.0–9.0		6.0–9.0		6.0–9.0		6.0–9.0	
Subpart Bb Hydrogenation of fatty acid	Sub-part Bb	BOD_5	0.45	0.45	0.15	0.15	0.30	0.30	0.15	0.15	0.30	0.30	0.15	0.15
		COD	0.75	0.75	0.25	0.25	0.50	0.50	0.25	0.25	0.50	0.50	0.25	0.25
		TSS	0.30	0.30	0.10	0.10	0.20	0.20	0.10	0.10	0.20	0.20	0.10	0.10
		Oil and grease	0.30	0.30	0.10	0.10	0.20	0.20	0.10	0.10	0.20	0.20	0.10	0.10
		pH	6.0–9.0		6.0–9.0		6.0–9.0		6.0–9.0		6.0–9.0		6.0–9.0	
Subpart C Soap manufacturing by fatty acid neutralization	Sub-part C	BOD_5	0.03	0.03	0.01	0.01	0.02	0.02	0.01	0.01	0.02	0.02	0.01	0.01
		COD	0.15	0.15	0.05	0.05	0.10	0.10	0.05	0.05	0.10	0.10	0.05	0.05
		TSS	0.06	0.06	0.02	0.02	0.04	0.04	0.02	0.02	0.04	0.04	0.02	0.02
		Oil and grease	0.03	0.03	0.01	0.01	0.02	0.02	0.01	0.01	0.02	0.02	0.01	0.01
		pH	6.0–9.0		6.0–9.0		6.0–9.0		6.0–9.0		6.0–9.0		6.0–9.0	
Subpart D Glycerin concentration	Sub-part D	BOD_5	4.50	4.50	1.50	1.50	0.80	0.80	0.40	0.40	0.80	0.80	0.40	0.40
		COD	13.50	13.50	4.50	4.50	2.40	2.40	1.20	1.20	2.40	2.40	1.20	1.20
		TSS	0.60	0.60	0.20	0.20	0.20	0.20	0.10	0.10	0.20	0.20	0.10	0.10
		Oil and grease	0.30	0.30	0.10	0.10	0.08	0.08	0.04	0.04	0.08	0.08	0.04	0.04
		pH	6.0–9.0		6.0–9.0		6.0–9.0		6.0–9.0		6.0–9.0		6.0–9.0	

Subpart E Glycerin distillation	Subpart E	BOD_5	1.50	1.50	0.50	0.50	0.60	0.60	0.30	0.30	0.60	0.60	0.30	0.30
		COD	4.50	4.50	1.50	1.50	1.80	1.80	0.90	0.90	1.80	1.80	0.90	0.90
		TSS	0.60	0.60	0.20	0.20	0.08	0.08	0.04	0.04	0.08	0.08	0.04	0.04
		Oil and grease	0.30	0.30	0.10	0.10	0.04	0.04	0.02	0.02	0.04	0.04	0.02	0.02
		pH	6.0–9.0		6.0–9.0		6.0–9.0		6.0–9.0		6.0–9.0		6.0–9.0	
Subpart F Soap flakes and powder	Subpart F	BOD_5	0.03	0.03	0.01	0.01	0.02	0.02	0.01	0.01	0.02	0.02	0.01	0.01
		COD	0.15	0.15	0.05	0.05	0.10	0.10	0.05	0.05	0.10	0.10	0.05	0.05
		TSS	0.03	0.03	0.01	0.01	0.02	0.02	0.01	0.01	0.02	0.02	0.01	0.01
		Oil and grease	0.03	0.03	0.01	0.01	0.02	0.02	0.01	0.01	0.02	0.02	0.01	0.01
		pH	6.0–9.0		6.0–9.0		6.0–9.0		6.0–9.0		6.0–9.0		6.0–9.0	
Subpart G Bar soaps	Subpart G	BOD_5	1.02	1.02	0.34	0.34	0.40	0.40	0.20	0.20	0.40	0.40	0.20	0.20
		COD	2.55	2.55	0.85	0.85	1.20	1.20	0.60	0.60	1.20	1.20	0.60	0.60
		TSS	1.74	1.74	0.58	0.58	0.68	0.68	0.34	0.34	0.68	0.68	0.34	0.34
		Oil and grease	0.12	0.12	0.04	0.04	0.06	0.06	0.03	0.03	0.06	0.06	0.03	0.03
		pH	6.0–9.0		6.0–9.0		6.0–9.0		6.0–9.0		6.0–9.0		6.0–9.0	
Subpart H Liquid soap	Subpart H	BOD_5	0.03	0.03	0.01	0.01	0.02	0.02	0.01	0.01	0.02	0.02	0.01	0.01
		COD	0.15	0.15	0.05	0.05	0.10	0.10	0.05	0.05	0.10	0.10	0.05	0.05
		TSS	0.03	0.03	0.01	0.01	0.02	0.02	0.01	0.01	0.02	0.02	0.01	0.01
		Oil and grease	0.03	0.03	0.01	0.01	0.02	0.02	0.01	0.01	0.02	0.02	0.01	0.01
		pH	6.0–9.0		6.0–9.0		6.0–9.0		6.0–9.0		6.0–9.0		6.0–9.0	
Subpart I Oleum sulfonation and sulfation	Subpart I	BOD_5	0.09	0.09	0.02	0.02	0.07	0.07	0.02	0.02	0.03	0.03	0.01	0.01
		COD	0.40	0.40	0.09	0.09	0.27	0.27	0.09	0.09	0.09	0.09	0.03	0.03
		TSS	0.15	0.15	0.03	0.03	0.09	0.09	0.03	0.03	0.06	0.06	0.02	0.02
		Surfactant	0.15	0.15	0.03	0.03	0.09	0.09	0.03	0.03	0.03	0.03	0.01	0.01
		Oil and grease	0.25	0.25	0.07	0.07	0.21	0.21	0.07	0.07	0.12	0.12	0.04	0.04
		pH	6.0–9.0		6.0–9.0		6.0–9.0		6.0–9.0		6.0–9.0		6.0–9.0	
Subpart J Air-SO_3 Sulfation and sulfonation	Subpart J	BOD_5	0.90	0.90	0.30	0.30	0.30	0.30	0.19	0.19	0.18	0.18	0.09	0.09
		COD	4.05	4.05	1.35	1.35	1.10	1.10	0.55	0.55	0.80	0.80	0.40	0 40
		TSS	0.09	0.09	0.03	0.03	0.04	0.04	0.02	0.02	0.04	0.04	0.02	0.02
		Surfactant	0.90	0.90	0.30	0.30	0.36	0.36	0.18	0.18	0.18	0.18	0.09	0.09
		Oil and grease	0.15	0.15	0.05	0.05	0.08	0.08	0.04	0.04	0.04	0.04	0.02	0.02
		pH	6.0–9.0		6.0–9.0		6.0–9.0		6.0–9.0		6.0–9.0		6.0–9.0	
Subpart K SO_3 solvent and vacuum sulfonation	Subpart K	BOD_5	0.90	0.90	0.30	0.30	0.20	0.20	0.10	0.10	0.20	0.20	0.10	0.10
		COD	3.05	3.05	1.35	1.35	0.90	0.90	0.45	0.45	0.90	0.90	0.45	0.45
		TSS	0.09	0.09	0.03	0.03	0.02	0.02	0.01	0.01	0.02	0.02	0.01	0.01
		Surfactant	0.90	0.90	0.30	0.30	0.20	0.20	0.10	0.10	0.20	0.20	0.10	0.10
		Oil and grease	0.10	0.10	0.05	0.05	0.04	0.04	0.02	0.02	0.04	0.04	0.02	0.02
		pH	6.0–9.0		6.0–9.0		6.0–9.0		6.0–9.0		6.0–9.0		6.0–9.0	

TABLE 2 Effluent Guidelines and Standards (Continued)

Category	Subpart	Effluent characteristic	BPCTCA effluent limitations				BATEA effluent limitations				New source standards of performance			
			Maximum for any 1 day		Average of daily values for 30 consecutive days shall not exceed		Maximum for any 1 day		Average of daily values for 30 consecutive days shall not exceed		Maximum for any 1 day		Average of daily values for 30 consecutive days shall not exceed	
			M[a]	E[a]	M	E	M	E	M	E	M	E	M	E
16. Soap and Detergent manufacturing (*cont.*) — Subpart L Sulfonic acid sulfation	Subpart L	BOD_5	0.90	0.90	0.30	0.30	0.20	0.20	0.10	0.10	0.20	0.20	0.10	0.10
		COD	4.05	4.05	1.35	1.35	0.90	0.90	0.45	0.45	0.90	0.90	0.45	0.45
		TSS	0.09	0.09	0.03	0.03	0.02	0.02	0.01	0.01	0.02	0.02	0.01	0.01
		Surfactant	0.90	0.90	0.30	0.30	0.20	0.20	0.10	0.10	0.20	0.20	0.10	0.10
		Oil and grease	0.15	0.15	0.05	0.05	0.04	0.04	0.02	0.02	0.04	0.04	0.02	0.02
		pH	6.0–9.0		6.0–9.0		6.0–9.0		6.0–9.0		6.0–9.0		6.0–9.0	
Subpart M Chlorosulfonic acid sulfation	Subpart M	BOD_5	0.90	0.90	0.30	0.30	0.30	0.30	0.15	0.15	0.30	0.30	0.15	0.15
		COD	4.05	4.05	1.35	1.35	1.50	1.50	0.75	0.75	1.50	1.50	0.75	0.75
		TSS	0.09	0.09	0.03	0.03	0.04	0.04	0.02	0.02	0.04	0.04	0.02	0.02
		Surfactant	0.90	0.90	0.30	0.30	0.30	0.30	0.15	0.15	0.30	0.30	0.15	0.15
		Oil and grease	0.15	0.15	0.05	0.05	0.06	0.06	0.03	0.03	0.06	0.06	0.03	0.03
		pH	6.0–9.0		6.0–9.0		6.0–9.0		6.0–9.0		6.0–9.0		6.0–9.0	
Subpart N Neutralization of sulfuric acid esters and sulfonic acids	Subpart N	BOD_5	0.03	0.03	0.01	0.01	0.02	0.02	0.01	0.01	0.02	0.02	0.01	0.01
		COD	0.15	0.15	0.05	0.05	0.10	0.10	0.05	0.05	0.08	0.08	0.04	0.04
		TSS	0.09	0.09	0.03	0.03	0.06	0.06	0.03	0.03	0.06	0.06	0.03	0.03
		Surfactant	0.06	0.06	0.02	0.02	0.04	0.04	0.02	0.02	0.04	0.04	0.02	0.02
		Oil and grease	0.03	0.03	0.01	0.01	0.02	0.02	0.01	0.01	0.02	0.02	0.01	0.01
		pH	6.0–9.0		6.0–9.0		6.0–9.0		6.0–9.0		6.0–9.0		6.0–9.0	
Subpart O Spray-dried detergents — Subpart Oa Spray-drying towers	Subpart Oa	BOD_5	0.03	0.03	0.01	0.01	0.02	0.02	0.01	0.01	0.02	0.02	0.01	0.01
		COD	0.15	0.15	0.05	0.05	0.08	0.08	0.04	0.04	0.08	0.08	0.04	0.04
		TSS	0.03	0.03	0.01	0.01	0.04	0.04	0.02	0.02	0.04	0.04	0.02	0.02
		Surfactant	0.06	0.06	0.02	0.02	0.04	0.04	0.02	0.02	0.04	0.04	0.02	0.02
		Oil and grease	0.015	0.015	0.005	0.005	0.01	0.01	0.005	0.005	0.01	0.01	0.005	0.005
		pH	6.0–9.0		6.0–9.0		6.0–9.0		6.0–9.0		6.0–9.0		6.0–9.0	

Subpart Ob	Sub-	BOD_5	0.24	0.24	0.08	0.08	0.12	0.12	0.06	0.06	0.12	0.12	0.06	0.06
Spray-drying towers but	part	COD	1.05	1.05	0.35	0.35	0.50	0.50	0.25	0.25	0.50	0.50	0.25	0.25
only when a high rate of	Ob	TSS	0.30	0.30	0.10	0.10	0.14	0.14	0.07	0.07	0.14	0.14	0.07	0.07
wet scrubbing is in oper-		Surfactant	0.45	0.45	0.15	0.15	0.20	0.20	0.10	0.10	0.20	0.20	0.10	0.10
ation which produces		Oil and grease	0.09	0.09	0.03	0.03	0.04	0.04	0.02	0.02	0.04	0.04	0.02	0.02
more wastewater than		pH	6.0–9.0		6.0–9.0		6.0–9.0		6.0–9.0		6.0–9.0		6.0–9.0	
can be recycled to process														
Subpart Oc	Sub-	BOD_5	0.02	0.02			0.02	0.02			0.02	0.02		
Fast turnaround opera-	part	COD	0.09	0.09			0.07	0.07			0.07	0.07		
tion of a spray tower	Oc[p]	TSS	0.02	0.02			0.02	0.02			0.02	0.02		
		Surfactant	0.03	0.03			0.02	0.02			0.02	0.02		
		Oil and grease	0.005	0.005			0.005	0.005			0.005	0.005		
		pH	6.0–9.0				6.0–9.0				6.0–9.0			
Subpart P	Sub-	BOD_5	0.60	0.60	0.20	0.20	0.10	0.10	0.05	0.05	0.10	0.10	0.05	0.05
Liquid detergents	part	COD	1.80	1.80	0.60	0.60	0.44	0.44	0.22	0.22	0.44	0.44	0.22	0.22
	Pa	TSS	0.015	0.015	0.005	0.005	0.01	0.01	0.005	0.005	0.01	0.01	0.005	0.005
Subpart Pa		Surfactant	0.39	0.39	0.13	0.13	0.10	0.10	0.05	0.05	0.10	0.10	0.05	0.05
Normal liquid detergent		Oil and grease	0.015	0.015	0.005	0.005	0.01	0.01	0.005	0.005	0.01	0.01	0.005	0.005
operations		pH	6.0–9.0		6.0–9.0		6.0–9.0		6.0–9.0		6.0–9.0		6.0–9.0	
Subpart Pb	Sub-	BOD_5	0.05	0.05			0.02	0.02			0.02	0.02		
Fast turnaround opera-	part	COD	0.15	0.15			0.07	0.07			0.07	0.07		
tion of automated fill	Pb[q]	TSS	0.002	0.002			0.002	0.002			0.002	0.002		
lines		Surfactant	0.04	0.04			0.02	0.02			0.02	0.02		
		Oil and grease	0.002	0.002			0.002	0.002			0.002	0.002		
		pH	6.0–9.0				6.0–9.0				6.0–9.0			
Subpart Q	Sub-	BOD_5	0.03	0.03	0.01	0.01	0.02	0.02	0.01	0.01	0.02	0.02	0.01	0.01
Detergents by dry	part	COD	0.21	0.21	0.07	0.07	0.14	0.14	0.07	0.07	0.14	0.14	0.07	0.07
blending	Q	TSS	0.03	0.03	0.01	0.01	0.02	0.02	0.01	0.01	0.02	0.02	0.01	0.01
		Surfactant	0.03	0.03	0.01	0.01	0.02	0.02	0.01	0.01	0.02	0.02	0.01	0.01
		Oil and grease	0.005	0.005	0.005	0.005	0.01	0.01	0.005	0.005	0.01	0.01	0.005	0.005
		pH	6.0–9.0		6.0–9.0		6.0–9.0		6.0–9.0		6.0–9.0		6.0–9.0	

[p] For Oc, the following applies: The maximum for any one day when the number of turnarounds exceeds six in any particular 30-consecutive-day periods shall be the sum of the appropriate value and that from Oa or Ob (whichever applies); the average of daily values for 30 consecutive days shall be the value (shown in Oc) multiplied by the number of turnarounds in excess of six and prorated to 30 days plus the appropriate value from Oa or Ob above.

[q] Subject to the following, there shall be no discharge of process wastewater pollutants to navigable waters. A process water impoundment which is designed, constructed, and operated so as to contain the precipitation from the 10-yr, 24-hr rainfall event for the area for which such impoundment is located may discharge the process water equivalent to the volume that falls in excess of that attributable to the 10-yr 24-hr rainfall event, when such occurs. During any calendar month it is permissible to discharge the difference between the precipitation for that month (that falls within the impoundment) and the evaporation volume from the impoundment.

TABLE 2 Effluent Guidelines and Standards (Continued)

Category	Subpart	Effluent characteristic	BPCTCA effluent limitations				BATEA effluent imitations				New source standards of performance			
			Maximum for any 1 day		Average of daily values for 30 consecutive days shall not exceed		Maximum for any 1 day		Average of daily values for 30 consecutive days shall not exceed		Maximum for any 1 day		Average of daily values for 30 consecutive days shall not exceed	
			M[a]	E[a]	M	E	M	E	M	E	M	E	M	E
16. Soap and detergent manufacturing (*cont.*)	Subpart R	BOD_5	0.03	0.03	0.01	0.01	0.02	0.02	0.01	0.01	0.02	0.02	0.01	0.01
		COD	0.15	0.15	0.05	0.05	0.10	0.10	0.05	0.05	0.10	0.10	0.05	0.05
Subpart R Drum-dried detergents		TSS	0.03	0.03	0.01	0.01	0.02	0.02	0.01	0.01	0.02	0.02	0.01	0.01
		Surfactant	0.03	0.03	0.01	0.01	0.02	0.02	0.01	0.01	0.02	0.02	0.01	0.01
		Oil and grease	0.03	0.03	0.01	0.01	0.02	0.02	0.01	0.01	0.02	0.02	0.01	0.01
		pH	6.0–9.0		6.0–9.0		6.0–9.0		6.0–9.0		6.0–9.0		6.0–9.0	
Subpart S Detergent bars and cakes	Subpart S	BOD_5	2.10	2.10	0.70	0.70	0.60	0.60	0.30	0.30	0.60	0.60	0.30	0.30
		COD	9.90	9.90	3.30	3.30	2.70	2.70	1.35	1.35	2.70	2.70	1.35	1.35
		TSS	0.60	0.60	0.20	0.20	0.20	0.20	0.10	0.10	0.20	0.20	0.10	0.10
		Surfactant	1.50	1.50	0.50	0.50	0.40	0.40	0.20	0.20	0.40	0.40	0.20	0.20
		Oil and grease	0.06	0.06	0.02	0.02	0.04	0.04	0.02	0.02	0.04	0.04	0.02	0.02
		pH	6.0–9.0		6.0–9.0		6.0–9.0		6.0–9.0		6.0–9.0		6.0–9.0	
17. Fertilizer manufacturing[23]	Subpart A	Total phosphorus as P	70	70	35	35	Same as [a] except substitute 25-yr, 24-hr rainfall for 10-yr, 24-hr rainfall				Same as [a] except substitute 25-yr, 24-hr rainfall for 10-yr 24-hr rainfall			
		Fluoride	30	30	15	15								
Subpart A Phosphate		TSS	50	50	25	25								
		pH	8.0–9.5		8.0–9.5									
Subpart B Ammonia	Subpart B	Ammonia as N	0.125	0.125	0.0625	0.0625	0.05	0.05	0.025	0.025	0.11	0.11	0.055	0.055
		pH	6.0–9.0		6.0–9.0		6.0–9.0		6.0–9.0		6.0–9.0		6.0–9.0	
Subpart C Urea	Subpart Ca	Ammonia as N	0.075	0.075	0.0375	0.0375	0.03	0.03	0.015	0.015	0.065	0.065	0.0325	0.0325
		Organic nitrogen as N	0.125	0.125	0.0625	0.0625	0.05	0.05	0.025	0.025	0.075	0.075	0.0375	0.0375
Subpart Ca Not prilled		pH	6.0–9.0		6.0–9.0									

Subpart Cb Prilled	Sub- part Cb	Ammonia as N	0.10	0.10	0.05	0.05	0.03	0.03	0.015	0.015	0.065	0.065	0.0325	0.0325
		Organic nitro- gen as N	0.25	0.25	0.125	0.125	0.075	0.075	0.0375	0.0375	0.125	0.125	0.0625	0.0625
		pH	6.0–9.0		6.0–9.0		6.0–9.0		6.0–9.0		6.0–9.0		6.0–9.0	
Subpart D Ammonia nitrate	Sub- part Da	Ammonia as N	0.075	0.075	0.0375	0.0375	0.015	0.015	0.0075	0.0075	0.05	0.05	0.025	0.025
		Nitrate as N	0.10	0.10	0.05	0.05	0.025	0.025	0.0125	0.0125	0.025	0.025	0.0125	0.0125
Subpart Da Aqueous solution		pH	6.0–9.0		6.0–9.0		6.0–9.0		6.0–9.0		6.0–9.0		6.0–9.0	
Subpart Db Prilled or granulated	Sub- part Db	Ammonia as N	0.20	0.20	0.10	0.10	0.015	0.015	0.0075	0.0075	0.10	0.10	0.05	0.05
		Nitrate as N	0.22	0.22	0.11	0.11	0.025	0.025	0.0125	0.0125	0.05	0.05	0.025	0.025
		pH	6.0–9.0		6.0–9.0		6.0–9.0		6.0–9.0		6.0–9.0		6.0–9.0	
Subpart E Nitric acid	Sub- part E	There shall be no discharge of process wastewater pollutants to navigable waters												
Subpart F Ammonium sulfate	Sub- part F	There shall be no discharge of process wastewater pollutants to navigable waters												
Subpart G Mixed and blend fertilizers	Sub- part G	There shall be no discharge of process wastewater pollutants to navigable waters												
18. Petroleum refining[24]	Sub- part Aa	BOD_5	22.7	8.0	12.0	4.25	2.5	0.92	2.0	0.75	11.8	4.2	6.3	2.2
Subpart A Topping		TSS	13.9	4.9	8.2	2.9	2.4	0.88	2.0	0.75	7.3	2.6	4.0	1.5
		COD[r]	117	41.2	60.3	21.3	10.0	3.5	8.0	2.8	61	21.7	32	11.2
		Oil and grease	6.9	2.5	3.7	1.3	0.50	0.18	0.40	0.14	3.6	1.3	1.9	0.7
Subpart Aa General		Phenolic compounds	0.168	0.060	0.076	0.027	0.012	0.0043	0.0090	0.0031	0.088	0.031	0.043	0.016
		Ammonia as N	2.81	0.99	1.27	0.45	0.68	0.24	0.51	0.18	2.8	1.0	1.3	0.45
		Sulfide	0.149	0.053	0.068	0.024	0.055	0.019	0.035	0.015	0.078	0.027	0.035	0.012
		Chromium (total)	0.345	0.122	0.20	0.071	0.124	0.044	0.105	0.037	0.18	0.064	0.105	0.037
		Chromium (6+)	0.0071	0.0025	0.0031	0.0011	0.0026	0.00097	0.0017	0.00062	0.0037	0.0013	0.0017	0.00062
		pH	6.0–9.0		6.0–9.0		6.0–9.0		6.0–9.0		6.0–9.0		6.0–9.0	

[r] If the chloride ion concentration in the effluent exceeds 1,000 mg/l, the Regional Administrator may substitute TOC for COD. Effluent limitations for TOC shall be based on effluent data from correlating TOC to BOD_5.

TABLE 2 Effluent Guidelines and Standards (Continued)

Category	Subpart	Effluent characteristic	BPCTCA effluent limitations				BATEA effluent limitations				New source standards of performance			
			Maximum for any 1 day		Average of daily values for 30 consecutive days shall not exceed		Maximum for any 1 day		Average of daily values for 30 consecutive days shall not exceed		Maximum for any 1 day		Average of daily values for 30 consecutive days shall not exceed	
			M[a]	E[a]	M	E	M	E	M	E	M	E	M	E
18. Petroleum refining (*cont*)	Subpart Ab1[s]	Size factors	1,000 bbl feedstock per stream day		Size factors		1,000 bbl feedstock per stream day		Size factors		1,000 bbl feedstock per stream day		Size factors	
Subpart Ab1 Size factors			0–49.9		1.02		0–49.9		1.02		0–49.9		1.02	
			50–99.9		1.21		50–99.9		1.21		50–99.9		1.21	
			100–149.9		1.44		100–149.9		1.44		100–149.9		1.44	
			150 or greater		1.57		150 or greater		1.57		150 or greater		1.57	
Subpart Ab2 Process factors	Subpart Ab2[s]	Process factors	Process configuration[t]		Process factors		Process configuration[t]		Process factors		Process configuration[t]		Process factors	
			1.0–3.99		0.60		1.0–3.99		0.60		1.0–3.99		0.60	
			4.0–6.99		1.00		4.0–6.99		1.00		4.0–6.99		1.00	
			7.0–9.99		1.66		7.0–9.99		1.66		7.0–9.99		1.66	
			10.0–12.99		2.77		10.0–12.99		2.77		10.0–12.99		2.77	
			13.0–15.0 or greater		4.09		13.0–15.0 or greater		4.09		13.0–15.0 or greater		4.09	
Subpart Ac1 Runoff	Subpart Ac1[u]	BOD_5	0.048	0.40	0.026	0.21	0.0105	0.088	0.0085	0.071	0.048	0.40	0.026	0.21
		TSS	0.029	0.24	0.017	0.14	0.010	0.084	0.0085	0.071	0.029	0.24	0.017	0.14
		COD[r]	0.37	3.10	0.19	1.6	0.028	0.24	0.022	0.19	0.37	3.1	0.19	1.6
		Oil and grease	0.015	0.126	0.008	0.067	0.0020	0.018	0.0016	0.014	0.015	0.126	0.0080	0.067
		pH	6.0–9.0		6.0–9.0		6.0–9.0		6.0–9.0		6.0–9.0		6.0–9.0	
Subpart Ac2 Ballast	Subpart Ac2[v]	BOD_5	0.048	0.40	0.026	0.21	0.0105	0.088	0.0085	0.071	0.048	0.40	0.026	0.21
		TSS	0.029	0.24	0.017	0.14	0.010	0.084	0.0085	0.071	0.029	0.24	0.017	0.14
		COD[r]	0.47	3.9	0.24	2.0	0.038	0.32	0.030	0.26	0.47	3.9	0.24	2.0
		Oil and grease	0.015	0.126	0.008	0.067	0.0020	0.018	0.0017	0.014	0.015	0.126	0.008	0.067
		pH	6.0–9.0		6.0–9.0		6.0–9.0		6.0–9.0		6.0–9.0		6.0–9.0	
Subpart Ad Once-through cooling water	Subpart Ad[w]	TOC	The quantity of pollutant properties controlled by this section, attributable to once-through cooling water, is excluded from the discharge allowed by Ab1 and Ab2 of this section. TOC not to exceed 5 mg/l											

[t] Calculation of the process configuration:

Process category	Process included	Weighting factor
Crude	Atmospheric crude distillation	
	Vacuum crude distillation	
	Desalting	1
Cracking and coking	Fluid catalytic cracking	
	Vis-breaking	
	Thermal cracking	
	Moving-bed catalytic cracking	
	Hydrocracking	
	Fluid coking	
	Delayed coking	6
Lubricating oil	Further defined in the development document	13
Asphalt	Asphalt production	
	Asphalt oxidation	
	Asphalt emulsifying	12

Example
Lubricating oil refinery 125 1,000 bbl/stream day throughput

Process	Capacity (1,000 bbl/ stream day)	Capacity relative to throughput	Weighting factor		Processing configuration
Crude:					
Atmospheric	125	1			
Vacuum	60	0.48			
Desalting	125	1			
Total		2.48	X 1	=	2.48
Cracking-FCC	41	0.328			
Hydrocracking	20	0.160			
Total		0.488	X 6	=	2.93
Lubricating oils	5.3	0.042			
	4.0	0.032			
	4.9	0.039			
Total		0.133	X 13	=	1.47
Asphalt	4.0	0.032	X 12	=	0.38
Refinery process configuration				=	7.26

[s] The limits stated in Aa (above) are to be multiplied by the factors of Ab1 and Ab2 to calculate the maximum average of daily values for 30 consecutive days.

[u] The allocation allowed for storm runoff flow, as kg/M^3 (lb/1,000 gal), shall be based solely on that storm flow which is treated in the main treatment system. All additional storm runoff (from tank fields and nonprocess areas) that has been segregated from the main waste storm for discharge shall not exceed a concentration of 35 mg/l of TOC or 15 mg/l of oil and grease when discharged. (Runoff: flow of storm water.)

[v] The allocation allowed for ballast water flow, or kg/M^3 (lb/1,000 gal) shall be based on those ballast waters treated at the refinery. (Ballast: flow of waters, from a ship which is treated at the refinery.)

[w] Once-through cooling shall mean those waters discharged that are used for the purpose of heat removal and that do not come into direct contact with any raw material, intermediate or finished product.

TABLE 2 Effluent Guidelines and Standards (Continued)

Category	Sub-part	Effluent characteristic	BPCTCA effluent limitations				BATEA effluent limitations				New source standards of performance			
			Maximum for any 1 day		Average of daily values for 30 consecutive days shall not exceed		Maximum for any 1 day		Average of daily values for 30 consecutive days shall not exceed		Maximum for any 1 day		Average of daily values for 30 consecutive days shall not exceed	
			M[a]	E[a]	M	E	M	E	M	E	M	E	M	E
18. Petroleum refining (*cont.*) Subpart B Cracking Subpart Ba General	Sub-part Ba	BOD_5	28.2	9.9	15.6	5.5	3.4	1.2	2.7	0.99	16.3	5.8	8.7	3.1
		TSS	17.1	6.1	10.2	3.6	3.2	1.2	2.7	0.99	9.9	3.5	5.8	2.0
		COD[r]	210	74	109	38.4	19.2	6.8	15.4	5.4	118	41.5	61	21.0
		Oil and grease	8.4	3.0	4.5	1.6	0.68	0.24	0.54	0.19	4.8	1.7	2.6	0.93
		Phenolic compounds	0.21	0.074	0.10	0.036	0.016	0.0055	0.001	0.0039	0.119	0.042	0.058	0.020
		Ammonia as N	18.8	6.6	8.5	3.0	4.6	1.6	3.5	1.2	18.8	6.6	8.6	3.0
		Sulfide	0.18	0.065	0.082	0.029	0.075	0.026	0.048	0.017	0.105	0.037	0.048	0.017
		Chromium (total)	0.43	0.15	0.25	0.088	0.16	0.053	0.14	0.049	0.24	0.084	0.14	0.049
		Chromium(6+)	0.0087	0.0031	0.0040	0.0014	0.0035	0.0013	0.0022	0.0008	0.0050	0.0018	0.0022	0.00081
		pH	6.0–9.0		6.0–9.0		6.0–9.0		6.0–9.0		6.0–9.0		6.0–9.0	
Subpart Bb1 Size factors	Sub-part Bb1[z]	Size factors	1,000 bbl feedstock per stream day		Size factors		1,000 bbl feedstock per stream day		Size factors		1,000 bbl feedstock per stream day		Size factors	
			0–34.9		0.89		0–34.9		0.89		0–34.9		0.89	
			35–74.9		1.00		35–74.9		1.00		35–74.9		1.00	
			75–109.9		1.14		75–109.9		1.14		75–109.9		1.14	
			110–149.9		1.31		110–149.9		1.31		110–149.9		1.31	
			150 or greater		1.41		150 or greater		1.41		150 or greater		1.41	
Subpart Bb2 Process factors	Sub-part Bb2[z]	Process factors	Process configuration[t]		Process factors		Process configuration[t]		Process factors		Process configuration[t]		Process factors	
			1.5–3.49		0.58		1.5–3.49		0.58		1.5–3.49		0.58	
			3.50–5.49		0.81		3.50–5.49		0.81		3.50–5.49		0.81	
			5.50–7.49		1.13		5.50–7.49		1.13		5.50–7.49		1.13	
			7.50–9.49		1.60		7.50–9.49		1.60		7.50–9.49		1.60	
			9.50–10.50 or greater		1.87		9.50–10.50 or greater		1.87		9.50–10.50 or greater		1.87	

Subpart	Subpart code	Parameter												
Subpart Bc1 Runoff	Subpart Bc1[u]	Same as Ac1												
Subpart Bc2 Ballast	Subpart Bc2[v]	Same as Ac2												
Subpart Bd Once-through cooling waste	Subpart Bd[w]	TOC	The quantity of pollutant properties controlled by this secton, attributable to once-through cooling water, is excluded from the discharge allowed by Bb1 and Bb2 of this section. TOC not to exceed 5 mg/l											
Subpart C Petrochemical; Subpart Ca General	Subpart Ca	BOD_5	34.6	12.1	18.4	6.5	4.6	1.7	3.7	1.3	21.8	7.7	11.6	4.1
		TSS	20.6	7.3	12.0	4.25	4.4	1.6	3.7	1.3	13.1	4.6	7.7	2.7
		COD[r]	210	74	109	38.4	22.0	7.6	17	6.1	133	47	69	24
		Oil and grease	11.1	3.9	5.9	2.1	0.90	0.32	0.72	0.26	6.6	2.4	3.5	1.3
		Phenolic compounds	0.25	0.088	0.120	0.0425	0.022	0.0077	0.015	0.0054	0.158	0.056	0.077	0.027
		Ammonia as N	23.4	8.25	10.6	3.8	5.6	2.0	4.2	1.5	23.4	8.3	10.7	3.8
		Sulfide	0.22	0.078	0.099	0.035	0.099	0.035	0.063	0.022	0.140	0.050	0.063	0.022
		Chromium (total)	0.52	0.183	0.30	0.107	0.22	0.080	0.19	0.068	0.32	0.116	0.19	0.068
		Chromium (6+)	0.0115	0.0040	0.0051	0.0018	0.0048	0.0017	0.0031	0.0011	0.0062	0.0024	0.0031	0.0011
		pH	6.0–9.0		6.0–9.0		6.0–9.0		6.0–9.0		6.0–9.0		6.0–9.0	
Subpart Cb1 Size factors	Subpart Cb1[y]	Size factors	1,000 bbl feedstock per stream day	Size factors			1,000 bbl feedstock per stream day	Size factors			1,000 bbl feedstock per stream day	Size factors		
			0–49.9	0.73			0–49.9	0.73			0–49.9	0.73		
			50–99.9	0.87			50–99.9	0.87			50–99.9	0.87		
			100–149.9	1.04			100–149.9	1.04			100–149.9	1.04		
			150 or greater	1.13			150 or greater	1.13			150 or greater	1.13		
Subpart Cb2 Process factors	Subpart Cb2[y]	Process factors	Process configuration[t]	Process factors			Process configuration[t]	Process factors			Process configuration[t]	Process factors		
			3.25–4.74	0.67			3.25–4.74	0.67			3.25–4.74	0.67		
			4.75–6.74	0.91			4.75–6.74	0.91			4.75–6.74	0.91		
			6.75–8.74	1.27			6.75–8.74	1.27			6.75–8.74	1.27		
			8.75–10.25 or greater	1.64			8.75–10.25 or greater	1.64			8.75–10.25 or greater	1.64		

[x] Same as [s] but substitute Bb1 and Bb2 for Ab1 and Ab2.

[y] Same as [s] but substitute Cb1 and Cb2 for Ab1 and Ab2.

TABLE 2 Effluent Guidelines and Standards (Continued)

Category	Sub-part	Effluent characterstic	BPCTCA effluent limitations				BATEA effluent limitations				New source standards of performance			
			Maximum for any 1 day		Average of daily values for 30 consecutive days shall not exceed		Maximum for any 1 day		Average of daily values for 30 consecutive days shall not exceed		Maximum for any 1 day		Average of daily values for 30 consecutive days shall not exceed	
			M[a]	E[a]	M	E	M	E	M	E	M	E	M	E
18. Petroleum refining (*cont.*) Subpart Cc1 Runoff	Subpart Cc1[u]	Same as Ac1												
Subpart Cc2 Ballast	Subpart Cc2[v]	Same as Ac2												
Subpart Cd Once-through cooling water	Subpart Cd[w]	TOC	The quality and quantity of pollutants properties controlled by this section, attributable to once-through cooling water, are excluded from the discharge allowed by Cb1 and Cb2 of this section. TOC not to exceed 5 mg/l											
Subpart D Lubricating oils	Subpart Da	BOD_5	50.6	17.9	25.8	9.1	7.8	2.7	6.3	2.2	34.6	12.2	18.4	6.5
		TSS	31.3	11.0	18.4	6.5	7.4	2.6	6.3	2.2	20.6	7.3	12.1	4.3
Subpart Da Petroleum production by topping, cracking, and lubricating oil manufacturing		COD[r]	360	127	187	66	40	13.8	32	11.0	245	87	126	45
		Oil and grease	16.2	5.7	8.5	3.0	1.4	0.50	1.1	0.40	10.5	3.8	5.6	2.0
		Phenolic compounds	0.38	0.133	0.184	0.065	0.034	0.12	0.024	0.0087	0.25	0.088	0.12	0.043
		Ammonia as N	23.4	8.3	10.6	3.8	5.6	2.0	4.2	1.5	23.4	8.3	10.7	3.8
		Sulfide	0.33	0.118	0.150	0.053	0.16	0.055	0.10	0.035	0.220	0.078	0.10	0.035
		Chromium (total)	0.77	0.273	0.45	0.160	0.36	0.13	0.31	0.11	0.52	0.180	0.31	0.105
		Chromium (6+)	0.017	0.0059	0.0076	0.0027	0.0081	0.0029	0.0052	0.0018	0.0115	0.0056	0.0052	0.0018
		pH	6.0–9.0		6.0–9.0		6.0–9.0		6.0–9.0		6.0–9.0		6.0–9.0	

Subpart Db1 Size factors	Sub-part Db1[s]	Size factors	1,000 bbl feedstock per stream day	Size factors			1,000 bbl feedstock per stream day	Size factors			1,000 bbl feedstock per stream day	Size factors		
			30–69.9	0.71			30–69.9	0.71			30–69.9	0.71		
			70–109.9	0.81			70–109.9	0.81			70–109.9	0.81		
			110–149.9	0.93			110–149.9	0.93			110–149.9	0.93		
			150–199.9	1.09			150–199.9	1.09			150–199.9	1.09		
			200 or greater	1.19			200 or greater	1.19			200 or greater	1.19		
Subpart Db2 Process factors	Sub-part Db2[s]	Process factors	Process configuration[t]	Process factors			Process configuration[t]	Process factors			Process configuration[t]	Process factors		
			6.0 or less–8.0	0.88			6.0 or less–8.0	0.88			6.0 or less–8.0	0.88		
			8.0–9.99	1.23			8.0–9.99	1.23			8.0–9.99	1.23		
			10.0–11.99	1.74			10.0–11.99	1.74			10.0–11.99	1.74		
			12.0–14 or greater	2.44			12.0–14 or greater	2.44			12.0–14 or greater	2.44		
Subpart Dc1 Runoff	Sub-part Dc1[u]	Same as Ac1												
Subpart Dc2 Ballast	Sub-part Dc2[v]	Same as Ac2												
Subpart Dd Once-through cooling water	Sub-part Dd[w]	TOC	The quantity of pollutant properties controlled by this section, attributable to once-through cooling water, is excluded from the discharge allowed by Db1 and Db2 of this section. TOC not to exceed 5 mg/l											
Subpart E Integrated	Sub-part Ea	BOD_5	54.4	19.2	28.9	10.2	8.8	3.2	7.1	2.6	41.6	14.7	22.1	7.8
		TSS	32.8	11.6	19.2	6.8	8.4	3.0	7.1	2.6	24.7	8.7	14.5	5.1
Subpart Ea General		COD[r]	388	136	198	70	47	16.8	38	13.4	295	104	152	54
		Oil and grease	17.1	6.0	9.1	3.2	1.7	0.60	1.4	0.48	12.6	4.5	6.7	2.4
		Phenolic compounds	0.40	0.14	0.192	0.068	0.041	0.015	0.029	0.010	0.30	0.105	0.14	0.051
		Ammonia as N	23.4	8.3	10.6	3.8	5.6	2.0	4.2	1.5	23.4	8.3	10.7	3.8
		Sulfide	0.35	0.124	0.158	0.056	0.19	0.066	0.12	0.042	0.26	0.093	0.12	0.042
		Chromium (total)	0.82	0.29	0.48	0.17	0.44	0.15	0.37	0.13	0.64	0.220	0.37	0.13
		Chromium (6+)	0.017	0.0062	0.0079	0.0028	0.0092	0.0033	0.0059	0.0021	0.013	0.0047	0.0059	0.0021
		pH	6.0–9.0		6.0–9.0		6.0–9.0		6.0–9.0		6.0–9.0		6.0–9.0	

[s] Same as [s] but substitute Db1 and Db2 for Ab1 and Ab2.

TABLE 2 Effluent Guidelines and Standards (Continued)

Category	Subpart	Effluent characteristic	BPCTCA effluent limitations				BATEA effluent limitations				New source standards of performance			
			Maximum for any 1 day		Average of daily values for 30 consecutive days shall not exceed		Maximum for any 1 day		Average of daily values for 30 consecutive days shall not exceed		Maximum for any 1 day		Average of daily values for 30 consecutive days shall not exceed	
			M[a]	E[a]	M	E	M	E	M	E	M	E	M	E
18. Petroleum refining (*cont.*)	Subpart Eb1[aa]	Size factors	1,000 bbl feedstock per stream day		Size factors		1,000 bbl feedstock per stream day		Size factors		1,000 bbl feedstock per stream day		Size factors	
Subpart Eb1 Size factors			70–144.9 145–219.9 220 or greater		0.69 0.89 1.02		70–144.9 145–219.9 220 or greater		0.69 0.89 1.02		70–144.9 145–219.9 220 or greater		0.69 0.89 1.02	
Subpart Eb2 Process factors	Subpart Eb2[aa]	Process factors	Process configuration[t]		Process factors		Process configuration[t]		Process factors		Process configuration[t]		Process factors	
			6.0 or less–7.49 7.5–8.99 9.0–10.5 or greater		0.78 1.00 1.30		6.0 or less–7.49 7.5–8.99 9.0–10.5 or greater		0.78 1.00 1.30		6.0 or less–7.49 7.5–8.99 9.0–10.5 or greater		0.78 1.00 1.30	
Subpart Ec1 Runoff	Subpart Ec1[u]	Same as Ac1												
Subpart Ec2 Ballast	Subpart Ec2[v]	Same as Ac2												
Subpart Ed Once-through cooling water	Subpart Ed[w]	TOC	The quantity of pollutant properties, controlled by this section, attributable to once-through cooling water, is excluded from the discharge allowed by Eb1 and Eb2 of this section. TOC not to exceed 5 mg/l											
19. Iron and steel manufacturing[25]	Subpart Aa	Ammonia	0.2736	0.2736	0.0912	0.0912	0.0126	0.0126	0.0042	0.0042	0.0126	0.0126	0.0042	0.0042
		Cyanide A	0.0657	0.0657	0.0219	0.0219	0.0003	0.0003	0.0001	0.0001	0.0003	0.0003	0.0001	0.0001
Subpart A By-product coke		Oil and grease	0.0327	0.0327	0.0109	0.0109	0.0126	0.0126	0.0042	0.0042	0.0126	0.0126	0.0042	0.0042
		Phenol	0.0045	0.0045	0.0015	0.0015	0.0006	0.0006	0.0002	0.0002	0.0006	0.0006	0.0002	0.0002
		TSS	0.1095	0.1095	0.0365	0.0365	0.0312	0.0312	0.0104	0.0104	0.0312	0.0312	0.0104	0.0104
Subpart Aa General		Sulfide					0.0003	0.0003	0.0001	0.0001	0.0003	0.0003	0.0001	0.0001
		pH	6.0–9.0		6.0–9.0		6.0–9.0		6.0–9.0		6.0–9.0		6.0–9.0	

Subpart Ab Coke plants utilizing desulfrization units	Sub-part Ab		The limits specified in Aa may be exceeded up to 15%				The limits specified in Aa may be exceeded up to 25%							
Subpart Ac Coke plants utilizing the indirect ammonia recovery process	Sub-part Ac		The limits specified in Aa may be exceeded up to 30%				The limits specified in Aa may be exceeded up to 70%							
Subpart B Beehive coke	Sub-part B		There shall be no discharge of process wastewater pollutants to navigable waters											
Subpart C Sintering	Sub-part C	TSS	0.0312	0.0312	0.0104	0.0104	0.0156	0.0156	0.0052	0.0052	0.0156	0.0156	0.0052	0.0052
		Fluoride					0.0126	0.0126	0.0042	0.0042	0.0126	0.0126	0.0042	0.0042
		Oil and grease	0.0063	0.0063	0.0021	0.0021	0.0063	0.0063	0.0021	0.0021	0.0063	0.0063	0.0021	0.0021
		Sulfide					0.00018	0.00018	0.00006	0.00006	0.00018	0.00018	0.00006	0.00006
		pH	6.0–9.0		6.0–9.0		6.0–9.0		6.0–9.0		6.0–9.0		6.0–9.0	
Subpart D Blast furnace (iron)	Sub-part D	TSS	0.0780	0.0780	0.0260	0.0260	0.0390	0.0390	0.0130	0.0130	0.0390	0.0390	0.0130	0.0130
		Cyanide A	0.0234	0.0234	0.0078	0.0078	0.0004	0.0004	0.00013	0.00013	0.0004	0.0004	0.00013	0.00013
		Phenol	0.0063	0.0063	0.0021	0.0021	0.0008	0.0008	0.00026	0.00026	0.0008	0.0008	0.00026	0.00026
		Ammonia	0.1953	0.1953	0.0651	0.0651	0.0156	0.0156	0.0052	0.0052	0.0156	0.0156	0.0052	0.0052
		Sulfide					0.0005	0.0005	0.00016	0.00016	0.0005	0.0005	0.00016	0.00016
		Fluoride					0.0312	0.0312	0.0104	0.0104	0.0312	0.0312	0.0104	0.0104
		pH	6.0–9.0		6.0–9.0		6.0–9.0		6.0–9.0		6.0–9.0		6.0–9.0	
Subpart E Blast furnace (ferromanganese)	Sub-part E	TSS	0.3129	0.3129	0.1043	0.1043	0.0780	0.0780	0.0260	0.0260	0.0780	0.0780	0.0260	0.0260
		Cyanide A	0.4689	0.4689	0.1563	0.1563	0.0008	0.0008	0.00026	0.00026	0.0008	0.0008	0.00026	0.00026
		Phenol	0.0624	0.0624	0.0208	0.0208	0.0016	0.0016	0.00052	0.00052	0.0016	0.0016	0.00052	0.00052
		Ammonia	1.5636	1.5636	0.5212	0.5212	0.0312	0.0312	0.0104	0.0104	0.0312	0.0312	0.0104	0.0104
		Sulfide					0.0009	0.0009	0.0003	0.0003	0.0009	0.0009	0.0003	0.0003
		Manganese					0.0156	0.0156	0.0052	0.0052	0.0156	0.0156	0.0052	0.0052
		pH	6.0–9.0		6.0–9.0		6.0–9.0		6.0–9.0		6.0–9.0		6.0–9.0	
Subpart F Basic oxygen furnace (semiwet air pollution control methods)	Sub-part F		There shall be no discharge of process wastewater pollutants to navigable waters											

[aa] Same as [a] but substitute Eb1 and Eb2 for Ab1 and Ab2.

TABLE 2 Effluent Guidelines and Standards (Continued)

			BPCTCA effluent limitations				BATEA effluent limitatons				New source standards of performance			
			Maximum for any 1 day		Average of daily values for 30 consecutive days shall not exceed		Maximum for any 1 day		Average of daily values for 30 consecutive days shall not exceed		Maximum for any 1 day		Average of daily values for 30 consecutive days shall not exceed	
Category	Sub-part	Effluent characteristic	M[a]	E[a]	M	E	M	E	M	E	M	E	M	E
19. Iron and steel manufacturing (*cont.*)	Sub-part G	TSS	0.0312	0.0312	0.0104	0.0104	0.0156	0.0156	0.0052	0.0052	0.0156	0.0156	0.0052	0.0052
Subpart G Basic oxygen furnace (wet air pollution control methods)		Fluoride					0.0126	0.0126	0.0042	0.0042	0.0126	0.0126	0.0042	0.0042
		pH	6.0–9.0		6.0–9.0		6.0–9.0		6.0–9.0		6.0–9.0		6.0–9.0	
Subpart H Open-hearth furnace	Sub-part H	TSS	0.0312	0.0312	0.0104	0.0104	0.0156	0.0156	0.0052	0.0052	0.0156	0.0156	0.0052	0.0052
		Fluoride					0.0126	0.0126	0.0042	0.0042	0.0126	0.0126	0.0042	0.0042
		Nitrate					0.0282	0.0282	0.0094	0.0094				
		Zinc					0.0030	0.0030	0.0010	0.0010	0.0030	0.0030	0.0010	0.0010
		pH	6.0–9.0		6.0–9.0		6.0–9.0		6.0–9.0		6.0–9.0		6.0–9.0	
Subpart I Electric-arc furnace (semiwet air pollution control methods)	Sub-part I	There shall be no discharge of process wastewater pollutants to navigable waters												
Subpart J Electric-arc furnace (wet air pollution control methods)	Sub-part J	TSS	0.0312	0.0312	0.0104	0.0104	0.0156	0.0156	0.0052	0.0052	0.0156	0.0156	0.0052	0.0052
		Fluoride					0.0126	0.0126	0.0042	0.0042	0.0126	0.0126	0.0042	0.0042
		Zinc					0.0030	0.0030	0.0010	0.0010	0.0030	0.0030	0.0010	0.0010
		pH	6.0–9.0		6.0–9.0		6.0–9.0		6.0–9.0		6.0–9.0		6.0–9.0	
Subpart K Vacuum degassing	Sub-part K	TSS	0.0156	0.0156	0.0052	0.0052	0.0078	0.0078	0.0026	0.0026	0.0078	0.0078	0.0026	0.0026
		Zinc					0.0015	0.0015	0.0005	0.0005	0.0015	0.0015	0.0005	0.0005
		Manganese					0.0015	0.0015	0.0005	0.0005	0.0015	0.0015	0.0005	0.0005
		Lead					0.0015	0.0015	0.00005	0.00005	0.00015	0.00015	0.00005	0.00005
		Nitrate					0.0141	0.0141	0.0047	0.0047				
		pH	6.0–9.0		6.0–9.0		6.0–9.0		6.0–9.0		6.0–7.0		6.0–9.0	
Subpart L Continuous coating	Sub-part L	TSS	0.0780	0.0780	0.0260	0.0260	0.0156	0.0156	0.0052	0.0052	0.0156	0.0156	0.0052	0.0052
		Oil and grease	0.0234	0.0234	0.0078	0.0078	0.0156	0.0156	0.0052	0.0052	0.0156	0.0156	0.0052	0.0052
		pH	6.0–9.0		6.0–9.0		6.0–9.0		6.0–9.0		6.0–9.0		6.0–9.0	

20. Nonferrous metals manufacturing[26]	Subpart A[bb]		There shall be no discharge of process wastewater pollutants to navigable waters											
Subpart A Bauxite refining														
Subpart B Primary aluminum smelting	Subpart B	Fluoride	2.0	2.0	1.0	1.0	0.1	0.1	0.05	0.05	0.05	0.05	0.025	0.025
		TSS	3.0	3.0	1.5	1.5	0.2	0.2	0.1	0.1	0.1	0.1	0.05	0.05
		pH	6.0–9.0		6.0–9.0		6.0–9.0		6.0–9.0		6.0–9.0		6.0–9.0	
Subpart C Secondary aluminum smelting	Subpart Ca		There shall be no discharge of process wastewater pollutants to navigable waters											
Subpart Ca General														
Subpart Cb Uses aluminum fluoride in its magnesium removal process ("demagging process")	Subpart Cb		There shall be no discharge of process wastewater pollutants to navigable waters											
Subpart Cc Use chlorine in its magnesium removal process	Subpart Cc	TSS			175	175	There shall be no discharge of process wastewater pollutants to navigable waters							
		COD			6.5	6.5								
		pH			7.5–9.0									
Subpart Cd Processes residues by wet methods	Subpart Cd	TSS			1.5	1.5	There shall be no discharge of process wastewater pollutants to navigable waters							
		Fluoride			0.4	0.4								
		Ammonia as N			0.01	0.01								
		Aluminum			1.0	1.0								
		Copper			0.003	0.003								
		COD			1.0	1.0								
		pH			7.5–9.0									

[bb] During any calendar month there may be discharged from the overflow of a process wastewater impoundment either a volume of process wastewater equal to the difference between the precipitation for that month that falls within the impoundment and the evaporation within the impoundment for that month or, if greater, a volume of process wastewater equal to the difference between the mean precipitation for that month that falls within the impoundment and the mean evaporation for that month as established by the National Climatic Center, National Oceanic and Atmospheric Administration, for the area in which such impoundment is located (or as otherwise determined if no monthly data have been established by the National Climatic Center).

TABLE 2 Effluent Guidelines and Standards (Continued)

Category	Sub-part	Effluent characteristic	BPCTCA effluent limitations				BATEA effluent limitations				New source standards of performance			
			Maximum for any 1 day		Average of daily values for 30 consecutive days shall not exceed		Maximum for any 1 day		Average of daily values for 30 consecutive days shall not exceed		Maximum for any 1 day		Average of daily values for 30 consecutive days shall not exceed	
			M[a]	E[a]	M	E	M	E	M	E	M	E	M	E
21. Phosphate manufacturing[27]														
Subpart A Phosphorus production	Subpart A	TSS	1.0	1.0	0.5	0.5	There shall be no discharge of process wastewater pollutants to navigable waters							
		Phosphorus (total)	0.30	0.30	0.15	0.15								
		Fluoride	0.10	0.10	0.05	0.05								
		Phosphorus (elemental)	No detectable quantity											
		pH	6.0–9.0		6.0–9.0									
Subpart B Phosphorus consuming	Subpart Ba		There shall be no discharge of process wastewater pollutants to navigable waters											
Subpart Ba Manufacturer of phosphoric acids, phosphorus pentoxide, or phosphorus pentasulfide														
Subpart Bb Phosphorus trichloride manufacturing	Subpart Bb	TSS	1.4	1.4	0.7	0.7	There shall be no discharge of process wastewater pollutants to navigable waters							
		Phosphorus (total)	1.6	1.6	0.8	0.8								
		Arsenic	0.0001	0.0001	0.00005	0.00005								
		Phosphorus (elemental)	No detectable quantity											
		pH	6.0–9.0		6.0–9.0									
Subpart Bc Phosphorus oxychloride manufacturing	Subpart Bc	TSS	0.3	0.3	0.15	0.15	There shall be no discharge of process wastewater pollutants to navigable waters							
		Phosphorus (total)	0.34	0.34	0.17	0.17								
		pH	6.0–9.0		6.0–9.0									

Subpart C Phosphate	Sub- part Ca		There shall be no discharge of process wastewater pollutants to navigable waters											
Subpart Ca Manufacturer of sodium tripoly phosphate or animal feed grade calcium phosphate														
Subpart Cb Manufacturer of human food grade calcium phosphate	Sub- part Cb	TSS	0.12	0.12	0.06	0.06	There shall be no discharge of process wastewater pollutants to navigable waters							
		Phosphorus (total)	0.06	0.06	0.03	0.03								
		pH	6.0–9.0		6.0–9.0									
22. Steam electric power generating[28]	Sub- part Aa	pH[cc]	6.0–9.0		6.0–9.0		6.0–9.0		6.0–9.0		6.0–9.0		6.0–9.0	
		PCB[dd]	No discharge		No discharge		No discharge		No discharge		No discharge		No discharge	
Subpart A Generating unit														
Subpart Aa General														
Subpart Ab Low-volume waste source	Sub- part Ab		The quantity of pollutants discharged shall not exceed the quantity determined by multiplying the flow of low-volume waste sources times the concentrations listed in Ab											
		TSS	100	None	30	None	100	None	30	None	100	None	30	None
		Oil and grease	20		15		20		15		20		15	
Subpart Ac Ash transport water	Sub- part Ac		The quantity of pollutants discharged shall not exceed the quantity determined by multiplying the flow of ash transport water times the concentration listed in Ac											
		TSS	100	None	30	None	100	None	30	None	100	None	30	None
		Oil and grease	20		15		20		15		20		15	
Subpart Ad Metal cleaning wastes	Sub- part Ad		The quantity of pollutants discharged shall not exceed the quantity determined by multiplying the flow of metal cleaning wastes times the concentration listed in Ad											
		TSS	100	None	30	None	100	None	30	None	100	None	30	None
		Oil and grease	20		15		20		15		20		15	
		Copper (total)	1.0		1.0		1.0		1.0		1.0		1.0	
		Iron (total)	1.0		1.0		1.0		1.0		1.0		1.0	

[cc] 6.0–9.0 does not apply to once-through cooling water.

[dd] PCB = polychlorinated biphenol compounds commonly used for transformer fluid.

TABLE 2 Effluent Guidelines and Standards (Continued)

Category	Subpart	Effluent characteristic	BPCTCA effluent limitations: Maximum for any 1 day		BPCTCA: Average of daily values for 30 consecutive days shall not exceed		BATEA effluent limitations: Maximum for any 1 day		BATEA: Average of daily values for 30 consecutive days shall not exceed		New source standards of performance: Maximum for any 1 day		New source: Average of daily values for 30 consecutive days shall not exceed	
			M[a]	E[a]	M	E	M	E	M	E	M	E	M	H
22. Steam electric power generating (*cont.*)	Subpart Ag1[ee]		The quantity of pollutants discharged shall not exceed the quantity determined by multiplying the flow of cooling tower blowdown sources times the concentration listed in Ag											
Subpart Ag1 Cooling tower blowdown (chlorine)		Free available chlorine	Maximum concentration 0.5 mg/l		Average concentration 0.2 mg/l		Maximum concentration 0.5 mg/l		Average concentration 0.2 mg/l		Maximum concentration 0.5 mg/l		Average concentration 0.2 mg/l	
Subpart Ag2 Cooling tower blowdown (anticorrosive compounds)	Subpart Ag2		Narrative ruling same as Ag1								Materials added for corrosion inhibition including but not limited to zinc, chromium, phosphorus			
		Zinc					1.0	None	1.0	None				
		Chromium					0.2		0.2					
		Phosphorus					5.0		5.0					
		Other corrosion-inhibiting materials					Established on a case-by-case basis		Established on a case-by-case basis		No detectable amounts		No detectable amounts	
Subpart Ah Thermal discharge	Subpart Ah	Heat	Heat may be discharged in blowdown from recirculating cooling water systems provided the temperature at which the blowdown is discharged does not exceed at any time the lowest temperature of recirculating cooling water prior to the addition of the makeup water											
Subpart B Small unit	Subpart Ba	pH[cc]	6.0–9.0		6.0–9.0		6.0–9.0		6.0–9.0		6.0–9.0		6.0–9.0	
Subpart Ba General		PCB[dd]	No discharge		No discharge		No discharge		No discharge		No discharge		No discharge	
Subpart Bb Low-volume waste source	Subpart Bb		The quantity of pollutants discharged shall not exceed the quantity determined by multiplying the flow of low volume waste sources times the concentration listed											
		TSS	100	None	30	None	100	None	30	None	100	None	30	None
		Oil and grease	20		15		20		15		20		15	

Subpart Bc Ash transport water	Subpart Bc						Narrative requirement is the same as Ac							
		TSS	100	None	30	None	100	None	30	None	100	None	30	None
		Oil and grease	20		15		20		15		20		15	
Subpart Bd Metal cleaning wastes	Subpart Bd						Narrative requirement is the same as Ad							
		TSS	100	None	30	None	100	None	30	None	100	None	30	None
		Oil and grease	20		15		20		15		20		15	
		Copper (total)	1.0		1.0		1.0		1.0		1.0		1.0	
		Iron (total)	1.0		1.0		1.0		1.0		1.0		1.0	
Subpart Be Boiler blowdown	Subpart Be						Narrative requirement is the same as Ae							
		TSS	100	None	30	None	100	None	30	None	100	None	30	None
		Oil and grease	20		15		20		15		20		15	
		Copper (total)	1.0		1.0		1.0		1.0		1.0		1.0	
		Iron (total)	1.0		1.0		1.0		1.0		1.0		1.0	
Subpart Bf Once-through cooling	Subpart Bf						Narrative requirement is the same as Af							
		Free available chlorine	Maximum concentraton 0.5 mg/l		Average concentration 0.2 mg/l		Maximum concentration 0.5 mg/l		Average concentration 0.2 mg/l		Maximum concentration 0.5 mg/l		Average concentration 0.2 mg/l	
Subpart Bg1 Cooling tower blowdown (anticorrosion compounds)	Subpart Bg1						Narrative requirement is the same as Ag1							
		Free available chlorine	Maximum concentration 0.5 mg/l		Average concentration 0.2 mg/l		Maximum concentration 0.5 mg/l		Average concentration 0.2 mg/l		Maximum concentration 0.5 mg/l		Average concentration 0.2 mg/l	
Subpart Bg2 Cooling tower blowdown (anticorrosion)	Subpart Bg2						Narrative requirement is the same as Ag2							
		Zinc	1.0	None	1.0	None	1.0	None	1.0	None	Materials added for corrosion inhibitor including, but not limited to, zinc, chromium, phosphate			
		Chromium	0.2		0.2		0.2		0.2					
		Phosphate	5.0		5.0		5.0		5.0					
		Other corrosion-inhibiting materials									No detectable amount		No detectable amount	
Subpart Bh Recirculating cooling water systems	Subpart Bh	Heat	Heat may be discharged in blowdown from recirculation cooling water systems provided the temperature at which the blowdown is discharged does not exceed at any time the lowest temperature of recirculating cooling water prior to the addition of the makeup water											

[ee] Neither free available chlorine nor total residual chlorine may be discharged from any unit for more than 2 hr, in any one day and not more than one unit in any plant may discharge free available or total residual chlorine at any one time unless the utility can demonstrate to the Regional Administrator or state (if state has NPDES permit issuing authority) that the unit in a particular location cannot operate at or below this level of chlorination.

TABLE 2 Effluent Guidelines and Standards (Continued)

Category	Sub-part	Effluent characteristic	BPCTCA effluent limitations				BATEA effluent limitations				New source standards of performance			
			Maximum for any 1 day		Average of daily values for 30 consecutive days shall not exceed		Maximum for any 1 day		Average of daily values for 30 consecutive days shall not exceed		Maximum for any 1 day		Average of daily values for 30 consecutive days shall not exceed	
			M[a]	E[a]	M	E	M	E	M	E	M	E	M	E
22. Steam electric power generating (*cont.*)	Sub-part Ca	pH[cc]	6.0–9.0		6.0–9.0		6.0–9.0		6.0–9.0		6.0–9.0		6.0–9.0	
Subpart C Old unit		PCB[dd]	No discharge		No discharge		No discharge		No discharge		No discharge		No discharge	
Subpart Ca General														
Subpart Cb Low-volume wastewater	Sub-part Cb		Narrative same as Ab											
		TSS	100	None	30	None	100	None	30	None				
		Oil and grease	20		15		20		15					
Subpart Cc Ash transport water	Sub-part Cc	TSS	100	None	30	None	100	None	30	None				
		Oil and grease	20		15		20		15					
Subpart Cd Metal cleaning wastes	Sub-part Cd		Narrative the same as Ad											
		TSS	100	None	30	None	100	None	30	None				
		Oil and grease	20		15		20		15					
		Copper (total)	1.0		1.0		1.0		1.0					
		Iron (total)	1.0		1.0		1.0		1.0					
Subpart Ce Boiler blowdown	Sub-part Ce		Narrative the same as Ae											
		TSS	100	None	30	None	100	None	30	None				
		Oil and grease	20		15		20		15					
		Copper (total)	1.0		1.0		1.0		1.0					
		Iron (total)	1.0		1.0		1.0		1.0					
Subpart Cf Once-through cooling	Sub-part Cf		Narrative the same as Af											
		Free available chlorine	Maximum concentration 0.5 mg/l		Average concentration 0.2 mg/l		Maximum concentration 0.5 mg/l		Average concentration 0.2 mg/l					

Subpart Cg1 Cooling tower blowdown (chlorine)	Subpart Cg1		Narrative the same as Ag1											
		Free available chlorine	Maximum concentration 0.5 mg/l		Average concentration 0.2 mg/l									
Subpart Cg2 Cooling tower blowdown (anticorrosion compounds)	Subpart Cg2		Narrative the same as Ag2											
		Zinc					1.0	None	1.0	None				
		Chromium					0.2		0.2					
		Phosphate					5.0		5.0					
		Other corrosion-inhibiting materials					Limit to be established on a case by case basis							
Subpart D Area runoff	Subpart D	TSS	Not to exceed 50 mg/l				Not to exceed 50 mg/l				Not to exceed 50 mg/l			
		pH	6.0–9.0		6.0–9.0		6.0–9.0		6.0–9.0		6.0–9.0		6.0–9.0	
Subpart Da Provision	Subpart Da		Any untreated overflow from facilities designed, contracted, and operated to treat the volume of material storage runoff and construction runoff which is associated with a 10-yr, 24-hr rainfall event shall not be subject to the limitations above											
23. Ferroalloy manufacturing[29]														
Subpart A Open electric furnaces with wet air pollution control devices	Subpart A	TSS	0.319	0.703	0.160	0.352	0.024	0.052	0.012	0.026	0.024	0.052	0.012	0.026
		Chromium (total)	0.006	0.014	0.0032	0.007	0.0008	0.0017	0.0004	0.0009	0.0008	0.0017	0.0004	0.0009
		Chromium (VI)	0.0006	0.0014	0.0003	0.0007	0.00008	0.0002	0.00004	0.0001	0.00008	0.0002	0.00004	0.0001
		Manganese (total)	0.064	0.141	0.032	0.070	0.008	0.017	0.0039	0.0086	0.008	0.017	0.0039	0.0086
		pH	6.0–9.0		6.0–9.0		6.0–9.0		6.0–9.0		6.0–9.0		6.0–9.0	
Subpart B Covered electric furnaces and other smelting operations with wet air pollution control devices	Subpart B//	TSS	0.419	0.922	0.209	0.461	0.032	0.071	0.016	0.035	0.032	0.071	0.016	0.035
		Chromium (total)	0.008	0.018	0.004	0.009	0.001	0.002	0.0005	0.0012	0.001	0.002	0.0005	0.0012
		Chromium (VI)	0.0008	0.0018	0.0004	0.0009	0.0001	0.0002	0.00005	0.0001	0.0001	0.0002	0.00005	0.0001
		Manganese (total)	0.084	0.184	0.042	0.092	0.011	0.023	0.005	0.012	0.011	0.023	0.005	0.012
		Cyanide (total)	0.006	0.009	0.002	0.005	0.0005	0.001	0.0003	0.0006	0.0004	0.001	0.0003	0.0006
		Phenols	0.004	0.013	0.004	0.009	0.0004	0.0009	0.0002	0.0005	0.0005	0.0009	0.0002	0.0005
		pH	6.0–9.0		6.0–9.0		6.0–9.0		6.0–9.0		6.0–9.0		6.0–9.0	

// Provided, however, that for nonelectric furnace smelting processes the units of effluent limitations set forth in the section shall read as kg/1,000 kg of product rather than kg/MWh, and the limitations (except pH) shall be 3.3 times those listed in B (above) (or for English units, lb/ton of product rather than lb/MWh) and the limitations (except for pH) shall be 3 times those listed in B (above).

TABLE 2 Effluent Guidelines and Standards (Continued)

Category	Subpart	Effluent characteristic	BPCTCA effluent limitations				BATEA effluent limitations				New source standards of performance			
			Maximum for any 1 day		Average of daily values for 30 consecutive days shall not exceed		Maximum for any 1 day		Average of daily values for 30 consecutive days shall not exceed		Maximum for any 1 day		Average of daily values for 30 consecutive days shall not exceed	
			M[a]	E[a]	M	E	M	E	M	E	M	E	M	E
23. Ferroalloy manufacturng (*cont.*)	Subpart C	TSS	2.659	5.319	1.330	2.659	0.271	0.542	0.136	0.271	0.271	0.542	0.136	0.271
Subpart C Slag processing		Chromium (total)	0.053	0.106	0.026	0.053	0.0054	0.011	0.0027	0.0054	0.0054	0.011	0.0027	0.0054
		Manganese (total)	0.532	1.064	0.266	0.532	0.054	0.108	0.027	0.054	0.054	0.108	0.027	0.054
		pH	6.0–9.0		6.0–9.0		6.0–9.0		6.0–9.0		6.0–9.0		6.0–9.0	
24. Leather tanning and finishing[30]	Subpart A	BOD_5	8.0	8.0	4.0	4.0	2.8	2.8	1.40	1.40	8.0	8.0	4.0	4.0
		TSS	10.0	10.0	5.0	5.0	3.0	3.0	1.50	1.50	10.0	10.0	5.0	5.0
Subpart A Hair pulp unhairing with chrome tanning and finishing		Chrome	0.20	0.20	0.1	0.1	0.1	0.1	0.05	0.05	0.10	0.20	0.05	0.10
		Oil and grease	1.50	1.50	0.75	0.75	1.06	1.06	0.53	0.53	1.06	1.50	0.53	0.75
		Sulfide					0.01	0.01	0.005	0.005				
		TKN					0.54	0.54	0.27	0.27				
		pH	6.0–9.0		6.0–9.0		6.0–9.0		6.0–9.0		6.0–9.0		6.0–9.0	
Subpart B Hair save unhairing with chrome tanning and finishing	Subpart B	BOD_5	9.2	9.2	4.6	4.6	3.2	3.2	1.60	1.60	9.2	9.2	4.6	4.6
		TSS	11.6	11.6	5.8	5.8	3.6	3.6	1.80	1.80	11.6	11.6	5.8	5.8
		Chrome	0.24	0.24	0.12	0.12	0.12	0.12	0.06	0.06	0.24	0.24	0.12	0.12
		Oil and grease	1.80	1.80	0.90	0.90	1.26	1.26	0.63	0.63	1.80	1.80	0.90	0.90
		Sulfide					0.012	0.012	0.006	0.006				
		TKN					0.64	0.64	0.32	0.32				
		Fecal coliform					400 counts/100 ml		400 counts/100 ml					
		pH	6.0–9.0		6.0–9.0		6.0–9.0		6.0–9.0		6.0–9.0		6.0–9.0	
Subpart C Unhairing with vegetable or alum tanning and finishing	Subpart C	BOD_5	7.6	7.6	3.8	3.8	2.6	2.6	1.30	1.30	7.6	7.6	3.8	3.8
		TSS	9.6	9.6	4.8	4.8	2.8	2.8	1.40	1.40	9.6	9.6	4.8	4.8
		Chrome	0.1	0.1	0.05	0.05	0.1	0.1	0.05	0.05	0.1	0.1	0.05	0.05
		Oil and grease	1.50	1.50	0.75	0.75	1.0	1.0	0.50	0.50	1.50	1.50	0.75	0.75
		Sulfide					0.01	0.01	0.005	0.005				
		TKN					0.5	0.5	0.25	0.25				
		Fecal coliform					400 counts/100 ml		400 counts/100 ml					
		pH	6.0–9.0		6.0–9.0		6.0–9.0		6.0–9.0		6.0–9.0		6.0–9.0	

Subpart D	Sub-	BOD_5	3.2	3.2	1.6	1.6	1.0	1.0	0.50	0.50	3.2	3.2	1.6	1.6
Finishing of tanned	part	TSS	4.0	4.0	2.0	2.0	1.2	1.2	0.60	0.60	4.0	4.0	2.0	2.0
hides	D	Chrome	0.2	0.2	0.1	0.1	0.04	0.04	0.02	0.02	0.20	0.20	0.10	0.10
		Oil and grease	0.5	0.5	0.25	0.25	0.48	0.48	0.24	0.24	0.50	0.50	0.25	0.25
		Sulfide					0.004	0.004	0.002	0.002				
		TKN					0.2	0.2	0.10	0.10				
		Fecal coliform					400 counts/100 ml		400 counts/100 ml					
		pH	6.0–9.0		6.0–9.0		6.0–9.0		6.0–9.0		6.0–9.0		6.0–9.0	
Subpart E	Sub-	BOD_5	9.6	9.6	4.8	4.8	3.2	3.2	1.60	1.60	9.6	9.6	4.8	4.8
Vegetable or chrome	part	TSS	12.0	12.0	6.0	6.0	3.6	3.6	1.80	1.80	12.0	12.0	6.0	6.0
tanning of unhaired	E[gg]	Chrome	0.12	0.12	0.06	0.06	0.12	0.12	0.06	0.06	0.12	0.12	0.06	0.06
hides		Oil and grease	1.80	1.80	0.90	0.90	1.26	1.26	0.63	0.63	1.80	1.80	0.90	0.90
		Sulfide					0.012	0.012	0.006	0.006				
		TKN					0.62	0.62	0.31	0.31				
		Fecal coliform					400 counts/100 ml		400 counts/100 ml					
		pH	6.0–9.0		6.0–9.0		6.0–9.0		6.0–9.0		6.0–9.0		6.0–9.0	
Subpart F	Sub-	BOD_5	5.6	5.6	2.8	2.8	1.4	1.4	0.70	0.70	5.6	5.6	2.8	2.8
Unhairing with chrome	part	TSS	6.8	6.8	3.4	3.4	1.6	1.6	0.80	0.80	6.8	6.8	3.4	3.4
tanning and no finishing	F[gg]	Chrome	0.20	0.20	0.10	0.10	0.06	0.06	0.03	0.03	0.20	0.20	0.10	0.10
		Oil and grease	0.70	0.70	0.35	0.35	0.68	0.68	0.34	0.34	0.70	0.70	0.35	0.35
		Sulfide					0.006	0.006	0.003	0.003				
		TKN					0.28	0.28	0.14	0.14				
		Fecal coliform					400 counts/100 ml		400 counts/100 ml					
		pH	6.0–9.0		6.0–9.0		6.0–9.0		6.0–9.0		6.0–9.0		6.0–9.0	
25a. Glass manufacturing[31–33]	Sub-	Phenol	0.0006	0.0006	0.0003	0.0003	There shall be no discharge of process wastewater pollutants to navigable waters							
Subpart A	part	COD	0.33	0.33	0.165	0.165								
Insulation fiber glass	A	BOD	0.024	0.024	0.012	0.012								
		TSS	0.03	0.03	0.015	0.015								
		pH	6.0–9.0		6.0–9.0									
Subpart B Sheet glass	Subpart B		There shall be no discharge of process wastewater pollutants to navigable waters											
Subpart C Rolled glass	Subpart C		There shall be no discharge of process wastewater pollutants to navigable waters											

[gg] Additional allocations equal to one-half the above effluent limitations for BOD_5 and TSS established in this section are allowed any point source subject to such effluent limitations with a production less than 17,000 kg hide per day.

TABLE 2 Effluent Guidelines and Standards (Continued)

Category	Subpart	Effluent characteristic	BPCTCA effluent limitations				BATEA effluent limitations				New source standards of performance			
			Maximum for any 1 day		Average of daily values for 30 consecutive days shall not exceed		Maximum for any 1 day		Average of daily values for 30 consecutive days shall not exceed		Maximum for any 1 day		Average of daily values for 30 consecutive days shall not exceed	
			M[a]	E[a]	M	E	M	E	M	E	M	E	M	E
25a. Glass manufacturing (*cont.*)	Subpart D	TSS	2.76	5.52	1.38	2.76	0.045	0.090	0.045	0.090	There shall be no discharge of process wastewater pollutants to navigable waters			
Subpart D Plate glass		pH	6.0–9.0		6.0–9.0		6.0–9.0		6.0–9.0					
Subpart E Float glass	Subpart E	TSS	2.00	0.0040	2.00	0.0040	0.70	0.0014	0.70	0.0014	0.70	0.0014	0.70	0.0014
		Oil	1.40	0.0028	1.40	0.0028	1.40	0.0028	1.40	0.0028	1.40	0.0028	1.40	0.0028
		Phosphorus	0.05	0.0001	0.05	0.0001	0.05	0.0001	0.05	0.0001	0.05	0.0001	0.05	0.0001
		pH	6.0–9.0		6.0–9.0		6.0–9.0		6.0–9.0		6.0–9.0		6.0–9.0	
Subpart F Automatic glass tempering	Subpart F	TSS	1.95	0.40	1.22	0.25	0.24	0.05	0.24	0.05	0.24	0.05	0.24	0.05
		Oil	0.64	0.13	0.64	0.13	0.49	0.10	0.49	0.10	0.49	0.10	0.49	0.10
		pH	6.0–9.0		6.0–9.0		6.0–9.0		6.0–9.0		6.0–9.0		6.0–9.0	
Subpart G Automatic glass laminating	Subpart G	TSS	4.40	0.90	4.40	0.90	0.88	0.18	0.88	0.18	0.88	0.18	0.88	0.18
		Oil	1.76	0.36	1.76	0.36	1.76	0.36	1.76	0.36	1.76	0.36	1.76	0.36
		Phosphorus	1.07	0.22	1.07	0.22	0.30	0.06	0.30	0.06	0.30	0.06	0.30	0.06
		pH	6.0–9.0		6.0–9.0		6.0–9.0		6.0–9.0		6.0–9.0		6.0–9.0	
Subpart H Glass container manufacturing	Subpart H	Oil	60.0	0.06	30.0	0.3	0.8	0.0008	0.4	0.0004	0.8	0.0008	0.4	0.0004
		TSS	140.0	0.14	70.0	0.07	0.8	0.0008	0.4	0.0004	0.8	0.0008	0.4	0.0004
		pH	6.0–9.0		6.0–9.0		6.0–9.0		6.0–9.0		6.0–9.0		6.0–9.0	
Subpart I Machine pressed and blown glass manufacturing	Subpart I	Oil	112.0	0.112	56.0	0.056	3.6	0.0036	1.8	0.0018	3.6	0.0036	1.8	0.0018
		TSS	280	0.28	140.0	0.14	3.6	0.0036	1.8	0.0018	3.6	0.0036	1.8	0.0018
		pH	6.0–9.0		6.0–9.0		6.0–9.0		6.0–9.0		6.0–9.0		6.0–9.0	
Subpart J Glass tubing	Subpart J	Oil	170.0	0.17	85.0	0.085	0.2	0.0002	0.1	0.0001	0.2	0.0002	0.1	0.0001
		TSS	460.0	0.46	230.0	0.23	0.2	0.0002	0.1	0.0001	0.2	0.0002	0.1	0.0001
		pH	6.0–9.0		6.0–9.0		6.0–9.0		6.0–9.0		6.0–9.0		6.0–9.0	

Subpart K Television picture tube envelope manufacturing	Subpart K	Oil	260.0	0.26	130.0	0.13	260.0	0.26	130.0	0.13	260.0	0.26	130.0	0.13
		TSS	260.0	0.26	130.0	0.13	120.0	0.12	60.0	0.06	120.0	0.2	60.0	0.06
		Fluoride	130.0	0.13	65.0	0.065	18.0	0.018	9.0	0.0009	18.0	0.018	9.0	0.0009
		Lead	9.0	0.009	4.5	0.0045	0.9	0.0009	0.45	0.00045	0.9	0.0009	0.45	0.00045
		pH	6.0–9.0		6.0–9.0		6.0–9.0		6.0–9.0		6.0–9.0		6.0–9.0	
Subpart L Incandescent lamp envelope manufacturing	Subpart La	Oil	230.0	0.23	115.0	0.115	46.0	0.045	23.0	0.023	45.0	0.045	23.0	0.023
		TSS	230.0	0.23	115.0	0.115	46.0	0.045	23.0	0.023	45.0	0.045	23.0	0.023
		pH	6.0–9.0		6.0–9.0		6.0–9.0		6.0–9.0		6.0–9.0		6.0–9.0	
Subpart La Any plant that produces incandescent lamps														
Subpart Lb Any plant that frosts incandescent lamps	Subpart Lb	Fluoride	136.0	0.14	68.0	0.07	14.0	0.014	7.0	0.007	14.0	0.014	7.0	0.007
		Ammonia	200.0	0.2	100.0	0.1	200.0	0.2	100.0	0.1	200.0	0.2	100.0	0.1
		TSS	170.0	0.17	85.0	0.09	34.0	0.034	17.0	0.017	34.0	0.034	17.0	0.017
		pH	6.0–9.0		6.0–9.0		6.0–9.0		6.0–9.0		6.0–9.0		6.0–9.0	
Subpart M Hand-pressed and blown manufacturing	Subpart Ma	Lead (mg/l)	2.0		1.0		0.2		0.1		0.2		0.1	
		Fluoride (mg/l)	30.0		15.0		4.0		2.0		4.0		2.0	
		TSS (mg/l)	50.0		25.0		10.0		5.0		10.0		5.0	
Subpart Ma Produces hand-pressed or blown *leaded* glassware, employs acid finishing technique and discharges greater than 50 gpd		pH	6.0–9.0		6.0–9.0		6.0–9.0		6.0–9.0		6.0–9.0		6.0–9.0	
Subpart Mb Produces *nonleaded* hand-pressed or blown glassware, employs acid finishing techniques and discharges greater than 50 gpd	Subpart Mb	Fluoride (mg/l)	30.0		15.0		4.0		2.0		4.0		2.0	
		TSS (mg/l)	50.0		25.0		10.0		5.0		10.0		5.0	
		pH	6.0–9.0		6.0–9.0		6.0–9.0		6.0–9.0		6.0–9.0		6.0–9.0	
Subpart Mc Produces *leaded* or *nonleaded*, does *not* employ acid finishing techniques and discharges greater than 50 gpd	Subpart Mc	TSS (mg/l)	50.0		25.0		10.0		5.0		10.0		5.0	
		pH	6.0–9.0		6.0–9.0		6.0–9.0		6.0–9.0		6.0–9.0		6.0–9.0	

TABLE 2 Effluent Guidelines and Standards (Continued)

Category	Subpart	Effluent characteristic	BPCTCA effluent limitations				BATEA effluent limitations				New source standards of performance			
			Maximum for any 1 day		Average of daily values for 30 consecutive days shall not exceed		Maximum for any 1 day		Average of daily values for 30 consecutive days shall not exceed		Maximum for any 1 day		Average of daily values for 30 consecutive days shall not exceed	
			M[a]	E[a]	M	E	M	E	M	E	M	E	M	E
25b. Asbestos manufacturing[34]; Subpart A Asbestos cement pipe	Subpart A	TSS	0.57	1.14	0.19	0.38	There shall be no discharge of process wastewater pollutants to navigable waters				0.57	1.14	0.19	0.38
		pH	6.0–9.0		6.0–9.0						6.0–9.0		6.0–9.0	
Subpart B Asbestos cement sheet	Subpart B	TSS	0.68	1.35	0.23	0.45	There shall be no discharge of process wastewater pollutants to navigable waters							
		pH	6.0–9.0		6.0–9.0									
Subpart C Asbestos paper (starch binder)	Subpart C	TSS	0.55	1.10	0.35	0.70	There shall be no discharge of process wastewater pollutants to navigable waters							
		pH	6.0–9.0		6.0–9.0									
Subpart D Asbestos paper (elastomeric binder)	Subpart D	TSS	0.55	1.10	0.35	0.70	There shall be no discharge of process wastewater pollutants to navigable waters				0.55	1.10	0.35	0.70
		pH	6.0–9.0		6.0–9.0						6.0–9.0		6.0–9.0	
Subpart E Asbestos millboard	Subpart E		There shall be no discharge of process wastewater pollutants to navigable waters											
Subpart F Asbestos roofing	Subpart F	COD	0.015	0.029	0.008	0.016	There shall be no discharge of process wastewater pollutants to navigable waters							
		TSS	0.010	0.020	0.006	0.012								
		pH	6.0–9.0		6.0–9.0									
Subpart G Asbestos floor tile	Subpart G	COD	0.14	0.30	0.09	0.18	There shall be no discharge of process wastewater pollutants to navigable waters							
		TSS	0.06	0.13	0.04	0.08								
		pH	6.0–9.0		6.0–9.0									

26. Rubber processing[35]	Sub-	TSS	0.096	0.096	0.064	0.064	0.096	0.096	0.064	0.064	0.096	0.096	0.064	0.064
Subpart A Tire and inner tube plants	part	Oil and grease	0.024	0.024	0.016	0.016	0.024	0.024	0.016	0.016	0.024	0.024	0.016	0.016
	A	pH	6.0–9.0		6.0–9.0		6.0–9.0		6.0–9.0		6.0–9.0		6.0–9.0	
Subpart B	Sub-	COD	12.00	12.00	8.00	8.00	3.12	3.12	2.08	2.08	12.00	12.00	8.00	8.00
Emulsion crumb rubber	part	BOD_5	0.60	0.60	0.40	0.40	0.12	0.12	0.08	0.08	0.60	0.60	0.40	0.40
	B	TSS	0.98	0.98	0.65	0.65	0.24	0.24	0.16	0.16	0.98	0.98	0.65	0.65
		Oil and grease	0.24	0.24	0.16	0.16	0.12	0.12	0.08	0.08	0.24	0.24	0.16	0.16
		pH	6.0–9.0		6.0–9.0		6.0–9.0		6.0–9.0		6.0–9.0		6.0–9.0	
Subpart C	Sub-	COD	5.91	5.91	3.94	3.94	3.12	3.12	2.08	2.08	5.91	5.91	3.94	3.94
Solution crumb rubber	part	BOD_5	0.60	0.60	0.40	0.40	0.12	0.12	0.08	0.08	0.60	0.60	0.40	0.40
	C	TSS	0.98	0.98	0.65	0.65	0.24	0.24	0.16	0.16	0.98	0.98	0.65	0.65
		Oil and grease	0.24	0.24	0.16	0.16	0.12	0.12	0.08	0.08	0.24	0.24	0.16	0.16
		pH	6.0–9.0		6.0–9.0		6.0–9.0		6.0–9.0		6.0–9.0		6.0–9.0	
Subpart D	Sub-	COD	10.27	10.27	6.85	6.85	2.66	2.66	1.78	1.78	10.27	10.27	6.85	6.85
Latex rubber	part	BOD_5	0.51	0.51	0.34	0.34	0.11	0.11	0.07	0.07	0.51	0.51	0.34	0.34
	D	TSS	0.82	0.82	0.55	0.55	0.21	0.21	0.14	0.14	0.82	0.82	0.55	0.55
		Oil and grease	0.21	0.21	0.14	0.14	0.11	0.11	0.07	0.07	0.21	0.21	0.14	0.14
		pH	6.0–9.0		6.0–9.0		6.0–9.0		6.0–9.0		6.0–9.0		6.0–9.0	
27. Timber products[36]	Sub-	BOD_5	1.5	0.09	0.5	0.03	There shall be no discharge of process waste-water pollutants to navigable waters				1.5	0.09	0.5	0.03
Subpart A Barking	part	TSS	6.9	0.431	2.3	0.144					6.9	0.431	2.3	0.144
	A	pH	6.0–9.0		6.0–9.0						6.0–9.0		6.0–9.0	
Subpart B Veneer	Sub-	BOD_5	0.72	0.045	0.24	0.015	There shall be no discharge of process wastewater pollutants to navigable waters							
	part	pH	6.0–9.0		6.0–9.0									
Subpart Ba Softwood	Ba													
Subpart Bb Hardwood	Sub- part Bb	BOD_5	1.62	0.10	0.54	0.034	There shall be no discharge of process wastewater pollutants to navigable waters							
		pH	6.0–9.0		6.0–9.0									
Subpart C Plywood	Sub- part C		There shall be no discharge of process wastewater pollutants to navigable waters											
Subpart D Hardboard dry process	Sub- part D		There shall be no discharge of process wastewater pollutants to navigable waters											

TABLE 2 Effluent Guidelines and Standards (Continued)

Category	Sub-part	Effluent characteristic	BPCTCA effluent limitations				BATEA effluent limitations				New source standards of performance			
			Maximum for any 1 day		Average of daily values for 30 consecutive days shall not exceed		Maximum for any 1 day		Average of daily values for 30 consecutive days shall not exceed		Maximum for any 1 day		Average of daily values for 30 consecutive days shall not exceed	
			M[a]	E[a]	M	E	M	E	M	E	M	E	M	E
27. Timber products (*cont.*)	Sub-part E	BOD_5	7.8	15.6	2.6	5.2	2.7	5.4	0.9	1.8	2.7	5.4	0.9	1.8
		TSS	16.5	33.0	5.5	11.0	3.3	6.6	1.1	2.2	3.3	6.6	1.1	2.2
Subpart E Hardboard wet process		pH	6.0–9.0		6.0–9.0		6.0–9.0		6.0–9.0		6.0–9.0		6.0–9.0	
Subpart F Wood preserving	Sub-part F	There shall be no discharge of process wastewater pollutants to navigable waters												
Subpart G Wood preserving steam	Sub-part G	COD	1,000	68.5	550	34.5	220	13.7	110	6.9	220	13.7	110	6.9
		Phenols	2.18	0.14	0.65	0.04	0.21	0.014	0.064	0.004	0.21	0.014	0.064	0.004
		Oil and grease	24.0	1.5	12.0	0.75	6.9	0.42	3.4	0.21	6.9	0.42	3.4	0.21
		pH	6.0–9.0		6.0–9.0		6.0–9.0		6.0–9.0		6.0–9.0		6.0–9.0	
Subpart H Wood preserving boultonizing	Sub-part H	There shall be no discharge of process wastewater pollutants to navigable waters												

Subpart I Wet storage	Subpart I	Debris	2.54	1.0	2.54	1.0	2.54	1.0	2.54	1.0	2.54	1.0	2.54	1.0
		pH	5.5–9.0		5.5–9.0		5.5–9.0		5.5–9.0		5.5–9.0		5.5–9.0	
Subpart J Log washing	Subpart J		There shall be no discharge of process wastewater pollutants to navigable waters											
Subpart K Sawmills and planing mills	Subpart K		There shall be no discharge of process wastewater pollutants to navigable waters											
Subpart L Finishing	Subpart L		There shall be no discharge of process wastewater pollutants to navigable waters											
Subpart M Particle board manufacturing	Subpart M		There shall be no discharge of process wastewater pollutants to navigable waters											
Subpart N Insulation board manufacturing	Subpart N	BOD_5	3.75	7.5	1.25	2.50	1.13	2.25	0.38	0.75	3.75	7.50	1.25	2.50
		TSS	9.40	18.8	3.13	6.25	2.85	5.70	0.85	1.90	9.40	18.80	3.13	6.25
		pH	6.0–9.0		6.0–9.0		6.0–9.0		6.0–9.0		6.0–9.0		6.0–9.0	
Subpart O Insulation board manufacturing with steaming or hardboard products	Subpart O	BOD_5	11.3	22.60	3.75	7.50	3.38	6.75	1.13	2.35	11.30	22.60	3.75	7.50
		TSS	9.40	18.80	3.13	6.25	2.85	5.70	0.85	1.90	9.40	18.80	3.13	6.25
		pH	6.0–9.0		6.0–9.0		6.0–9.0		6.0–9.0		6.0–9.0		6.0–9.0	

REFERENCES

1. "Pulp, Paper, and Paperboard Point Source Category," *Federal Register,* vol. 39, no. 104, pt. II, Effluent Guidelines and Standards, May 29, 1974.
2. "Builders Paper and Board Manufacturing Point Source Category," *Federal Register,* vol. 39, no. 9, pt. II, Effluent Guidelines and Standards, January 14, 1974.
3. "Builders Paper and Board Manufacturing Point Source Category," *Federal Register,* vol. 39, no. 91, pt. III, Effluent Guidelines and Standards, May 9, 1974.
4. "Meat Products Point Source Category," *Federal Register,* pt. II, Small Processor Subcategory, Effluent Limitations and Guidelines, August 28, 1974.
5. "Meat Products Point Source Category," *Federal Register,* vol. 39, no. 41, pt. II, Effluent Guidelines and Standards, February 28, 1974.
6. "Dairy Products Processing Industry Point Source Category," *Federal Register,* vol. 39, no. 103, pt. III, Effluent Limitations Guidelines and Pretreatment Standards Application, May 28, 1974.
7. "Grain Mills Point Source Category," *Federal Register,* pt. II, Effluent Limitations Guidelines and Standards, March 20, 1974.
8. "Grain Mills Point Source Category," *Federal Register,* vol. 39, no. 181, pt. II, Effluent Limitations Guidelines for Existing Sources and Pretreatment Standards for New Sources, September 17, 1974.
9. "Canned and Preserved Fruits and Vegetables Processing Point Source Category," *Federal Register,* vol. 39, no. 56, pt. III, Effluent Guidelines and Standards, March 21, 1974.
10. "Canned and Preserved Seafood Processing Point Source Category," *Federal Register,* vol. 39, no. 56, pt. III, Effluent Guidelines and Standards, March 21, 1974.
11. "Canned and Preserved Seafood Processing Point Source Category," *Federal Register,* vol. 39, no. 124, pt. II, Effluent Limitations Guidelines, June 26, 1974.
12. "Beet Sugar, Processing Point Source Subcategory," *Federal Register,* vol. 39, no. 22, pt. II, Effluent Guidelines and Standards, January 31, 1974.
13. "Liquid and Crystalline Cane Sugar Refining Subcategory," *Federal Register,* vol. 39, no. 55, pt. III, Effluent Limitations Guidelines and Proposed Pretreatment Standards, March 20, 1974.
14. "Textile Industry Point Source Category," *Federal Register,* vol. 39, no. 130, pt. II, Effluent Guidelines and Standards, July 5, 1974.
15. "Cement Manufacturing Point Source Category," *Federal Register,* vol. 39, no. 35, pt. III, Effluent Guidelines and Standards, February 20, 1974.
16. "Feedlots Point Source Category," *Federal Register,* vol. 39, no. 32, pt. II, Effluent Guidelines and Standards, February 14, 1974.
17. "Electroplating Point Source Category, Copper, Nickel, Chromium and Zinc on Ferrous and Nonferrous Materials Subcategory," *Federal Register,* vol. 39, no. 61, pt. II, Effluent Guidelines and Standards, March 28, 1974.
18. "Organic Chemicals Manufacturing Point Source Category," *Federal Register,* vol. 39, no. 81, pt. I, Effluent Guidelines and Standards and Proposed Application to Pretreatment Standards, April 25, 1974.
19. "Inorganic Chemicals Manufacturing Point Source Category," *Federal Register,* vol. 39, no. 49, pt. II, Effluent Limitations Guidelines and Proposed Guidelines for Existing Sources to Pretreatment Standards for Incompatible Pollutants, March 12, 1974.
20. "Plastics and Synthetics Point Source Category," *Federal Register,* vol. 39, no. 67, pt. II, Effluent Guidelines and Standards, April 5, 1974.
21. "Plastics and Synthetics Point Source Category," *Federal Register,* vol. 39, no. 184, pt. II, Proposed Effluent Limitations and Guidelines for Existing Sources and Standards of Performance and Pretreatment Standards for New Sources, September 20, 1974.
22. "Soap and Detergent Manufacturing Point Source Category," *Federal Register,* vol. 39, no. 72, pt. II, Effluent Limitations Guidelines, April 12, 1974.
23. "Fertilizer Manufacturing Point Source Category," *Federal Register,* vol. 39, no. 68, pt. III, Effluent Guidelines and Standards and Proposed Limitations, April 8, 1974.
24. "Petroleum Refining Point Source Category," *Federal Register,* vol. 39, no. 91, pt. II, Effluent Guidelines and Standards, May 9, 1974.
25. "Iron and Steel Manufacturing Point Source Category," *Federal Register,* vol. 39, no. 126, pt. II, Effluent Guidelines and Standards, June 28, 1974.
26. "Nonferrous Metals Manufacturing Point Source Category," *Federal Register,* vol. 39, no. 68, pt. II, Effluent Guidelines and Standards and Proposed Limitations, April 8, 1974.

27. "Phosphate Manufacturing Point Source Category," *Federal Register,* vol. 39, no. 35, pt. II, Effluent Guidelines and Standards, February 20, 1974.
28. "Steam Electric Power Generating Point Source Category," *Federal Register,* vol. 39, no. 196, Effluent Guidelines and Standards, October 8, 1974.
29. "Ferroalloy Manufacturing Point Source Category," *Federal Register,* vol. 39, no. 37, pt. II, Effluent Limitations Guidelines and Standards, February 22, 1974.
30. "Leather Tanning and Finishing Point Source Category," *Federal Register,* vol. 39, no. 69, pt. III, Effluent Limitations Guidelines, April 9, 1974.
31. "Glass Manufacturing Point Source Category," *Federal Register,* vol. 39, no. 163, pt. II, Proposed Effluent Limitations Guidelines and Standards of Performance and Pretreatment Standards, August 21, 1974.
32. "Glass Manufacturing Point Source Category," *Federal Register,* vol. 39, no. 32, pt. III, Effluent Guidelines and Standards, February 14, 1974.
33. "Glass Manufacturing Point Source Category, Insulation Fiberglass Subcategory," *Federal Register,* vol. 39, no. 15, pt. III, Effluent Limitations Guidelines, January 22, 1974.
34. "Asbestos Manufacturing Point Source Category," *Federal Register,* vol. 39, no. 39, pt. II, Effluent Limitations Guidelines, February 26, 1974.
35. "Rubber Processing Point Source Category," *Federal Register,* vol. 39, no. 36, pt. II, Tire and Inner Tube Plants, Emulsion Crumb Rubber, Solution Crumb Rubber and Latex Rubber Subcategories, February 21, 1974.
36. "Timber Products Processing Point Source Category," *Federal Register,* vol. 39, no. 76, pt. II, Effluent Guidelines and Standards, April 18, 1974.

Index